Compliments of the
author
Art Sherman

McGraw-Hill Series in MECHANICAL ENGINEERING

Robert M. Drake, Jr.
Stephen J. Kline
Consulting Editors

Beggs, *Mechanism*
Cambel and Jennings, *Gas Dynamics*
Csanady, *Theory of Turbomachines*
Durelli, Phillips, and Tsao, *Introduction to the Theoretical and Experimental Analysis of Stress and Strain*
Eckert, *Introduction to Heat and Mass Transfer*
Eckert and Drake, *Heat and Mass Transfer*
Gröber, Erk, and Grigull, *Fundamentals of Heat Transfer*
Ham, Crane, and Rogers, *Mechanics of Machinery*
Hartenberg and Denavit, *Kinematic Synthesis of Linkages*
Hartman, *Dynamics of Machinery*
Hinze, *Turbulence*
Jacobsen and Ayre, *Engineering Vibrations*
Kays and London, *Compact Heat Exchangers*
Phelan, *Fundamentals of Mechanical Design*
Raven, *Automatic Control Engineering*
Sabersky, *Elements of Engineering Thermodynamics*
Schenck, *Theories of Engineering Experimentation*
Schlichting, *Boundary Layer Theory*
Shigley, *Dynamic Analysis of Machines*
Shigley, *Kinematic Analysis of Mechanisms*
Shigley, *Mechanical Engineering Design*
Shigley, *Theory of Machines*
Spalding and Cole, *Engineering Thermodynamics*
Stoecker, *Refrigeration and Air Conditioning*
Sutton and Sherman, *Engineering Magnetohydrodynamics*
Wilcock and Booser, *Bearing Design and Application*

Engineering Magnetohydrodynamics

GEORGE W. SUTTON
General Electric Company
and
University of Pennsylvania

ARTHUR SHERMAN
General Electric Company

McGRAW-HILL BOOK COMPANY
New York St. Louis San Francisco Toronto London Sydney

ENGINEERING MAGNETOHYDRODYNAMICS

Library of Congress Catalog Card Number 64-7871

62382

The authors would like to dedicate this volume to their wives, Evelyn D. Sutton and Hennie L. Sherman, whose inspiration, sacrifice, and inexhaustible patience made possible its completion.

PREFACE

This book is the outgrowth of notes prepared for a graduate course which was first given at the Towne School of the University of Pennsylvania in 1960 to 1961. The purpose of the course was to introduce engineers to the concepts of plasma physics and magnetohydrodynamics from a physical viewpoint. Following this philosophy, the concepts, notation, and mathematical techniques used by physicists are generally used throughout the book. In addition, most derivations are given twice: from a physical viewpoint by tracking individual particles, and also more rigorously from kinetic theory. By use of this physical approach it is hoped that students will be sufficiently prepared to follow new developments in plasma physics as well as in plasma engineering. It is hoped that this book will therefore be a bridge between plasma physics and engineering magnetohydrodynamics.

The subject of magnetohydrodynamics has only recently become important to the engineering profession, although it has been studied for many years by physicists. This change has occurred because of the recent applications of plasma physics to several new technological developments. One such problem is the attenuation and reflection of microwaves by rocket exhausts, where the electron density becomes large enough for the exhaust flame to become electrically conducting. More recently, propagation of radio waves has become of extreme importance for hypersonic vehicles, where the temperature behind the surrounding shock layer is sufficiently high to ionize the constituents of air.

Another technology which has recently become extremely important is nuclear fusion. Although this is at present mainly in the research phase, the experimental equipment requires considerable engineering design. Of course, when and if nuclear fusion is perfected and becomes economically important, there will be a large need for engineers to design, construct, and test the fusion plants.

Still another area which utilizes magnetohydrodynamics is electrical propulsion, which is one of several proposed methods for achieving interplanetary travel. With the use of a plasma for the working fluid which is accelerated by a magnetic field, specific impulses up to 10,000 sec or greater are attainable.

The fact that the air in the shock layer which surrounds hypersonic vehicles is ionized has prompted research on methods of magnetically interacting with the flow to produce various effects, including control of drag or angle of attack, and boundary-layer control to increase the transition Reynolds number or to reduce the hypersonic heat transfer. The magnetic field could also be used to permit radio wave propagation through the plasma.

Finally, research is currently in progress on the direct conversion into electric energy of the thermal and kinetic energy in a flowing plasma. Although this is an old concept, new methods for obtaining the required ionization and new refractory materials to confine the plasma may make this method of direct conversion a reality.

In studying the large amount of literature in the field of magnetohydrodynamics, it is possible to discern three paths by which the topic has been developed. The first might be called *classical magnetohydrodynamics*, in which experiments were performed on mercury, and theories were developed to explain the observations; the best-known example of this is Hartmann flow of a viscous incompressible conducting fluid. In other cases it is assumed that the fluid possesses an electrical conductivity which is infinitely large, and is the electrical counterpart of a nonviscous, non-heat-conducting fluid. Although these assumptions lead to mathematical simplifications, in most cases they are unrealistic. In addition, many such mathematical problems which have been solved have no practical applications as yet. It appears that this approach is closer to applied mathematics than to engineering magnetohydrodynamics.

The second path is *gaseous electronics*. This field is mainly concerned with electrical discharges in gases, and has yielded a large body of knowledge on the physical and radiation properties of ionized gases. However, neither the flow nor the presence of a magnetic field are usually considered, and the gas is usually far from equilibrium.

The final path is that due to the astrophysicists, such as Chapman, Cowling, and Jeans. This is essentially the kinetic theory of gases, which was initiated by Boltzmann and Maxwell, and which is continued today by Spitzer, Rosenbluth, Burgers, and others. This approach has been given the name of *statistical plasma mechanics* by Professor Burgers, with the subtitle, "The bridge between particle mechanics and continuum mechanics."† It starts with the consideration of the motion of particles, and develops both the macroscopic conservation equations and the transport properties. For the purposes of this book, this last approach seems to be most suitable for introducing the various topics, and in addition, is self-consistent. Where applicable, the other two topics will be covered.

Part I deals mainly with the properties of ionized gases in magnetic and electric fields, and essentially follows the microscopic viewpoint. In the introduction (Chap. 1) the concepts of ionized gases and plasmas are described, together with the various magnetohydrodynamic regimes. Next, electromagnetic field theory is reviewed in Chap. 2. Since a particle approach is to be utilized, the laws of Coulomb, Ampère, and

† In Francis H. Clauser (gen. ed.), *Plasma Dynamics*, Addison-Wesley Publishing Company, Inc., Reading, Mass., 1960.

Faraday are presented first, and Maxwell's equations are then derived from them. The properties of the electromagnetic field are derived, followed by radiation from a moving charge, so that radiation from a plasma can be treated later. In Chap. 3, motion of an individual charged particle is considered. The various drift motions and adiabatic invariants are derived.

Kinetic theory is introduced in Chap. 4 with the distribution function of a gas in equilibrium. Next, Boltzmann's equation is derived, and several collisionless problems are solved to demonstrate its utility. Finally, the conservation equations are derived. None of these equations require detailed consideration of the collision term. To demonstrate the use of the collision term, the electrical conductivity of a gas is derived in Chap. 5. Mixtures of gases are also considered, and ion slip is presented.

In all the above, it has been assumed that the state of the ionized gas is known. Chapter 6 develops statistical mechanics, which is then used to determine the degree of ionization of a gas in equilibrium and also when currents are present.

Finally, Chap. 7 deals with radiation from and wave motion in plasmas. Principally, longitudinal and transverse wave motions, including collisional damping, are treated. For most of the discussion, a two-fluid macroscopic viewpoint (species-momentum equations) is taken, although the topic of collisionless damping is discussed from the microscopic (Boltzmann equation) viewpoint.

Part II deals with the macroscopic motion of electrically conducting compressible fluids. In Chap. 8 the magnetohydrodynamic approximations are presented first, followed by a derivation of the similarity parameters. The latter are especially useful for the scaling of phenomena.

The description of macroscopic fluid motions is first introduced in Chap. 9 by a brief discussion of infinitesimal wave motions (Alfvén waves) proceeding to a more detailed study of finite magnetohydrodynamic discontinuities or shock waves.

Next, the subject of magnetohydrodynamic channel flows is treated. In Chap. 10 exact solutions to channel-flow problems are considered in order to achieve greater insight into the nature of these flows. After this idealized approach, the more useful approximate methods of estimating channel-flow behavior are considered in Chap. 11. These can all be conveniently classified under the heading of the quasi-one-dimensional approximation.

Finally, Part II is concluded with the treatment of magnetohydrodynamic boundary layers in Chap. 12. Here the approximations inherent in the analysis are discussed and some typical examples presented.

Part III describes some applications of magnetohydrodynamics in terms of the material which has already been developed. Propulsion and power generation are developed in separate chapters. These chapters are mainly descriptive, since detailed derivations are clearly beyond the scope of this book. However, it is hoped that the students will have gained an understanding of the physical phenomena involved in these devices, which is the objective of this work.

The authors wish to express their gratitude to Dr. Hsuan Yeh, director of the Towne School of the University of Pennsylvania; Dr. Joseph Farber of General Electric Company, and Dr. Boris Podolsky of Xavier University, for encouraging the authors to undertake this book. They would, as well, like to acknowledge the support of the U.S. Air Force Office of Scientific Research for some of the work described. The authors are also indebted to the General Electric Company and the Massachusetts Institute of Technology for providing the necessary facilities for the preparation of the manuscript, and to Miss Marie Coonahan and Miss Barbara Wheatland for their patient and careful typing of the manuscript. Finally, for many stimulating discussions and insights, the authors wish to thank their many associates, including Drs. Jack Kerrebrock, Henry Hurwitz, Jr., David BenDaniel, Lewi Tonks, and James Fay.

GEORGE SUTTON
ARTHUR SHERMAN

CONTENTS

SYMBOLS Numbers denote chapters in which symbol is used

a speed of sound, **9, 11, 14**
channel half height, **10**

a_e fraction of enthalpy change due to power generation, **14**

a^* channel aspect ratio, **14**

A Helmholz free energy, **6**
cross-sectional area, **11, 14**
Alfvén speed, **8, 9**

$A_1(s)$ integral defined by (5.48), **5**

$\mathbf{A}$ magnetic potential, **2, 3, 4**

A_M emission constant, **6**

b_e fraction of pressure drop due to Lorentz force, **14**

b impact parameter, **4, 5**
generator height, **14**

$\mathbf{b}$ induced magnetic induction

$\mathbf{B}$ magnetic induction

c_f skin friction coefficient

c speed of light, **1, 2**

c_0 speed of light in vacuum, **2, 7**

$\mathbf{c}$ particle random thermal velocity $= \mathbf{w} - \mathbf{v}$

C_V specific heat at constant volume

C_P specific heat at constant pressure

C perimeter

c_d total shear-stress coefficient, **10**

c_H heat-transfer coefficient, **10**

d Debye shielding length, **1, 4, 5, 6**
electrode pitch, **14**

$\mathbf{d}$ charge displacement, **4**

$\mathbf{D}$ electric displacement vector, **2**

D general Debye length, **6**

$\mathfrak{D}_{rs}$ coefficient of diffusion

e electronic charge, **2, 3, 4, 5, 6, 7, 14**

e sum of internal and thermal energy per unit mass, **4, 8, 9, 10, 11**

$\mathbf{e}_i$ unit vector in i^{th} direction

E_0 ionization energy

E total energy, **6**
internal energy, **11**

$\mathbf{E}$ electric field with respect to laboratory

$\mathbf{E}^*$ electric field in coordinates moving with mass average gas velocity

E_1 amplitude of sinusoidally varying electric field, **7**

$\mathcal{E}$ dimensionless electric field $(\mathbf{E}/\mu_0 n_e e)$ vector, **7**

f velocity distribution function, **4, 5, 7**
mass fraction of un-ionized atoms, **5**
frequency, **14**

$\mathbf{f}$ surface force vector

$\mathbf{F}$ force on a particle, **2, 3, 4, 5**
body force per unit volume, **8, 12**

g degeneracy of an atomic energy level, **6**

$\mathbf{g}$ relative velocity, **4, 5**
gravitational vector, **2**

$\mathbf{G}$ center of mass velocity, **5, 6**
group velocity, **9**

G ratio of internal partition functions or statistical weights, **6**

$\mathbf{G}^{**}$ gradient driving force (5.142)

h Planck's constant, **6, 7, 11**
static enthalpy, **4, 5, 8, 9, 10, 11, 14**
film coefficient for heat transfer, **14**
generator width, **14**

H total enthalpy, **4, 9, 11, 14**
hamiltonian, **4**

$\mathbf{H}$ magnetic field intensity

H_a Hartmann number, **10**

$\mathcal{H}$ ohmic heating, **12**

I_{sp} specific impulse, **13**

i $\sqrt{-1}$

I	total current
	total impulse, 13
	magnetic-interaction parameter, 8, 10, 11, 12, 14
i,j,k	orthogonal unit vectors
$\mathcal{I}$	imaginary part of
j	conduction current vector
J	electric current vector
J*	surface current vector
k	Boltzmann's constant
k	wave number vector
K	ratio of voltage to open-circuit voltage, 10, 14
	permittivity, 2
K_0	permittivity of vacuum, 2
$\mathcal{K}$	thermal conductivity, 4, 5, 8, 11, 12
dl	element of electrical or particle path
L	characteristic length
L	lagrangian, 2
l	electrode pitch, 10
m	particle mass, 3, 4, 5, 6, 7, 11
	mass flux, 9
$\dot{m}$	total mass flow
$\mathfrak{M}^*$	ratio of Mach number to initial value
M	magnetization
$\mathfrak{M}$	Mach number
$\mathfrak{M}_M$	magnetohydrodynamic Mach number
M	molecular weight
n	quantum number, 6
	number density of particles, 2, 3, 4, 5, 7, 11
	coefficient in friction law, 14
n^*	moles, 12
n	normal to a surface
N	total number of particles, 4, 7
	amplitude of sinusoidally varying electron density, 7
$\mathfrak{N}$	degrees of freedom, 3
N_u	Nusselt number, 13
p	hydrostatic pressure
p	dipole moment vector, 2
	generalized momentum vector, 4
p, p_{ij}	pressure tensor
P	power density, total power, 14
	dimensionless pressure = $p/\rho u^2$, 11
	partition function, 6, 14
	(number density of seed)/(number density of seed plus inert), 11
$\mathbf{P}_s$	dynamical friction vector of s species
P	polarization vector
P_m	magnetic Prandtl number
P_R	Prandtl number
q	generalized spatial vector, 4
	velocity vector, 10
	heat-flux vector, 4, 5, 10
q	ratio of sound speed to Alfvén speed, squared
Q_{rs}	collision cross section, 4, 5, 7
Q	heat, 14
r_L	Larmor or cyclotron radius, 3
r	spatial radius vector
R_δ	Reynolds number based on boundary-layer thickness, 12
R	collision radius, 4, 5
	gas constant ($k/\langle m \rangle$), 8, 9, 11, 14
R_m	magnetic Reynolds number, 8, 9, 10, 12
R_L	load resistance, 14
R_e	Reynolds number, 8, 10, 12
$\mathcal{R}$	universal gas constant, 8
	real part of, 7, 14
s	force-law exponent, 5
	parameter in Laplace transform, 12
S	entropy, 4, 9, 14
	magnetic force number, 8
S	Poynting vector, 2
d**S**	element of surface
S_t	Stanton number, 14

t time
t distance tangential to surface
T temperature

$u(r)$ potential energy
u,v,w components of velocity in x, y, z directions
u phase velocity
U velocity (constant), 7, 10, 14
U dimensionless velocity, 11

v mean velocity with respect to laboratory coordinates
V electric potential
amplitude of sinusoidally varying velocity, 7
V diffusion or drift velocity vector
$d\mathcal{V}$ volume
V_1 shock velocity, 9

w particle velocity vector with respect to laboratory
W energy, work, 2, 14

X mole fraction, 11, 14
generalized force, 6
x,y,z spatial coordinates (also, x_1, x_2, x_3)

Z number of charges on a particle, 1, 2, 6, 7
ratio of friction coefficient to twice the magnetic-interaction parameter, 14
current streamline function, 10

α electric field pitch angle, 14
degree of ionization, 6, 11
polarization constant, 4, 5
magnetic diffusivity, $(\mu_0\sigma)^{-1}$, 8, 9
power-supply specific weight, 13
constant, 11
$\boldsymbol{\alpha}$ thermal-diffusion-coefficient tensor
β phase angle, 7
Hall constant $= (en_e)^{-1}$, 8
Hall parameter $= \omega\tau$, 5, 14

$\boldsymbol{\beta}$ heat conduction due to diffusion coefficient tensor, 5

γ_i dynamical friction vector in Fokker-Planck equation, 5
γ_{ij} dispersion coefficient tensor in Fokker-Planck equation, 5
γ ratio of specific heats
mass advantage, 13
Γ gamma function

δ boundary-layer thickness, 10
a small change in a quantity
δ_{ij} Dirac delta function
δ_s energy loss factor for s species, 5, 14

ϵ quantum energy level, 6
a small quantity, 2
sum of internal and random kinetic energies, 4
azimuthal angle, 5
ϵ_{int} internal energy, 4
η,ξ dimensionless boundary-layer coordinates, 12
η resistivity, 14
viscosity, 5, 8, 10
η_L local static conversion efficiency, 14
η_p polytropic efficiency
η_C Compressor efficiency, 14
η_g generator efficiency, 14

θ temperature ratio, 12
dimensionless temperature difference, 10
Θ molecular property, 4

κ wave number, 7

λ chemical activity, 6
characteristic quantum wavelength, 6
mean free path, 1, 5
wavelength, 14
Λ ratio of Debye length to average impact parameter (5.110)

$\bar{\mu}$ mean molecular weight

μ chemical potential, 6
magnetic permeability, 1, 5
μ_0 magnetic permeability of vacuum, 2
$\boldsymbol{\mu}$ magnetic moment vector, 3
$\boldsymbol{\mu}$ mobility tensor, 5
ν kinematic viscosity, 9, 12
collision frequency, 4, 5, 7, 14
stochiometric ratio, 6
radiation frequency, 6
ξ length scale, 11

$\boldsymbol{\pi}$ electromagnetic stress tensor, 2
$\boldsymbol{\pi}^M$ magnetic field stress tensor, 2
$\boldsymbol{\pi}^E$ electric field stress tensor, 2

ρ mass density
ρ_e charge density $= \sum_s n_s e Z_s$
ρ_{e_t} true charge density, 2
ρ_0 free charge density, 2
ρ, θ, ϕ polar coordinates

$\tilde{\sigma}$, σ' reduced electrical conductivity
$\boldsymbol{\sigma}$ electrical conductivity
σ_0 surface charge density, 2, 11
scalar electrical conductivity

τ dimensionless time, 10
specific volume, 9
collision time, 4, 5, 10, 14
$\boldsymbol{\tau}$ shear stress tensor

ϕ viscous dissipation function, 4 (8.18)
electrical field potential, 2, 10, 14
ϕ^* magnetic scalar potential, 2

Φ complex electric potential, 14
viscous dissipation function (8.34)

χ work function, 6
scattering angle, 5, 7

ψ fluid dynamic stream function
electric current stream function, 10
$\boldsymbol{\psi}$ viscous force vector (8.12)

ω circular frequency, 7, 8, 9
angular frequency of rotation, 6
Larmor or cyclotron frequency, 3, 5, 14
exponent in conductivity expression, 11
ω_p plasma frequency, $[e^2\bar{n}_e/m_eK_0]^{\frac{1}{2}}$
ω_i probability of ith configuration, 6
$\tilde{\omega}_i$ degeneracy of ith energy level, 6

Ω element of solid angle
$\boldsymbol{\Omega}$ collision frequency tensor, 5

SUBSCRIPTS

chem	chemical
d	drift or diffusion
e	electron, electrical
el	electronic
eff	effective
E	electric
f	friction, fast
g	gas, guiding center
H	Hall
i,j,k	orthogonal directions
in	into
I	ion, imaginary
m	magnetic, maximum
min	minimum
M	metal
n	neutral
p	polarization
R	real
rej	rejected
rs	between the r and s species

r,s	species
s	slow, stagnation
t	true tangent
tr	translational
T	total
w	wall
x,y,z	cartesian coordinate directions
μ	magnetization
0	entrance, initial, reference value
1	inlet
2	exit
$\perp$	perpendicular
$\parallel$	parallel
∞	infinite
∇	gradients
$< >$	average

SUPERSCRIPTS

$(\;)'$	perturbation quantity
$(\bar{\;})$	mean quantity
$(\tilde{\;})$	dimensionless quantity, mean quantity
$(\;)^0$	total or stagnation conditions
$(\hat{\;})$	Laplace transform

part I

BASIC PRINCIPLES

1

INTRODUCTION

1.1 DEFINITIONS

Magnetohydrodynamics can be regarded as a combination of fluid mechanics and electromagnetism, that is, the behavior of electrically conducting fluids in the presence of magnetic and electric fields. The equations governing fluid flow are familiar to most students of fluid mechanics; similarly, the magnetic and electric fields are governed by a set of equations known as *Maxwell's equations*. Whereas the equations of fluid flow consist of one vector and two scalar equations, Maxwell's equations consist of two vector and two scalar equations. Since many problems require the simultaneous solution of all these equations, Maxwell's equations are developed in Chap. 2. Fortunately, though the equations of fluid mechanics are notoriously nonlinear, Maxwell's equations are usually linear, and therefore there is hope of solving problems even when Maxwell's equations are added.

There exists a controversy concerning the proper name for this subject. Magnetohydrodynamics is particularly inappropriate because one is usually not concerned with water, and one is interested in not only the dynamics but also the kinematics and energetics of a given situation. To rectify this situation, many other names have been proposed, such as magneto-fluid-dynamics, magneto-gas-dynamics, magneto-plasma-dynamics, magneto-fluid-mechanics, etc. Unfortunately, there is no universal acceptance of any of these, although they are frequently used to describe appropriate problems. This book is concerned mostly with the engineering aspects of these topics, which includes the appropriate plasma physics, mathematics, and applications. For this reason, the title of *engineering magnetohydrodynamics* seems most suitable, at least at present.

Another suitable name could be *plasma engineering*, but this title does not indicate the presence of either a magnetic field or flow.

In addition to deriving the appropriate differential equations, the properties of the fluid must also be specified. These usually consist of the caloric equation, the equation of state, and the various transport properties of viscosity, thermal conductivity, diffusion, and electrical conductivity, which is a special form of diffusion. These properties are treated in Part I.

Most of these properties are concerned with an ionized gas. An ordinary gas consists of gaseous molecules, each of which is electrically neutral; that is, each molecule contains the same number of positive charges in its nucleus as negatively charged electrons in its shells. Of course, these particles may be polarizable or may consist of permanent dipoles. However, in an ionized gas a large number of particles have a net positive charge and others have a net negative charge. Thus, an electric field will cause these particles to drift. Actually, the properties only become interesting when the carriers of negative charge are mostly electrons, since because of their small mass they possess a high mobility.

It is useful to make a careful distinction between electrons and ions; electrons are particles with a negative unit charge and a rest mass of 1/1,845 of a proton; ions may have any number of unit charges, either positive or negative, but the nucleus always contains at least one proton.

Gases usually become ionized by collisional processes. The electrons in the shell are attracted to the nucleus by coulombic forces, much in the same manner as the moon or artificial satellites are attracted to the earth by gravitational forces. This attractive force is just balanced by the centrifugal force of the electron or satellite (see Fig. 1.1). One therefore states that the electrons (or satellites) are in a potential well. For a satellite, there are an infinite number of stable orbits, but for an atom, there are only discrete stable orbits for each electron. The orbit in which the electron has the minimum energy is called the *ground state*, and is a consequence of the discrete energy levels of quantum mechanics.

Now for an electron (or satellite) to escape from its stable or initial orbit, additional kinetic energy must be supplied to it. For the satellite, one must use a rocket to supply the additional energy. But for the electron, the energy may be supplied in a number of ways. The atom may absorb an energetic photon, or an energetic atom or electron may collide with the atom in question. This collision may result in a transfer of energy to the atom, which then usually shows up in increased kinetic energy of the outermost electron. As a result, the electron may escape entirely. The amount of energy required to remove the outermost electron is called the *first ionization potential* (singly ionized); that required to remove the second electron is called the *second ionization potential* (doubly ionized); etc.

When an electron escapes from an atom or a molecule, it is said to be *ionized*. Under these conditions, the motion of the electron is no longer circular about any one atom, but is subject to the local electric and magnetic fields. Occasionally, it will pass closely to an atom or ion and will therefore have its velocity and direction changed. This is called a *close encounter* or *collision*. The distance along its trajectory that an electron moves between close encounters is called the *free path;* and the average distance for all electrons is called the *electron mean free path*. Mean free paths can be defined for other particles in a similar manner.

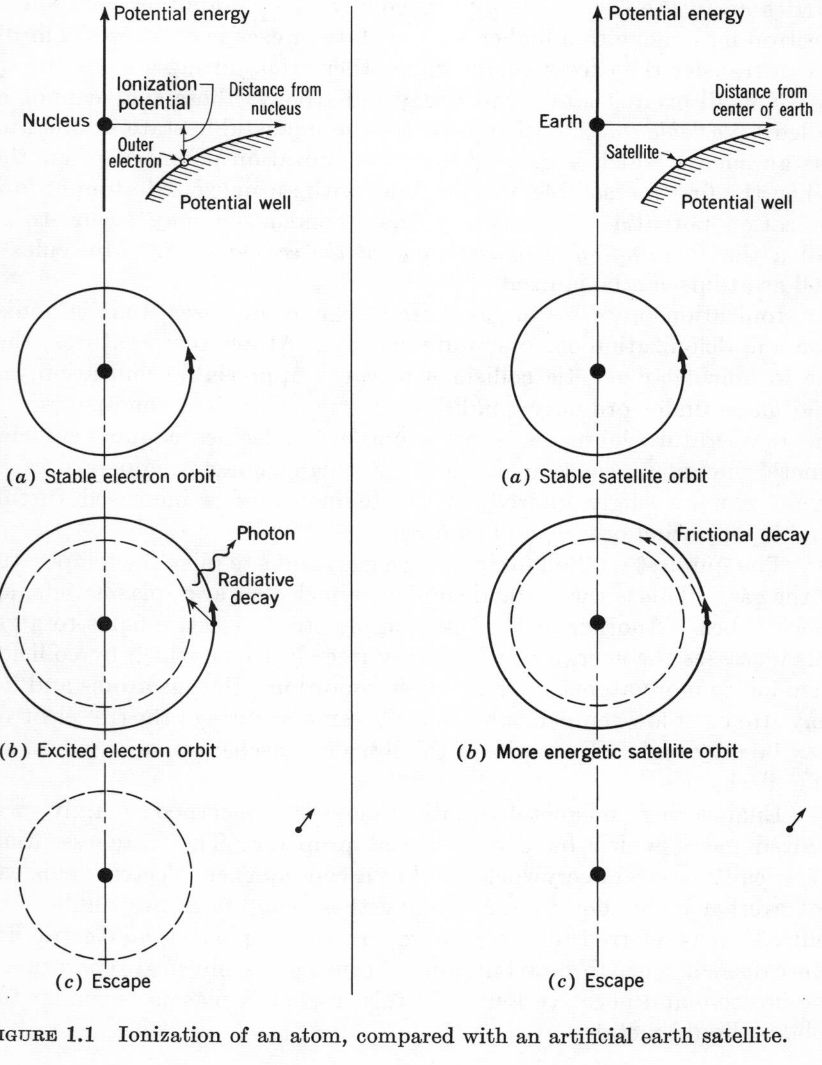

FIGURE 1.1 Ionization of an atom, compared with an artificial earth satellite.

During collisions, the electron may gain or lose energy. It can also be captured by a positive ion, which is then deionized. An electron can also be captured by a neutral particle; this is called *attachment* and leads to the formation of negatively charged ions.

To ionize an atom, the entire ionization energy need not be supplied in one collision. For example, during a particular collision the increase in kinetic energy of the electron may be sufficient only to move it into a larger orbit. The atom or molecule is then electronically "excited." Then, three things may occur. First, the electron can decay radiatively; that is, it can move back to its stable orbit and emit a photon which carries away the excess energy. Secondly, due to another collision the electron may move to a higher excited state or escape entirely. Thirdly, it can transfer the excess energy to another atom during a collision.

Not all excited states can decay radiatively; those that cannot are called *metastable states.* In some cases the metastable state in one atom has an energy which is greater than the ionization potential of another. When the first metastable atom collides with an unexcited atom of lower ionization potential, ionization of the second atom may occur; this is called the *Penning effect* or *collisions of the second kind.* Molecules as well as atoms can be ionized.

Ionization processes in gases are dynamic processes; that is, ionization and deionization occur simultaneously. At low temperatures, there are insufficient energetic collisions to cause appreciable ionization, and cold gases under ordinary conditions are not electrical conductors. As the temperature increases, some atoms or molecules acquire sufficient kinetic energy to cause ionization. At high enough temperatures, all atoms can be singly ionized; if the temperature is increased further, double ionization occurs, and so forth.

The simplest method for ionizing a gas is thus to raise the temperature of the gas. This is the method employed in electric arcs, plasma jets, and shock tubes. Another method is to apply strong electric fields to a gas: this increases the energy of a few stray free electrons, which by collisions then ionize more atoms. Under these conditions, the gas atoms and ions may still be at low temperatures, but the temperatures of the free electrons may be very high. Examples of this are glow discharges, neon tubes, and ring discharges.

Engineering magnetohydrodynamics is concerned mainly with ionized gases which have one special property: They are essentially electrically neutral everywhere, and as a consequence, electric fields cannot exert a major body force. When these conditions are fulfilled, the ionized gas is referred to as a *plasma.* In such a plasma, an electric field can cause currents to flow but cannot cause gross physical separation of the positive and negative ions. In this respect, a plasma is similar to a solid or liquid metal.

The inclusion of the plasma completes the states of matter: There are conducting and nonconducting solids, liquids, and now gases. For the nonconductors, the only body forces are gravitational and electric field gradients, whereas for the conductors the main body forces are gravitational and magnetic. On all matter, surface forces in the form of pressure and electric fields can be exerted; but magnetic surface forces can be exerted only on conductors, whether solids, liquids, or plasmas.

1.2 CHARACTERISTIC NUMBERS

In gases there exist some characteristic lengths which help specify the various regimes. For a nonconducting gas there is only one such length: the mean free path, which is the average distance that a particle moves, owing to thermal agitation, between collisions. All the transport properties can be specified in terms of this mean free path. In addition, the ratio of the mean free path to the size of the object or container determines the flow regime, that is, whether the flow is free-molecular or continuum.

In an ionized gas there is a profusion of characteristic lengths. First, there are many mean free paths: the electron mean free path for collisions with ions, the electron mean free path for collisions with neutral particles, the ion mean free path for collisions with neutral particles, etc. These different mean free paths result in entirely different phenomena. Also, in a magnetic field a charged particle moves in a helical path between collisions; the radius of curvature of the path in a plane normal to the helix axis is called the *gyro radius* or *Larmor radius*. This radius depends on the magnetic field strength, the charge on the particle, and the particle velocity. However, it is sometimes useful to use the mean thermal velocity to define the gyro radius. It turns out that the ratio of the gyro radius to the mean free path determines the nature of the transport properties; if this ratio is large, the transport properties are scalar, but if the ratio is small, some or all of the properties can be written as second-rank tensors.

Another characteristic length is the Debye shielding length: This is the maximum distance over which an ionized gas may be nonneutral, on the average, and depends on the number density of charged particles and their mean thermal speed. It is in terms of the Debye length that a plasma is defined: The size of the apparatus or object must be much larger than the Debye length, and the ionized gas must be initially electrically neutral. (Note that this definition is not explicitly dependent on the degree of ionization of the gas or on the necessity for the electron temperature to be equal to the ion temperature.) The Debye length is also the maximum distance over which the coulombic field of an ion is effective.

A plasma has the same relation to a nonconducting gas that a metallic conducting solid or liquid has to a dielectric solid or liquid; namely, electric fields cause electric currents but in general can cause no net charge separation, and therefore no net electrical body force on the gas, although a surface force is still possible. This fact causes considerable simplification of the conservation equations: the ionized gas may be considered to be a single fluid which is electrically conducting, and the transport and other properties may always be calculated, at least in principle, from the state of the gas. This simplification is important for most flow applications, but there are some obvious examples where this simplification may not be used; for example, shock-wave structures, low-density flows, electronic vacuum tubes, and in the vicinity of surfaces immersed in a plasma. In these cases, the conservation equations for each electrical species must be utilized.

The characteristic lengths are not the only new phenomena in an ionized gas, for new velocities are introduced. In a nonconducting gas, there are only two characteristic velocities: the acoustic (mechanical) velocity, which is close to the mean thermal velocity, and the velocity of electromagnetic waves, which depends only on the dielectric constant or the polarizability of the gas.

In an ionized gas, there are a minimum of three thermal velocities: electrons, ions, and neutral particles. In addition, the velocity of electromagnetic waves is altered and depends on their frequency. Finally, if a magnetic field is present, and if the gas is sufficiently conducting, a new wave is possible: propagation of the magnetic field itself, called the *Alfvén wave,* which is generally coupled to the acoustic wave. The velocity depends on the average acoustic velocity and the magnitude and direction of the magnetic field.

Finally, wherever there are characteristic lengths and characteristic velocities, there are characteristic frequencies. For example, in a nonconducting gas, the collision frequency is the ratio of the particle velocity to the mean free path. Similarly, in an ionized gas, the electrons, ions, and neutral particles have characteristic collision frequencies. In addition, each type of charged particle has a characteristic gyro frequency associated with its helical motion in a magnetic field. Finally, there is a frequency for coupled motion of charged particles with local electric fields; these are the so-called "plasma frequencies."

There are a large number of relations between the various lengths, frequencies, and velocities. For example, the ratio of the electron mean free path to the electron gyro radius is equal to the ratio of the electron gyro frequency to the electron collision frequency. The Debye length is equal to the ratio of the electron mean thermal velocity to the electron plasma frequency. Also, the Alfvén velocity is equal to the ratio of the geometric mean ion-and-electron gyro frequencies to the electron plasma frequency, times the speed of light.

It is also possible to regroup the lengths, frequencies, and velocities into dimensionless numbers, such as the number of electrons in a sphere having a radius equal to the Debye length, etc. Other numbers apply to transport properties other than electrical, such as the familiar Reynolds number, Prandtl number, Knudsen number, etc. In addition, a conducting fluid has a magnetic Reynolds number, which is proportional to the effect of the flow on the magnetic field; a magnetic interaction parameter, which is the influence of the magnetic field on the flow; etc. These numbers are important for defining the flow regimes and for justifying certain simplifying assumptions. Many of these dimensionless numbers are not yet named.

1.3 MAGNETOHYDRODYNAMIC REGIMES

The previous section has indicated that a large number of characteristic lengths are used to specify the state of a plasma. To give a better understanding of the relationship between these lengths, Kantrowitz and Petschek[1] have mapped onto the state of a gas five regimes (see Fig. 1.2). The gas chosen was deuterium, primarily because this gas is of interest for thermonuclear fusion. In addition, deuterium has only one electron; when this electron is removed from the stable orbit around the nucleus, the atom is then singly ionized and has no other electronic shell structure. It therefore has a very simple structure and acts as a point charge of atomic mass 2, except at very high temperatures when the colliding charged particles can penetrate through the coulombic barrier to the nucleus.

The plot is in terms of the number of electrons per cubic centimeter and temperature in electron volts. Actually, the latter is the mean thermal energy of the deuterium ions or electrons, and the electron volts are simply the maximum voltage of a potential barrier that the electron can penetrate. Other coordinates could have been used, such as the familiar pressure-volume, or enthalpy-entropy. However, with ionized gases the two most important parameters are electron density and temperature, and it has become customary to use the units of per cubic centimeter (cm^{-3}) and electron volts (ev), respectively.

The plot has also been made for a special condition involving the magnetic pressure. It will be shown later that the electromagnetic Lorentz force can be represented as a gradient of $B^2/2\mu_0$, which is the square of the magnetic field divided by twice the permeability. The Lorentz force in an ionized gas tends to accelerate or decelerate it in the same manner as gradients in the hydrostatic pressure. Thus, the term $B^2/2\mu_0$ is called the *magnetic pressure* π^M. Now the values of the magnetic field used in Fig. 1.2 are such that the magnetic pressure is exactly equal to the gas pressure. In various applications one is normally interested in other values of the ratio of magnetic pressure to gas pressure. For example, in a magnetohydrodynamic power generator, this ratio must be the reciprocal of the magnetic Reynolds number, and since the latter is usually much less than unity, the magnetic pressure ratio must be much greater than unity. As another example, in thermonuclear fusion experiments, the ratio of magnetic pressure to gas pressure is as high as 10^5. Under these circumstances, gradients in the magnetic field can accelerate the plasma *irrespective* of the pressure gradients in the gas. Thus, a value of the magnetic pressure ratio of unity is the *lowest* value that one may consider for useful magnetohydrodynamics of ionized gases. The dashed lines in Fig. 1.2 show the required magnetic field strength for fulfilling this condition. Also, in Fig. 1.2, the typical geometrical length has been taken as 1 cm, since in many cases this is approximately the typical size of laboratory apparatus.

The diagram in Fig. 1.2 has four boundaries. At the right side, the electron thermal velocities become close to the speed of light c_0; that is, they are relativistic. Although this is possible to achieve with a particle

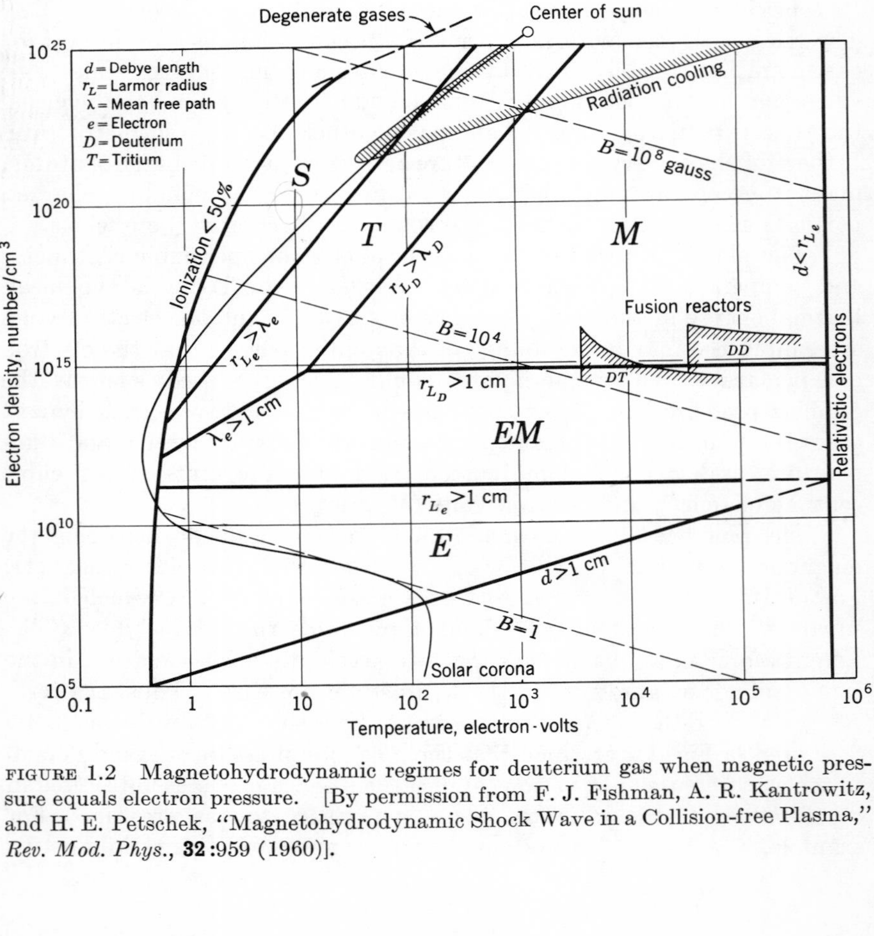

FIGURE 1.2 Magnetohydrodynamic regimes for deuterium gas when magnetic pressure equals electron pressure. [By permission from F. J. Fishman, A. R. Kantrowitz, and H. E. Petschek, "Magnetohydrodynamic Shock Wave in a Collision-free Plasma," *Rev. Mod. Phys.*, **32**:959 (1960)].

accelerator, it is quite difficult to achieve with the large number density of electrons in a plasma. It can also be shown that the ratio of the Debye shielding length d to the electron Larmor radius is given by

$$\frac{d}{r_{L_e}} \approx \frac{\langle c \rangle_e}{c_0} \sqrt{\frac{\pi^M}{p}} \tag{1.1}$$

where $\langle c \rangle_e$ is the mean thermal electron velocity, c_0 is the speed of light in vacuum, p is the pressure, and π^M is the magnetic pressure. Thus, for practical cases, $d \ll r_{L_e}$. This produces a very important simplification which will be used later, namely, that when an electron enters the coulombic field of an ion, *the presence of the magnetic field can be neglected.* Thus, the interaction of an electron with an ion does not depend upon the orientation of the electron-velocity vector with respect to the magnetic field.

The left boundary represents conditions at which 50 per cent thermal ionization is achieved; in the region to the left of this boundary the ionization is less than 50 per cent. The lower limit has too low a particle density. Consequently the Debye shielding length becomes larger than the size of the apparatus, and the ionized gas is not a plasma.

The upper boundary indicates the regime in which the electrons are so tightly packed that their spins interact with one another. This produces a profound effect on the forces between the charged particles so that they no longer act like a perfect gas. This is the situation in metals, but for gases the pressure required to achieve this state is beyond laboratory or solar gravitational means. This state is called *degenerate,* and will be explained in Chap. 6.

The interior of the four boundaries is divided into five regions as follows:

S = scalar
T = tensor
M = magnetic
EM = electromagnetic
E = electric

In the S region, the gas is so dense that the electron Larmor radius is larger than the electron mean free path. As noted previously, this implies that all properties of the gas are scalar. Thus, in the S region, the gas behaves as a single fluid whose properties are not affected by the presence of the magnetic field.

The T region is the region where the electron Larmor radius is less than a mean free path, but the ion Larmor radius is still greater than an ion mean free path. Those properties which depend on electrons are second-rank tensors, whereas those properties which are controlled by the ions are still scalar. To be specific, the electrical conductivity is controlled by electrons, so that this is a tensor. The ions have greater momentum than electrons, so that viscosity is controlled by the ions and is therefore scalar. Thermal conduction depends about equally on each, and so the thermal conductivity is tensor.

To the right of the T region, all properties are tensor. Thus, they are controlled by the magnetic field, and this is therefore named the M region.

When the ion Larmor radius becomes larger than the size of the apparatus, the ions will no longer follow helical paths around the magnetic field lines. Thus, their motion will not be controlled by the presence of the magnetic field. However, the electron Larmor radius can still be smaller than the apparatus, and thus their gross motion is controlled by the magnetic field. The ion motion is caused by electric fields due to any charge separation that develops as a result of electron motion. Since magnetic fields cause electron motion and the charge-separation electric fields cause ion motion, this region is called the EM region.

Finally, when the electron Larmor radius exceeds the size of the apparatus, the magnetic field is too small to affect the plasma motion, but electric fields will still cause currents. This is the E region, and its lower bound occurs where the Debye length exceeds the size of the apparatus. Below the lower boundary of the E region, the particles not only do not interact with one another (since the mean free path exceeds 1 cm), but gross charge separation can occur. Under these conditions, the situation cannot be described in terms of gas properties, but can be described in terms of particle motions. This is the region of vacuum-tube operation.

Several other regions have been superimposed on this diagram. At the top of the diagram is the radiation-cooling region. In this region a particle loses an appreciable part of its energy in the time it takes to move a distance of one centimeter, with the average thermal velocity. In this region one cannot usually achieve a steady state. The upper bound is blackbody radiation; the lower bound is that due to radiation which is emitted by an electron when it interacts with the coulombic field of an ion, called *bremsstrahlung*.

Also shown are the conditions on the sun. Notice that the interior of the sun is in the radiation-cooled region. Actually, in the interior of the sun, the radiative transfer must equal the thermonuclear heat generation to be in equilibrium, but this is not exactly the same criterion.

Also shown in Fig. 1.2 are the conditions required to achieve continuous thermonuclear reactions for the deuterium-tritium and deuterium-deuterium reactors. At the left-hand vertical boundaries the reaction energy is equal to the bremsstrahlung. The upper boundaries represent a net energy production of 100 watts/cm^3. Actually, the typical dimension for a thermonuclear reactor is closer to a meter, and the required ratio of magnetic pressure to gas pressure is closer to 10^5. Thus, thermonuclear reactors will be much further in the *M* region, instead of at its lower boundary.

The other applications will generally be in the *T* region. These include MHD power generators and most plasma propulsion devices. Some of the latter are in the *M* and the *EM* regions, and at least one device is in the *E* region.

The material in this book is concerned mainly with the *M*, *T*, and *S* regions. The *M* and *S* regions are simpler to describe than the *T* region; thus the *M* region is discussed first, in which collisions between particles will be neglected. The *S* region will be developed later, and finally the *T* region.

REFERENCE CITED

1. Kantrowitz, A. R., and H. E. Petschek: "An Introductory Discussion of Magnetohydrodynamics," in R. Landshoff (ed.), *Magnetohydrodynamics*, pp. 3–15, Stanford University Press, Stanford, Calif., 1957.

GENERAL REFERENCES

Alfvén, H.: *Cosmical Electrodynamics*, Oxford University Press, Fair Lawn, N.J., 1953.

Allis, W. P. (ed.): *Nuclear Fusion*, D. Van Nostrand Company, Inc., Princeton, N.J., 1960.

Bershader, D., and Rolf Landshoff: "Magnetohydrodynamics," in V. L. Streeter (ed.), *Handbook of Fluid Dynamics*, McGraw-Hill Book Company, New York, 1961.

Bishop, A. S.: *Project Sherwood*, Addison-Wesley Publishing Company, Inc., Reading, Mass., 1958.

Clauser, F. H. (gen. ed.): *Symposium on Plasma Dynamics*, Addison-Wesley Publishing Company, Inc., Reading, Mass., 1960.

Cole, G. H. A.: "Some Aspects of Magnetohydrodynamics," *Advan. Phys.*, **5**: 452–497 (1956); *Quart. Suppl. Phys. Mag.*

Cowling, T. G.: *Magnetohydrodynamics*, Interscience Publishers, Inc., New York, 1957.

Delcroix, J. L.: *Introduction to the Theory of Ionized Gases*, translation by M. Clark, Jr., D. J. BenDaniel, and J. M. BenDaniel, Interscience Publishers, Inc., New York, 1960.

Dungey, J. W.: *Cosmic Electrodynamics*, Cambridge University Press, New York, 1958.

Engineering Aspects of Magnetohydrodynamics: C. Mannal and N. W. Mather (eds.), *Proc. 2d Symp.*, Columbia University Press, New York, 1962; N. W. Mather and G. W. Sutton (eds.), *Proc. 3d Symp.*, Gordon and Breach, Science Publishers, Inc., New York, 1964.

Ferraro, V. C. A., and C. Plumpton: *Magneto-fluid Mechanics*, Oxford University Press, Fair Lawn, N.J., 1961.

Frenkiel, F. N., and W. R. Sears (eds.): *International Symposium of Magnetofluid Dynamics,* National Academy of Sciences, 1960; see also *Rev. Mod. Phys.,* **32** (October, 1960).

Glasstone, S., and R. Lovberg: *Controlled Thermonuclear Reactions,* D. Van Nostrand Company, Inc., Princeton, N.J., 1960.

International Summer Course in Plasma Physics (Riso), Danish Atomic Energy Commission, 1960.

Landshof, R. K. M.: "Magnetohydrodynamics," in *The McGraw-Hill Encyclopedia of Science and Technology,* vol. 8, p. 55, McGraw-Hill Book Company, New York, 1960.

Lehnert, B. (ed.): *Electromagnetic Phenomena in Cosmical Physics,* Cambridge University Press, New York, 1958.

Leontovich, M. A. (ed.): *Plasma Physics and the Problem of Controlled Nuclear Reactions,* Pergamon Press, New York, 1959–1961.

Linhart, J. G.: *Plasma Physics,* North Holland Publishing Company, Amsterdam, 1960.

Lockheed Symposia on Magnetohydrodynamics: R. Landshoff (ed.), vol. I, *Magnetohydrodynamics,* 1957, and vol. II, *Plasma in a Magnetic Field,* 1958; D. Bershader (ed.), vol. IV, *Magnetohydrodynamics of Conducting Fluids,* 1959, and vol. V, *Plasma Hydromagnetics,* 1960, Stanford University Press, Stanford, Calif.

Longmire, C. L., J. L. Tuck, and W. B. Thompson (eds.): *Plasma Physics and Thermonuclear Research,* Pergamon Press, New York, 1959.

Lundquist, S.: "Studies in Magneto-hydrodynamics," *Arkiv Fysik,* **5**(15):297 (February, 1952).

Montgomery, D. C., and D. A. Tidman, *Plasma Kinetic Theory,* McGraw-Hill Book Company, New York, 1964.

Pai, S. I.: *Magnetogasdynamics,* Prentice-Hall, Inc., Englewood Cliffs, N.J., 1962.

Post, R. F.: "Controlled Fusion Research: An Application of the Physics of High Temperature Plasmas," *Rev. Mod. Phys.,* **28**:338–362 (1956).

Ratcliffe, J. A.: *The Magneto-ionic Theory and Its Application to the Ionosphere,* Cambridge University Press, New York, 1959.

Resler, E. L., and W. R. Sears: "Prospects for Magneto-aerodynamics," *J. Aeron. Sci.,* **25**:235 (April, 1958).

Rose, D. J., and M. Clark: *Plasmas and Controlled Fusion,* John Wiley & Sons, Inc., New York, 1961.

Spitzer, L.: *Physics of Fully Ionized Gases,* vol. 2, Interscience Publishers, Inc., New York, 1962.

Theory of Neutral and Ionized Gases (Grenoble Université), John Wiley & Sons, Inc., New York, 1960.

Vlasov, A. A.: *Many-particle Theory and Its Application to Plasma,* Gordon and Breach, Science Publishers, Inc., New York, 1961.

2

THE ELECTROMAGNETIC FIELD

2.1 INTRODUCTION—UNITS

The electromagnetic field can be introduced from either of two points of view: particle or continuum. If one starts from the continuum, then one can derive the laws which affect a given particle, and vice versa. However, in this section the particle approach is used because it is more consistent with the method of development of this book.

Historically, two systems of units have been used in electromagnetism: electrostatic and magnetic. These two systems are confusing and require conversion factors. To eliminate this confusion, the mksc system has been devised, in which the basic units are the meter, kilogram, second, and coulomb. The first three are self-explanatory. The charge on an electron is $(-)1.60207 \times 10^{-19}$ coulomb, and the symbol for this magnitude of charge is e. Thus,

$$e = 1.60207 \times 10^{-19} \text{ coulomb}$$

An ampere is the flow of charges through a surface equal to one coulomb per second; thus it is sometimes more convenient to let one coulomb equal one ampere-second. The number of net charges on a given particle is Z. Thus, for an electron, $Z = -1$. All charges are negative or positive multiples of e, and e is the smallest unit of charge. When a particle has a net charge Ze, it will be treated as a point charge; that is, the electron shell structure and nuclear structure will be neglected. This is permissible at moderate temperatures because colliding charged particles will not penetrate beyond the coulombic field. Charges are also conserved; whenever a negatively charged particle is formed a positively charged particle must also be formed.

From the basic units, other units can be evolved. For example, mass density is kilograms per cubic meter. The unit of force is called a newton and is given by Newton's second law. Thus, one newton equals 1 kg-m/sec^2. Work or energy is the joule; this is the energy required to move a force of one newton one meter; hence one joule equals 1 kg-m^2/sec^2. The unit of power is a watt, which is equal to one joule per second, or 1 kg-m^2/sec^3. A watt is also defined as an ampere-volt, which therefore defines the volt as 1 kg-m^2/(sec^2)(coulomb). Finally pressure is defined as newtons per square meter, equal to kilograms per meter per second per second, and one atmosphere pressure equals 1.013×10^5 newtons/m^2. Electric fields are in volts per meter, and magnetic fields in volt-seconds per square meter. The volt-second is also called the weber. Ordinarily, magnetic fields are given in units of gauss; 10^4 gauss equal 1 weber/m^2. Other units are the henry, which is 1 volt-sec/amp, and the farad, which is 1 amp-sec/volt. Other units will be derived as required.

2.2 ELECTROSTATICS

Electrostatics deals with the forces between stationary charged particles in the absence of magnetic fields; these forces are called *coulombic*. Charged particles are also subjected to forces from an electric field, and electric fields are caused by charged particles; thus electrostatics is also concerned with electric fields.

Electrostatics can also deal with moving charges, if a frame of reference exists in which all charges appear to be stationary.

2.2.1 Coulomb's Law. The fundamental law of electrostatics is Coulomb's law (1785), which states that two charged particles exert a mutual force, in a direction parallel to a line connecting the two particles, which varies inversely as the square of the separation distance and is proportional to the product of the charges (see Fig. 2.1). Consider two particles with charges eZ_1 and eZ_2. Then the force on particle 2 due to

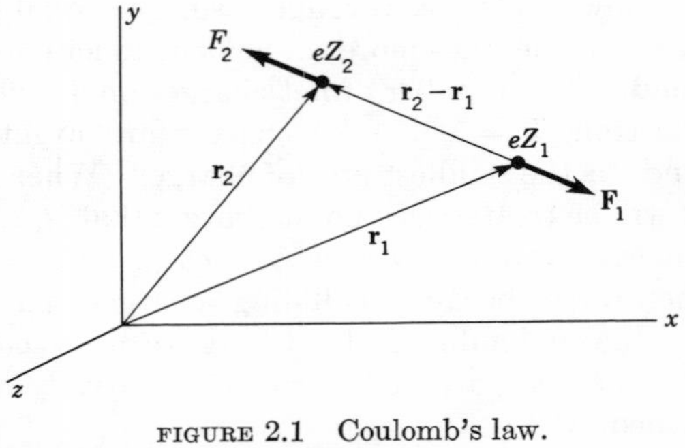

FIGURE 2.1 Coulomb's law.

particle 1 is

$$\mathbf{F}_2(\mathbf{r}_2) = \frac{e^2 Z_1 Z_2}{4\pi K_0} \frac{(\mathbf{r}_2 - \mathbf{r}_1)}{|\mathbf{r}_2 - \mathbf{r}_1|^3} \tag{2.1}$$

and the force on charge 1 due to the presence of charge 2 is

$$\mathbf{F}_1(\mathbf{r}_1) = \frac{e^2 Z_1 Z_2}{4\pi K_0} \frac{(\mathbf{r}_1 - \mathbf{r}_2)}{|\mathbf{r}_2 - \mathbf{r}_1|^3} \tag{2.2}$$

Here $\mathbf{r}_1$ and $\mathbf{r}_2$ are vectors to the particles from an origin, and $(4\pi K_0)^{-1}$ is the proportionality constant in vacuum,

$$(4\pi K_0)^{-1} = 8.988 \times 10^9 \left(\frac{\text{newton-m}^2}{\text{amp}^2\text{-sec}^2} = \frac{\text{volt-m}}{\text{amp-sec}} \right) \tag{2.3}$$

K_0 is called the *permittivity of vacuum.* Note that if particle 1 is held stationary, then the force on particle 2 is conservative. This leads to the concept that the (stationary) charges create electric fields. Thus, the force on 2 can be regarded as the product of its charge and the local electric field at $\mathbf{r}_2$, or

$$\mathbf{F}_2(\mathbf{r}_2) = eZ_2\mathbf{E}(\mathbf{r}_2) \tag{2.4}$$

where the electric field at $\mathbf{r}_2$ is given by

$$\mathbf{E}(\mathbf{r}_2) = \frac{eZ_1}{4\pi K_0} \frac{\mathbf{r}_2 - \mathbf{r}_1}{|\mathbf{r}_2 - \mathbf{r}_1|^3} \tag{2.5}$$

An important assumption is that the forces exerted on charge 2 by other charged particles are independent of each other; that is, the forces are superimposable. Then the *total* electric field at point 2 is given by the sum of expressions similar to (2.5), or

$$\mathbf{E}(\mathbf{r}_2) = \sum_{i \neq 2}^{n} \frac{Z_i e}{4\pi K_0} \frac{\mathbf{r}_2 - \mathbf{r}_i}{|\mathbf{r}_2 - \mathbf{r}_i|^3}$$

or, dropping the subscript 2,

$$\mathbf{E}(\mathbf{r}) = \sum_{\substack{i=1 \\ (\mathbf{r}_i \neq \mathbf{r})}}^{n} \frac{Z_i e}{4\pi K_0} \frac{\mathbf{r} - \mathbf{r}_i}{|\mathbf{r} - \mathbf{r}_i|^3} \tag{2.6}$$

Note that if there is a point charge at $\mathbf{r}$, this must *not* be included in the summation.

The total electric field due to the n stationary charges is conservative; that is, if charge 2 is moved around a small path and returned to its original position, no net work has been expended.† Thus,

$$\oint \mathbf{F}_2(\mathbf{r}) \cdot d\mathbf{r} = eZ_2 \oint \mathbf{E} \cdot d\mathbf{r} = 0$$

† The particle motion must be sufficiently slow so that radiation is negligible.

Use of Stokes' theorem leads immediately to

$$\nabla \times \mathbf{E} = 0 \tag{2.7}$$

which is also directly derivable from (2.6). Since the curl of a gradient is also equal to zero, one may let the quasi-stationary electric field be the negative gradient of a potential, or, from (2.6),

$$\mathbf{E} = -\nabla \phi = \frac{e}{4\pi K_0} \sum_i Z_i \frac{\mathbf{r} - \mathbf{r}_i}{|\mathbf{r} - \mathbf{r}_i|^3} \tag{2.8}$$

which can be integrated immediately to

$$\phi(\mathbf{r}) = \frac{e}{4\pi K_0} \sum_i \frac{Z_i}{|\mathbf{r} - \mathbf{r}_i|} \tag{2.9}$$

Generally, we are interested in a continuum in which the individual charges cannot be distinguished. Instead of individual charges, one uses the *local free charge density* ρ_e (in units of coulombs per cubic meter), which is the sum of the charges in a small volume $\Delta\mathcal{V}$, divided by that volume:†

$$\rho_e = \lim_{\Delta\mathcal{V} \to \epsilon} e \frac{\sum_i Z_i}{\Delta\mathcal{V}} \tag{2.10}$$

Obviously, there must be a large number of charged particles in the small volume to define the charge density as a continuum property. In a gas there are ions and atoms of several species s. For example, all free electrons can be called species 1; all positively charged hydrogen atoms 2; all singly positively charged helium atoms 3; etc. Thus, the charge and mass of all particles belonging to the same species are the same. If the number density of each species is n_s, then $\sum_i eZ_i = \Delta\mathcal{V} \sum_s n_s e Z_s$, and (2.10) becomes

$$\rho_e = e \sum_s n_s Z_s \tag{2.11}$$

In (2.9), instead of summing over each particle, one can then treat each small volume element as having a net charge $eZ_i = \rho_e \, \Delta\mathcal{V}$; finally one may integrate instead of summing, to obtain

$$\phi(\mathbf{r}) = \frac{1}{4\pi K_0} \int_{\mathcal{V}} \frac{\rho_e(\mathbf{r}') \, d\mathcal{V}'}{|\mathbf{r} - \mathbf{r}'|} \tag{2.12}$$

where the integration is performed with $\mathbf{r}$ fixed. Now, integrals such as (2.12) are not convenient to use, and it is desirable to convert (2.12) into

† An alternative definition is given by

$$\rho_e(\mathbf{r}) = \sum_i eZ_i \, \delta(\mathbf{r} - \mathbf{r}_i)$$

where δ is the Dirac delta function.

a differential equation. To do this, the surface integral of (2.6) is calculated. It is convenient to calculate the contribution to the surface integral from each charge separately, with the origin taken at each charge. For the ith charge, the element of surface is

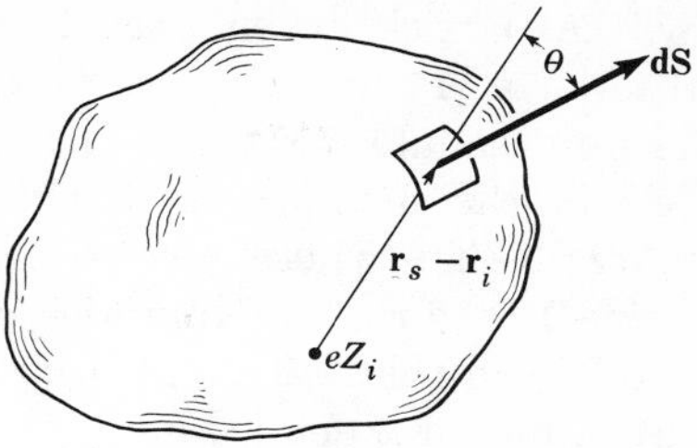

FIGURE 2.2 Gauss' law.

$$dS = \frac{d\Omega|\mathbf{r}_s - \mathbf{r}_i|^2}{\cos\theta}$$

where $d\Omega$ is an element of solid angle measure about the particle (see Fig. 2.2). Also, $(\mathbf{r}_s - \mathbf{r}_i) \cdot \mathbf{dS} = |\mathbf{r}_s - \mathbf{r}_i|\, dS \cos\theta$. Thus,

$$\int_s \mathbf{E}(\mathbf{r}_s) \cdot \mathbf{dS}(\mathbf{r}_s) = \frac{eZ_i}{4\pi K_0} \int_s d\Omega = \frac{eZ_i}{K_0} \tag{2.13}$$

since $\int_s d\Omega = 4\pi$. Performing the integration over all particles on the interior of the volume, one obtains

$$\int_s \mathbf{E} \cdot \mathbf{dS} = \frac{1}{K_0} \int_v \rho_e \, d\mathcal{V} \tag{2.14}$$

The contribution to the surface integral from all charges exterior to the volume is zero, because the integral $\int_s d\Omega = 0$. Use of Gauss' theorem with (2.14) yields Gauss' law:

$$\nabla \cdot \mathbf{E} = \frac{\rho_e}{K_0} \tag{2.15}$$

Finally, use of (2.8) yields Poisson's equation:

$$\nabla^2 \phi = -\frac{\rho_e}{K_0} \tag{2.16}$$

2.2.2 Polarization. In some problems, an additional property becomes important: the polarizability of particles. Some molecules are dipoles in their normal state; that is, the charge centroid of the electrons does not coincide with the charge centroid of the positive nucleus. In the presence of an electric field, these particles tend to rotate so that the lines of centers of the two charge centroids are parallel to the electric field. Other particles are not ordinarily dipoles; that is, the two charge centroids coincide. However, in the presence of an electric field, the centroids may separate, with the positively charged centroid in the direction of the field. In both cases, energy will be absorbed by the particle when placed in an electric field. Thus, a dipole can absorb or return energy to the field, and the polarization of the medium should be taken into account. Consider a single neutral particle in the medium, with net positive charge $+Ze$ and net negative charge $-Ze$, whose charge centroids are separated by a distance $\mathbf{l}$, where $\mathbf{l}$ is directed from the negative charge centroid to the positive charge centroid. The polarization of the particle is measured by its dipole moment defined as

$$\mathbf{p} = Ze\mathbf{l} \tag{2.17}$$

The potential field ϕ_p from such a dipole can be calculated by summing the field from both charge centroids and by letting $|\mathbf{l}|$ become vanishingly small. The result is

$$\phi_p(\mathbf{r}) = \frac{1}{4\pi K_0} \mathbf{p}_i \cdot \frac{(\mathbf{r} - \mathbf{r}_i)}{|\mathbf{r} - \mathbf{r}_i|^3} \tag{2.18}$$

The total dipole moment $\mathbf{P}_p$ is the sum of the individual dipole moments per unit volume. If each particle of the s species has an average dipole moment $\langle \mathbf{p}_s \rangle$, then the total dipole moment is $\mathbf{P}_p = \sum_s n_s \langle \mathbf{p}_s \rangle$, and the dipole of a small volume $\Delta \mathcal{V}$ is $\mathbf{P}_p \, \Delta \mathcal{V}$. Thus, the dipole electric field potential becomes

$$\phi_p(\mathbf{r}) = -\frac{1}{4\pi K_0} \int_{\mathcal{V}} \frac{\mathbf{P}_p(\mathbf{r}') \cdot (\mathbf{r}' - \mathbf{r}) \, d\mathcal{V}}{|\mathbf{r}' - \mathbf{r}|^3} \tag{2.19a}$$

where the dipole moment and volume element are located at $\mathbf{r}'$ during integration.

Now,

$$\begin{aligned} \nabla \cdot \frac{\mathbf{P}_p}{|\mathbf{r}|} &= \frac{1}{|\mathbf{r}|} \nabla \cdot \mathbf{P}_p + \mathbf{P}_p \cdot \nabla \frac{1}{|\mathbf{r}|} \\ &= \frac{1}{|\mathbf{r}|} \nabla \cdot \mathbf{P}_p - \frac{\mathbf{P}_p \cdot \mathbf{r}}{|\mathbf{r}|^3} \end{aligned}$$

Thus, with the use of Gauss' theorem, (2.19a) can be written as

$$\phi_p(\mathbf{r}) = -\frac{1}{4\pi K_0} \left[\int_v \frac{\nabla' \cdot \mathbf{P}_p(\mathbf{r}') \, d\mathcal{V}'}{|\mathbf{r}' - \mathbf{r}|} - \int_s \frac{\mathbf{P}_p \cdot d\mathbf{S}}{|\mathbf{r}' - \mathbf{r}|} \right] \tag{2.19b}$$

It can be seen that the influence of polarization can be thought of as consisting of an *apparent* charge density $-\nabla \cdot \mathbf{P}_p$ throughout the volume, and an apparent surface charge $\mathbf{P}_p$ distributed over the surface of the region. If the surface of the region is extended to infinity, and at infinity $\mathbf{P}_p$ vanishes, then the surface integral in (2.19b) can be neglected, so that

$$\phi_p(\mathbf{r}) = -\frac{1}{4\pi K_0} \int_v \frac{\nabla' \cdot \mathbf{P}_p(\mathbf{r}') \, d\mathcal{V}'}{|\mathbf{r}' - \mathbf{r}|} \tag{2.19c}$$

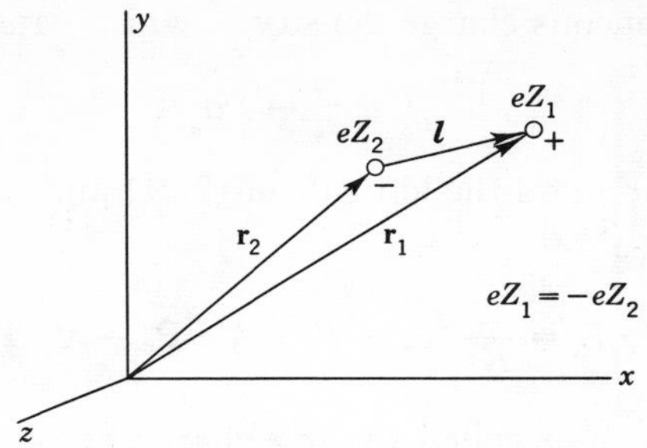

FIGURE 2.3 Polarization due to free charges.

Note that in a uniformly polarized region there is no contribution to the electric potential from the interior of the region, since $\nabla \cdot \mathbf{P}_p = 0$.

The total electric field potential is obtained by adding (2.19c) to (2.12):

$$\phi(\mathbf{r}) = \frac{1}{4\pi K_0} \int_v \frac{\rho_e(\mathbf{r}') - \nabla' \cdot \mathbf{P}_p(\mathbf{r}')}{|\mathbf{r} - \mathbf{r}'|} \, d\mathcal{V} \tag{2.20}$$

Then (2.14) becomes

$$\int_s \mathbf{E} \cdot \mathbf{dS} = \frac{1}{K_0} \int_v (\rho_e - \nabla \cdot \mathbf{P}_p) \, d\mathcal{V} \tag{2.21}$$

The term $-\nabla \cdot \mathbf{P}_p$, therefore, is an apparent charge density caused by a gradient in the polarization. The total charge density ρ_{e_t} is defined as the sum of the charge density due to charged particles and the apparent charge density due to polarization, as follows:

$$\rho_{e_t} = \rho_e - \nabla \cdot \mathbf{P}_p \tag{a}$$

In the same manner, charge nonneutrality of charged particles in a gas gives rise to an apparent polarization (see Fig. 2.3). Consider two equal and opposite free charges in a gas. The dipole moment for these two charges is

$$\mathbf{p}_e = eZ_1\mathbf{l} = eZ_1(\mathbf{r}_1 - \mathbf{r}_2) = eZ_1\mathbf{r}_1 - eZ_1\mathbf{r}_2 = eZ_1\mathbf{r}_1 + eZ_2\mathbf{r}_2$$

The dipole moment associated with each charge is therefore $eZ_i\mathbf{r}_i$, where $\mathbf{r}_i$ is measured from some origin. The total dipole moment per unit volume is the sum of the dipole moments of the particles; hence,

$$\mathbf{P}_e = \lim_{\Delta\mathcal{V}\to\epsilon} \frac{\sum_i eZ_i\mathbf{r}_i}{\Delta\mathcal{V}}$$
$$= \lim_{\Delta\mathcal{V}\to\epsilon} \frac{\int \rho_e \mathbf{r} \, d\mathcal{V}}{\int d\mathcal{V}}$$

The inhomogeneous charge density ρ_e' which causes this polarization may be defined as

$$\rho_e' = -\nabla \cdot \mathbf{P}_e \tag{b}$$

Use of Gauss' theorem on the left side of (2.21) and addition of (*b*) to the right side of (2.21) yield

$$\nabla \cdot \mathbf{E} = \frac{1}{K_0}(\rho_e - \rho_e' - \nabla \cdot \mathbf{P}_e - \nabla \cdot \mathbf{P}_p) \tag{c}$$

The difference $\rho_e - \rho_e'$ is called the *free* charge density ρ_0,

$$\rho_0 = \rho_e - \rho_e' = \rho_e + \nabla \cdot \mathbf{P}_e \tag{d}$$

while the total polarization is given by

$$\mathbf{P} = \mathbf{P}_e + \mathbf{P}_p \tag{e}$$

Use of (*d*) and (*e*) in (*c*) and rearrangement yield

$$\nabla \cdot (K_0\mathbf{E} + \mathbf{P}) = \rho_0 \tag{f}$$

Now, the electric displacement $\mathbf{D}$ is defined as

$$\mathbf{D} = K_0\mathbf{E} + \mathbf{P} \tag{2.22}$$

so that (*f*) becomes

$$\nabla \cdot \mathbf{D} = \rho_0 \tag{2.23}$$

If the polarization is proportional to $\mathbf{E}$, then the displacement is also proportional to the electric field

$$\mathbf{D} = K\mathbf{E} \tag{2.24}$$

where K is the permittivity of the medium. The ratio K/K_0 is the dielectric constant for the medium. Finally, subtraction of (*d*) from (*a*) shows that

$$\rho_0 = \rho_{e_t} + \nabla \cdot \mathbf{P} \tag{g}$$

which is in agreement with the usual formulas of electrodynamics.

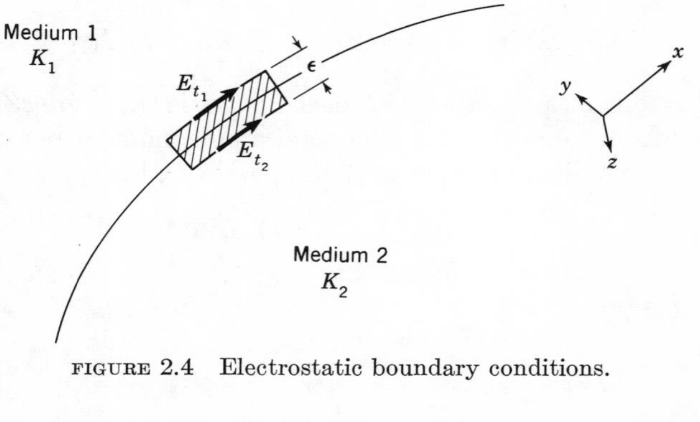

FIGURE 2.4 Electrostatic boundary conditions.

2.2.3 Electrostatic Boundary Conditions. The boundary conditions between two different media can be obtained from the integral relations. First, consider the shaded area in Fig. 2.4. Around the periphery, $\oint \mathbf{E} \cdot \mathbf{dl} = 0$ from $\nabla \times \mathbf{E} = 0$, which leads to

$$E_{t_1} = E_{t_2} \tag{2.25}$$

where t refers to the tangential direction. For both media, $E_t = -\partial\phi/\partial x$, so that

$$\left(\frac{\partial \phi}{\partial x}\right)_1 = \left(\frac{\partial \phi}{\partial x}\right)_2 \tag{h}$$

which integrates immediately to

$$\phi_1 = \phi_2 \tag{2.25a}$$

on all portions of an interface. Equations (2.25) and (2.25a) are completely equivalent. The constant of integration of (2.25a) is zero; otherwise there would be a different potential on either side of the boundary which would give rise to infinite values of the normal electric field.

Next, consider a small volume enclosing the boundary with an area $\mathbf{dS}$ and a height h (see Fig. 2.5). For this volume, Gauss' law is

$$\int \mathbf{D} \cdot \mathbf{dS} = \int \rho_0 \, d\mathcal{V}$$

or

$$D_{n_1} \, dS_1 + D_{n_2} \, dS_2 = \rho_0 \epsilon \, dS \tag{i}$$

if ϵ is very small. The term $\rho_0\epsilon$ is the amount of charge per unit area of the surface dS; this is called σ_0 coulombs/m^2. Now as $h \to 0$, $dS_1 \to dS_2$, and recalling that $\mathbf{D}_i = K_i\mathbf{E}_i$ and $\mathbf{E} = -\nabla\phi$, this boundary condition becomes

$$K_1\left(\frac{\partial \phi}{\partial n}\right)_1 - K_2 \frac{\partial \phi_2}{\partial n} = \sigma_0 \tag{2.26}$$

Equations (2.25), or (2.25a), and (2.26) are the two boundary conditions for the electric field. Although they were derived for stationary fields, they are also valid for time-varying fields, as long as K_1 and K_2 are constant.

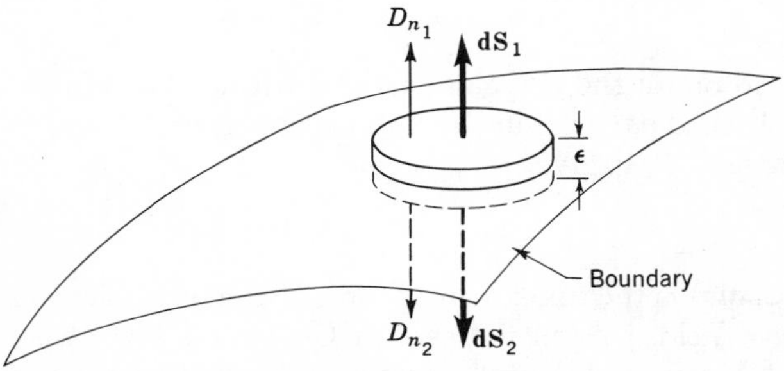

FIGURE 2.5 Boundary condition for **D**.

2.3 MAGNETOSTATICS

It has been experimentally observed that when electric currents flow in two wires, a mutual force is exerted between them. In analogy with electrostatics, magnetostatics treats only quasi-stationary situations. The force law is similar to Coulomb's law; the force varies inversely as the square of the distance between the wires and is proportional to the product of the two currents. But in addition, the force depends on the relative orientation of the wires. In vector notation, the magnetic force law is

$$\mathbf{dF}(\mathbf{r}) = \frac{\mu_0}{4\pi} \frac{II'}{|\mathbf{r} - \mathbf{r}'|^3} \mathbf{dl} \times [\mathbf{dl}' \times (\mathbf{r} - \mathbf{r}')] \tag{2.27}$$

where I is the total current in the wire and $\mathbf{dl}$ is an element of wire at $\mathbf{r}$, I' is the total current and $\mathbf{dl}'$ is an element of the wire at $\mathbf{r}'$, and $\mu_0/4\pi$ is the constant of proportionality, given by

$$\frac{\mu_0}{4\pi} = 10^{-7} \text{ newtons/amp}^2 = 10^{-7} \text{ volt-sec/amp-m} \tag{2.28}$$

μ_0 is called the *permeability of vacuum.* If we define a magnetic field $\mathbf{B}(\mathbf{r})$ at $\mathbf{r}$, due to all current elements at $\mathbf{r}'$, then from (2.27) the expression for $\mathbf{B}(\mathbf{r})$ is

$$\mathbf{B}(\mathbf{r}) = \frac{\mu_0}{4\pi} \int_{l'} \frac{I'(\mathbf{r}')\, \mathbf{dl}' \times (\mathbf{r} - \mathbf{r}')}{|\mathbf{r} - \mathbf{r}'|^3} \tag{2.29}$$

which is called the *Biot and Savart law.* The force law then takes on the following simple form:

$$\mathbf{dF}(\mathbf{r}) = I(\mathbf{r})\, \mathbf{dl}(\mathbf{r}) \times \mathbf{B} \tag{2.30}$$

which is known as *Ampère's law* (1825). The current is the charge crossing the cross section of the wire per second. If A is the cross section, then $I = n_s e Z_s A w_s$, where s is the charged species which is moving in the wire. Thus $I\, \mathbf{dl} = (n_s e Z_s A\, dl)\mathbf{w}_s$, where it is assumed that the particle velocity is in the direction of the wire. The force on the wire is therefore

$$\mathbf{dF} = n_s e Z_s A\, dl\, \mathbf{w}_s \times \mathbf{B}$$

and is exerted on all the charged particles within the volume $A\, dl$. The number of charged particles in this volume is $n_s A\, dl$; hence the force on *one* of these particles F_s is given by

$$\mathbf{F}_s = eZ_s \mathbf{w}_s \times \mathbf{B} \tag{2.30a}$$

Equation (2.30*a*) is the fundamental force law on a particle due to motion in a magnetic field. As in the case of Coulomb's law, it is desirable to convert (2.29) into a differential equation. To do this, the vector product of **B** is taken over the surface of a closed volume. Expansion of the resulting triple product yields

$$\int_s \mathbf{B}(\mathbf{r}) \times d\mathbf{S}(\mathbf{r}) = \frac{\mu_0}{4\pi} \int_s \int_{l'} \frac{(\mathbf{r}_s - \mathbf{r}')(I'\, d\mathbf{l}' \cdot d\mathbf{S})}{|\mathbf{r}_s - \mathbf{r}'|^3} - \frac{\mu_0}{4\pi} \int_s \int_{l'} \frac{I'\, d\mathbf{l}'\, [(\mathbf{r}_s - \mathbf{r}') \cdot d\mathbf{S}]}{|\mathbf{r}_s - \mathbf{r}'|^3}$$

Integration of the first term with respect to $d\mathbf{S}$ yields zero since $d\mathbf{l}'$ is a constant vector with respect to that integration. For the second term, let $dS = |\mathbf{r} - \mathbf{r}'|^2\, d\Omega/\cos\theta$, and use Stokes' law for the left side. The result is

$$-\int_{\mathcal{V}} (\nabla \times \mathbf{B})\, d\mathcal{V} = -\mu_0 \int_{l'} I'\, d\mathbf{l}' \tag{2.31}$$

where the integral on the right is over the entire volume. For a distributed current,

$$I'\, d\mathbf{l}' = \mathbf{J}'\, dS'\, dl' = \mathbf{J}'\, d\mathcal{V}' \tag{2.32}$$

where dS' is an element of area normal to $\mathbf{J}$, and $\mathbf{J}$ is the current density and is in the direction of current flow. Substitution of (2.32) into (2.31) yields

$$\int_{\mathcal{V}} (\nabla \times \mathbf{B})\, d\mathcal{V} = \mu_0 \int_{\mathcal{V}} \mathbf{J}\, d\mathcal{V}$$

Since the shape of the volume is arbitrary, the integrands must be equal, or

$$\nabla \times \mathbf{B} = \mu_0 \mathbf{J} \tag{2.33}$$

Equation (2.33) holds when $\mathbf{J}$ includes the *total* current density in a medium. For moving charges, the current density is given by the sum (over all particles in a small volume) of products of the charge on each particle and its velocity with respect to laboratory coordinates divided by that volume, or

$$\mathbf{J} = \frac{\sum_i eZ_i\, w_i}{\Delta\mathcal{V}} = \sum_s n_s e Z_s \mathbf{v}_s \tag{j}$$

where $\mathbf{v}_s$ is the average velocity of the s species. Note that this current is *not* time-averaged. If some charged particles are executing helical or cycloidal motion, their velocity can be decomposed into a circular motion plus the motion of the center of curvature $\mathbf{w}_d$, called the *guiding-center velocity* (or sometimes *drift* velocity), so that

$$\mathbf{w} = \mathbf{w}_d + \boldsymbol{\omega} \times \mathbf{r}$$

where $\boldsymbol{\omega}$ is the angular velocity vector, and $\mathbf{r}$ is the radius of curvature. Associated with the circular motion of a charged particle is a circular current $I = eZ\omega/2\pi$, for which a *magnetic moment* is defined as follows:

$$\boldsymbol{\mu}_i = \frac{I\pi r^2\boldsymbol{\omega}}{\omega} \tag{2.34}$$

The sum of all such magnetic moments per unit volume is the magnetization $\mathbf{M}_\mu$ due to circular motion of charged particles,

$$\mathbf{M}_\mu = \lim_{\Delta\mathcal{V}\to\epsilon} \frac{\sum_i \boldsymbol{\mu}_i}{\Delta\mathcal{V}} = \sum_s n_s\langle\boldsymbol{\mu}_s\rangle \tag{2.35}$$

where $\langle\boldsymbol{\mu}_s\rangle$ is the average magnetic moment, and n_s is the number density of the s species. With this definition of $\mathbf{M}_\mu$, (2.33) can be written as follows:

$$\nabla \times \mathbf{B} = \mu_0\mathbf{J}_d + \mu_0 \nabla \times \mathbf{M}_\mu \equiv \mu_0\mathbf{J} \tag{2.36}$$

where $\mathbf{J}_d$ is the drift current associated with the motion of the guiding centers of charged particles, and $\nabla \times \mathbf{M}_\mu$ represents an apparent magnetization current. The proof is given in Sec. 3.12. Rearrangement of (2.36) yields

$$\nabla \times \mathbf{H} = \mathbf{J}_d \tag{2.37}$$

where $\mathbf{H}$, called the *magnetic field strength*, is

$$\mathbf{H} = \frac{\mathbf{B}}{\mu_0} - \mathbf{M}_\mu \tag{2.38}$$

If the magnetization is proportional to the magnetic field, then Eq. (2.38) can be written as

$$\mathbf{H} = \frac{\mathbf{B}}{\mu} \tag{2.39}$$

where μ is the permeability of the gas. Note the distinction between μ, which is the permeability, and $\boldsymbol{\mu}$, which is the magnetic moment.

In addition to the magnetic moment associated with the circular motion of charges $\mathbf{M}_\mu$, some particles, for example, electrons, have an intrinsic magnetic moment leading to a magnetization $\mathbf{M}_p$. If one thinks of this magnetic moment as a circulation of charges, then this should give rise to a magnetization current $\nabla \times \mathbf{M}_p$. This procedure leads to some conceptual difficulties.[1] Furthermore, the smallest element of current in the present treatment is the electron, and therefore the circulating charges which give rise to the permanent magnetic moment of electrons or other atomic particles are not considered to be macroscopic currents. Thus in the present treatment $\nabla \times \mathbf{M}_p$ associated with the intrinsic magnetic moment of atomic particles will *not* be regarded as a macroscopic current.

Problems involving $\mathbf{M}_p$ arise primarily in magnetic materials where the magnetization $\mathbf{M}_p$ can be important. In gases this effect is negligible, owing to the much smaller number density of atomic particles. For completeness, however, note that the magnetic field strength is given by

$$\mathbf{H} = \frac{\mathbf{B}}{\mu_0} - \mathbf{M}_\mu - \mathbf{M}_p$$

and (2.38) is modified to

$$\nabla \times \mathbf{B} = \mu_0(\mathbf{J} + \nabla \times \mathbf{M}_p) \qquad (2.38a)$$

while (2.37) remains the same.

Equation (2.29) also reveals another property of $\mathbf{B}$. Note that

$$\nabla_r \frac{1}{|\mathbf{r} - \mathbf{r}'|} = -\frac{\mathbf{r} - \mathbf{r}'}{|\mathbf{r} - \mathbf{r}'|^3}$$

so that (2.29) becomes

$$\mathbf{B}(\mathbf{r}) = \frac{\mu_0}{4\pi} \int_{l'} I'(\mathbf{r}')\, \nabla_r \frac{1}{|\mathbf{r} - \mathbf{r}'|} \times d\mathbf{l}'$$

Now, $\nabla_r(1/|\mathbf{r} - \mathbf{r}'|) \times I'\, d\mathbf{l}' = \nabla_r \times (I'\, d\mathbf{l}'/|\mathbf{r} - \mathbf{r}'|)$ where the operator ∇_r operates only on $\mathbf{r}$. Thus,

$$\mathbf{B}(\mathbf{r}) = \frac{\mu_0}{4\pi} \nabla_r \times \int \frac{I'\, d\mathbf{l}'}{|\mathbf{r} - \mathbf{r}'|} = \frac{\mu_0}{4\pi} \nabla_r \times \int \frac{\mathbf{J}\, d\mathcal{V}}{|\mathbf{r} - \mathbf{r}'|} \qquad (2.40)$$

Since $\nabla \cdot \nabla \times (\;\;) = 0$, (2.40) shows that

$$\nabla \cdot \mathbf{B} = 0 \qquad (2.41)$$

In analogy with the electric field potential, a magnetic field potential $\mathbf{A}$ may be defined by means of (2.40) as follows:

$$\mathbf{A}(r) = \frac{\mu_0}{4\pi} \int \frac{\mathbf{J}'\, d\mathcal{V}'}{|\mathbf{r} - \mathbf{r}'|} \qquad (2.42)$$

so that

$$\mathbf{B} = \nabla \times \mathbf{A} \qquad (2.43)$$

The differential form for $\mathbf{A}$ can be obtained directly by substitution of (2.43) into (2.33),

$$\nabla^2 \mathbf{A} = -\mu_0 \mathbf{J} \qquad (2.44)$$

where $\nabla \cdot \mathbf{A}$ has been taken as zero for convenience. The operator $\nabla^2 \mathbf{A}$ is defined for cartesian components of $\mathbf{A}$. Equations (2.42) and (2.44) are usually simpler to use than (2.29) and (2.33).

Finally, the boundary conditions must be evaluated. From (2.41), the normal components of $\mathbf{B}$ across a surface must be equal, or

$$B_{n_1} = B_{n_2} \qquad (2.45)$$

and since $\mathbf{H} = \mathbf{B}_0/\mu_0 - \mathbf{M} = \mathbf{B}/\mu$,

$$\mu_1 H_{n_1} = \mu_2 H_{n_2} \tag{2.46}$$

For the tangential component, from (2.33),

$$B_{t_1} - B_{t_2} = \mu_0 J^* \tag{2.47}$$

where J^* is the total surface current between the two regions and can be due to both guiding-center current and magnetization current. If the two kinds of currents are separated, (2.47) becomes

$$B_{t_1} - B_{t_2} = \mu_0 J_d^* + \mu_0(M_{1\mu} - M_{2\mu}) \tag{2.48}$$

where J_d^* is the guiding-center surface current. In terms of the magnetic field strength H, (2.48) can be written as

$$H_{t_1} - H_{t_2} = \mu_0 J_d^*$$

These boundary conditions can also be written in terms of the magnetic potential. From $\nabla \cdot \mathbf{A} = 0$, the normal component of $\mathbf{A}$ is continuous. For the tangential component, construct a surface $\epsilon\, dt$ (see Fig. 2.4) normal to the surface which separates the two regions, and integrate (2.43) over the shaded surface $dS = \epsilon\, dt$:

$$\int (\nabla \times \mathbf{A}) \cdot \mathbf{e}_3\, dS = \int \mathbf{B} \cdot \mathbf{e}_3\, dS$$

The left side becomes the line integral for ϵ small, so that

$$(A_{t_1} - A_{t_2})\, dt = B_3 \epsilon\, dt$$

As $\epsilon \to 0$, the right side must also go to zero, since B_3 is finite; thus,

$$A_{t_1} = A_{t_2} \tag{2.49}$$

Since both the normal and tangential components of A are continuous,

$$\mathbf{A}_1 = \mathbf{A}_2 \tag{2.50}$$

Next, a small volume $\epsilon\, dS$ is constructed around the surface (see Fig. 2.5). Integration of (2.44) in this volume yields

$$\int \nabla \cdot \nabla A_i\, d\mathcal{V} = \mu_0 \int J_i\, d\mathcal{V}$$

where $i = 1, 2$, or 3. Use of Gauss' theorem yields

$$\int \nabla A_i \cdot d\mathbf{S} = \mu_0 J_i \epsilon\, dS$$

or

$$dS\left[\left(\frac{\partial A_i}{\partial n}\right)_1 - \left(\frac{\partial A_i}{\partial n}\right)_2\right] = \mu_0 J_i \epsilon\, dS$$

If there is a surface current, then $J_i\epsilon$ is the surface current J^*. Thus,

$$\left(\frac{\partial A_t}{\partial n}\right)_1 - \left(\frac{\partial A_t}{\partial n}\right)_2 = \mu_0 J^* \tag{2.51}$$

This current includes both magnetization currents and guiding-center currents. In terms of guiding-center currents only, (2.51) becomes

$$\frac{1}{\mu_1}\left(\frac{\partial A_t}{\partial n}\right)_1 - \frac{1}{\mu_2}\left(\frac{\partial A_t}{\partial n}\right)_1 = J_d^* \tag{2.52}$$

For the normal component of A across the surface, $J_n\epsilon \to 0$ as $\epsilon \to 0$, so that

$$\left(\frac{\partial A_n}{\partial n}\right)_1 = \left(\frac{\partial A_n}{\partial n}\right)_2 \tag{2.53}$$

These boundary conditions also apply when the situation is nonsteady.

The magnetic potential vector **A** is obviously somewhat difficult to use. For the special case of zero guiding-center currents, (2.37) yields $\nabla \times \mathbf{H} = 0$. Then **H** can be a gradient of a magnetic scalar potential ϕ^*:

$$\mathbf{H} = -\nabla\phi^* \tag{2.54}$$

Furthermore, $\mathbf{B} = \mu\mathbf{H}$, and from (2.41) and (2.54),

$$\nabla \cdot (\mu\,\nabla\phi^*) = 0 \tag{2.55}$$

even when magnetization exists. In the special case of constant permeability μ = const, and (2.55) reduces to Laplace's equation. In the absence of currents, the boundary conditions for ϕ^* are particularly simple: Both ϕ^* and its normal derivative across a surface must be continuous.

2.4 THE ELECTROMAGNETIC FIELD

In the time-independent or quasi-stationary case, the electrostatic and magnetostatic fields are completely uncoupled. This is no longer true in time-dependent problems. For example, if a closed loop of wire is placed in a magnetic field but is cut at one point, and if the shape of the loop or the magnetic field is changed, then a voltage will appear between the two ends of the wire. This voltage is given as follows:

$$\Delta\phi = -\frac{d}{dt}\int_s \mathbf{B} \cdot \mathbf{dS} \tag{2.56}$$

where **dS** is an element of area enclosed by the loop. Equation (2.56) is Faraday's law of induction (1830). The appearance of a potential between the ends of the loop means that a line integral of an electric field must exist; let this electric field be $\mathbf{E}'$. Then $\Delta\phi = -\int_l \mathbf{E}' \cdot \mathbf{dl}$, and with the use of Stokes' theorem, (2.56) becomes

$$\nabla \times \mathbf{E}' = -\frac{\partial \mathbf{B}}{\partial t} \tag{2.57}$$

In addition to the induced field, there may also be present an electrostatic field, $\mathbf{E}'' = -\nabla\phi$. Accordingly, the total electric field can be defined as

$$\mathbf{E} = \mathbf{E}' + \mathbf{E}'' \tag{2.58}$$

Use of (2.43) and (2.57) and integration then yield

$$\mathbf{E} = -\frac{\partial \mathbf{A}}{\partial t} + \mathbf{E}''$$

or

$$\mathbf{E} = -\frac{\partial \mathbf{A}}{\partial t} - \nabla\phi \tag{2.59}$$

We next derive the expression for the complete electric current in a nonstatic situation. The influx of charges into a volume must be equal to the increase in charges in the volume, or

$$-\int \mathbf{J} \cdot d\mathbf{S} = \frac{d}{dt}\int \rho_e \, d\mathcal{V} \tag{k}$$

where the charge current is given by (j) of Sec. 2.3, and ρ_e is given by (2.11). Use of Gauss' theorem on the left side of (k) yields

$$\nabla \cdot \mathbf{J} = -\frac{\partial \rho_e}{\partial t} \tag{2.60}$$

The charge current can be decomposed into a drift current $\mathbf{J}_d$, the effect of helical motion of individual particles, and polarization caused by charge separation. Thus we let

$$\mathbf{J} = \mathbf{J}_d + \nabla \times \mathbf{M}_\mu + \frac{\partial \mathbf{P}_e}{\partial t} \tag{l}$$

In addition to the current caused by the motion of charges, changes in the dipole moment appear to be a current, because of the motion of the charges in the dipole. Thus $(\partial/\partial t)\nabla \cdot \mathbf{P}_p$ may be added to the both sides of (l). With the use of (l), (2.60) becomes

$$\nabla \cdot \left(\mathbf{J}_d + \nabla \times \mathbf{M}_\mu + \frac{\partial \mathbf{P}}{\partial t}\right) = -\frac{\partial \rho_{e_t}}{\partial t} \tag{2.61}$$

Now the right side of (2.61) is the total change in charge density due to both charged species and dipoles; thus the term in parenthesis in (2.61) must represent the total current $\mathbf{J}_t$:

$$\begin{aligned} \mathbf{J}_t &= \mathbf{J}_d + \nabla \times \mathbf{M}_\mu + \frac{\partial \mathbf{P}}{\partial t} \\ &= \mathbf{J} + \frac{\partial \mathbf{P}_p}{\partial t} \\ &= \sum_s n_s e Z_s \mathbf{v}_s + \frac{\partial \mathbf{P}_p}{\partial t} \end{aligned} \tag{m}$$

Now $\nabla \cdot \nabla \times \mathbf{M}_\mu \equiv 0$, and use of (*g*), Sec. 2.2.2, yields

$$\nabla \cdot \mathbf{J}_d = -\frac{\partial \rho_0}{\partial t} \tag{2.62}$$

We are now in a position to derive the dynamical form for (2.37). If the divergence of (2.37) is taken, there is obtained

$$\nabla \cdot \nabla \times \mathbf{H} = \nabla \cdot \mathbf{J}_d \tag{n}$$

Now the left side of (*n*) is identically equal to zero, while the right side, from (2.62) and (2.24), is

$$\nabla \cdot \mathbf{J}_d = -\frac{\partial \rho_0}{\partial t} = -\nabla \cdot \frac{\partial \mathbf{D}}{\partial t} \tag{o}$$

and is nonzero. To make the right side of (*n*) identically equal to zero, it is therefore necessary to add to (2.37) a term $\partial \mathbf{D}/\partial t$, which is called the *displacement current.* Thus, (2.37) becomes

$$\nabla \times \mathbf{H} = \mathbf{J}_d + \frac{\partial \mathbf{D}}{\partial t} \tag{2.63}$$

Equation (2.63) can also be written in a different form with the substitution of (2.38*a*) and (2.62) into (2.63):

$$\nabla \times \mathbf{B} = \mu_0 \mathbf{J} + \mu_0 K_0 \frac{\partial \mathbf{E}}{\partial t} + \mu_0 \nabla \times \mathbf{M}_p \tag{2.64}$$

or

$$\nabla \times \mathbf{B} = \mu_0 \left(\mathbf{J}_d + \frac{\partial \mathbf{P}}{\partial t} + \nabla \times \mathbf{M} + K_0 \frac{\partial \mathbf{E}}{\partial t} \right) \tag{2.65}$$

Now, (2.23), (2.41), (2.57), and (2.63) or (2.64) are known as *Maxwell's equations.* They are repeated below in their usual form:

$$\nabla \cdot \mathbf{D} = \rho_0 \tag{Ia}$$

$$\nabla \cdot \mathbf{B} = 0 \tag{IIa}$$

$$\nabla \times \mathbf{E} = -\frac{\partial \mathbf{B}}{\partial t} \tag{IIIa}$$

$$\nabla \times \mathbf{H} = \mathbf{J}_d + \frac{\partial \mathbf{D}}{\partial t} \tag{IVa}$$

or

$$\nabla \cdot \mathbf{E} = \frac{\rho_e}{K_0} = \frac{1}{K_0} \sum_s n_s e Z_s \tag{Ib}$$

$$\nabla \cdot \mathbf{B} = 0 \tag{IIb}$$

$$\nabla \times \mathbf{E} = -\frac{\partial \mathbf{B}}{\partial t} \tag{IIIb}$$

$$\nabla \times \mathbf{B} = \mu_0 \left(\mathbf{J} + K_0 \frac{\partial \mathbf{E}}{\partial t} + \nabla \times \mathbf{M}_p \right) \tag{IVb}$$

Equations (I) and (II) can be considered initial conditions. For example, if the divergence of (III) is taken, one obtains

$$\frac{\partial}{\partial t}(\nabla \cdot \mathbf{B}) = 0$$

or

$$\nabla \cdot \mathbf{B} = \text{const}$$

Thus, if $\nabla \cdot \mathbf{B} = 0$ initially, it will remain so. Again, the divergence of (IVa) may be taken. With the use of (2.62), one obtains

$$\frac{\partial}{\partial t}(\nabla \cdot \mathbf{D} - \rho_0) = 0$$

which again shows that if $\nabla \cdot \mathbf{D} = \rho_0$ initially, it will remain so. Or the divergence of (IVb) may be taken, yielding

$$\frac{\partial}{\partial t}\left(\nabla \cdot \mathbf{E} - \frac{\rho_e}{K_0}\right) = 0$$

so that if $\nabla \cdot \mathbf{E} = \rho_e/K_0$ initially, it will remain so.

2.5 ELECTROMAGNETIC FORCES AND ENERGY

2.5.1 Electromagnetic Forces. The combined coulombic and ampere force on a single charged particle from (2.4) and (2.30a) is

$$\mathbf{F}_s = eZ_s(\mathbf{E} + \mathbf{w}_s \times \mathbf{B}) \tag{2.66}$$

We next determine whether the total force per unit volume on an ionized gas can be expressed exclusively in terms of electromagnetic field quantities. To simplify the analysis, assume that polarization and magnetization effects are absent. The sum of the forces on the charges per unit volume gives the force per unit volume as follows:

$$\mathbf{F} = \rho_e\mathbf{E} + \mathbf{J} \times \mathbf{B} \tag{2.67}$$

From (2.15), $\rho_e = K_0\nabla \cdot \mathbf{E}$; and from (2.64), $\mathbf{J} = \mu_0^{-1}\nabla \times \mathbf{B} - K_0\,\partial\mathbf{E}/\partial t$, so that (2.67) becomes

$$\mathbf{F} = K_0\mathbf{E}(\nabla \cdot \mathbf{E}) + \frac{(\nabla \times \mathbf{B}) \times \mathbf{B}}{\mu_0} - K_0\frac{\partial \mathbf{E}}{\partial t} \times \mathbf{B} \tag{2.68}$$

The last term in (2.68) can be expressed as

$$\begin{aligned}-K_0\frac{\partial \mathbf{E}}{\partial t} \times \mathbf{B} &= -K_0\frac{\partial}{\partial t}(\mathbf{E} \times \mathbf{B}) + K_0\mathbf{E} \times \frac{\partial \mathbf{B}}{\partial t} \\ &= -K_0\frac{\partial}{\partial t}(\mathbf{E} \times \mathbf{B}) - K_0\mathbf{E} \times (\nabla \times \mathbf{E})\end{aligned} \tag{2.69}$$

where Maxwell's equation (III) was used to eliminate $\partial\mathbf{B}/\partial t$. Substitution of (2.69) into (2.68) yields

$$\mathbf{F} = K_0[\mathbf{E}(\nabla\cdot\mathbf{E}) - \mathbf{E}\times(\nabla\times\mathbf{E})] - \frac{\mathbf{B}\times(\nabla\times\mathbf{B})}{\mu_0} - K_0\frac{\partial}{\partial t}(\mathbf{E}\times\mathbf{B}) \tag{2.70}$$

Equation (2.70) can be made symmetrical in **B** and **E** by addition of $\mathbf{B}(\nabla\cdot\mathbf{B})$ since $\nabla\cdot\mathbf{B} = 0$ from Maxwell's equation (II). Thus, (2.70) becomes

$$\mathbf{F} = K_0[\mathbf{E}(\nabla\cdot\mathbf{E}) - \mathbf{E}\times(\nabla\times\mathbf{E})] + \frac{1}{\mu_0}[\mathbf{B}(\nabla\cdot\mathbf{B}) - \mathbf{B}\times(\nabla\times\mathbf{B})] - K_0\frac{\partial}{\partial t}(\mathbf{E}\times\mathbf{B}) \tag{2.71}$$

Consider the electric field force. In the x_j direction ($j = 1, 2, 3$), this becomes

$$E_j\left(\frac{\partial E_1}{\partial x_1} + \frac{\partial E_2}{\partial x_2} + \frac{\partial E_3}{\partial x_3}\right) - E_k\left(\frac{\partial E_k}{\partial x_j} - \frac{\partial E_j}{\partial x_k}\right) + E_l\left(\frac{\partial E_j}{\partial x_l} - \frac{\partial E_l}{\partial x_j}\right) \tag{2.72}$$

Addition and subtraction of $E_j(\partial E_j/\partial x_j)$ allows (2.72) to be written as

$$E_j\left(\frac{\partial E_1}{\partial x_1} + \frac{\partial E_2}{\partial x_2} + \frac{\partial E_3}{\partial x_3}\right) + E_1\frac{\partial E_j}{\partial x_1} + E_2\frac{\partial E_j}{\partial x_2} + E_3\frac{\partial E_j}{\partial x_3} - E_1\frac{\partial E_1}{\partial x_j} - E_2\frac{\partial E_2}{\partial x_j} - E_3\frac{\partial E_3}{\partial x_j} \tag{2.73}$$

or

$$\sum_i\left(E_j\frac{\partial E_i}{\partial x_i} + E_i\frac{\partial E_j}{\partial x_i}\right) - \frac{1}{2}\frac{\partial E^2}{\partial x_j} \tag{2.74}$$

The first and second terms in (2.74) can be combined; and the derivative of the last term can be changed to $\delta_{ij}(\partial/\partial x_i)$. Then (2.74) becomes

$$\sum_i\frac{\partial}{\partial x_i}(E_iE_j - \tfrac{1}{2}\delta_{ij}E^2) \tag{2.75}$$

A similar procedure may be used in the other two directions. The terms of the tensor $E_iE_j - \frac{1}{2}\delta_{ij}E^2$ may be regarded as the i, j components of a dyadic $\mathbf{EE} - \frac{1}{2}E^2\mathsf{I}$, where the components of the unit diadic I are δ_{ij}. Furthermore, the operation $\sum_i \partial/\partial x_i$ can be regarded as a divergence of a dyadic T; that is,

$$\nabla\cdot\mathsf{T} = \sum_j \mathbf{e}_i\frac{\partial T_{ij}}{\partial x_j} \tag{2.76}$$

Then (2.75) can be written as

$$\nabla \cdot (\mathbf{EE} - \tfrac{1}{2}E^2\mathsf{I}) \tag{2.77}$$

A similar procedure can be used for the magnetic forces in (2.71). As a result, (2.71) may be written as

$$\mathbf{F} = \nabla \cdot [K_0(\mathbf{EE} - \tfrac{1}{2}E^2\mathsf{I}) + \mu_0^{-1}(\mathbf{BB} - \tfrac{1}{2}\mathbf{B}^2\mathsf{I})] - K_0 \frac{\partial}{\partial t}(\mathbf{E} \times \mathbf{B}) \tag{2.78}$$

Finally, a tensor whose divergence yields a force per unit volume is regarded as a stress tensor. Thus, the terms in the brackets of (2.78) are regarded as the electromagnetic stress tensor, and are designated as $\boldsymbol{\pi}$.

$$\boldsymbol{\pi} = K_0(\mathbf{EE} - \tfrac{1}{2}E^2\mathsf{I}) + \mu_0^{-1}(\mathbf{BB} - \tfrac{1}{2}B^2\mathsf{I}) \tag{2.79}$$

The remaining term in (2.78) is the time rate of change of a vector. Generally, a vector whose time rate of change yields a force may be regarded as a momentum vector. Thus, $K_0(\mathbf{E} \times \mathbf{B})$ is regarded as the electromagnetic momentum. If a vector $\mathbf{S}$ is defined as $\mathbf{E} \times \mathbf{B}/\mu_0$, then this becomes $K_0\mu_0\mathbf{S}$. It will be shown later that the speed of light in a vacuum is $c_0^2 = (K_0\mu_0)^{-1}$; thus (2.78) may be written as

$$\mathbf{F} = \nabla \cdot \boldsymbol{\pi} - \frac{1}{c_0^2}\frac{\partial \mathbf{S}}{\partial t} \tag{2.80}$$

Whereas mechanical stress tensors exist only in a substance, it is important to note that the electromagnetic stresses exist even in vacuum. As an illustration, consider a magnetic field in the z direction. The components of $\boldsymbol{\pi}^M$ are then

$$\boldsymbol{\pi}^M = \frac{1}{2}\begin{bmatrix} -B_z^2 & 0 & 0 \\ 0 & -B_z^2 & 0 \\ 0 & 0 & B_z^2 \end{bmatrix} \tag{2.81}$$

Thus, the magnetic lines of flux exhibit a *tension* in the z direction, parallel to the magnetic field; but transverse to the magnetic field they are in compression. Thus, magnetic lines of flux can be visualized as rubber bands; lateral displacements cause a restoring pressure while longitudinal displacements cause a restoring tension.

As examples of this concept, consider first a single flexible turn of a coil of wire (see Fig. 2.6a). When energized by a current, the magnetic forces cause the loop to become perfectly circular. This force per unit length of the wire can be calculated by integrating the radial component of $\mathbf{j} \times \mathbf{B}$ over a cross section of the wire. One can also visualize this effect as a result of the difference in magnetic pressure exerted on the inside of the wire compared to the outside; that is, the force per unit length of wire is given by the radial component of the magnetic pressure, integrated over the surface area of the wire.

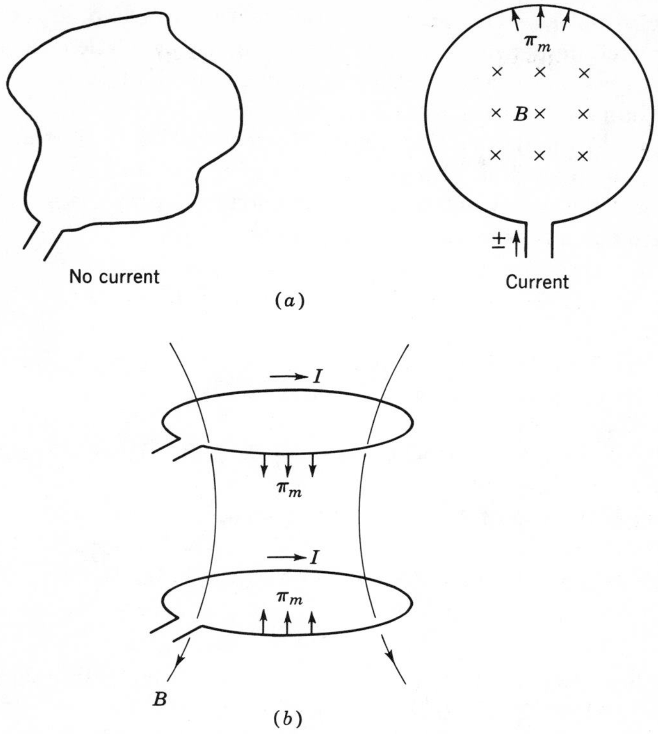

FIGURE 2.6 Illustrations of magnetic pressure.

Next consider two such loops whose planes are parallel to each other, energized in the same direction (see Fig. 2.6*b*). The magnetic lines of flux link the two loops. The net forces on each loop are such that the loops are pulled toward each other. Again, this can be calculated from the Lorentz force; or one can visualize this effect as due to the tension along lines of magnetic flux.

2.5.2 Effect of Polarization and Magnetization. The inclusion of polarization and magnetization causes additional complications in the expressions for the electromagnetic force, and unanimity of opinion on the subject does not exist. The Minkowski formulation[1] replaces K_0 and μ_0 by K and μ, respectively; while in another formulation, the stress tensor remains the same as in vacuum.[1] The justification for the latter is that the polarization and magnetization forces are then properly included. This can be understood if (2.66) is interpreted such that eZ_i is a *partial* charge on a particle, and this partial charge has velocity w_i. Then in (2.67) the charge density ρ_e is the net free charge density, given by the particles which have a *net* charge, and $\mathbf{J}$ is the total current due to motion of charged particles, time variations of polarization, and the motion of dipoles. These are described further in Chap. 4. However, $\mathbf{J}$ does not include permanent magnetic moments of particles such as electrons because the size of the current element, if indeed one exists, is smaller than the scale of measurement.

2.5.3 Magnetostriction and Electrostriction. If the electrical properties of materials change with density (due to compression), then the material exhibits electro- or magnetostrictive properties. This introduces into the stress tensor the additional terms

$$-\frac{1}{2}\left(E^2\rho\,\frac{\partial K}{\partial \rho} + \frac{B^2}{\mu^2}\,\rho\,\frac{\partial \mu}{\partial \rho}\right)\mathsf{I} \tag{2.82}$$

In the Minkowski formulation, the electromagnetic force per unit volume is then defined as in (2.78) and (2.79):

$$\mathbf{F} = \nabla \cdot \boldsymbol{\pi} - \frac{\partial}{\partial t}\,(\mathbf{D} \times \mathbf{B}) \tag{2.83}$$

which, with the use of Maxwell's equations, becomes

$$\mathbf{F} = \rho_0\mathbf{E} + \mathbf{J}_d \times \mathbf{B} - \tfrac{1}{2}E^2\,\nabla K - \tfrac{1}{2}H^2\,\nabla\mu + \nabla\left[\tfrac{1}{2}\rho E^2\,\frac{\partial K}{\partial \rho} + \tfrac{1}{2}\rho H^2\,\frac{\partial \mu}{\partial \rho}\right] \tag{2.84}$$

The applicability of (2.84) to an ionized gas is discussed further in Ref. 2; however, in Ref. 2, $\mu = \mu(\rho,T)$ only.

2.5.4 Electromagnetic Energy. Associated with electric and magnetic fields are also field energies, which are analogous to field momenta. These may be calculated by considering the interchange of mechanical energy with electromagnetic energy. Consider a number of independent charged particles in an electromagnetic field, and neglect all other processes which change the energy of the particles, except for the electromagnetic field. Then the force on a single particle s is given by (2.66). The rate of energy increase of this particle is $\mathbf{F}_s \cdot \mathbf{w}_s$; thus the total rate of energy increase of the energy $\mathbf{w}$ of all particles is

$$\frac{dW}{dt} = \sum_s \mathbf{F}_s \cdot \mathbf{w}_s = \sum_s Z_s e(\mathbf{E} + \mathbf{w}_s \times \mathbf{B}) \cdot \mathbf{w}_s \tag{a}$$

The last term in (a) is identically equal to zero; that is, a magnetic field cannot change the energy of a particle. Then (a) becomes

$$\frac{dW}{dt} = \int \mathbf{E} \cdot \mathbf{J}\, d\mathcal{V} \tag{b}$$

where the integral has replaced the summation, and where $\mathbf{J}\,d\mathcal{V}$ is taken as $\sum_s Z_s e\mathbf{w}_s$ summed over a small volume. Use of Maxwell's (IVa) for the current yields

$$\int (\mathbf{E} \cdot \mathbf{J})\, d\mathcal{V} = \int \left(\mathbf{E} \cdot \nabla \times \mathbf{H} - \mathbf{E} \cdot \frac{\partial \mathbf{D}}{\partial t}\right) d\mathcal{V} \qquad (c)$$

Now $\quad \mathbf{E} \cdot \nabla \times \mathbf{H} = \nabla \cdot (\mathbf{H} \times \mathbf{E}) + \mathbf{H} \cdot \nabla \times \mathbf{E}$

Thus (c) becomes

$$\int \mathbf{E} \cdot \mathbf{J}\, d\mathcal{V} = \int \left[\mathbf{H} \cdot \nabla \times \mathbf{E} - \mathbf{E} \cdot \frac{\partial \mathbf{D}}{\partial t} - \nabla \cdot (\mathbf{E} \times \mathbf{H})\right] d\mathcal{V}$$

In the first term in the brackets, Maxwell's equation (IIIa) is used; and the last term is converted into a surface integral. The result is

$$\int \mathbf{E} \cdot \mathbf{J}\, d\mathcal{V} = -\int \left(\mathbf{H} \cdot \frac{\partial \mathbf{B}}{\partial t} + \mathbf{E} \cdot \frac{\partial \mathbf{D}}{\partial t}\right) d\mathcal{V} - \int (\mathbf{E} \times \mathbf{H}) \cdot d\mathbf{S} \qquad (d)$$

If μ and K are constant, (d) becomes

$$\int \mathbf{E} \cdot \mathbf{J}\, d\mathcal{V} = -\int \frac{\partial}{\partial t}\left(\frac{K}{2} E^2 + \frac{\mu}{2} H^2\right) d\mathcal{V} - \int (\mathbf{E} \times \mathbf{H}) \cdot d\mathbf{S} \qquad (2.85)$$

or, in differential form,

$$\mathbf{E} \cdot \mathbf{J} = -\frac{\partial}{\partial t}\left(\frac{K}{2} E^2 + \frac{\mu}{2} H^2\right) - \nabla \cdot (\mathbf{E} \times \mathbf{H}) \qquad (2.86)$$

Equations (2.85) and (2.86) are known as *Poynting's theorem:* The first term on the right side is the time rate of change of the local electromagnetic field energy; the second term is a *flux* vector, called *Poynting's vector*. From these equations, Poynting's vector represents an *outward* flux of electromagnetic energy. Thus, the rate at which the electromagnetic field increases the energy of a group of particles is equal to the rate of *decrease* of the electromagnetic field energy *plus* the influx of Poynting's vector.

For magnetohydrodynamic devices, there is a more convenient form of (b), which is somewhat more general. Use of $\mathbf{E} = -\nabla\phi - \partial\mathbf{A}/\partial t$ in (b) yields

$$\begin{aligned}\int \mathbf{E} \cdot \mathbf{J}\, d\mathcal{V} &= -\int (\nabla\phi) \cdot \mathbf{J}\, d\mathcal{V} - \int \mathbf{J} \cdot \frac{\partial \mathbf{A}}{\partial t}\, d\mathcal{V} \\ &= -\int \nabla \cdot (\phi\mathbf{J})\, d\mathcal{V} + \int \phi\nabla \cdot \mathbf{J}\, d\mathcal{V} - \int \mathbf{J} \cdot \frac{\partial \mathbf{A}}{\partial t}\, d\mathcal{V} \qquad (e)\end{aligned}$$

Now, from (2.61), $\nabla \cdot \mathbf{J} = -\partial\rho_{e_t}/\partial t$ in the second term of (e), while the first term can be converted into a surface integral. Thus,

$$\int \mathbf{E} \cdot \mathbf{J}\, d\mathcal{V} = -\int \phi\mathbf{J} \cdot d\mathbf{S} - \int \phi \frac{\partial \rho_{e_t}}{\partial t}\, d\mathcal{V} - \int \mathbf{J} \cdot \frac{\partial \mathbf{A}}{\partial t}\, d\mathcal{V} \qquad (2.87)$$

Thus, the change in energy of the fluid due to electromagnetic fields can appear in three ways: In the first term, the energy appears as a current to electrodes in the device. The second and third terms apply to electrodeless machines and represent the coupling to external circuits; the second term is capacitive while the third term is inductive. These three terms represent the three ways in which energy can be interchanged with a plasma by electromagnetic means.

2.6 ELECTROMAGNETIC WAVES

Maxwell's equations are also wave equations. This can be seen most easily by assuming that the medium is linear; that is, μ and K are constant. Then substitution of $\mathbf{H} = \mu_0^{-1}\nabla \times \mathbf{A}$ and $\mathbf{D} = -K(\nabla\phi + \partial\mathbf{A}/\partial t)$ into Maxwell's equation (IV*a*) yields

$$\nabla^2\mathbf{A} - \nabla\left(\nabla \cdot \mathbf{A} + \mu K \frac{\partial\phi}{\partial t}\right) = -\mu J_d + \mu K \frac{\partial^2\mathbf{A}}{\partial t^2} \tag{2.88}$$

A similar type of equation can be obtained for the potential by substitution of

$$\mathbf{D} = -K\left(\nabla\phi + \frac{\partial\mathbf{A}}{\partial t}\right)$$

into Maxwell's equation (I*a*):

$$\nabla^2\phi - \mu K \frac{\partial^2\phi}{\partial t^2} + \frac{\partial}{\partial t}\left(\nabla \cdot \mathbf{A} + \mu K \frac{\partial\phi}{\partial t}\right) = -\frac{\rho_0}{K} \tag{2.89}$$

Equations (2.88) and (2.89) can be uncoupled by the use of the Lorentz condition,

$$\nabla \cdot \mathbf{A} + \mu K \frac{\partial\phi}{\partial t} = 0 \tag{2.90}$$

so that they become

$$\nabla^2\mathbf{A} - \mu K \frac{\partial^2\mathbf{A}}{\partial t^2} = -\mu_0\mathbf{J}_d \tag{2.91}$$

$$\nabla^2\phi - \mu K \frac{\partial^2\phi}{\partial t^2} = -\frac{\rho_0}{K} \tag{2.92}$$

Thus the equations for **A** and ϕ are wave equations; in fact, all electromagnetic field vectors can be described by wave equations. Equations (2.91) and (2.92) also reduce to the previous static equations when the derivatives with respect to time are zero. The wave properties of (2.91) and (2.92) can be demonstrated by considering **A** and ϕ to be given by

$$\mathbf{A} = \mathbf{A}_0 f_1(\mathbf{n} \cdot \mathbf{r} \pm ct) \tag{a}$$

$$\phi = \phi_0 f_2(\mathbf{n} \cdot \mathbf{r} \pm ct) \tag{b}$$

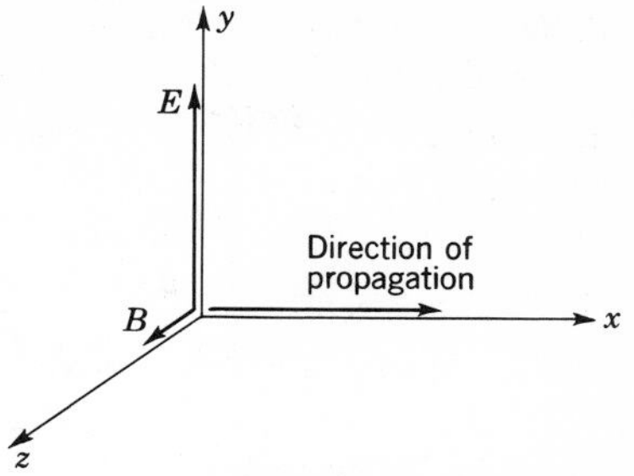

FIGURE 2.7 Plane wavefront.

where **r** is the distance from the origin, **n** is a unit vector which is normal to the wavefront, and f_1, f_2 are arbitrary functions. Then substitution of (*a*) and (*b*) into the homogeneous forms of (2.91) and (2.92) shows that (*a*) and (*b*) are solutions, provided that the phase velocity $c = (\mu K)^{-\frac{1}{2}}$. Thus, in the absence of current $\mathbf{J}_d$ and charge density ρ_0, the form of the wave is unchanged, and it propagates normal to the wavefront with velocity c. Surprisingly enough, these waves can propagate even in vacuum, in which case $c = (\mu_0 K_0)^{-\frac{1}{2}} = c_0$ turns out to be exactly the velocity of light; and therefore light is a form of electromagnetic radiation. This discovery by Maxwell was one of the milestones of the last century. Furthermore, waves of all frequencies propagate with the same velocity in vacuum.

Let us consider a plane wave propagating in the x direction in a vacuum. Since it is assumed that the wave is plane, the electric field has no variations in the yz plane, but only in the x direction. In a vacuum $\nabla \cdot \mathbf{E} = 0$; thus there can be no component of **E** in the direction of propagation x. Thus $E_x = 0$, but E_y and E_z can exist. Thus, the electric field vector always lies in the plane normal to the direction of propagation (see Fig. 2.7). Also,

$$-\frac{\partial \mathbf{B}}{\partial t} = \nabla \times \mathbf{E} = -\mathbf{j}\left(\frac{\partial E_z}{\partial x}\right) + \mathbf{k}\left(\frac{\partial E_y}{\partial x}\right)$$

Thus, **B** always lies in the wavefront. Furthermore, **E** and **B** are related. This can be seen by considering **E** to be given as follows:

$$\mathbf{E} = \mathbf{j}E(x - ct) \qquad (c)$$

Then

$$\frac{\partial \mathbf{B}}{\partial t} = -\nabla \times \mathbf{E} = -\mathbf{k}E'(x - ct) \qquad (d)$$

Integration of (*d*) yields

$$\mathbf{B} = \frac{\mathbf{k}}{c} E(x - ct) \qquad (e)$$

Thus, $B = E/c$ and follows a right-handed rule with respect to the direction of propagation and the electric field (see Fig. 2.7). But notice that the magnitude of **B** is quite small in an electromagnetic wave. Since **B** and **E** are both normal to the wavefront, Poynting's vector $\mathbf{E} \times \mathbf{H}$ is in the x direction, that is, in the direction of propagation. Thus the electromagnetic energy propagates in the direction of the wave. The magnitude of Poynting's vector is

$$\mathbf{E} \times \mathbf{H} = \frac{\mathbf{n}E^2}{c\mu} \qquad (f)$$

This can be rearranged as follows, since $KE^2 = \mu H^2$, from (*e*):

$$\mathbf{E} \times \mathbf{H} = \mathbf{n}c\{\tfrac{1}{2}KE^2 + \tfrac{1}{2}\mu H^2\} \qquad (2.93)$$

which shows that the local Poynting vector is equal to the product of the local density of electromagnetic energy and the velocity of light, in the direction of propagation.

The electromagnetic pressure is given by the Maxwell stress tensor. For the example above, this becomes

$$\boldsymbol{\pi}^E = \tfrac{1}{2}KE^2 \begin{bmatrix} -1 & 0 & 0 \\ 0 & +1 & 0 \\ 0 & 0 & -1 \end{bmatrix} \qquad (2.94)$$

$$\boldsymbol{\pi}^M = \tfrac{1}{2}\mu H^2 \begin{bmatrix} -1 & 0 & 0 \\ 0 & -1 & 0 \\ 0 & 0 & +1 \end{bmatrix} \qquad (2.95)$$

Since $\mu H^2 = KE^2$, from (*e*), the total stress tensor is

$$\boldsymbol{\pi} = \tfrac{1}{2}(\mu H^2 + KE^2) \begin{bmatrix} -1 & 0 & 0 \\ 0 & 0 & 0 \\ 0 & 0 & 0 \end{bmatrix} \qquad (2.96)$$

that is, the only component of the total Maxwell stress tensor is a pressure in the direction of propagation whose magnitude is equal to the local electromagnetic energy density.

2.6.1 Origin of Electromagnetic Waves. The above relations have dealt with the propagation of electromagnetic waves through nondispersive media, without consideration of their origin. These waves can be created by the acceleration of charges. This can be shown by considering a single particle with charge eZ and velocity $\mathbf{w}$ in a vacuum. For convenience, we will consider the radiation from this particle as it passes through a fixed point, letting this point be the origin for a set of coordinates. Also, for convenience, the z coordinate will be taken in the direction of the particle velocity; that is, $\mathbf{w} = \mathbf{k}w(t)$. The current due to this particle is therefore

$$\mathbf{J} = eZw\mathbf{k}\ \delta(x)\ \delta(y)\ \delta(z) \qquad (2.97)$$

where $\delta(x)$ is the Dirac delta function, with the following properties:

$$\begin{aligned} x > 0 \qquad & \delta(x) = 0 \\ x < 0 \qquad & \delta(x) = 0 \\ x = 0 \qquad & \delta(x) = \infty \\ \int_{-\epsilon}^{+\epsilon} & \delta(x)\, dx = 1 \end{aligned}$$

The representation given in (2.97) is necessary to indicate that the particle is located at the origin. With (2.97), then (2.92) becomes

$$\nabla^2 \mathbf{A} - \frac{1}{c_0^2}\frac{\partial^2 \mathbf{A}}{\partial t^2} = -\mu_0 eZ\mathbf{k}w(t)\,\delta(x)\,\delta(y)\,\delta(z) \tag{2.98}$$

From (2.98) it is obvious that the only component of **A** due to this particle is A_z. Furthermore, (2.98) is spherically symmetric, so that it is convenient to use spherical coordinates. But it is first necessary to represent the right side of (2.98) in spherical coordinates. To do this, let

$$\delta(x)\,\delta(y)\,\delta(z) = G(r)\,\delta(r) \tag{a}$$

where $G(r)$ is a normalizing factor to ensure that

$$\textstyle\iiint \delta(x)\,\delta(y)\,\delta(z)\,dx\,dy\,dz = 1 \tag{b}$$

In spherical coordinates, the element of volume corresponding to $dx\,dy\,dz$ is $4\pi r^2\,dr$; hence from (*a*) and (*b*),

$$1 = \textstyle\int G(r)\cdot 4\pi r^2\,\delta(r)\,dr \tag{c}$$

If we define $\int_0^\epsilon \delta(r)\,dr = 1$, then (*c*) requires that

$$G = \frac{1}{4\pi r^2} \tag{d}$$

Substitution of (*d*) into (*a*) and into (2.98) yields

$$\frac{1}{r^2}\frac{\partial}{\partial r}\left(r^2\frac{\partial A_z}{\partial r}\right) - \frac{1}{c_0^2}\frac{\partial^2 A_z}{\partial t^2} = -\frac{\mu_0 eZw(t)\,\delta(r)}{4\pi r^2} \tag{e}$$

It is assumed that for $t \le 0$ there is no radiation, so that

$$A_z(r,0) = \left(\frac{\partial A_z}{\partial t}\right)(r,0) = 0$$

Integration of (*e*) from 0 to ϵ gives the boundary condition on A_z at $r = \epsilon$:

$$\left[r^2\frac{\partial A_z}{\partial r}\right]_{r=\epsilon} = -\frac{\mu_0 eZw(t)}{4\pi} + \frac{1}{c_0^2}\int_0^\epsilon \frac{\partial^2 A_z}{\partial t^2}r^2\,dr \tag{f}$$

The last term in (*f*) goes to zero as $\epsilon \to 0$. Next, the Laplace transform is taken of (*e*) and (*f*), for $r \ge \epsilon$:

$$\left[r^2\frac{\partial \hat{A}}{\partial r}\right]_{r=\epsilon} = -\frac{\mu_0 eZ\hat{w}(s)}{4\pi} \tag{g}$$

$$\frac{1}{r^2}\frac{\partial}{\partial r}\left(r^2\frac{\partial \hat{A}}{\partial r}\right) - \frac{s^2}{c_0^2}\hat{A} = 0 \qquad r > \epsilon \tag{h}$$

where $\hat{A}$ and $\hat{w}$ are the Laplace transforms of A_z and w, respectively. Equation (h) may be simplified by a change of dependent variable to $r\hat{A}(r)$,

$$\frac{\partial^2}{\partial r^2}(r\hat{A}) - \frac{s^2}{c_0^2}(r\hat{A}) = 0 \tag{i}$$

whose solution is

$$r\hat{A} = a_1 e^{-(s/c_0)r} + b_1 e^{(s/c_0)r} \tag{j}$$

Since the potential $\hat{A}$ must go to zero as $r \to \infty$, then $b_1 = 0$. Boundary condition (g) gives

$$a_1 = \frac{\mu_0 eZ\hat{w}}{4\pi} \tag{k}$$

so that (j) becomes

$$\hat{A}(s) = \frac{\mu_0 eZ\hat{w}}{4\pi r} e^{-(s/c_0)r} \tag{l}$$

whose inverse is

$$A_z(r,t) = \frac{\mu_0 eZw(t - r/c_0)}{4\pi r} \tag{2.99}$$

that is, the potential corresponds to the particle position at a preceding time. Equation (2.99) is to be compared to (2.42), which is derived for a steady case in the absence of propagation. Solutions such as those given by (2.99) are called *retarded* potentials, since the potential for $r > 0$ corresponds to an event which occurred at a preceding time. Equation (2.99) is correct only if $w/c_0 \ll 1$; otherwise there is a relativistic correction which requires the right side of (2.99) to be divided by $1 - (\mathbf{w} \cdot \mathbf{r})/rc_0$. The generalization of (2.99) to a particle of arbitrary position and velocity is

$$\mathbf{A}(\mathbf{r},t) = \frac{\mu_0 eZw(t - |\mathbf{r} - \mathbf{r}'|/c_0)}{4\pi|\mathbf{r} - \mathbf{r}'|} \tag{2.100}$$

To calculate the electric potential from (2.99), the Lorentz condition (2.90) is used:

$$\begin{aligned} \frac{\partial \phi}{\partial t} &= -\frac{\nabla \cdot \mathbf{A}}{\mu_0 K_0} = -\frac{1}{\mu_0 K_0}\frac{\partial A_z}{\partial z} \\ &= -\frac{eZ}{4\pi K_0 r}\left[\frac{-\dot{w}(t - r/c_0)}{c_0} - \frac{w}{r}\right]\frac{\partial r}{\partial z} \end{aligned} \tag{m}$$

At distances far from the origin, the term w/r may be neglected; also $\partial r/\partial z = z/r = \cos\theta$, where θ is the angle between r and the z axis. Then integration of (m) yields

$$\phi = \frac{eZw(t - r/c_0)\cos\theta}{4\pi r K_0 c_0} \tag{2.101}$$

Next, the electric field is calculated from $\mathbf{E} = -\nabla\phi - \partial\mathbf{A}/\partial t$. From (2.101),

$$\nabla\phi = \frac{eZ}{4\pi c_0 K_0}\left[\frac{\cos\theta}{r}\nabla(w) + w\cos\theta\,\nabla(r^{-1}) + \frac{w}{r}\nabla\cos\theta\right]$$

$$= \frac{eZ}{4\pi c_0 K_0}\left[-\frac{\dot{w}}{rc_0}\mathbf{e}_r\cos\theta + w\cos\theta\left(-\frac{\mathbf{e}_r}{r^2}\right) - \frac{w}{r^2}\mathbf{e}_\theta\sin\theta\right] \qquad (n)$$

At distances far from the origin, only the first term in the brackets of (n) is important. Also, from (2.99),

$$\frac{\partial\mathbf{A}}{\partial t} = \mathbf{k}\frac{\mu_0 eZ}{4\pi r}\dot{w}\left(t - \frac{r}{c_0}\right) \qquad (o)$$

Since $\mathbf{k} = \mathbf{e}_r\cos\theta - \mathbf{e}_\theta\sin\theta$, (o) becomes

$$\frac{\partial\mathbf{A}}{\partial t} = \frac{\mu_0 eZ\dot{w}(t - r/c_0)}{4\pi r}(\mathbf{e}_r\cos\theta - \mathbf{e}_\theta\sin\theta) \qquad (p)$$

Use of (n) and (p) yields

$$\mathbf{E} = \mathbf{e}_\theta\frac{\dot{w}(t - r/c_0)\sin\theta}{4\pi c_0{}^2K_0 r}eZ \qquad (2.102)$$

Equation (2.102) gives the electric field for large r due to the acceleration in the z direction of the particle, and is independent of the direction of the instantaneous velocity of the particle. Note that $\mathbf{E}$ is normal to $\mathbf{r}$, so that the electric field again lies in the wavefront. The generalization of (2.103) to an arbitrary direction of acceleration yields

$$\mathbf{E}(\mathbf{r}) = \frac{eZ[\dot{\mathbf{w}}(t - r/c)\times\mathbf{r}]\times\mathbf{r}}{4\pi c_0{}^2K_0 r^3} \qquad (2.103)$$

where r is the distance between the particle and the point at which the electric field is measured. Equation (2.103) is valid if $w/c_0 \ll 1$; otherwise corrections for relativity are required, as follows:[3]

$$\mathbf{E}(\mathbf{r}) = \frac{eZ[\dot{\mathbf{w}}(t - r/c_0)\times(\mathbf{r} - r\mathbf{w}/c)]\times\mathbf{r}}{4\pi c_0{}^2K_0 r^3(1 - \mathbf{r}/r\cdot\mathbf{w}/c_0)^3} \qquad (2.104)$$

For the far field, the magnetic field is obtained from Maxwell's equation (III) as follows:

$$\frac{\partial\mathbf{B}}{\partial t} = -\nabla\times\mathbf{E} = \frac{-\mathbf{e}_\phi}{r}\frac{\partial}{\partial r}(rE_\theta) \qquad (q)$$

Substitution of (2.102) for E_θ yields

$$\frac{\partial\mathbf{B}}{\partial t} = \frac{\mathbf{e}_\phi eZ\ddot{w}(t - r/c_0)\sin\theta}{4\pi c_0{}^3K_0 r} \qquad (r)$$

Integration yields

$$\mathbf{B} = \frac{\mathbf{e}_\phi e Z \dot{w}(t - r/c_0) \sin \theta}{4\pi c_0{}^3 K_0 r} \tag{s}$$

But $\mathbf{e}_\phi = \mathbf{e}_r \times \mathbf{e}_\theta$; hence (*s*) becomes

$$\mathbf{B} = \frac{\mathbf{e}_r \times \mathbf{e}_\theta}{c_0} \cdot \frac{eZ\dot{w}(t - r/c_0) \sin \theta}{4\pi c_0{}^2 K_0 r} \tag{t}$$

Thus,

$$\mathbf{B}(r,t) = \frac{\mathbf{r}}{rc_0} \times \mathbf{E}(r,t) \tag{u}$$

so that **B** also is normal to **r** and therefore lies in the wavefront.

The energy radiated from the accelerating charge is obtained by integration of Poynting's vector over a sphere of radius r:

$$\dot{W} = \int (\mathbf{E} \times \mathbf{H}) \cdot d\mathbf{S} \tag{v}$$

An element of area is $2\pi r^2 \sin \theta \, d\theta$, and use of (2.102) and (*s*) yields

$$\dot{W} = \frac{2\pi e^2 Z^2 |\dot{\mathbf{w}}|^2}{\mu_0 c_0 (4\pi K_0)^2 c_0{}^4} \int_0^\pi \sin^3 \theta \, d\theta \tag{w}$$

The integral in (*w*) is $\frac{4}{3}$; thus the radiated power is

$$\dot{W} = \frac{2}{3} \frac{e^2 Z^2 |\dot{\mathbf{w}}|^2}{4\pi K_0 c_0{}^3} \tag{2.105}$$

Equation (2.105) will be used later to calculate radiation from charged particles during a collision and also from charged particles which are moving in helical paths because of the presence of magnetic fields.

2.7 TRANSFORMATION TO MOVING COORDINATES—SPECIAL RELATIVITY

Up until now, the coordinates x, y, z, t which we have chosen were fixed to the laboratory. However, in magnetohydrodynamics, it is necessary to consider problems in moving coordinates. Suppose the moving coordinates travel in the x direction with steady velocity v; then the moving coordinates are related to the stationary coordinates by $x' = x - vt$, $y' = y$, $z' = z$, $t' = t$. Such a transformation is called a *galilean transformation*, and it is easily shown that Newton's laws of motion are invariant under such a transformation. This transformation can be written as follows:

$$\begin{Bmatrix} x' \\ y' \\ z' \\ t' \end{Bmatrix} = \begin{bmatrix} 1 & 0 & 0 & -v \\ 0 & 1 & 0 & 0 \\ 0 & 0 & 1 & 0 \\ 0 & 0 & 0 & 1 \end{bmatrix} \begin{Bmatrix} x \\ y \\ z \\ t \end{Bmatrix}$$

However, Maxwell's equations change their form when a galilean transformation is used, but these differential equations should be the same in both sets of coordinates. This paradox was resolved by Einstein, by postulating that the speed of light in both sets of coordinates is the same. If the origins of both sets of coordinates happen to coincide at the instant when a spherically symmetric light pulse is emitted from a particle at the origin, then the equations of motion for the wavefront of the light pulse in both sets of coordinates are

$$\begin{aligned} x^2 + y^2 + z^2 - c^2t^2 &= 0 \\ x'^2 + y'^2 + z'^2 - c^2t'^2 &= 0 \end{aligned} \tag{2.106}$$

The left sides of Eqs. (2.106) may be regarded as a vector with four components: x_1, x_2, x_3, x_4, where $x_1 = x$, $x_2 = y$, $x_3 = z$, and $x_4 = ict$. The magnitude of this vector is clearly the same in both sets of coordinates. The transformation from one set of coordinates to the other may be written in terms of four direction cosines $\gamma_{ij'}$:

$$\begin{Bmatrix} x_1' \\ x_2' \\ x_3' \\ x_4' \end{Bmatrix} = \begin{bmatrix} \gamma_{1'1} & 0 & 0 & \gamma_{1'4} \\ 0 & 1 & 0 & 0 \\ 0 & 0 & 1 & 0 \\ \gamma_{4'1} & 0 & 0 & \gamma_{4'4} \end{bmatrix} \begin{Bmatrix} x_1 \\ x_2 \\ x_3 \\ x_4 \end{Bmatrix} \tag{2.107}$$

Two of these may be chosen arbitrarily: Let $\gamma_{1'1} = \alpha$ and $\gamma_{4'1} = i\alpha\beta$. So that the coordinates in the (′) system are orthogonal, the products of the direction cosines must be zero,

$$\begin{aligned} \alpha(i\alpha\beta) + \gamma_{1'4}(\gamma_{4'4}) &= 0 \\ \alpha(\gamma_{1'4}) + i\alpha\beta(\gamma_{4'4}) &= 0 \end{aligned}$$

from which $\gamma_{1'4} = \mp i\alpha\beta$; $\gamma_{4'4} = \pm\alpha$. The upper sign is taken to allow time to be positive. Finally, the length of the vector must not change under a transformation, so that the value of the determinant of the above matrix must be unity. This gives

$$\alpha\gamma_{4'4} - \gamma_{1'4}i\alpha\beta = 1$$

from which $\alpha = 1/\sqrt{1 - \beta^2}$. The matrix then becomes

$$\begin{bmatrix} \dfrac{1}{\sqrt{1-\beta^2}} & 0 & 0 & \dfrac{i\beta}{\sqrt{1-\beta^2}} \\ 0 & 1 & 0 & 0 \\ 0 & 0 & 1 & 0 \\ -\dfrac{i\beta}{\sqrt{1-\beta^2}} & 0 & 0 & \dfrac{1}{\sqrt{1-\beta^2}} \end{bmatrix} \tag{2.108}$$

Applying this transformation to the four-component vector yields

$$\begin{aligned} x' &= \frac{x - \beta ct}{\sqrt{1-\beta^2}} \\ y' &= y \\ z' &= z \\ t' &= \frac{t - \beta x/c}{\sqrt{1-\beta^2}} \end{aligned} \qquad (2.109)$$

The velocity of the (′) coordinate system is $\beta c(1 - \beta^2)^{-\frac{1}{2}}$. Obviously, when $\beta \ll 1$, this reduces to the galilean transformation with $\beta = v/c$. In terms of the four coordinates x_1, x_2, x_3, x_4, the Lorentz condition (2.90) can be written as $\partial A_k/\partial x_k = 0$ if we define $A_1 = A_1$, $A_2 = A_2$, $A_3 = A_3$, and $A_4 = i\phi/c$. It can be shown that Maxwell's equation (in vacuum) can be written in the form

$$\sum_{k=1}^{4} \frac{\partial f_{hk}}{\partial x_k} = 0 \qquad (h = 1,2,3,4) \qquad \sum_{h \neq j \neq k}^{3} \frac{\partial f_{jk}}{\partial x_h} = 0 \qquad (2.110)$$

if one defines $f_{kh} = \partial A_h/\partial x_k - \partial A_k/\partial x_h$. The tensor f_{kh} is called the *field tensor* and has the components

$$f_{kh} = \begin{bmatrix} 0 & B_z & -B_y & -i\dfrac{E_x}{c} \\ -B_z & 0 & B_x & -i\dfrac{E_y}{c} \\ B_y & -B_x & 0 & -i\dfrac{E_z}{c} \\ \dfrac{iE_x}{c} & \dfrac{iE_y}{c} & \dfrac{iE_z}{c} & 0 \end{bmatrix} \qquad (2.111)$$

Then upon applying the Lorentz transformation, in moving coordinates the field quantities are $f'_{kh} = \gamma_{kl} f_{lm} \gamma_{hm}$, or

$$\begin{aligned} E'_x &= E_x \\ E'_y &= \frac{E_y - \beta c B_z}{\sqrt{1-\beta^2}} \\ E'_z &= \frac{E_z + \beta c B_y}{\sqrt{1-\beta^2}} \\ B'_x &= B_x \\ B'_y &= \frac{B_y + \beta E_z/c}{\sqrt{1-\beta^2}} \\ B'_z &= \frac{B_z - \beta E_y/c}{\sqrt{1-\beta^2}} \end{aligned} \qquad (2.112)$$

If $\beta \ll 1$, then $\mathbf{B}' \simeq \mathbf{B}$ and $\mathbf{E}' \simeq \mathbf{E} + \mathbf{v} \times \mathbf{B} \cdot \mathbf{E}'$ is the electric field in coordinates moving with velocity $\mathbf{v}$; that is, $\mathbf{E}' = \mathbf{E}^*$. Referring to the motion of a particle (2.66), we can write this force equation as

$$\mathbf{F} = eZ[\mathbf{E}^* + (\mathbf{w} - \mathbf{v}) \times \mathbf{B}] \tag{2.113}$$

This expression will be used later. In summary, we have seen that in moving coordinates the apparent electric field is altered, but not the magnetic field, as long as the velocity is much smaller than that of light. If β is not small, (2.113) must of course be modified.

REFERENCES CITED

1. Fano, R. M., L. J. Chu, and R. B. Adler: *Electromagnetic Fields, Energy and Forces*, John Wiley & Sons, Inc., New York, 1960.
2. Chu, Boa-Teh: "Thermodynamics of Electrically Conducting Fluids," *Phys. Fluids*, **2**:473–484 (1959).
3. Sommerfeld, A.: *Electrodynamics*, p. 254, Academic Press Inc., New York, 1952. Equation (2.104) is easily transformed to Sommerfeld's equation (8).

GENERAL REFERENCES

Abraham, Max, and Richard Becker: *The Classical Theory of Electricity and Magnetism*, 2d ed., translation by John Dougall, Hafner Publishing Company, Inc., New York, 1950.

Jackson, John David: *Classical Electrodynamics*, John Wiley & Sons, Inc., New York, 1962.

Landau, L., and E. Lifshitz: *The Classical Theory of Fields*, Addison-Wesley Publishing Company, Inc., Reading, Mass., 1951.

Landau, L. D., and E. M. Lifshitz: *Electrodynamics of Continuous Media*, Pergamon Press, New York, 1960.

Lehnert, B. (ed.): *Electromagnetic Phenomena in Cosmical Physics*, Cambridge University Press, New York, 1958.

Panofsky, Wolfgang, and Melba Phillips: *Classical Electricity and Magnetism*, Addison-Wesley Publishing Company, Inc., Reading, Mass., 1962.

Sommerfeld, Arnold: *Electrodynamics*, Academic Press Inc., New York, 1952.

Stratton, Julius A.: *Electromagnetic Theory*, McGraw-Hill Book Company, New York, 1941.

3

MOTION OF CHARGED PARTICLES

3.1 INTRODUCTION

In this chapter, the motion of a charged particle is considered in the absence of collisions with either the walls or other particles. Under these conditions, the motion of each particle is governed by the local electric and magnetic fields, while the total current and the electric and magnetic fields must obey Maxwell's equations macroscopically. In general, the motion in the absence of magnetic fields in steady electric fields is not interesting, in the absence of collisions; consequently, the presence of magnetic fields is assumed, which results in helical motion of the charged particles. To be collisionless, during an orbit the particle must not touch the walls; thus all Larmor radii must be much smaller than the typical geometrical length. Also, to be collisionless, the mean free paths of the various particles must be equal to or greater than the size of the apparatus and thus also larger than the Larmor radii. Thus, the plasma is in the M region.

In this chapter, the motion in combined electric and magnetic fields will be analyzed, and the resultant properties of the plasma will be obtained.

3.2 MOTION IN A UNIFORM MAGNETIC FIELD

Consider a particle with velocities $w_{\parallel}$ parallel to the magnetic field and $w_{\perp}$ in the plane perpendicular to $\mathbf{B}$. The force on the particle is $eZ\mathbf{w} \times \mathbf{B}$, which is always perpendicular to the velocity vector of the particle in the plane perpendicular to B. Thus, in that plane the motion must be circular, with the acceleration $w_{\perp}^2/r_L$, where r_L is the radius of curvature of the path. Use of Newton's law yields

$$eZw_\perp B = \frac{mw_\perp^2}{r_L}$$

or

$$\frac{eZB}{m} = \frac{w_\perp}{r_L} = \omega \qquad (3.1)$$

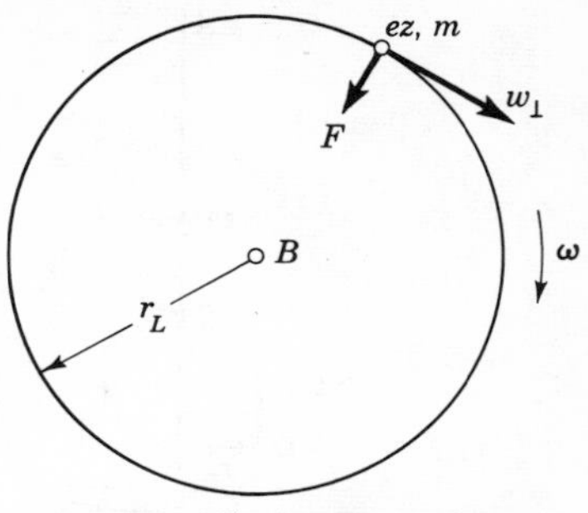

FIGURE 3.1 Cyclotron motion of a particle.

where ω is the circular frequency of rotation of the particle (see Fig. 3.1). This frequency is the particle cyclotron frequency, and depends only on the charge, magnetic field, and mass of the particle. The radius of curvature is called the *Larmor* or *gyro radius;* thus $r_L = w_\perp/\omega$; it depends on the particle velocity. Usually the rms speed of the species is used to determine the Larmor radius.

The component of velocity parallel to **B** is not changed by the magnetic field; hence the total motion is helical about an axis parallel to **B**. The center of curvature of the motion of a particle appears to be "locked onto" a particular magnetic flux line, and the path of the particle encloses the same magnetic flux lines. Note that positively and negatively charged particles gyrate in different directions. With **B** out of the paper, positively charged particles rotate clockwise, and negatively charged particles rotate counterclockwise.

3.3 MOTION IN UNIFORM ELECTRIC AND MAGNETIC FIELDS

In the presence of other fields, such as gravitation or electrostatic fields, as well as magnetic fields, the motion of charged particles will generally have an additional component of velocity superimposed on the helical motion caused by the presence of the magnetic field. In a plane perpendicular to the magnetic field, the motion will then be trochoidal or epicycloidal. This can be decomposed into the gyration of the particle and the motion of the center of curvature of the path (see Fig. 3.2).

The center of curvature is called the *guiding center;* its velocity is called the *guiding-center velocity* $\mathbf{V}_{gc}$. For steady uniform fields, the guiding-center velocity is called the *drift velocity* $\mathbf{V}_d$; for time-varying electric fields, the *polarization velocity* $\mathbf{V}_p$. For a curving **B** field, the velocity is called *curvature drift velocity* $\mathbf{V}_c$. In this section, the expression for $\mathbf{V}_d$ is derived; subsequent sections consider the other guiding-center velocities.

We consider first a uniform electric field. Any component of an electric field which is parallel to the magnetic field will cause a uniform acceleration in this direction. For the other component of the electric

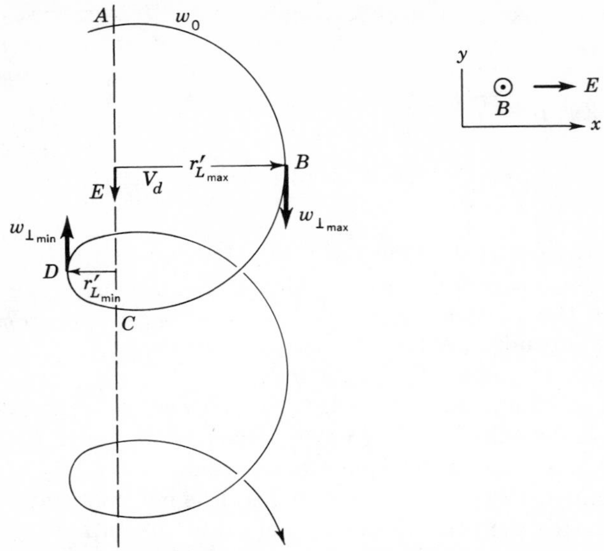

FIGURE 3.2 Motion of a positively charged particle in uniform crossed fields.

field, in a plane perpendicular to **B**, use is made of Newton's law,

$$\mathbf{F}_\perp = m\ddot{\mathbf{r}}$$

or

$$eZ(\mathbf{E}_\perp + \mathbf{w}_\perp \times \mathbf{B}) = m\ddot{\mathbf{r}} \tag{3.2}$$

where $\mathbf{r}$ is the projection of the radius vector in the plane normal to **B**. Next, assume that $\mathbf{w}_\perp$ consists of two components $\mathbf{V}_d + \mathbf{c}'_\perp$, and that the spatial vector consists of $\mathbf{r}_d + \mathbf{r}'_\perp$. Then (3.2) becomes

$$eZ(\mathbf{E}_\perp + \mathbf{V}_d \times \mathbf{B} + \mathbf{c}'_\perp \times \mathbf{B}) = m(\ddot{\mathbf{r}}_d + \ddot{\mathbf{r}}_\perp) \tag{3.3}$$

Since $\mathbf{V}_d = \dot{\mathbf{r}}_d$ and $\mathbf{c}'_\perp = \dot{\mathbf{r}}_\perp$, (3.3) can be separated into two equations. Furthermore, assume that $E_\perp$ is responsible only for V_d and r_d. Then

$$eZ(\mathbf{E}_\perp + \mathbf{V}_d \times \mathbf{B}) = m\ddot{\mathbf{r}}_d \tag{3.4}$$

$$eZ\mathbf{c}'_\perp \times \mathbf{B} = m\ddot{\mathbf{r}}'_\perp \tag{3.5}$$

Finally, if $\mathbf{V}_d$ is constant, then $\ddot{\mathbf{r}}_d = \dot{\mathbf{V}}_d = 0$, so that $\mathbf{V}_d$ is given by

$$\mathbf{E}_\perp = -\mathbf{V}_d \times \mathbf{B} \tag{3.6}$$

Actually we wish to know $\mathbf{V}_d$ explicitly. To obtain this vector, multiply (3.6) by **B**. Then

$$\mathbf{V}_d = \mathbf{E}_\perp \times \frac{\mathbf{B}}{B^2} \tag{3.7}$$

This is the average particle motion and is called the *drift* or *guiding-center velocity;* it is perpendicular to both the electric and magnetic fields. On the other hand, the motion relative to $\mathbf{V}_d$ is the same as in the previous section, as can be seen by comparison of (3.1) with (3.5). Thus the relative motion is circular about this velocity. Since the particle may also have a uniform velocity parallel to **B**, the total motion is helical about a line parallel to **B** which moves with the drift velocity $\mathbf{V}_d$.

This motion can be explained by examination of the motion of a positively charged particle with an initial velocity parallel to **E** (see Fig. 3.2). The electric field accelerates the particle in the **E** direction, and the magnetic field exerts a force perpendicular to **B** and to the particle velocity. At point B the particle will have acquired its maximum velocity. Since the cyclotron frequency is constant and $r_L = w_\perp/\omega$, the radius of curvature is maximum at point B, and the particle travels in the $-y$ direction the fastest. From B to C, the electric field decelerates the particle and reduces its velocity until the particle reaches point D, at which the radius of curvature $r'_\perp$ is a minimum. From this point the particle is accelerated again until it reaches point E, after which the cycle repeats itself. The net effect is a steady motion of the guiding center in the $-y$ direction. Thus the particle is no longer "locked" onto one of the magnetic flux lines but drifts across them. However, the circular motion always encompasses the same number of magnetic flux lines.

This drift velocity is independent of both the charge and mass of the particle, as well as initial velocity. Thus all charged particles will drift in the same direction. If the plasma is electrically neutral, no net electric current can exist.

This same technique can be used to analyze the motion in a gravitational field. The force on the particle is now $m\mathbf{g}$ instead of $eZ\mathbf{E}$. Thus,

$$\mathbf{V}_d = \frac{m}{eZ}\frac{\mathbf{g} \times \mathbf{B}}{B^2} = \frac{\mathbf{g} \times \mathbf{B}/B}{\omega} \tag{3.8}$$

Now each species will have a different drift velocity; and the ion drift velocity will be much larger than the electron drift current. Thus a net electric current will result. Also, the average force on a particle is $eZ\mathbf{V}_d \times \mathbf{B} = -\mathbf{g}m$, so that the drift velocity causes a Lorentz force which exactly balances the gravitational force.

If **B** becomes very small, the Larmor radius becomes very large, and these analyses no longer apply.

3.4 MOTION IN UNIFORM MAGNETIC FIELD—TIME-VARYING ELECTRIC FIELD

As in the previous section, consider only the component of the electric field perpendicular to the magnetic field. We wish to determine the particle motion when the electric field is changing slowly with respect to time, as follows:

$$\mathbf{E}(t) = \mathbf{E}_0 + \dot{\mathbf{E}}t + \cdots$$

where $\mathbf{E}$ is parallel to $\mathbf{E}_0$. Then (3.2) can be resolved into components when $\mathbf{E}$ is restricted to lie in the x direction, as follows:

$$\frac{m}{eZ}\dot{w}_x - Bw_y = E_{x_0} + \dot{E}_x t + \cdots \tag{3.9}$$

$$\frac{m}{eZ}\dot{w}_y + Bw_x = 0 \tag{3.10}$$

Substitution of w_x from (3.9) into (3.10) yields

$$\left(\frac{m}{eZB}\right)^2 \ddot{w}_y + w_y = \frac{-E_{x_0}}{B} - \frac{\dot{E}_x t}{B} + \cdots$$

The homogeneous solution to the above equation is the usual cyclotron rotation. The particular solution is

$$w_y = -\frac{E_{x_0}}{B} - \frac{\dot{E}_x t}{B} = -\frac{E_x(t)}{B} = V_{d_y}$$

$$w_x = \frac{\dot{E}_x}{\omega B} = V_{p_x}$$

Thus, in addition to the drift velocity $\mathbf{V}_d$ caused by the instantaneous value of $\mathbf{E}$, there is an additional component due to the time variation of $\mathbf{E}$, in the direction of $\mathbf{E}$. This is called the *polarization drift*, and in general is given by

$$\mathbf{V}_p = \frac{m}{eZB^2}\frac{\partial \mathbf{E}}{\partial t} \tag{3.11}$$

The name arises from the similarity to the polarization current of Maxwell's equations.

3.5 MOTION IN AN INHOMOGENEOUS MAGNETIC FIELD

A large number of applications in thermonuclear fusion, geophysics, and astrophysics are concerned with inhomogeneous magnetic fields and zero electric fields. These inhomogeneous fields also lead to drift velocities $\mathbf{V}_d$ of the guiding center so that the guiding center is not locked onto the same magnetic field line even in the absence of electric fields.

The general problem of obtaining the motion of the guiding center in an arbitrary inhomogeneous magnetic field is very difficult. To simplify the analysis we will consider the guiding-center motion in the vicinity of a point in space at which all derivatives of any component

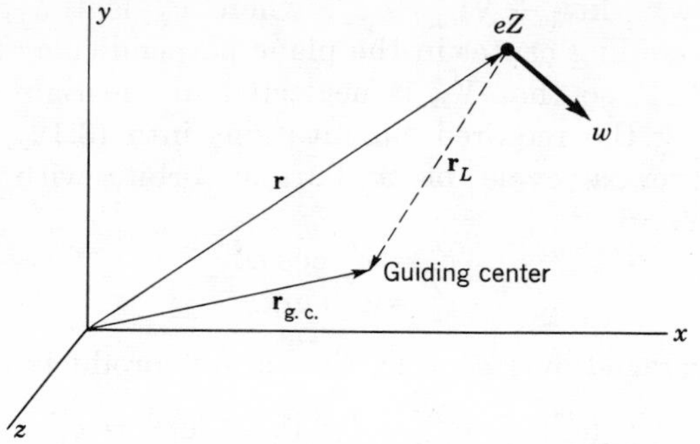

FIGURE 3.3 Motion of guiding center.

of **B** may exist, but at which point $\mathbf{B} = (0,0,B_z)$. We proceed by defining the guiding-center velocity as follows (see Fig. 3.3):

$$\mathbf{V}_{gc} = \dot{\mathbf{r}}_{gc} = \dot{\mathbf{r}} + \dot{\mathbf{r}}_L \tag{3.12}$$

where $\mathbf{r}$ is the vector to the particle, and $\mathbf{r}_L$ is the vector from the particle to the guiding center, e.g., the Larmor radius. Thus $\dot{\mathbf{r}}$ is just the particle velocity $\mathbf{w}$, and $\mathbf{r}_L$ is

$$\mathbf{r}_L = m\mathbf{w} \times \frac{\mathbf{B}}{eZB^2}$$

Differentiation of $\mathbf{r}_L$ with respect to time yields

$$\dot{\mathbf{r}}_L = \frac{m}{eZ}\left(\frac{1}{B^2}\frac{d\mathbf{w}}{dt} \times \mathbf{B} + \frac{\mathbf{w}}{B^2} \times \frac{d\mathbf{B}}{dt} - \frac{2\mathbf{w} \times \mathbf{B}}{B^3}\frac{dB}{dt}\right) \tag{3.13}$$

The term $d\mathbf{w}/dt$ is given by Newton's law,

$$\frac{d\mathbf{w}}{dt} = \frac{eZ}{m}(\mathbf{w} \times \mathbf{B}) \tag{3.14}$$

and

$$\frac{d\mathbf{B}}{dt} = (\mathbf{w} \cdot \nabla)\mathbf{B} + \frac{\partial \mathbf{B}}{\partial t} \tag{3.15}$$

Only steady magnetic fields are to be considered; so the last term in (3.15) is neglected. Similarly,

$$\frac{dB}{dt} = \mathbf{w} \cdot (\nabla B)$$

Furthermore, at the point under consideration, B is taken only in the z direction so that

$$\begin{aligned}\nabla B &= \left(\mathbf{i}\frac{\partial}{\partial x} + \mathbf{j}\frac{\partial}{\partial y} + \mathbf{k}\frac{\partial}{\partial z}\right)\sqrt{B_x^2 + B_y^2 + B_z^2} \\ &= \mathbf{i}\frac{\partial B_z}{\partial x} + \mathbf{j}\frac{\partial B_z}{\partial y} + \mathbf{k}\frac{\partial B_z}{\partial z} = \nabla B_z\end{aligned}$$

Next, we let $\mathbf{w} = \mathbf{k}w_\parallel + \mathbf{V}_{gc\perp} + \mathbf{c}'_\perp$, where $\mathbf{c}'_\perp$ is the particle motion relative to the guiding center in the plane perpendicular to **B**. We also assume $\mathbf{V}_{gc\perp} \ll \mathbf{c}'_\perp$, so that $\mathbf{V}_{gc}$ is neglected in the right side of (3.13). After performing the required substitutions into (3.12), the right side is averaged over a cycle of a Larmor orbit, with the following approximations:

$$c'_x = c'_\perp \cos \omega t$$
$$c'_y = c'_\perp \sin \omega t$$

Thus, when averaged over a cycle, the various products become

$$\langle c'^2_x \rangle = \langle c'^2_y \rangle = \tfrac{1}{2}|c'_\perp|^2 \qquad |c'_\perp|^2 = c'^2_\perp$$
$$\langle c'_x c'_y \rangle = 0$$
$$\langle w'_\parallel c'_x \rangle = \langle w'_\parallel c'_y \rangle = 0$$
$$\langle w_\parallel{}^2 \rangle = w_\parallel{}^2$$

These manipulations are tedious, but the result is

$$\mathbf{V}_{gc} = \mathbf{k}w_\parallel + \frac{m}{eZB^2}\left[w_\parallel{}^2(-\mathbf{i}B_{y,z} + \mathbf{j}B_{x,z}) + \tfrac{1}{2}\mathbf{k}c_\perp{}^2(B_{y,x} - B_{x,y}) + \frac{c'_\perp{}^2}{2}(-\mathbf{i}B_{z,y} + \mathbf{j}B_{z,x})\right] \tag{3.16}$$

where $B_{y,z} = \partial B_y/\partial z$, etc. The terms in the **k** direction correspond to motion along the field line. They will be treated in Sec. 3.9. The other terms become

$$-\mathbf{i}B_{y,z} + \mathbf{j}B_{x,z} = \mathbf{B} \times (\mathbf{B} \cdot \nabla)\frac{\mathbf{B}}{B^2} \tag{3.17}$$

$$-\mathbf{i}B_{z,y} + \mathbf{j}B_{z,x} = \mathbf{B} \times \frac{\nabla B_z}{B} \tag{3.18}$$

with the use of vector identities.

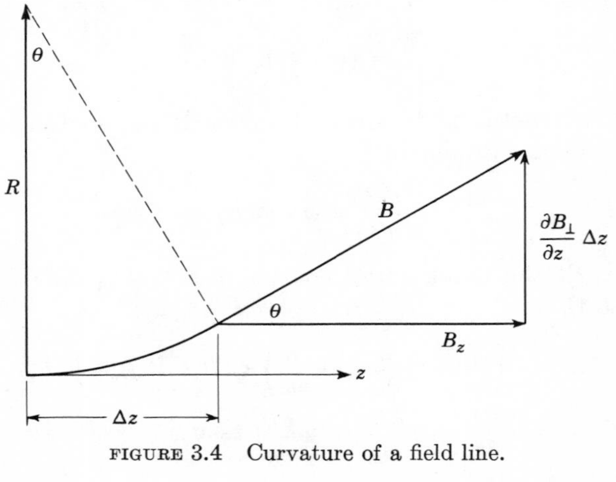

FIGURE 3.4 Curvature of a field line.

The term in (3.17) can be easily understood. Consider

$$\mathbf{i}B_{x,z} + \mathbf{j}B_{y,z} = \frac{\partial \mathbf{B}_\perp}{\partial z}$$

This is the variation of the perpendicular magnetic field $B_\perp$ in the z direction (see Fig. 3.4). The angle θ is $\Delta z(\partial B_\perp/\partial z)/B_z$. Thus, the radius of curvature R is $(\theta/\Delta z)^{-1} = [(\partial B_\perp/\partial z)/B_z]^{-1}$. Equation (3.17) is obtained by taking the vector product of $\partial \mathbf{B}_\perp/\partial z$ with $\mathbf{B}$; thus,

$$-\mathbf{i}B_{y,z} + \mathbf{j}B_{x,z} = \mathbf{B} \times \frac{\mathbf{R}}{R^2} \tag{3.19}$$

This drift therefore occurs because of curvature of the magnetic field lines, and is perpendicular to the plane of curvature. It is therefore called the *curvature drift* $\mathbf{V}_c$ and from (3.19, 3.16) is

$$\mathbf{V}_c = \frac{w_\parallel{}^2 m}{eZB^2} \frac{\mathbf{B} \times \mathbf{R}}{R^2} \tag{3.20}$$

This drift motion is simple to explain. Consider a particle moving along a curved field line with a helical motion (see Fig. 3.5). Because of the motion along the line, the particle is subjected to a centrifugal force $-mw_\parallel{}^2\mathbf{R}/R^2$ at right angles to $\mathbf{B}$. This replaces the force $m\mathbf{g}$ in Eq. (3.8). Thus,

$$\mathbf{V}_c = -\frac{mw_\parallel{}^2}{eZB^2} \frac{\mathbf{R} \times \mathbf{B}}{R^2}$$

in agreement with (3.20). Thus, field-line curvature will produce drifts so that the particle guiding center will not remain fixed to the same magnetic field line.

The other term in (3.16), corresponding to (3.18), is caused by gradients in the magnitude of the magnetic field. Figure 3.6 shows this motion

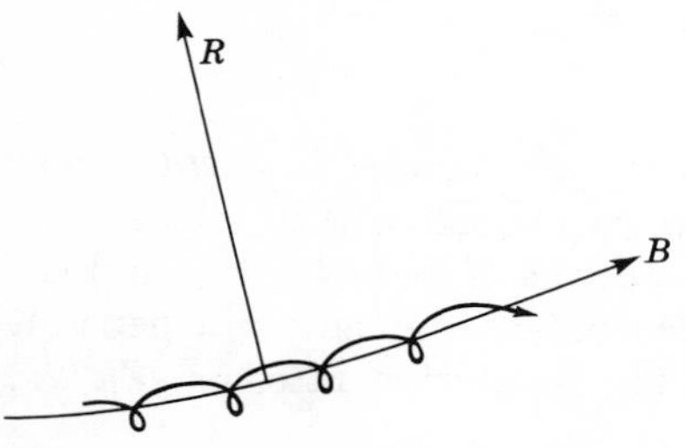

FIGURE 3.5 Motion along a curved field line.

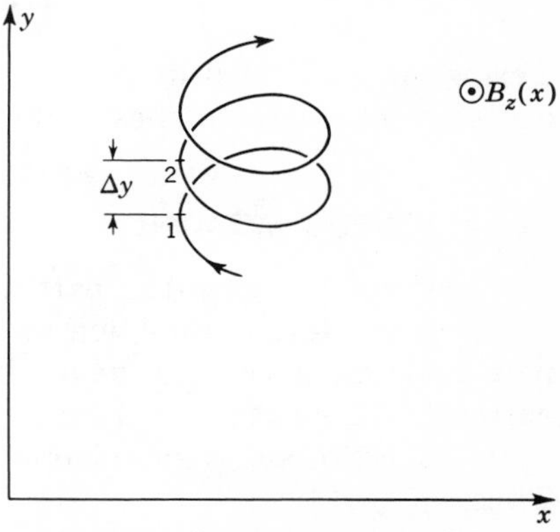

FIGURE 3.6 Drift in a magnetic field gradient.

where $\mathbf{B} = \mathbf{k}B_z(x)$. The force on the particle in the x direction is given by

$$F_x = eZw_yB_z(x) = eZw_y\left[B_z\Big|_{x_0} + \frac{\partial B_z}{\partial x}\Big|_{x_0}(x - x_0)\right]$$

This equation of motion may next be integrated between times t_1 and t_2 to give the net motion in the x direction, which is obviously zero, since the net force in the x direction is zero between times t_1 and t_2.

$$\int_{t_1}^{t_2} eZw_y\left[B_z\Big|_{x_0} + \frac{\partial B_z}{\partial x}\Big|_{x_0}(x - x_0)\right]dt = m\int_{t_1}^{t_2}\frac{dw_x}{dt}\,dt = 0$$

or, letting $w_y = dy/dt$,

$$B_z\Big|_{x_0}\int_{t_1}^{t_2}\frac{dy}{dt}\,dt = -\frac{\partial B_z}{\partial x}\Big|_{x_0}\int(x - x_0)\frac{dy}{dt}\,dt$$

Thus,

$$B_z\Big|_{x_0}\delta y = -\frac{\partial B_z}{\partial x}\Big|_{x_0}\int(x - x_0)\,dy$$

The motion is almost circular; thus the integral on the right is just the area of the Larmor orbit $\pi r_L{}^2 = \pi w_\perp{}^2/\omega^2$. Thus,

$$\delta y = \frac{1}{B_z}\frac{\partial B_z}{\partial x}\frac{\pi w_\perp{}^2}{\omega^2}$$

The time for the passage from 1 to 2 is approximately the cyclotron time $2\pi/\omega$. Thus,

$$V_{d_y} = \frac{\delta y}{\delta t} = \frac{1}{2}\frac{1}{B_z}\frac{\partial B_z}{\partial x}\frac{w_\perp{}^2}{\omega} = \frac{mw_\perp{}^2}{2eZB_z{}^2}\frac{\partial B_z}{\partial x}$$

In vector form this becomes identical to that given by (3.16) and (3.18):

$$\mathbf{V}_d = \frac{mw_\perp{}^2}{2eZB^3}\,\mathbf{B}\times(\nabla B_z) \tag{3.21}$$

This is the gradient drift velocity. Note that the guiding center always drifts across magnetic lines of the same intensity.

3.6 MAGNETIC MOMENT

Each of the gyrating particles creates a magnetic moment whose vector is opposite in direction to the applied magnetic field. This magnetic moment is equal to the product of the area of the orbit $\pi r_L{}^2$ and the current. The current is the charge which passes a given point per unit time, which becomes the charge times the revolution rate, or $eZ\omega/2\pi$. Thus,

$$\boldsymbol{\mu} = -\pi r_L{}^2 eZ\frac{\omega}{2\pi}\frac{\mathbf{B}}{B}$$

or, letting $eZ = \omega m/B$ and $w_\perp = r_L\omega$,

$$\boldsymbol{\mu} = -\frac{1}{2}\frac{mw_\perp{}^2}{B}\frac{\mathbf{B}}{B} \tag{3.22}$$

The average magnetic moment of all particles of a given species is $\langle\mu\rangle = \frac{1}{2}\langle mw_\perp{}^2\rangle/B$. The magnetization is the total magnetic moment per unit volume, or

$$\mathbf{M}_\mu = -\tfrac{1}{2}n\,\langle mw_\perp{}^2\rangle\frac{\mathbf{B}}{B^2} \tag{3.23}$$

for each species. The term $\frac{1}{2}\langle mw_\perp{}^2\rangle$ is equal to $\mathfrak{N}kT/2$, where $\mathfrak{N}$ is the number of degrees of freedom. Since $\mathfrak{N}_\perp = 2$, then

$$n\left\langle\frac{mw_\perp{}^2}{2}\right\rangle = nkT_\perp = p_\perp$$

by analogy with the perfect-gas law. Thus, the ratio of the contribution to H from magnetization to that from the magnetic field is

$$\frac{\mu_0 M_\mu}{B} = \frac{1}{2}\frac{p_\perp}{B^2/2\mu_0} = \frac{p_\perp}{2\pi^M} \tag{3.24}$$

for each species. This is just half the ratio of the "static" transverse pressure to the magnetic pressure. Thus, if $p_\perp$ is comparable to π^M, then the magnetization must be taken into account in Maxwell's equation. However, in thermonuclear devices, this pressure ratio is usually very small. In high-density devices, the total pressure is usually comparable to π^M, but the degree of ionization is usually small, so that the partial pressure of ionized species is also small and the magnetization can be neglected.

3.7 ADIABATIC INVARIANTS

Particles which do not have their energy changed by either electric or magnetic fields have certain properties which do not change; these are called the *adiabatic invariants*. The simplest adiabatic invariant is the total kinetic energy of the particle, by virtue of the fact that the magnetic field causes a force which is always normal to the particle velocity. Therefore, if we take the product of the charge flowing around the orbit and the electric field, this will be equivalent to the change in kinetic energy of the particle, which must be zero in the absence of an electric field.

$$\Delta(\text{KE}) = eZ\oint \mathbf{E}\cdot d\mathbf{l} = eZ\int(\nabla\times\mathbf{E})\cdot d\mathbf{S} = eZ\frac{d}{dt}\int\mathbf{B}\cdot d\mathbf{S} = 0 \tag{3.25}$$

where Stokes' theorem and Faraday's law have been used. Hence

$$\int\mathbf{B}\cdot d\mathbf{S} = \text{const}$$

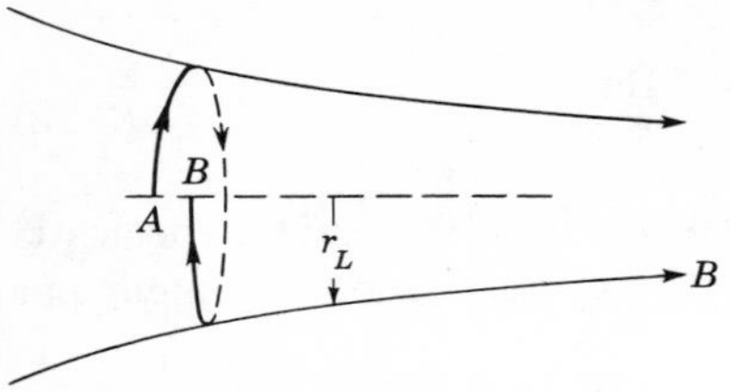

FIGURE 3.7 Particle motion in a converging magnetic field.

Consider a stationary inhomogeneous magnetic field which does not vary with time. A particle will follow a path shown in Fig. 3.7. Since **B** is assumed to vary slowly, the points A and B will be close to each other so that the surface normal to **B** will be approximately πr_L^2. Thus,

$$\pi r_L^2 B = \text{const} \tag{3.26}$$

which shows that the number of flux lines encompassed by an orbit remains constant. This is true even if the particle drifts, and is consistent with the previous result that if r_L is a constant, the particle drifts in such a way that the local magnetic field remains constant. Equation (3.26) can also be considered an adiabatic invariant.

Use of $r_L = mw_\perp/eZB$ in (3.26) yields

$$\frac{m^2 w_\perp^2}{e^2 Z^2 B^2} \pi B \equiv \left(\frac{1}{2}\frac{m w_\perp^2}{B}\right) \frac{2\pi m}{e^2 Z^2} = \text{const}$$

Since the mass and charge of a particle remain constant, the quantity in parentheses also remains constant. But this quantity is just the magnetic moment of a particle. Thus,

$$\mu = \frac{1}{2}\frac{m w_\perp^2}{B} = \text{const} \tag{3.27}$$

This is another adiabatic invariant. This result is also true if the magnetic field varies with time. More detailed analyses have shown that the variation of magnetic field during a particle orbit must be small for this result to be exact, or

$$\frac{1}{\omega B}\frac{dB}{dt} < 0.1 \tag{3.28}$$

Another invariant can be derived from (3.26). Since the number of flux lines encompassed by a particle orbit is constant, as the magnetic field lines are squeezed together the particles also are squeezed together. Thus, the number density of particles is proportional to B, or

$$\frac{n}{B} = \text{const} \tag{3.29}$$

for the same group of particles.

The energy and magnetic moment invariants can be used to derive the equation of motion along the field line. First, (3.27) can be rewritten as

$$\mu B_\parallel = \tfrac{1}{2} m w_\perp^2 = \mathcal{E} - \tfrac{1}{2} m w_\parallel^2 \tag{3.30}$$

where $\mathcal{E} = \frac{1}{2}m(w_\parallel{}^2 + w_\perp{}^2)$ is the total particle energy. Differentiation of (3.30) with respect to time yields

$$\mu\left(\frac{\partial B_\parallel}{\partial t} + w_\parallel \frac{\partial B_\parallel}{\partial l}\right) = \frac{d\mathcal{E}}{dt} - mw_\parallel \frac{dw_\parallel}{dt} \tag{3.31}$$

where l is the distance along a field line. The change in energy can be caused by changes in both $w_\perp$ and $w_\parallel$. For $w_\perp$,

$$\frac{d\mathcal{E}_\perp}{dt} = \frac{eZ\oint E_\perp r_L\, d\theta}{\tau} = \frac{eZ\omega}{2\pi}\frac{\partial B_\parallel}{\partial t}\pi r_L{}^2$$

where use has been made of Faraday's law. This can be rewritten as

$$\frac{d\mathcal{E}_\perp}{dt} = \mu\frac{\partial B_\parallel}{\partial t} \tag{3.32}$$

The change in $w_\parallel$ due to electric fields parallel to l is

$$\frac{d\mathcal{E}_\parallel}{dt} = w_\parallel eZE_\parallel \tag{3.33}$$

Combination of (3.31), (3.32), and (3.33) and division by $w_\parallel$ yield

$$\mu\frac{\partial B_\parallel}{\partial l} = -m\frac{dw_\parallel}{dt} + eZE_\parallel$$

But $\partial B_\parallel/\partial l$ is the same as $\nabla B_\parallel$; thus the equation of motion in the direction of the magnetic field is finally

$$m\frac{dw_\parallel}{dt} = -\mu\,\nabla B_\parallel + eZE_\parallel \tag{3.34}$$

Note that the term $\mathbf{w} \times \mathbf{B}$ is contained in $\mu\,\nabla B$.

Finally, there is an adiabatic invariant associated with the component of velocity parallel to the magnetic field: over a closed path, the line integral $\oint w_\parallel\, dl$ is a constant. If the path is closed, this implies that when the particle returns to its initial position both the magnetic field and electric field, if time-varying, have returned to their initial values. The proof that $\oint w_\parallel\, dl = \text{const}$ may be obtained by differentiation with respect to time and substitution of (3.34),

$$\frac{d}{dt}\int w_\parallel\, dl = \int \frac{dw_\parallel}{dt}\, dl = -\frac{\mu}{m}\int\frac{\partial B_\parallel}{\partial l}\, dl - \frac{eZ}{m}\oint\frac{\partial\phi}{\partial l}\, dl$$

where use has been made of $\mathbf{E} = -\nabla\phi - \partial\mathbf{A}/\partial t$; but $A_\parallel = 0$. Thus,

$$\frac{d}{dt}\int w_\parallel\, dl = -\frac{\mu}{m}[B_\parallel(\tau) - B_\parallel(0)] - \frac{eZ}{m}[\phi(\tau) - \phi(0)]$$

or

$$\frac{d}{dt}\oint w_\parallel\, dl = 0 \tag{3.35}$$

if the initial and final values of B and ϕ are identical.

The various adiabatic invariants are summarized below:

1. Kinetic energy: $\frac{m}{2}(w_\perp{}^2 + w_\parallel{}^2) = \text{const} \qquad (\mathbf{E} = 0)$ (3.36)

2. Magnetic moment: $\mu = \frac{1}{2}\frac{mw_\perp{}^2}{B} = \text{const}$ (3.27)

   (*a*) $\pi r_L{}^2 B = \text{const}$ (3.26)

   (*b*) $\frac{n}{B} = \text{const}$ (3.29)

3. Longitudinal invariant: $\oint w_\parallel \, dl = \text{const}$ (3.35)

3.8 SPECIFIC HEATS

In the absence of gradients and curvature of the magnetic field, particles perform helical motions about field lines. If there is a gradient in the magnetic field, in addition to the helical motion about field lines, the particle will drift, but in a direction such that the magnitude of the magnetic field remains the same (see Fig. 3.6). If the field is curved, the particles also drift in such a manner that they shift to magnetic field lines of the same magnitude. Thus, at any one point in an equalized plasma, the number density of charged particles of a given species is proportional to the local magnetic field, as given by (3.29):

$$n \sim B \tag{3.37}$$

The average magnetic moment for particles near a given point is

$$\langle\mu\rangle = \frac{\langle\frac{1}{2}mw_\perp{}^2\rangle}{B}$$

so that

$$n\langle\mu\rangle = \frac{p_\perp}{B}$$

The magnetic moment of a particle remains fixed. If the plasma has existed long enough for the particle to be located randomly, $\langle\mu\rangle$ will be a constant everywhere. Thus,

$$p_\perp \sim nB \tag{3.38}$$

Use of (3.37) in (3.38) yields

$$p_\perp \sim n^2$$

or, multiplying by the average particle mass,

$$p_\perp \sim \rho^2 \tag{3.39}$$

In an ordinary gas, $p \sim \rho^\gamma$ for adiabatic compression. Thus, for the ionized particles in a collisionless plasma, the specific heat ratio for $p_\perp$ appears to be 2. This can also be seen by considering transverse compression: Since the plasma is collisionless, only the two transverse components of velocity are affected. For each velocity component there is a degree of freedom, and the specific heat ratio is $\gamma = (\mathfrak{N} + 2)/\mathfrak{N}$. Thus if $\mathfrak{N} = 2$, then $\gamma = 2$ in agreement with the previous result.

In the direction parallel to B, a parallel pressure may be defined as

$$p_\parallel = n \left\langle \frac{m w_\parallel^2}{2} \right\rangle \tag{3.40}$$

The longitudinal adiabatic invariant states that $\int w_\parallel \, dl = \text{const.}$ As the magnetic field is increased, the flux path that the particle travels over becomes smaller, and thus the velocity increases. Thus,

$$w_\parallel \sim B \tag{3.41}$$

Use of (3.41) and (3.37) in (3.40) yields

$$p_\parallel \sim n^3 \tag{3.42}$$

so that $\gamma_\parallel = 3$. Here only one component of velocity can be changed during longitudinal compression; so $\gamma_\parallel = (\mathfrak{N} + 2)/\mathfrak{N} = 3$, in agreement with (3.42).

3.9 MOTION IN THE DIRECTION OF THE MAGNETIC FIELD—"MAGNETIC MIRROR"

In Secs. 3.3 to 3.6, the drift motion of charged particles perpendicular to magnetic lines of flux was derived. In this section, the motion in the direction of the magnetic field lines is considered in the absence of an electric field. From (3.25), the total kinetic energy of a charged particle remains constant; and from (3.27), the transverse kinetic energy is proportional to the absolute value of the magnetic field. As a charged particle moves in a helical path along a field line, if the magnetic field increases, $w_\perp$ will also increase, but at the expense of $w_\parallel$. Thus, the particle velocity in the direction of the magnetic field will be decreased, and may actually be reduced to zero, or reversed. Consider (3.34) with $E = 0$ (see Fig. 3.8):

$$m \frac{dw_\parallel}{dt} = -\mu \frac{dB_z}{dz} \tag{3.43}$$

where the local magnetic field has been taken in the z direction. Equation (3.43) shows that when B_z increases in the z direction, there is a force on the particle in the direction opposite to the gradient dB_z/dz. If the particle is moving in the $+z$ direction, Eq. (3.43) may also be written as

$$m w_\parallel \frac{dw_\parallel}{dz} = -\mu \frac{dB_z}{dz}$$

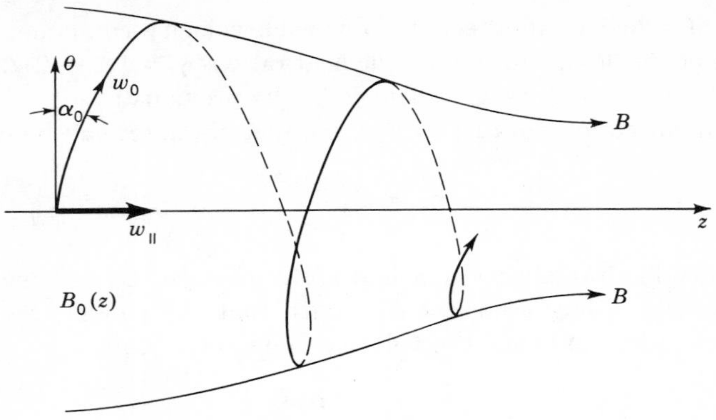

FIGURE 3.8 Magnetic mirror.

This can be integrated immediately to

$$m\left(\frac{w_{\parallel}^2}{2} - \frac{w_{\parallel_0}^2}{2}\right) = -\mu(B_z - B_{z_0}) \tag{3.44}$$

where $w_{\parallel_0}$ is the axial velocity when the magnetic field is B_{z_0}. Thus, as the particle moves in the $+z$ direction, B_z will increase, which requires that $w_{\parallel}$ decrease. In fact, if $B_z - B_{z_0} = \frac{1}{2}mw_{\parallel_0}^2$ at some point, the particle velocity $w_{\parallel}$ will be zero. If at that point $\partial B_z/\partial z$ is also positive, Eq. (3.43) shows that the particle will be reflected. This arrangement is a magnetic mirror for trapped particles. If, however,

$$\frac{1}{2}mw_{\parallel_0}^2 > \frac{1}{2}mw_{\perp_0}^2 \frac{(B_z - B_{z_0})}{B_{z_0}}$$

then the particle will continue through the mirror and not be trapped. Since $w_{\parallel_0}/w_{\perp_0} = \tan\alpha_0$, the helix angle, the requirement for reflection is

$$\cos^2\alpha_0 < \frac{B_{z_0}}{B_{z,\max}} \tag{3.45}$$

Particles whose helix angle is larger than α_0 will obviously escape.

Particles whose guiding center is off axis will also be reflected in accordance with Eq. (3.45). In addition, they will be subjected to curvature and gradient drifts, but these drifts are in the circumferential (θ) direction and therefore are not lost from the magnetic field. However, collisions between particles will allow radial losses.

These considerations are important for certain nuclear fusion experiments, in which high-energy particles are trapped between two magnetic mirrors. They also explain part of the phenomenon of the Van Allen belts which surround the earth. Energetic particles from the sun acquire

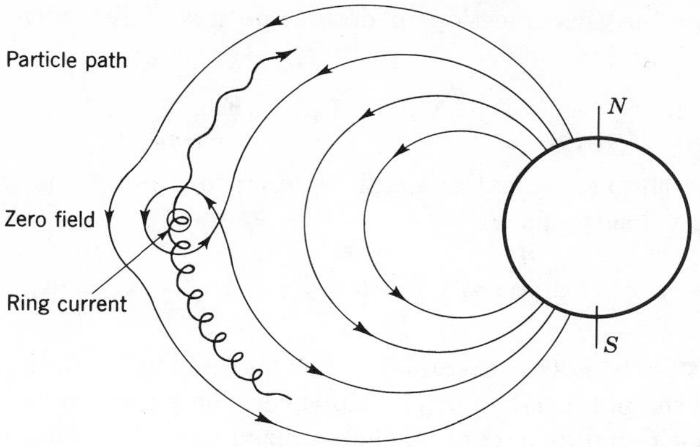

FIGURE 3.9 Source of aurora polaris.

a magnetic moment with respect to the earth's magnetic field by either collision or radioactive decay. Once they have this moment, they are trapped and are reflected from pole to pole, and owing to curvature and gradients in the earth's magnetic field, they also drift circumferentially until their circumferential density is uniform.

Charged particles from the sun also create a ring current around the earth's magnetosphere (see Fig. 3.9). Associated with this ring current is a magnetic field which cancels the earth's magnetic field in its immediate vicinity. Since B becomes very small and the magnetic moment remains constant, those particles in the low-magnetic-field region gain a very large meridional velocity (1,000 to 5,000 km/sec). Their high longitudinal velocity through the region of low magnetic field reduces the magnetic moment of the particles so that they descend to low altitudes along their magnetic field line and excite the electronic states of air atoms by collision; this is the aurora polaris. The aurora polaris sheet is quite thin, about 10^3 m, which indicates that the region of low magnetic field is quite small. Also, the aurora as seen from the earth tends to wave back and forth. This is an indication that the reaction between the ring current and the earth's magnetic field is variable, causing the ring current to wander.[1]

3.10 HAMILTONIAN FORMULATION

Hamilton's equations are useful for certain purposes, and the equations of motion of charged particles are sometimes presented in this form.[2] The hamiltonian is the sum of the particle kinetic and potential energy, where in this case the latter is the electric potential. However, the use of the particle positional coordinates and momenta as the generalized coordinates will not generate the Lorentz force on the particle, $eZ\mathbf{w} \times \mathbf{B}$.

To examine this question in detail one may start with Lagrange's equations of motion,

$$\frac{d}{dt}\boldsymbol{\nabla}_{\dot{q}}L - \boldsymbol{\nabla}_q L = \mathbf{F} \tag{3.46}$$

where $\boldsymbol{\nabla}_q$ is the usual spatial gradient operator, and $\boldsymbol{\nabla}_{\dot{q}}$ is the gradient operator in velocity space:

$$\boldsymbol{\nabla}_{\dot{q}} = \mathbf{i}\frac{\partial}{\partial \dot{q}_1} + \mathbf{j}\frac{\partial}{\partial \dot{q}_2} + \mathbf{k}\frac{\partial}{\partial \dot{q}_3} \tag{3.47}$$

Note that $\boldsymbol{\nabla}_q$ does *not* operate on $\dot{q}$. The lagrangian is usually the kinetic energy less the potential energy. However, the potential energy may be initially considered as part of the generalized force F. Thus, $L = \frac{1}{2}mw^2$, and $\mathbf{F} = Ze(\mathbf{E} + \mathbf{w} \times \mathbf{B})$. Use of the electric and magnetic potentials yields

$$\mathbf{F} = eZ\left[-\boldsymbol{\nabla}\phi - \frac{\partial \mathbf{A}}{\partial t} + \mathbf{w} \times (\boldsymbol{\nabla} \times \mathbf{A})\right]$$

Expansion of the last term yields

$$\mathbf{F} = eZ\left[-\boldsymbol{\nabla}\phi - \frac{\partial \mathbf{A}}{\partial t} - (\mathbf{w} \cdot \boldsymbol{\nabla})\mathbf{A} + \boldsymbol{\nabla}(\mathbf{w} \cdot \mathbf{A})\right]$$

The second and third terms in the brackets are the rate of change of $\mathbf{A}$ as seen by a particle with velocity $\mathbf{w}$, and are usually denoted by $-d\mathbf{A}/dt$. This may also be written as

$$\frac{\partial \mathbf{A}}{\partial t} + (\mathbf{w} \cdot \boldsymbol{\nabla})\mathbf{A} \equiv \frac{d\mathbf{A}}{dt} \equiv \frac{d}{dt}\boldsymbol{\nabla}_w(\mathbf{w} \cdot \mathbf{A}) \equiv \frac{d}{dt}\boldsymbol{\nabla}_w(\mathbf{w} \cdot \mathbf{A} - \phi)$$

since $\boldsymbol{\nabla}_w \phi = 0$. The generalized force then becomes

$$\mathbf{F} = eZ\left[\frac{d}{dt}\boldsymbol{\nabla}_w(\phi - \mathbf{w} \cdot \mathbf{A}) - \boldsymbol{\nabla}(\phi - \mathbf{w} \cdot \mathbf{A})\right] \tag{3.48}$$

The form of $\mathbf{F}$ is similar to that of L in Eq. (3.46). Thus a new lagrangian may be formed:

$$L' = L - eZ(\phi - \mathbf{w} \cdot \mathbf{A}) = \tfrac{1}{2}mw^2 - eZ(\phi - \mathbf{w} \cdot \mathbf{A}) \tag{3.49}$$

This is similar to the usual form, except for the additional term $\mathbf{w} \cdot \mathbf{A}$ which accounts for the Lorentz force. To proceed to Hamilton's equations, one next finds the generalized momenta. It is obvious that if the generalized spatial coordinates are selected arbitrarily, then the momenta cannot also be selected arbitrarily. The correct momenta are given by

$$\mathbf{p} = \boldsymbol{\nabla}_{\dot{q}}L'$$

where $\mathbf{q}$ are the coordinates, and $\dot{\mathbf{q}}$ are the rates of change of the coordinates. Since $\mathbf{A}$ is a function of the spatial coordinates, let $\mathbf{x} = \mathbf{q}$ so that the particle velocities are $\mathbf{w} = \dot{\mathbf{q}}$. Thus,

$$\mathbf{p} = \nabla_w L' = m\mathbf{w} + eZ\mathbf{A} \tag{3.50}$$

Next, the hamiltonian is formed as follows:

$$H = \mathbf{p} \cdot \dot{\mathbf{q}}_i - L' \equiv \mathbf{p} \cdot \mathbf{w} - L'$$

Use of (3.49) and (3.50) yields

$$\begin{aligned} H &= \frac{1}{2m} (\mathbf{p} - e\mathbf{A}) \cdot (\mathbf{p} - e\mathbf{A}) + eZ\phi \\ \text{or} \qquad H &= \tfrac{1}{2} m w^2 + eZ\phi \end{aligned} \tag{3.51}$$

Finally, the equation of motion is

$$\frac{\partial H}{\partial q_i} = \frac{dp_i}{dt}$$

$$\text{or} \qquad \nabla_q H = \frac{d\mathbf{p}}{dt} \tag{3.52}$$

3.11 ELECTRIC CURRENTS IN AN IONIZED GAS

The definition of the actual *free* current at a point in a gas is

$$\mathbf{J} = \sum_s n_s e Z_s \langle \mathbf{w} \rangle_s \tag{3.53}$$

where $\langle \mathbf{w} \rangle$ indicates the average over all velocities of the s species. This is a time average of the particle motion and must be carefully distinguished from the *drift* velocity which is a time average of a guiding center. For a single particle,

$$\mathbf{w}_s = \mathbf{V}_{d_s} - \boldsymbol{\omega}_s \times \mathbf{r}_{L_s}$$

so that (3.53) becomes

$$\mathbf{J} = \sum_s n_s e Z_s \mathbf{V}_{d_s} - \sum_s n_s e Z_s \langle \boldsymbol{\omega}_s \times \mathbf{r}_{L_s} \rangle \tag{3.54}$$

The second term on the right of (3.54) is that due to the magnetization associated with the orbital motion of the charged particles, and according to Maxwell's equations must be given by

$$\mathbf{J}_M \equiv - \sum_s n_s e Z_s \langle \boldsymbol{\omega}_s \times \mathbf{r}_{L_s} \rangle = \nabla \times \mathbf{M}_\mu \tag{3.55}$$

We will prove this result by considering a surface dx long and counting the rate at which particles go through it (see Fig. 3.10). These parti-

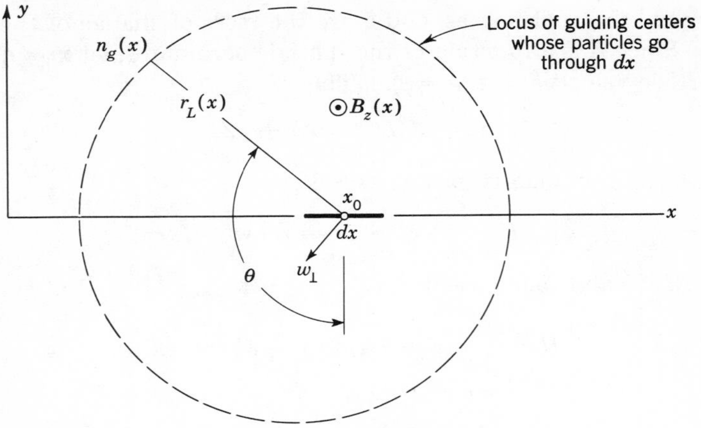

FIGURE 3.10 Magnetization current.

cles are associated with guiding centers which are a distance $r_L(x)$ away from dx, with a number density of guiding centers $n_g(x)$. For simplicity we consider the plasma to be uniform in the z direction. The particle flux associated with the guiding centers at θ is therefore

$$d\dot{n}_y = -n(x_0, \theta)w_\perp \sin \theta \frac{d\theta}{2\pi}$$

where $n(x_0, \theta)\, d\theta$ is the number density of charged particles at x_0 whose guiding centers lie between angles θ and $\theta + d\theta$, where θ is measured with respect to the $-y$ direction. The factor 2π is a normalizing factor since

$$n(x_0) = \frac{1}{2\pi} \int_0^{2\pi} n(x_0, \theta)\, d\theta = n(x)$$

in a uniform gas. Now the density $n(x_0, \theta)$ at x_0 associated with the guiding centers at θ is not equal to the density of guiding centers $n_g(x)$, in an inhomogeneous field. This occurs because if the magnetic field at x is less than at x_0, the particles will become compressed at x_0, in accordance with the law $n/B =$ const. Thus,

$$n(x_0,\theta) = n_g(x) \frac{B(x_0)}{B(x)} \tag{3.56}$$

Both $n_g(x)$ and $B(x)$ may be expanded in Taylor series, for $\dfrac{r_L}{B}\dfrac{dB}{dx} \ll 1$:

$$n_g(x) = n_g(x_0) \left[1 + \frac{\partial n_g/\partial x}{n_{0_g}} (x - x_0) \right] \tag{3.57}$$

$$B(x) = B(x_0) \left[1 + \frac{\partial B/\partial x}{B_0} (x - x_0) \right] \tag{3.58}$$

Also

$$x - x_0 = -r_L \sin \theta = -\frac{w_\perp m}{eZB_0} \sin \theta \tag{3.59}$$

where variations in r_L may be neglected since they will contribute only second-order terms. Combination of (3.56) to (3.59) and neglecting second-order terms yield

$$n(x_0,\theta) = n_g(x_0)\left[1 - \frac{w_\perp m}{eZB_0}\sin\theta\left(n_{0_g}^{-1}\frac{\partial n_g}{\partial x} - B_0^{-1}\frac{\partial B}{\partial x}\right)\right] \tag{3.60}$$

The particle flux per unit area through dx is therefore

$$\dot{n}_y = \frac{-n_g(x_0)w_\perp}{2\pi}\int_0^{2\pi}\left[1 - \frac{w_\perp m}{eZB_0}\sin\theta\left(n_{0_g}^{-1}\frac{\partial n_g}{\partial x} - B_0^{-1}\frac{\partial B}{\partial x}\right)\right]\sin\theta\, d\theta$$

or, after integration,

$$\dot{n}_y = n_g\frac{mw_\perp^2}{2eZB_0}\left(n_{0_g}^{-1}\frac{\partial n_g}{\partial x} - B_0^{-1}\frac{\partial B}{\partial x}\right) \tag{3.61}$$

Next, the total current will be calculated, assuming constant composition and $w_\perp$ so that $dp_\perp/p_\perp = dn_g/n_g$ and $p_\perp = (n_g/2)mw_\perp^2$; then[3]

$$J_{M_y} = \frac{\partial p_\perp/\partial x}{B} - p_\perp\frac{\partial B/\partial x}{B^2} \tag{3.62}$$

We next compare (3.62) to $\nabla \times \mathbf{M}_\mu$. Now

$$\mathbf{M}_\mu = -\frac{p_\perp}{B}\mathbf{k}$$

Thus,
$$(\nabla \times \mathbf{M}_\mu)_y = -\frac{\partial}{\partial x}M_\mu = \frac{\partial}{\partial x}\frac{p_\perp}{B} = \frac{\partial p_\perp/\partial x}{B} - \frac{p_\perp(\partial B/\partial x)}{B^2} \tag{3.63}$$

Comparison of (3.62) with (3.63) confirms that

$$\mathbf{J}_M = \nabla \times \mathbf{M}_\mu \tag{3.64}$$

for each species, and hence for the entire gas, which is a well-known result. Substitution of (3.55) into (3.54) yields

$$\mathbf{J} = \mathbf{J}_{\text{drift}} + \nabla \times \mathbf{M}_\mu \tag{3.65}$$

But Maxwell's equations require that

$$\mu_0^{-1}\nabla \times \mathbf{B} = \nabla \times \mathbf{H} + \nabla \times \mathbf{M}_\mu \tag{3.66}$$

Comparison of (3.65) and (3.66) shows that the true current is

$$\mu_0\mathbf{J} = \nabla \times \mathbf{B} \tag{3.67}$$

and the drift current is

$$\mathbf{J}_{\text{drift}} = \nabla \times \mathbf{H} \tag{3.68}$$

Unfortunately, these relationships are sometimes reversed. To avoid confusion, only the true current will be used in the remainder of this book.

This confusion arises because of the type of magnetic moment under consideration. We can distinguish two types of magnetic moments:

(1) Magnetic moments caused by rotation of the electron field around a nucleus; electron spin; and nuclear spin. This magnetic moment is attached to the particle, and as the particle moves, does *not* contribute to the free current. (2) The other magnetic moment is caused by the *curved* motion of a charged particle. Whether the path is curved or not curved, this particle contributes to the current. Therefore the free current in a gas is clearly given by (3.67). It is not always convenient to calculate the free currents in a gas from (3.67); usually one calculates the drift current $\mathbf{J}_d$ and then adds the magnetization current due to particle orbits $\mathbf{J}_M$. Thus, if one calculates the current from $\nabla \times \mathbf{H}$, one must *always* add to this the magnetization current due to the free charges.

3.12 MAGNETIC FIELD PRESSURE

From the previous discussion, it is seen that

$$\frac{\nabla \times \mathbf{B}}{\mu_0} = \sum_s n_s e Z_s \mathbf{V}_{ds} + \nabla \times \mathbf{M}_\mu \tag{3.69}$$

Consider an inhomogeneous magnetic field $\mathbf{B} = \mathbf{k}B_z(x)$ and a stationary state of the plasma. Then, from (3.21),

$$\sum_s n_s e Z_s \mathbf{V}_{ds} = \mathbf{j}\,\frac{\Sigma \frac{1}{2} n_s m_s w_{\perp s}^2}{B^2}\,\frac{\partial B_z}{\partial x} = \mathbf{j}\,\frac{p_\perp}{B^2}\,\frac{\partial B_z}{\partial x} \tag{3.70}$$

From (3.23), the total magnetic moment is

$$\mathbf{M}_\mu = -\frac{1}{2}\sum_s n_s \langle m w_\perp{}^2\rangle_s \frac{\mathbf{B}}{B^2} = -\frac{p_\perp \mathbf{B}}{B^2} \tag{3.71}$$

Substitution into Eq. (3.69) yields

$$-\frac{1}{\mu_0}\,\mathbf{j}\,\frac{\partial B_z}{\partial x} = \mathbf{j}\,\frac{p_\perp}{B_z{}^2}\,\frac{\partial B_z}{\partial x} - \mathbf{j}\,\frac{p_\perp}{B_z{}^2}\,\frac{\partial B_z}{\partial x} + \frac{\mathbf{j}}{B_z}\,\frac{\partial p_\perp}{\partial x}$$

which can be integrated to yield

$$\frac{B_z{}^2}{2\mu_0} + p_\perp = \text{const} \tag{3.72}$$

Thus the sum of the magnetic pressure and the transverse plasma pressure must be a constant for this situation. From Maxwell's equations, $B_z{}^2/2\mu_0$ is the normal magnetic stress. Thus for the plasma to be stationary the sum of the magnetic pressure and the gas pressure must be constant.

Note that it was implied that B_z had a gradient. Actually, the magnetic field tends to diffuse through a plasma. B_z can have a stationary gradient only if $\partial \mathbf{B}/\partial t = 0$, which in turn requires that $\nabla \times \mathbf{E} = 0$. This is true only if there are no collisions between charged particles, which implies perfect conductivity.

REFERENCES CITED

1. Chapman, S.: "Sun Storms and the Earth: The Aurora Polaris and the Space around the Earth," *Am. Scientist*, September, 1961, pp. 249–284.
2. Goldstein, H.: *Classical Mechanics*, p. 20, Addison-Wesley Publishing Company, Inc., Reading, Mass., 1959.
3. Tonks, L.: "Particle Transport, Electric Currents, and Pressure Balance in Magnetically Immobilized Plasma," *Phys. Rev.*, **97**:1443–1445 (1955).

GENERAL REFERENCES

Chandrasekhar, S.: *Plasma Physics*, notes compiled by S. K. Trehan, The University of Chicago Press, Chicago, 1960.

Clauser, F. H. (gen. ed.): *Symposium on Plasma Dynamics*, Addison-Wesley Publishing Company, Inc., Reading, Mass., 1960.

Drummond, J. E. (ed.): *Plasma Physics*, McGraw-Hill Book Company, New York, 1961.

Glasstone, S., and R. Lovberg: *Controlled Thermonuclear Reactions*, D. Van Nostrand Company, Inc., Princeton, N.J., 1960.

International Summer Course in Plasma Physics (Riso), Danish Atomic Energy Commission, 1960.

Landshof, R. K. M.: "Magnetohydrodynamics," *The McGraw-Hill Encyclopedia of Science and Technology*, vol. 8, p. 55, McGraw-Hill Book Company, New York, 1960.

Linhart, J. G.: *Plasma Physics*, North Holland Publishing Company, Amsterdam, 1960.

Longmire, C. L., J. L. Tuck, W. B. Thompson (eds.): *Plasma Physics and Thermonuclear Research*, Pergamon Press, New York, 1959.

Rose, D. J., and M. Clark: *Plasmas and Controlled Fusion*, John Wiley & Sons, Inc., New York, 1961.

Spitzer, L.: *Physics of Fully Ionized Gases*, vol. 2, Interscience Publishers, Inc., New York, 1962.

Vlasov, A. A.: *Many-particle Theory and Its Application to Plasma*, Gordon and Breach, Science Publishers, Inc., New York, 1961.

4

STATISTICAL BEHAVIOR OF PLASMAS

4.1 INTRODUCTION

In Chap. 3 collisions between particles were neglected. However, in a gas at normal pressure and temperature, a single particle experiences about 10^9 collisions/sec. Therefore, the instantaneous velocity of a single particle will change 10^9 times/sec, and each of the 10^9 different velocities will be determined mainly by the geometry of each collision rather than by the external forces acting on the gas. Electric fields, pressure gradients, etc., usually introduce only a small perturbation in the motion of the individual particles. When there exists a large number of collisions and the perturbing effect of external fields on the particle motion is small, it is no longer convenient to analyze the motion of individual particles. Instead, the *average* perturbing effect on a large number of particles is analyzed.

In addition to the large number of collisions, the particles have a distribution of speeds; that is, they are not isoenergetic. The collisions between particles not only change the direction of motion, but in addition, one particle can transfer part or all of its kinetic energy to another particle. Thus, if one started with an isoenergetic gas, in which each particle has the same speed, then collisions would cause the particles to develop a spread in velocities. Thus, it is not convenient to treat *all* the particles simultaneously, but instead one treats those particles which at a given time have velocities in some small range $\Delta\mathbf{c}$. To accomplish this, one introduces the velocity distribution function. In this chapter, this will be defined and derived for a gas which is isotropic, that is, for the S region.

As an example, the collision frequency will be obtained for hard spheres, with and without mean motion. The concept of the distribution function will be enlarged to obtain Boltzmann's equation from which several important properties of a plasma will be obtained. Finally, Boltzmann's equation will be used to obtain the conservation equations.

4.2 DISTRIBUTION FUNCTIONS

As indicated above, one is interested in the number of particles dN which occupy a given spatial region and which have random thermal velocities with components between c_1 and $c_1 + dc_1$, c_2 and $c_2 + dc_2$, c_3 and $c_3 + dc_3$. The spatial coordinates are x_1, x_2, and x_3. This number dN will be proportional to both the volume element $dx_1\,dx_2\,dx_3 \equiv d\mathbf{x}$ and the velocity increment $dc_1\,dc_2\,dc_3 \equiv d\mathbf{c}$. Thus,

$$dN = f(\mathbf{c},\mathbf{x},t)\,d\mathbf{x}\,d\mathbf{c} \tag{4.1}$$

The weighting factor f is called the *velocity distribution function.* Note that the individual particle velocities $\mathbf{c}$ as used above are also coordinates and do *not* depend on $\mathbf{x}$. From this point of view, $\mathbf{x}$ is called *geometry space,* $\mathbf{c}$ is called *velocity space,* and the combined coordinates $\mathbf{x}$ and $\mathbf{c}$ are called *phase space.* Obviously, each separate species s will have its own distribution function f_s; thus electrons, hydrogen atoms, positive hydrogen ions, negative hydrogen ions, and helium atoms will each have their *own* distribution function. Thus f_s is the number density of the s species in phase space.

4.3 AVERAGES

The number density of a given species s which has velocities between $\mathbf{c}$ and $\mathbf{c} + d\mathbf{c}$ is obviously, from (4.1),

$$dn_s = \frac{dN_s}{d\mathbf{x}} = f_s\,d\mathbf{c} \tag{4.2}$$

To obtain the total particle number density per unit volume n_s, one integrates f_s over the entire velocity range:

$$n_s = \iiint_{-\infty}^{\infty} f_s\,dc_1\,dc_2\,dc_3 \equiv \int f_s\,d\mathbf{c} \tag{4.3}$$

For (4.3) to be meaningful, $f_s(\mathbf{x},\mathbf{c},t) \to 0$ as $c \to \pm\infty$.

The mass partial density of species s is obtained by multiplying the number density n_s by the mass per particle m_s:

$$\rho_s = n_s m_s \tag{4.4}$$

The total mass density is the sum of the partial mass densities:

$$\rho = \sum_s \rho_s = \sum_s n_s m_s \tag{4.5}$$

Temperature is defined as follows:

$$\frac{(\text{Total random kinetic energy})_s}{\text{Unit volume}} = \tfrac{3}{2} n_s k T_s \tag{4.6}$$

The factor of $\frac{3}{2}$ arises from $\frac{1}{2}kT$ of energy associated with each degree of freedom, and there are three degrees of freedom associated with translation. This must be multiplied by the number density to obtain the total kinetic energy of the s species per unit volume. Now, each particle has $\frac{1}{2}m_s c^2$ of random kinetic energy; the number of such particles with velocities between $\mathbf{c}$ and $\mathbf{c} + d\mathbf{c}$ is just $f_s\, d\mathbf{c}$. Thus, the kinetic energy associated with these particles is $\frac{1}{2}m_s c^2 f_s\, d\mathbf{c}$. The total thermal kinetic energy of the s species is therefore

$$n_s \langle \tfrac{1}{2} m_s c^2 \rangle_s = \tfrac{3}{2} n_s k T_s = \int \frac{1}{2} m_s c^2 f_s \, d\mathbf{c} \tag{4.7}$$

In general, the average of *any* property may be obtained by integration of that property over the distribution function; thus,

$$n_s \langle A \rangle = \int A(\mathbf{c}) f_s \, d\mathbf{c}$$

The quantity A may be scalar, vector, or tensor.

4.4 FLUXES

In the same manner in which averages are defined, one may define the average flux of some property Θ_s of a particle of species s. The flux of Θ_s for a single particle through a surface $d\mathbf{s}$ which is stationary with respect to the laboratory is given by

$$\Theta_s \mathbf{w} \cdot d\mathbf{s}$$

where $\mathbf{w}$ is the particle velocity with respect to laboratory coordinates, and is to be distinguished from the random thermal velocity of the particle, $\mathbf{c}$.

The total flux is obtained by integration over the distribution function; hence the total flux for the s species is

$$\text{Flux} = \left(\int \Theta_s \mathbf{w} f_s \, d\mathbf{w}\right) \cdot d\mathbf{s}$$

Therefore the flux vector is

$$\textbf{Flux vector} = \int \Theta_s \mathbf{w} f_s \, d\mathbf{w} \equiv n_s \langle \Theta \mathbf{w} \rangle_s \tag{4.8}$$

4.4.1 Particle Flux. With $\Theta_s = 1$, the flux is obviously the particle-number flux, as follows:

$$\textbf{Particle flux vector} = \int \mathbf{w} f_s \, d\mathbf{w} = n_s \langle \mathbf{w} \rangle_s \tag{4.9}$$

We define the average velocity $\mathbf{v}_s$ of the s species as the ratio of the particle-flux vector to the number density of s species; thus,

$$\mathbf{v}_s = \frac{1}{n_s} \int \mathbf{w} f_s \, d\mathbf{w} = \langle w \rangle_s \tag{4.10}$$

4.4.2 Mass Flux. To obtain the mass flux of the s species, let $\Theta_s = m_s$; then

$$\textbf{Mass flux vector} = \dot{\mathbf{m}}_s = \int m_s \mathbf{w} f_s \, d\mathbf{w} = n_s m_s \langle \mathbf{w} \rangle_s = \rho_s \mathbf{v}_s \tag{4.11}$$

from (4.4) and (4.10). The total mass-flux vector $\dot{\mathbf{m}}$ is obtained by summing (4.11) over all species:

$$\dot{\mathbf{m}} = \sum_s \dot{\mathbf{m}}_s = \sum_s \rho_s \mathbf{v}_s \tag{4.12}$$

Now the total mass density is the sum of the partial mass densities given by (4.12). From (4.5) and (4.12) the mass-average velocity may be defined as

$$\mathbf{v} = \frac{\dot{\mathbf{m}}}{\rho} = \frac{\sum_s \rho_s \mathbf{v}_s}{\sum_s \rho_s} \tag{4.13}$$

Now for an individual particle, two "thermal" velocities can be defined. The first, $\mathbf{c}$, is the random velocity with respect to the mass-average velocity $\mathbf{v}$,

$$\mathbf{c}_s = \mathbf{w}_s - \mathbf{v} \tag{4.14}$$

while the other, $\mathbf{c}_s'$, is defined with respect to the average velocity of only that species,

$$\mathbf{c}_s' = \mathbf{w}_s - \mathbf{v}_s \tag{4.15}$$

The distribution function can be written in terms of $\mathbf{w}$, $\mathbf{c}$, or $\mathbf{c}'$; all forms are equally valid. From (4.10), it is obvious that the average value of $\langle \mathbf{c}' \rangle_s = 0$. But the average of $\langle \mathbf{c} \rangle_s$ from (4.15) is not necessarily zero, but is the difference between the species-average velocity $\mathbf{v}_s$ and the mass-average velocity $\mathbf{v}$. Thus $\langle \mathbf{c} \rangle_s$ is the diffusion velocity $\mathbf{V}_s$ of that species:

$$\mathbf{V}_s = \mathbf{v}_s - \mathbf{v} = \langle \mathbf{c} \rangle_s = \frac{1}{n_s} \int \mathbf{c} f_s \, d\mathbf{c} \tag{4.16}$$

Substitution of (4.16) into (4.12) yields

$$\dot{\mathbf{m}} = \sum_s \rho_s \mathbf{V}_s + \mathbf{v} \sum_s \rho_s$$

From (4.13) $\dot{\mathbf{m}}$ is given by the last term in the above equation; thus the sum of the mass diffusions is zero:

$$\sum_s \rho_s \mathbf{V}_s = 0 \tag{4.17}$$

4.4.3 Electric Current. The charge flux or electric current $\mathbf{J}_s$ with respect to laboratory coordinates is obtained by letting $\Theta_s = eZ_s$; thus,

$$\mathbf{J}_s = n_s e Z_s \mathbf{v}_s = n_s e Z_s \mathbf{V}_s + n_s e Z_s \mathbf{v} \tag{4.18}$$

The total electric current is obtained by summing over all species; hence,

$$\mathbf{J} = \sum \mathbf{J}_s = \sum_s n_s e Z_s \mathbf{V}_s + \mathbf{v} \sum_s n_s e Z_s = \mathbf{j} + \mathbf{v}\rho_e \tag{4.19}$$

The conduction current $\mathbf{j}$ is the first term on the right side of (4.19); the second term is the convection current. If the gas is electrically neutral, then

$$\rho_e = \sum_s n_s e Z_s = 0 \tag{4.20}$$

so that the total current is equal to the conduction current, $\mathbf{J} = \mathbf{j}$. The conduction current of the s species is therefore given by

$$\mathbf{j}_s = eZ_s \int \mathbf{c} f_s \, d\mathbf{c} = eZ_s n_s \mathbf{V}_s \tag{4.21}$$

and the total conduction current is given by

$$\mathbf{j} = \sum_s \mathbf{j}_s = \sum_s n_s e Z_s \mathbf{V}_s \tag{4.22}$$

4.4.4 Momentum Flux. If $\boldsymbol{\Theta}_s$ is a vector with components $\Theta_1{}^s$, $\Theta_2{}^s$, and $\Theta_3{}^s$, then the flux of one of the components of $\boldsymbol{\Theta}_s$ with respect to laboratory coordinates is

$$\text{Flux}_i = \mathbf{e}_i \int \Theta_i{}^s \mathbf{w} f_s \, d\mathbf{w} \tag{4.23}$$

The total flux can therefore be expressed as a diadic:

$$\textbf{Flux} = \int \boldsymbol{\Theta}_s \mathbf{w} f_s \, d\mathbf{w} \tag{4.23a}$$

The momentum flux with respect to laboratory coordinates is obtained by letting $\boldsymbol{\Theta}_s = m_s \mathbf{w}$; then with the use of (4.14), (4.16), and (4.23*a*), the momentum flux of the s species becomes

$$\rho_s(\mathbf{vv} + \mathbf{V}_s\mathbf{v} + \mathbf{v}\mathbf{V}_s) + \rho_s\langle\mathbf{cc}\rangle_s \tag{4.24}$$

The first term is the partial fraction of the total mass-averaged momentum; the second is the diffusion of momentum flux; the third is the momentum of diffusion. The last term is the momentum flux associated with random motion only; this is therefore the partial-pressure tensor of the s species. In component form this becomes

$$\mathbf{p}_s = \rho_s \begin{bmatrix} \langle c_1c_1\rangle & \langle c_1c_2\rangle & \langle c_1c_3\rangle \\ \langle c_2c_1\rangle & \langle c_2c_2\rangle & \langle c_2c_3\rangle \\ \langle c_3c_1\rangle & \langle c_3c_2\rangle & \langle c_3c_3\rangle \end{bmatrix}_s \tag{4.24a}$$

or, in subscript notation,

$$p_{ij_s} = \rho_s \langle c_i c_j \rangle_s \tag{4.24b}$$

It is obvious that the pressure tensor is symmetric since

$$\langle c_i c_j \rangle_s = \langle c_j c_i \rangle_s$$

according to the averaging procedure. In addition, the trace of a tensor which is the sum of the diagonal terms is an invariant. It therefore appears that the trace may be associated with the partial pressure of the s species as follows:

$$p_s = \frac{1}{3} \rho_s \sum_i \langle c_i c_i \rangle_s = \frac{\rho_s}{3} \langle c^2 \rangle_s = n_s k T_s \tag{4.25}$$

from (4.7). Thus, it is implicitly assumed here that each species obeys the perfect-gas law. This will be modified for charged particles in Chap. 6.

The *total-momentum-flux tensor* is obtained by summing (4.24) over all species:

$$\text{Total momentum flux} = \rho \mathbf{v}\mathbf{v} + \sum_s \mathbf{p}_s \tag{4.26}$$

where use has been made of (4.17). The first term in (4.26) is the total mass momentum, and the second term is the total-pressure tensor $\mathbf{p}$:

$$\mathbf{p} = \sum_s \mathbf{p}_s$$

The total hydrostatic pressure is

$$p = \sum_s p_s = \sum_s n_s k T_s$$

If the temperature of each species is identical, equal to T, then

$$p = nkT \tag{4.27}$$

where n is the total number density of particles $\sum_s n_s$. The total-shear-stress tensor is given by

$$\boldsymbol{\tau} = \mathbf{p} - p\mathbf{I}$$

where $\mathbf{I}$ is the identity tensor; or in subscript notation,

$$\tau_{ij} = p_{ij} - p\delta_j$$

4.4.5 Energy Flux. To obtain the energy flux, let

$$\Theta_s = \epsilon_{\text{int}_s} + \tfrac{1}{2}m_s w^2$$

where ϵ_{int_s} is the internal energy of a given particle (vibrational, rotational, electronic, chemical), and $\frac{1}{2}m_s w^2$ is obviously the kinetic energy of translation with respect to laboratory coordinates. Use of (4.8) and (4.14) yields

$$\textbf{Energy flux}_s = \mathbf{v}[\tfrac{1}{2}\rho_s v^2 + n_s\langle\epsilon_{\text{int}}\rangle_s + \tfrac{1}{2}\rho_s\langle c^2\rangle_s] + \tfrac{1}{2}\rho_s v^2 \mathbf{V}_s + \rho_s \mathbf{v}(\mathbf{v}\cdot\mathbf{V}_s) + \mathbf{v}\cdot\mathbf{p}_s + \int \mathbf{c}(\epsilon_{\text{int}_s} + \tfrac{1}{2}m_s c^2) f_s \, d\mathbf{c} \qquad (4.28)$$

The last term in (4.28) is the energy flux due to random motion; thus this is the heat-conduction vector $\mathbf{q}_s$:

$$\mathbf{q}_s = \int \mathbf{c}\left(\epsilon_{\text{int}_s} + \frac{1}{2}m_s c^2\right) f_s \, d\mathbf{c}$$

To interpret the remaining terms in (4.28), we may note that

$$\mathbf{p}_s = \boldsymbol{\tau}_s + p_s \mathbf{I}$$

so that

$$\mathbf{v}\cdot\mathbf{p}_s = \mathbf{v}\cdot\boldsymbol{\tau}_s + p_s\mathbf{v}$$

Also, $\frac{1}{2}m_s\langle c^2\rangle_s = \frac{3}{2}kT_s$ by definition; hence (4.28) may be rearranged as follows:

$$\textbf{Energy flux}_s = \rho_s\mathbf{v}\left(\frac{\langle\epsilon_{\text{int}}\rangle_s}{m_s} + \frac{3}{2}\frac{kT_s}{m_s} + \frac{p_s}{\rho_s}\right) + \tfrac{1}{2}\rho_s v^2\mathbf{v} + \tfrac{1}{2}\rho_s v^2 \mathbf{V}_s + \rho_s\mathbf{v}(\mathbf{v}\cdot\mathbf{V}_s) + \mathbf{v}\cdot\boldsymbol{\tau}_s + \mathbf{q}_s \qquad (4.29)$$

Now $[\langle\epsilon_{\text{int}}\rangle_s + \frac{3}{2}kT_s]/m_s$ is the thermodynamic energy per unit mass of the s species, and with the addition of p_s/ρ_s becomes the enthalpy of the s species.

The total energy flux is obtained by summing (4.29) over all species to obtain

$$\textbf{Total energy flux} = \rho\mathbf{v}(\tfrac{1}{2}v^2 + h) + \mathbf{q} + \mathbf{v}\cdot\boldsymbol{\tau} \qquad (4.30)$$

where h is the enthalpy per unit mass of mixture,

$$h = \frac{\sum_s \rho_s h_s}{\rho} \qquad (4.30a)$$

$\mathbf{q}$ is the total-heat-flux vector $\sum_s \mathbf{q}_s$, and $\boldsymbol{\tau}$ is the total-stress tensor. The total enthalpy H is given by

$$H = \tfrac{1}{2}v^2 + h \qquad (4.30b)$$

Thus the first term in (4.30) is the convection of total enthalpy, the second term is the flux of energy due to random motion, and the last term is flow work.

4.5 ISOTROPIC EQUILIBRIUM DISTRIBUTION FUNCTION

In this section, the expression for the equilibrium distribution function in the *absence* of an external force will be derived. Under these conditions, the distribution function should be invariant to a rotation of coordinates; hence it should be isotropic. Only one species is considered; hence the subscript s is dropped. Consider now isotropic motion relative to a coordinate system moving with uniform velocity. In this case we wish to study the distribution function $f(\mathbf{c})$, where $\mathbf{c}$ is the random or thermal velocity. Let us also define the following distribution functions: Let $f_1(c_1)\,dc_1$ be equal to the fraction of particles per unit volume having velocities in the x_1 direction between c_1 and $c_1 + dc_1$, and define $f_2(c_2)\,dc_2$ and $f_3(c_3)\,dc_3$ similarly. The fraction of particles having a total velocity between $(c_1^2 + c_2^2 + c_3^2)^{\frac{1}{2}}$ and $[(c_1 + dc_1)^2 + (c_2 + dc_2)^2 + (c_3 + dc_3)^2]^{\frac{1}{2}}$ is thus the product of the three distribution functions and is also equal to $(f/n)\,dc_1\,dc_2\,dc_3$; hence,

$$f\,dc_1\,dc_2\,dc_3 = nf_1f_2f_3\,dc_1\,dc_2\,dc_3 \tag{4.31}$$

Now if the gas is isotropic, the velocities in the three orthogonal directions are independent of each other and are therefore *uncorrelated*. Therefore, f can be a function only of the absolute velocity of the particle; that is, $f = f(\sqrt{c_1^2 + c_2^2 + c_3^2})$, or more conveniently, $f = f(c_1^2 + c_2^2 + c_3^2)$. Equation (4.31) then becomes

$$f(c_1^2 + c_2^2 + c_3^2) = nf_1(c_1)f_2(c_2)f_3(c_3) \tag{4.32}$$

The f without a subscript is not to be confused with f_1, f_2, or f_3. Next, the logarithm of (4.32) is taken:

$$\ln f(c_1^2 + c_2^2 + c_3^2) = \ln f_1(c_1) + \ln f_2(c_2) + \ln f_3(c_3) + \ln n \tag{4.33}$$

Differentiation of (4.33) with respect to c_1, c_2, and c_3, respectively, yields the following three equations:

$$\begin{aligned} 2c_1\frac{f'}{f} &= \frac{f_1'}{f_1} \\ 2c_2\frac{f'}{f} &= \frac{f_2'}{f_2} \\ 2c_3\frac{f'}{f} &= \frac{f_3'}{f_3} \end{aligned} \tag{4.34}$$

Rearrangement of (4.34) yields

$$\frac{f'}{f} = \frac{f_1'(c_1)}{2c_1f_1} = \frac{f_2'(c_2)}{2c_2f_2} = \frac{f_3'(c_3)}{2c_3f_3} \tag{4.35}$$

Since each part of (4.35) depends only on its own variable, each part

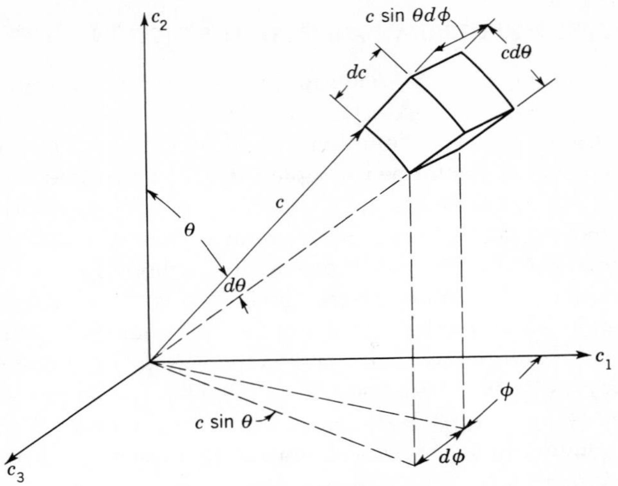

FIGURE 4.1 Velocity space.

must be a constant; thus,

$$\frac{f'}{f}(c^2) = -b \tag{4.36}$$

We have changed the independent variable in Eq. (4.36) to c^2, which is the square of the *absolute* velocity of the particle, since $c_1^2 + c_2^2 + c_3^3 = c^2$. Integration of Eq. (4.36) yields

$$\ln f = -bc^2 + \ln a$$

or

$$f = ae^{-bc^2} = ae^{-b(c_1^2+c_2^2+c_3^2)} \tag{4.37}$$

The constants of integration may be obtained from the definition of number density and temperature [(4.3) and (4.7)]. The element of volume in velocity space $dc_1\, dc_2\, dc_3$, which is written as $d\mathbf{c}$, is shown in Fig. 4.1.

Thus the element of volume is also $(c\, d\theta)(c \sin\theta\, d\phi)(dc)$. In (4.37), however, $f = f(c)$ only; hence we may integrate immediately with respect to θ and ϕ:

$$dc_1\, dc_2\, dc_3 = \int_0^\pi \sin\theta\, d\theta \int_0^{2\pi} d\phi \cdot c^2\, dc = 2 \cdot 2\pi c^2\, dc = 4\pi c^2\, dc \tag{4.38}$$

Thus, Eq. (4.3) becomes

$$n_s = 4\pi \int_0^\infty ae^{-bc^2} c^2\, dc = \frac{a}{b^{\frac{3}{2}}} \pi^{\frac{3}{2}} \tag{4.39}$$

Equation (4.7) becomes

$$\begin{aligned} \tfrac{3}{2}kT_s &= \frac{4\pi m_s}{2n_s} a \int_0^\infty c^4 e^{-bc^2}\, dc \\ &= \frac{4\pi a m_s}{2n_s} \frac{3}{8} \frac{\sqrt{\pi}}{b^{\frac{5}{2}}} \end{aligned} \tag{4.40}$$

or finally,

$$n_s k T_s = \frac{m_s}{2} \frac{a}{b^{\frac{5}{2}}} \pi^{\frac{3}{2}} \tag{4.40a}$$

Division by (4.39) yields

$$b = \frac{m_s}{2kT_s}$$

which, when substituted into Eq. (4.39), yields

$$a = n_s \left(\frac{m_s}{2kT_s\pi}\right)^{\frac{3}{2}}$$

Finally, the distribution function is

$$\begin{aligned} f_s &= n_s \left(\frac{m_s}{2\pi k T_s}\right)^{\frac{3}{2}} e^{-(m_s/2kT_s)c^2} \\ &= n_s \left(\frac{m_s}{2\pi k T_s}\right)^{\frac{3}{2}} e^{-(m_s/2kT_s)(c_1^2+c_2^2+c_3^2)} \end{aligned} \tag{4.41}$$

Since f_s is also equal to the product $nf_{1_s}(c_1)f_{2_s}(c_2)f_{3_s}(c_3)$, then (4.41) yields

$$f_{i_s}(c_i) = \left(\frac{m_s}{2kT_s\pi}\right)^{\frac{1}{2}} e^{-(m_s c_i^2)/2kT_s} \tag{4.42}$$

The distribution function of (4.41) is isotropic; that is, there is no preferred orientation, in accordance with the original assumption.

4.6 PROPERTIES OF THE ISOTROPIC DISTRIBUTION FUNCTION

The number density of particles of species s having speeds between $|\mathbf{c}|$ and $|\mathbf{c} + \mathbf{dc}|$ is just the product of f and the volume in velocity space $4\pi c^2\, dc$, or

$$f_s\, d\mathbf{c} = 4\pi c^2 n_s \left(\frac{m_s}{2\pi k T_s}\right)^{\frac{3}{2}} e^{-m_s c^2/2kT_s}\, dc$$

Thus the distribution function for speeds between $|\mathbf{c}|$ and $|\mathbf{c} + \mathbf{dc}|$ is

$$F_s(|\mathbf{c}|) = 4\pi n_s c^2 \left(\frac{m_s}{2\pi k T_s}\right)^{\frac{3}{2}} e^{-m_s c^2/2kT_s} \tag{4.43}$$

which is shown in Fig. 4.2.

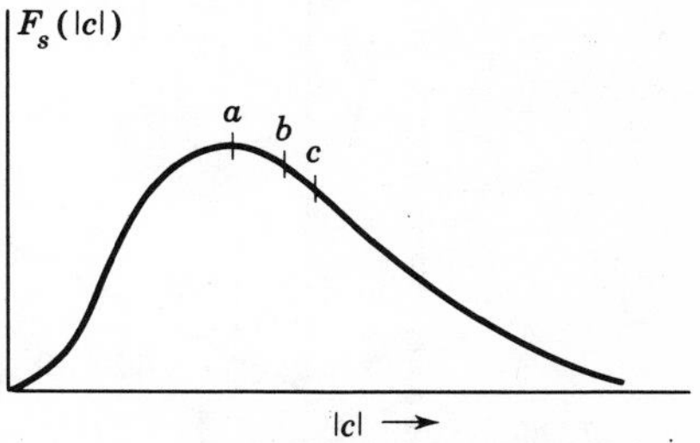

FIGURE 4.2 Isotropic distribution function: (a) Most probable speed $c = \sqrt{2kT_s/m_s}$; (b) mean speed $\langle c\rangle = \sqrt{8kT_s/\pi m_s}$; ($c$) rms speed $\langle c^2\rangle^{1/2} = \sqrt{3kT_s/m_s}$

The maximum value of F_s is the most probable speed. Its value is determined by differentiation of (4.43) with respect to c, which yields

$$c_{\max} = \sqrt{\frac{2kT_s}{m_s}} \tag{4.44}$$

The rms speed is defined in terms of the thermal velocity (4.6); thus,

$$\sqrt{\langle c^2 \rangle} = \sqrt{\frac{3kT_s}{m_s}} \tag{4.45}$$

In addition, there is the mean thermal speed, which is the centroid of the area of Fig. 4.2,

$$\langle c \rangle = \frac{\int F_s(c)c\,dc}{\int F_s(c)\,dc} = 4\pi\left(\frac{m_s}{2\pi kT_s}\right)^{\frac{3}{2}} \int c^3 e^{-m_s c^2/2kT_s}\,dc$$

or

$$\langle c \rangle = \sqrt{\frac{8kT_s}{\pi m_s}} \tag{4.46}$$

Thus, the rms speed $\langle c^2 \rangle^{\frac{1}{2}}$ is larger than the mean speed $\langle c \rangle$ by a factor of 1.086. This mean thermal speed is to be distinguished from the average vector velocity $\langle \mathbf{c} \rangle$ which of course is zero for an isotropic velocity distribution. The mean speed $\langle c \rangle$ for electrons is shown in Fig. 4.3.

If the species s has a mean velocity $\mathbf{v}_s$ and the distribution function is isotropic about $\mathbf{v}_s$, then the distribution function in laboratory coordi-

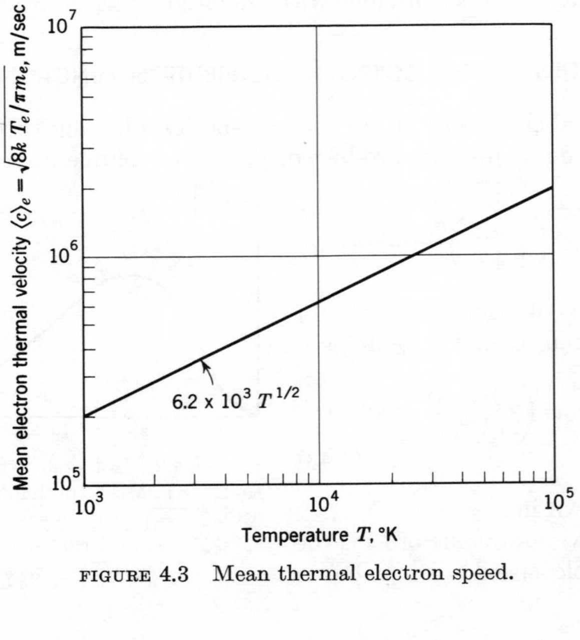

FIGURE 4.3 Mean thermal electron speed.

nates is obtained by use of the transformation $\mathbf{c} = \mathbf{w} - \mathbf{v}_s$, so that

$$f_s(\mathbf{w}) = n_s \left(\frac{m_s}{2\pi k T_s}\right)^{\frac{3}{2}} e^{-(m_s/2kT_s)[(w_1-v_{1_s})^2+(w_2-v_{2_s})^2+(w_3-v_{3_s})^2]}$$

or

$$f_s(\mathbf{w}) = n_s \left(\frac{m_s}{2\pi k T_s}\right)^{\frac{3}{2}} e^{-(m_s/2kT_s)|\mathbf{w}-\mathbf{v}|^2} \tag{4.47}$$

It is easily verified that $n_s^{-1}\int f_s \mathbf{w}\, d\mathbf{w} = \mathbf{v}_s$.

The isotropic velocity distribution is obtained only under very special conditions. One sufficient but not necessary condition is that the gas be in equilibrium. In general, the distribution function is not isotropic in the presence of temperature, pressure, density, and potential gradients.

4.7 KNUDSEN DIFFUSION

Consider a box which contains a gas at equilibrium, but which also has a small hole at one end connected to a vacuum (see Fig. 4.4). If the size of the hole is smaller than, or comparable to, a mean free path in the gas, then the gas efflux will not be governed by the usual equations of compressible flow, because the gas cannot be treated as a continuum. However, the problem is solved easily with the use of the distribution function. At the hole, all particles go from the inside of the box to the outside; none returns. Thus, there are no particles with velocities in the range $0 > c_1 > -\infty$. The particle mean velocity through the hole is then obtained by the usual averaging procedure:

$$\langle c_1 \rangle = n^{-1} \int_0^{\infty} dc_1 \int_{-\infty}^{\infty} dc_2 \int_{-\infty}^{\infty} dc_3\, f(c)c_1$$

Note that the lower limit of integration for c_1 is 0, since at the hole there are no particles with a velocity less than this. If the distribution function is maxwellian, then $\langle c_1 \rangle$ integrates to

$$\langle c_1 \rangle = \sqrt{\frac{kT}{2m\pi}}$$

or with the definition $\langle c \rangle = \sqrt{8kT/\pi m}$,

$$\langle c_1 \rangle = \tfrac{1}{4}\langle c \rangle \tag{4.48}$$

The number of particles which pass through the hole per unit time per unit area of the hole is obtained by averaging nc_1 in a manner similar to (4.48); the result is obviously $\frac{1}{4}n\langle c \rangle$, where n is the number density of the particles in the box. The mass flux is obtained by averaging nmc_1; this result is obviously $\frac{1}{4}nm\langle c \rangle$ or $\frac{1}{4}\rho\langle c \rangle$, where ρ is the mass density in the box.

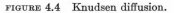

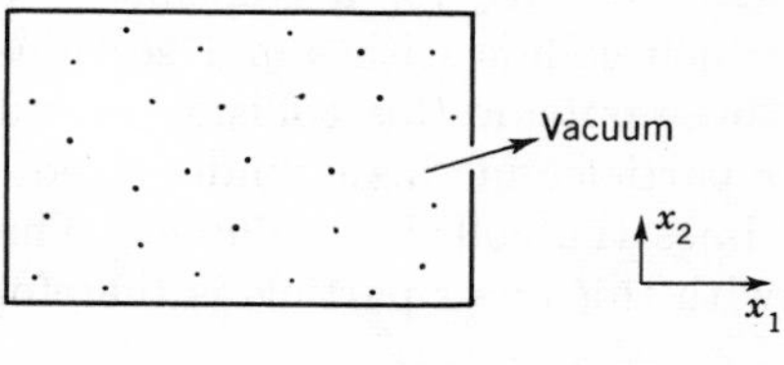

FIGURE 4.4 Knudsen diffusion.

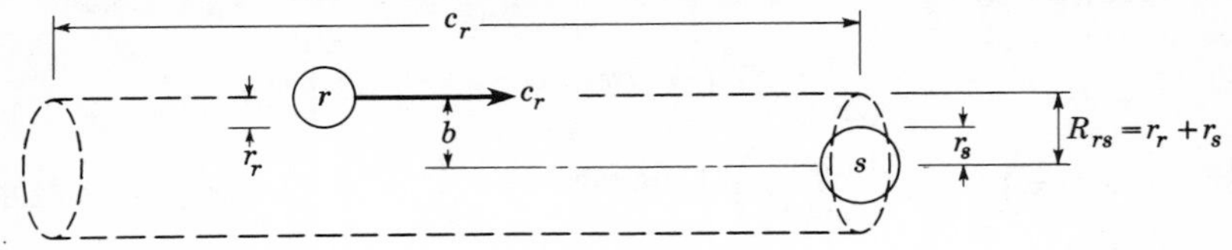

FIGURE 4.5 Collision cylinder.

It is obvious that these results can be true only if the mean mass motion in the box due to the efflux is very small; that is, these results cannot possibly apply if initially there was only one particle in the box. When this requirement is fulfilled, the efflux is called *Knudsen diffusion.* It is a simple method for obtaining a definite particle flow; one needs to know only the temperature in the box (to obtain $\langle c \rangle$) and the area of the hole accurately.

4.8 Collision Frequency

The collision frequency is another quantity that is frequently used. However, there are actually four collision frequencies. These are defined below:

$\nu_{rs}(c)$ = collisions per unit time between *one* particle of r species having speed c, and all particles of the s species.

$\nu_r(c)$ = collisions per unit time between one particle of r species having speed c and all species (but may exclude r).

$\langle \nu_{rs} \rangle$ = average collisions per unit time between r species and s species.

$\langle \nu_r \rangle$ = average collisions per unit time between r species and all species (but may exclude r).

The last three collision frequencies can be obtained from the first, with additional information. Hence, the expression for ν_{rs} will be derived first.

4.8.1 Approximate Calculation of Collision Frequency. We will first derive the expression for ν_{rs} approximately, assuming that the particles are hard, elastic spheres with radii of r_r and r_s, respectively. From Fig. 4.5, it is apparent that the center-line collision parameter b must be less than R_{rs} for a collision to occur. All r particles with velocity c_r which collide with s in 1 sec must lie in the collision cylinder $\pi R_{rs}^2 c_r$; all those outside this collision cylinder will miss particle s. The number of r particles in this cylinder is equal to the number density of r particles times the collision volume. The number of collisions of all r particles with this one s particle is therefore

$$n_r \pi R_{rs}^2 c_r$$

To obtain the total number of collisions per unit volume of r particles with all s particles, we must multiply this by the number of s particles:

$$n_r n_s \pi R_{rs}^2 c_r \tag{4.49}$$

To obtain the number of collisions per second that one r-type particle experiences, we must divide (4.49) by n_r; finally,

$$\nu_{rs}(c_r) = n_s \pi R_{rs}^2 c_r$$

or

$$\nu_{rs}(c_r) = n_s Q_{rs} c_r \tag{4.50}$$

where $\pi R_{rs}^2 = Q_{rs}$ is called the cross section for collisions between r and s particles; it is apparent that $Q_{rs} = Q_{sr}$. If there are many species, the collision frequency for the rth species is given by

$$\nu_r(c) = c_r \sum_s n_s Q_{rs} = \sum_s \nu_{rs} \tag{4.51}$$

where s can include r or not, depending upon the use. If a total number density of particles is defined as

$$n = \sum_s n_s \tag{4.52}$$

where s may or may not include r, then an average cross section Q_r can be defined as follows:

$$\nu_r = c_r n \frac{\Sigma n_s Q_{rs}}{n} = c_r n Q_r$$

or

$$Q_r = \sum \frac{n_s}{n} Q_{rs} \tag{4.53}$$

The time between collisions is obviously the reciprocal of the collision frequency:

$$\tau_r = \frac{1}{\nu_r} \tag{4.54}$$

The free path of a particle is defined as the distance that a particle travels between collisions; this is equal to the product of its velocity and the time between collisions, or

$$\lambda_r = c_r \tau_r = \frac{c_r}{\nu_r}$$
$$\tau_r = \frac{1}{\nu_r} = \frac{\lambda_r}{c_r} \tag{4.55}$$

Equations (4.50) to (4.55) are close to being correct. However, they ignore the fact that the particles actually have a velocity distribution function and that the other particles with which the r particles collide are also in motion. Finally, real particles are not hard spheres. For example, electrically neutral particles at first attract each other, then

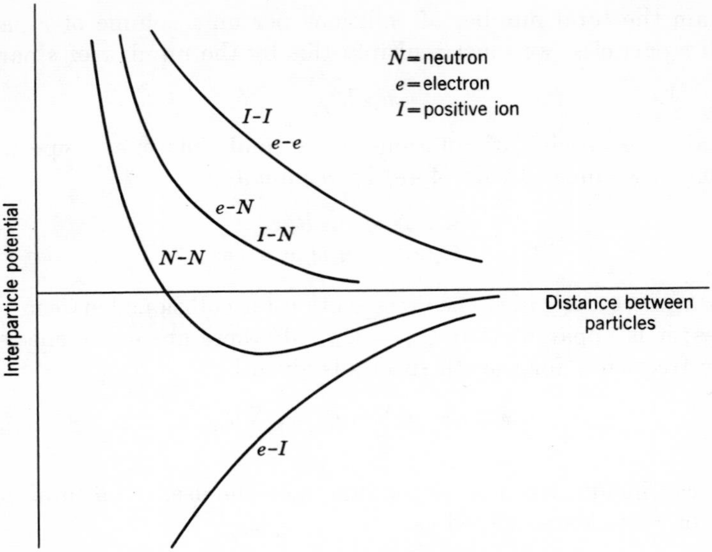

FIGURE 4.6 Interparticle potentials.

repel. Electrons are attracted by neutral particles and by ions, the latter over relatively large distances. Thus, for real particles, the closest distance of approach R_{rs} depends upon the relative velocity between the two colliding particles, $g_{rs} = |\mathbf{c}_r - \mathbf{c}_s|$, and the impact parameter b. The distance of closest approach occurs when the initial relative kinetic energy along the line of centers is equal to the interparticle potential ϕ. Some typical interparticle potentials are shown in Fig. 4.6. Positive slopes indicate attraction, and negative slopes repulsion.

The actual interaction potentials represent a considerable complication. The collision cross section is then not a simply defined quantity but depends upon the purpose for which it will be used: diffusion, momentum transport, or heat conduction; the collision frequency for each of these will generally be different.

4.8.2 Effect of Thermal Motion on Collision Frequency.[1] In this section we will consider mainly the effect of thermal motion of both species; however, we will illustrate this with two models for the cross section: Q_{rs} equal to a constant (so-called "constant cross section") and Q_{rs} inversely proportional to the relative velocity (so-called "constant-frequency model" or "maxwellian molecule"). The effect of thermal motion will be represented by taking the distribution function for each species as maxwellian about its own temperature T_s.

Consider collisions between species r particle and s particles, with velocities $\mathbf{c}_r$ and $\mathbf{c}_s$ and a collision radius $R_{rs} = r_r + r_s$ which depends only on $|\mathbf{c}_r - \mathbf{c}_s|$. The number of collisions between one r and all s particles having velocities between $\mathbf{c}_r$ and $\mathbf{c}_r + d\mathbf{c}_r$ and $\mathbf{c}_s$ and $\mathbf{c}_s + d\mathbf{c}_s$ is equal to the number of s particles in this velocity range in a collision cylinder of base πR_{rs}^2 and height equal to $g = |\mathbf{c}_r - \mathbf{c}_s|$. The number density of s particles in this velocity range is given by

$$f_s \, d\mathbf{c}_s$$

and the volume is

$$\pi R_{rs}^2 g = Q_{rs} g$$

The collision frequency for r particles having velocity $\mathbf{c}_r$ is then obtained by integration over $d\mathbf{c}_s$:

$$\nu_{rs}(c_r) = \int_{-\infty}^{\infty} Q_{rs} g f_s \, d\mathbf{c}_s \tag{4.56}$$

Now g is a function of c_r, c_s, and the angle θ between the vectors $\mathbf{c}_r$ and $\mathbf{c}_s$. Thus it is necessary to express $d\mathbf{c}_s$ and g as a function of $|c_s|$ and θ. This is done by orienting the coordinates of $\mathbf{c}_s$ along $\mathbf{c}_r$ and expressing $\mathbf{c}_s$ in terms of spherical coordinates,

$$d\mathbf{c}_s = c_s^2 \, d\phi \sin\theta \, d\theta \, dc_s \tag{4.57}$$

and

$$g^2 = c_r^2 + c_s^2 - 2c_r c_s \cos\theta \tag{4.58}$$

Thus, (4.56) becomes

$$\nu_{rs}(c_r) = -2\pi \int_0^{\pi} \int_0^{\infty} Q_{rs} f_s \sqrt{c_r^2 + c_s^2 - 2c_r c_s \cos\theta} \; c_s^2 \, dc_s \, d(\cos\theta)$$

where $2\pi = \int_0^{2\pi} d\phi$. Integration with respect to $\cos\theta$ yields

$$\nu_{rs}(c_r) = \frac{2\pi}{3} \int_0^{\infty} \frac{Q_{rs} f_s}{c_r c_s} [(c_r + c_s)^3 \pm (c_r - c_s)^3] c_s^2 \, dc_s$$

The term $c_r - c_s$ is the minimum *relative* velocity, and by definition must be positive. The + sign is to be used if $c_r < c_s$ and the − sign if $c_s < c_r$. Thus, the integral must be broken into two parts as follows:

$$\nu_{rs}(c_r) = \frac{4n_s\pi}{3} \left(\frac{m_s}{2\pi k T_s}\right)^{\frac{3}{2}} \times \left[\int_0^{c_r} Q_{rs} \frac{c_s^2}{c_r} (c_s^2 + 3c_r^2) e^{-m_s c_s^2/2kT_s} \, dc_s + \int_{c_r}^{\infty} Q_{rs} c_s (c_r^2 + 3c_s^2) e^{-m_s c_s^2/2kT_s} \, dc_s \right] \tag{4.59}$$

where it has been assumed that f_s is maxwellian. For Q_{rs} = const, integration yields

$$\nu_{rs}(c_r) = \frac{n_s}{\sqrt{\pi}} Q_{rs} \frac{(2kT_s/m_s)}{c_r} \psi\left(c_r \sqrt{\frac{m_s}{2kT_s}}\right) \tag{4.60}$$

where

$$\psi(x) = xe^{-x^2} + (2x^2 + 1) \int_0^x e^{-y^2} \, dy \tag{4.61}$$

Equation (4.60) predicts the collision frequency of r particles having a velocity c_r, when the s particles have a maxwellian velocity distribution. For $c_r \to 0$, the collision frequency becomes constant, since

$$\lim_{c_r \to 0} \left(\frac{\psi}{c_r}\right) = 2\sqrt{\frac{m_s}{2kT_s}} \tag{4.62}$$

In other words, if c_r is very small, the number of collisions which it suffers depends only on the rate at which s particles collide with it. Under these conditions, the r particle hardly moves between collisions, and thus the free path for such particles is essentially zero. On the other hand, for very fast r particles, $\psi(x) \to \sqrt{\pi}\, x^2 = \sqrt{\pi}\, c_r^2(m_s/2kT_s)$; thus,

$$\lim_{c_r \to \infty} \nu_{rs}(c_r) = n_s Q_{rs} c_r \tag{4.63}$$

and the free path c_r/ν_{rs} for these particles is

$$\lim_{c_r \to \infty} \lambda_{rs}(c_r) = \frac{1}{n_s Q_{rs}} \tag{4.64}$$

which is in agreement with our approximate formula, in which the motion of the s particles was neglected. When c_r is very large compared to c_s, the motion of the s particles has no effect; hence the excellent agreement between (4.63) and the approximate relation (4.50).

For maxwellian particles, the cross section is taken inversely proportional to the relative velocity; that is, $Q_{rs}(g) = \alpha/g$; then

$$\nu_{rs}(c_r) = \alpha n_s \tag{4.65}$$

and is independent of the velocity of the r particle.

If the r particles are very light, then the average value of c_r is much larger than $\sqrt{2kT_s/m_s}$, which is approximately the average thermal speed of the s particles. Thus, for all light particles except the very slowest, x is large, and the approximation of (4.64) may be used; that is, if Q_{rs} is constant, the mean free path is very close to constant.

4.8.3 Total Collision Frequency. To obtain the total collision frequency of particles r with the s particles, we must multiply $\nu_{rs}(c_r)$ by the number of r particles with velocities between $\mathbf{c}_r$ and $\mathbf{c}_r + d\mathbf{c}_r$, which is

$$f_r(c_r)\, d\mathbf{c}_r = 4\pi c_r^2\, dc_r f_r$$

and finally integrate from $c_r = 0$ to $c_r = \infty$ as follows:

$$\nu_{rs} = \frac{4\pi}{n_r} \int_0^\infty c_r^2 f_r \nu_{rs}(c_r)\, dc_r \tag{4.66}$$

As before, we will assume a maxwellian distribution for the r particles. For Q_{rs} constant, we will use (4.60). Then

$$\langle \nu_{rs} \rangle = 4\pi Q_{rs} \left(\frac{m_r}{2\pi k T_r}\right)^{\frac{3}{2}} \frac{2n_s k T_s}{\sqrt{\pi}\, m_s} \int_0^\infty c_r e^{-m_r c_r^2/2kT_r}\, \psi\left(c_r \sqrt{\frac{m_s}{2kT_s}}\right) dc_r$$

In terms of the variable $x = c_r \sqrt{m_s/2kT_s}$, this becomes

$$\langle \nu_{rs} \rangle = \frac{4Q_{rs}}{\pi} \frac{(m_r/2kT_r)^{\frac{3}{2}}}{(m_s/2kT_s)^2} \int_0^\infty e^{-(m_r T_s/m_s T_r)x^2}\, x\psi(x)\, dx \tag{4.67}$$

Substitution of $\psi(x)$ from (4.60) yields the following expression for the integral:

$$\int_0^\infty [x^2 e^{-x^2(1+m_r T_s/m_s T_r)} + (2x^2 + 1)x e^{-m_r T_s/m_s T_r} \int_0^x e^{-y^2}\, dy]\, dx$$

The first term becomes

$$\frac{\sqrt{\pi}}{4(1+\beta)^{\frac{3}{2}}}$$

where $$\beta = \frac{m_r T_s}{m_s T_r}$$

For the second term, it is convenient to replace y by Kx and integrate with respect to K, since the limits of integration with respect to K are 0 and 1. Then $dy = x\, dK$, and the second integral becomes

$$\int_0^1 dK \int_0^\infty x^2(2x^2 + 1)e^{-x^2(K^2+\beta)}\, dx$$

Integration with respect to x yields

$$\int_0^1 \left[\frac{3\sqrt{\pi}}{4}(K^2 + \beta)^{-\frac{5}{2}} + \frac{\sqrt{\pi}}{4}(K^2 + \beta)^{-\frac{3}{2}}\right] dK$$

The first term in the integral above yields

$$\frac{3\sqrt{\pi}}{4}\left[\frac{1}{3\beta}\frac{K}{(K^2+\beta)^{\frac{3}{2}}} + \frac{2}{3}\frac{K}{\beta^2(K^2+\beta)^{\frac{1}{2}}}\right]_0^1 = \frac{3\sqrt{\pi}}{4}\left[\frac{1}{3\beta}\frac{1}{(1+\beta)^{\frac{3}{2}}} + \frac{2}{3}\frac{1}{\beta^2(1+\beta)^{\frac{1}{2}}}\right]$$

The second term in the integral becomes

$$\frac{\pi}{4}\frac{1}{\beta(1+\beta)^{\frac{1}{2}}}$$

Addition of these integrals yields

$$\frac{\sqrt{\pi}}{4}\left[\frac{1}{(1+\beta)^{\frac{3}{2}}}+\frac{1}{\beta(1+\beta)^{\frac{3}{2}}}+\frac{2}{\beta^2(1+\beta)^{\frac{1}{2}}}+\frac{1}{\beta(1+\beta)^{\frac{1}{2}}}\right]$$
$$=\frac{\sqrt{\pi}}{2}(1+\beta)^{\frac{1}{2}}\beta^{-2} \quad (4.68)$$

Substitution of (4.68) into (4.67) yields

$$\langle\nu_{rs}\rangle = \frac{2Q_{rs}}{\sqrt{\pi}} n_s(2k)^{\frac{1}{2}}\left(\frac{T_r}{m_r}+\frac{T_s}{m_s}\right)^{\frac{1}{2}} \quad (4.69)$$

Note that the summation rule of (4.51) should be replaced by the following to give the total collision frequency of the r particle:

$$\langle\nu_r\rangle = \sum_s \langle\nu_{rs}\rangle \quad (4.70)$$

Some typical cases are presented below.

(*a*) *Collisions with Like Particles*

$$\langle\nu_{11}\rangle = \sqrt{2}\, Q_{11}\sqrt{\frac{8}{\pi}k\frac{T_1}{m_1}}\, n_1 \quad (4.71)$$

Comparison with (4.46) yields

$$\langle\nu_{11}\rangle = \sqrt{2}\, Q_{11}\langle c\rangle_1 n_1 \quad (4.72)$$

which is a factor of $\sqrt{2}$ larger than the approximate formula of (4.50). This correction occurs because the motion of the second particle has been taken into account.

(*b*) *Electron Collisions with Atoms.* Under most circumstances, $m_eT_a/m_aT_e \ll 1$; then

$$\langle\nu_{ea}\rangle = n_aQ_{ea}\sqrt{\frac{8}{\pi}\frac{kT_e}{m_e}} = n_aQ_{ea}\langle c\rangle_e \quad (4.73)$$

(*c*) *Combined Electron Collisions with Electrons and Ions.* If the atom in (4.73) above is ionized, Q_{eI} is determined by the geometry of collision in a manner which will be described later. Q_{ee} and Q_{eI} both occur under an inverse-square law (although with different signs), but because the second electron is able to rebound, it turns out that $Q_{ee} = \frac{1}{2}Q_{eI}$. Let us also assume that (4.72) and (4.73) are correct when referred to an *average* cross section. Then, in a fully ionized gas, in which $n_e = n_I$,

$$\langle\nu_e\rangle = \langle\nu_{ee}+\nu_{eI}\rangle = n_e\left(1+\frac{\sqrt{2}}{2}\right)Q_{eI}\langle c\rangle_e \quad (4.74)$$

(*d*) *Constant Collision Frequency.* If $Q_{rs}(g) = \alpha/g$, then the results of (4.65) hold. Integration over f_r and division by n_r yield

$$\nu_{rs} = \alpha n_s = Q_{rs} n_s \langle c \rangle_r \tag{4.75}$$

Thus the average collision cross section is

$$Q_{rs} = \frac{\alpha}{\langle c \rangle_r} \tag{4.76}$$

(e) *Collision Frequency—Electron Current.* When an electron current flows through a gas, the distribution function is given approximately by the maxwellian distribution function about the mean electron velocity $\mathbf{v}_e$. Because of the large thermal velocities of electrons in comparison to the ions and neutral particles, the velocity of the latter may be neglected and (4.63) applies. However, if there is relative motion $\mathbf{v}_{es}$ between the electrons and the s species, the velocity $\mathbf{c}_e$ must be replaced by the actual *relative* velocity $|\mathbf{v}_{es} + \mathbf{c}_e|$; that is,

$$g = \sqrt{v_{es}^2 + c_e{}^2 - 2v_{es}c_e \cos\theta} \tag{4.77}$$

so that

$$\nu_{es}(c_e) = n_s Q_{es} \sqrt{v_{es}^2 + c_e{}^2 - 2v_e c_e \cos\theta} \tag{4.78}$$

To obtain $\langle \nu_{es} \rangle$, $\nu_{es}(c_e)$ must be multiplied by $d\mathbf{c} = 2\pi \sin\theta \, d\theta c^2 \, dc$, similar to the procedure in (4.66). Thus,

$$\langle \nu_{es} \rangle = -2\pi n_s \left(\frac{m_e}{2\pi k T_e} \right)^{\frac{3}{2}} \int_0^\pi \int_0^\infty Q_{es} \sqrt{v_{es}^2 + c_e{}^2 - 2v_e c_e \cos\theta} \times e^{-m_e c^2/2kT_e} c_e{}^2 \, dc_e \, d(\cos\theta)$$

This integration is formally identical to (4.59); thus for a constant cross section,

$$\langle \nu_{es} \rangle = \frac{n_s}{\sqrt{\pi}} Q_{es} \left(\frac{2kT_e}{m_e} \right) \frac{1}{v_e} \psi \left(\frac{v_e}{\sqrt{m_e/2kT_e}} \right) \tag{4.79}$$

where $\psi(x)$ is given by (4.61). For convenience, we may take $\psi(x)$ to be

$$\psi(x) \approx 2x + \sqrt{\pi}\, x^2 \tag{4.80}$$

which gives the proper results for $x \to 0$ and $x \to \infty$. Combination of (4.80) and (4.79) yields

$$\langle \nu_{es} \rangle = n_s (v_e + \langle c \rangle_e) Q_{es} \tag{4.81}$$

Thus it is seen that the mean thermal velocity of the electrons must be augmented by the velocity of the electrons through the s particles.

4.9 MEAN FREE PATH

There are two different methods of defining the mean free path in a gas. The first is the total distance that a particle moves per unit time, divided by the average collision frequency, or

$$\langle \lambda_{rs} \rangle = \frac{\langle c_r \rangle}{\langle \nu_{rs} \rangle} \tag{4.82}$$

For like particles of constant cross section, use of (4.71) yields

$$\langle \lambda_{rr} \rangle = \frac{1}{\sqrt{2}\, n_r Q_{rr}} \tag{4.83}$$

whereas for electrons colliding with atoms, the result is

$$\langle \lambda_{ea} \rangle = \frac{1}{n_a Q_{ea}} \tag{4.84}$$

The other mean is the instantaneous average of the free path for each particle:

$$\langle \lambda_{rs} \rangle = \int f_r \frac{c}{\lambda_{rs}(c)}\, d\mathbf{c} \tag{4.85}$$

This is more difficult to evaluate; for constant cross sections, the mean free path calculated from (4.85) for like particles is 4 per cent lower than (4.83). Generally, (4.82) is the usual method which is used.

4.10 BOLTZMANN'S EQUATION

In the previous sections we examined the properties associated with a maxwellian distribution function. In this section we would like to derive the effects on the distribution function when the state of the gas is changing.[2] We must start with the definition of the hamiltonian H of a single charged particle:

$$H = \text{kinetic energy} + \text{potential energy}$$

The importance of the hamiltonian lies in the ability to then write the equations of motion in a particularly symmetrical form:

$$\begin{aligned} \frac{dq_i}{dt} &= \frac{\partial H}{\partial p_i}\,(q_i,p_i,t) \\ \frac{dp_i}{dt} &= -\,\frac{\partial H}{\partial q_i}\,(q_i,p_i,t) \end{aligned} \tag{4.86}$$

where p_i and q_i are generalized momenta and coordinates. Let us consider a group of particles having momenta between p_i and $p_i + dp_i$, and coordinates between q_i and $q_i + dq_i$. The volume occupied by these particles in these momenta–space coordinates is

$$\Delta = \delta p_1 \, \delta p_2 \, \delta p_3 \, \delta q_1 \, \delta q_2 \, \delta q_3 \tag{4.87}$$

We wish to discover how Δ changes with time, that is, whether the phase space occupied by these same particles changes. To determine this, we differentiate (4.87) with respect to time:

$$\frac{d\Delta}{dt} = \left[\frac{d}{dt}(\delta p_1)\,\delta q_1 + \frac{d}{dt}(\delta q_1)\,\delta p_1\right]\delta p_2\,\delta p_3\,\delta q_2\,\delta q_3 + \cdots \tag{4.88}$$

Now
$$\frac{d}{dt}(\delta p_1) = \delta\left(\frac{dp_1}{dt}\right) = -\delta\left(\frac{\partial H}{\partial q_1}\right) = -\frac{\partial}{\partial p_1}\left(\frac{\partial H}{\partial q_1}\right)\delta p_1 \tag{4.89}$$

and
$$\frac{d}{dt}(\delta q_1) = \delta\left(\frac{dq_1}{dt}\right) = \delta\left(\frac{\partial H}{\partial p_1}\right) = \frac{\partial}{\partial q_1}\left(\frac{\partial H}{\partial p_1}\right)\delta q_1 \tag{4.90}$$

Substitution of (4.89) and (4.90) into (4.88) yields

$$\frac{d\Delta}{dt} = \left(\frac{\partial^2 H}{\partial q_1\,\partial p_1} - \frac{\partial^2 H}{\partial p_1\,\partial q_1}\right)\Delta + \cdots = 0 \tag{4.91}$$

This is interpreted as stating that the phase *volume* occupied by a system of particles does not change as the particles move. This is known as *Liouville's theorem*. The number of such particles in Δ is

$$n_\Delta = f(q_i,p_i)\,\delta q_1\,\delta q_2\,\delta q_3\,\delta p_1\,\delta p_2\,\delta p_3 = f\cdot\Delta \tag{4.92}$$

Differentiation of (4.92) with respect to time yields

$$\frac{dn_\Delta}{dt} = \Delta\frac{df}{dt} + f\frac{d\Delta}{dt}$$

Since we are following the *same* particles, $dn_\Delta/dt = 0$, and from (4.91), $d\Delta/dt = 0$. Therefore,

$$\frac{df}{dt} = 0 \tag{4.93}$$

If, however, collisions between particles occur, then some particles will have their velocities changed. Hence in general,

$$\frac{df}{dt} = \left(\frac{\partial f}{\partial t}\right)_c \tag{4.94}$$

where the term $(\partial f/\partial t)_c$ represents the effects of collisions. Obviously, $(\partial f/\partial t)_c$ is zero in the absence of interaction between the particles, or when the gas is in equilibrium. Equation (4.94) can now be rewritten in terms of the coordinates and momenta:

$$\frac{df}{dt}(q_i,p_i,t) = \frac{\partial f}{\partial t} + \frac{\partial f}{\partial q_i}\frac{dq_i}{dt} + \frac{\partial f}{\partial p_i}\frac{dp_i}{dt} = \left(\frac{\partial f}{\partial t}\right)_c \tag{4.95}$$

The repeated subscript indicates summation over $i = 1, 2, 3$. Use of (4.86) in (4.95) yields

$$\frac{\partial f}{\partial t} + \frac{\partial H}{\partial p_i}\frac{\partial f}{\partial q_i} - \frac{\partial H}{\partial q_i}\frac{\partial f}{\partial p_i} = \left(\frac{\partial f}{\partial t}\right)_c$$

or

$$\frac{\partial f}{\partial t} + \{f,H\} = \left(\frac{\partial f}{\partial t}\right)_c \tag{4.96}$$

The braces $\{f,H\}$ are known as the *Poisson brackets*, and are shorthand for the required operations. Finally, if the distribution function depends only on the hamiltonian, then we may write

$$\frac{\partial f}{\partial q_i} = \frac{df}{dH}\frac{\partial H}{\partial q_i} \qquad \left(\frac{\partial f}{\partial t}\right)_c = 0$$

$$\frac{\partial f}{\partial p_i} = \frac{df}{dH}\frac{\partial H}{\partial p_i}$$

and (4.96) becomes

$$\frac{\partial f}{\partial t} = 0 \tag{4.97}$$

This indicates that at any given point f does not change with time. If $f = f(H)$, the system is called *ergodic;* (4.97) indicates that the distribution function for ergodic systems is stationary. In general, the expressions for our distribution functions will not depend solely on H; thus it is not necessary to use the generalized momenta or coordinates. Thus, one may choose the particle positional coordinates and velocities so that $f = f(x_i,w_i,t)$; thus,

$$\frac{df}{dt} = \frac{\partial f}{\partial t} + \sum_i \frac{dx_i}{dt}\frac{\partial f}{\partial x_i} + \sum_i \frac{dw_i}{dt}\frac{\partial f}{\partial w_i} = \left(\frac{\partial f}{\partial t}\right)_c \tag{4.98}$$

For a given particle, dx_i/dt is the particle velocity w_i, and dw_i/dt is the particle acceleration, which for electromagnetic forces becomes

$$\frac{dw_i}{dt} = m^{-1}eZ[E_i + (\mathbf{w} \times \mathbf{B})_i]$$

so that (4.98) becomes

$$\frac{\partial f}{\partial t} + \sum_i w_i \frac{\partial f}{\partial x_i} + \sum_i \frac{eZ}{m}[E_i + (\mathbf{w} \times \mathbf{B})_i]\frac{\partial f}{\partial w_i} = \left(\frac{\partial f}{\partial t}\right)_c$$

or

$$\frac{\partial f}{\partial t} + \mathbf{w} \cdot \nabla f + \frac{eZ}{m}(\mathbf{E} + \mathbf{w} \times \mathbf{B}) \cdot \nabla_w f = \left(\frac{\partial f}{\partial t}\right)_c \tag{4.99}$$

The collisional term $(\partial f/\partial t)_c$ is zero only in the absence of collisions between particles or when equilibrium has been established, in which case collisions do not affect the distribution function. When $(\partial f/\partial t)_c$ is zero, (4.99) is called *Vlasov's equation;* more generally it is called *Boltzmann's equation.* It is also important to note that there is a different Boltzmann equation for each species in the gas.

In the remainder of this chapter, solutions to (4.99) will be obtained; these solutions will then be used to derive some important properties of ionized gases.

4.11 FILLING OF A VACUUM BY A COLLISIONLESS NEUTRAL GAS[3]

The first problem involves only the first and second terms in (4.99). For simplicity, the problem will be one-dimensional (see Fig. 4.7). Consider a vacuum, infinite in the x and y directions, but bounded by a thin membrane at $z = \pm a$. For $|z| > a$, the gas is in equilibrium; that is,

$$t \leq 0: \quad \begin{array}{ll} f = \text{maxwellian} & |z| > a \\ f = 0 & |z| < a \end{array} \tag{4.100}$$

For this case, Boltzmann's equation becomes

$$\frac{\partial f}{\partial t} + w_z \frac{\partial f}{\partial z} = 0 \tag{4.101}$$

The solution to (4.101) can be obtained by means of the Laplace transform, and is

$$f(t,z,w_z) = f(0, z - w_z t, w_z) \tag{4.102}$$

which can be verified by substitution. Equation (4.102) states that the particles within a given region dz are those which have traveled into it from a distance $w_z t$ from it. The boundary conditions (4.100) therefore become

$$\left.\begin{array}{lll} f(w_z) = \text{maxwellian} & \text{when } |z - w_z t| > a \\ f = 0 & \text{when } |z - w_z t| < a \end{array}\right\} t > 0 \tag{4.103}$$

Equation (4.103) becomes

$$f = \text{maxwellian when} \quad \left\{\begin{array}{l} -\infty < w_z < (z-a)/t \\ \infty > w_z > (z+a)/t \end{array}\right\} \tag{4.104}$$

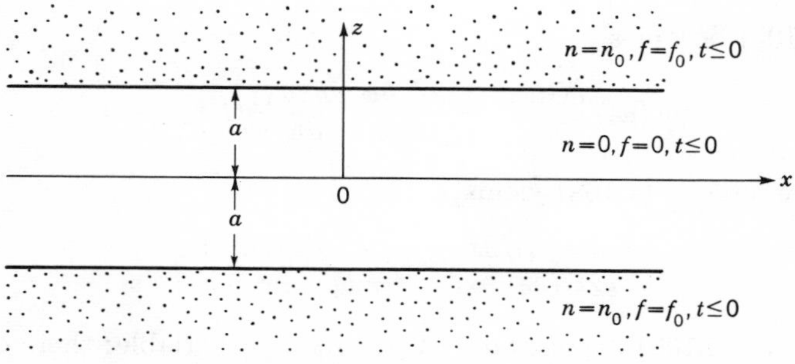

FIGURE 4.7 Filling of a vacuum.

To obtain the number density inside, the distribution function is integrated over the limits of (4.104),

$$n(z,t) = n_0\left(\frac{m}{2\pi kT}\right)^{\frac{3}{2}}\int_{-\infty}^{\infty} e^{-mw_x^2/2kT}\,dw_x\int_{-\infty}^{\infty} e^{-mw_y^2/2kT}\,dw_y \times\left(\int_{-\infty}^{(z-a)/t} e^{-mw_z^2/2kT}\,dw_z + \int_{(z+a)/t}^{\infty} e^{-mw_z^2/2kT}\,dw_z\right)$$

which integrates immediately to

$$\frac{n}{n_0} = 1 + \frac{1}{2}\left[\operatorname{erf}\left(\frac{z-a}{t}\sqrt{\frac{m}{2kT}}\right) - \operatorname{erf}\left(\frac{z+a}{t}\sqrt{\frac{m}{2kT}}\right)\right] \tag{4.105}$$

The criterion for neglecting collisions is that the collision time $\tau > a\sqrt{m/2kT}$ or $\tau > a/\langle c\rangle$. Since the mean free path is $\tau\langle c\rangle$, this becomes $\lambda > a$. Thus, the mean free path must be larger than a for this analysis to apply.

4.12 EQUILIBRIUM DISTRIBUTION FUNCTION IN AN ELECTRIC FIELD

For the second example, a case is chosen which is steady in time; also, to simplify the problem, only a steady electric field in the x_1 direction is considered: $E_1 = -\partial\phi/\partial x_1$; that is, the problem is one-dimensional. Then (4.99) becomes

$$w_1\frac{\partial f}{\partial x_1} - \frac{eZ}{m}\frac{\partial\phi}{\partial x_1}\frac{\partial f}{\partial w_1} = 0 \tag{4.106}$$

It is assumed that $f = nf_1(x_1,w_1)f_2(x_2,w_2)f_3(x_3,w_3)$. Substitution into (4.106) yields the following, since $\partial/\partial x_2 = \partial/\partial x_3 = 0$:

$$w_1\frac{\partial f_1}{\partial x_1} - \frac{eZ}{m}\frac{\partial\phi}{\partial x_1}\frac{\partial f_1}{\partial w_1} = 0 \tag{4.107}$$

Equation (4.107) can be solved by separation of variables: Let

$$f_1(x_1,w_1) = F(w_1)G(x_1)$$

Then (4.107) becomes

$$w_1F(w_1)\frac{dG(x_1)}{dx_1} - \frac{eZ}{m}\frac{\partial\phi}{\partial x_1}\frac{dF(w_1)}{dw_1}G(x_1) = 0 \tag{4.108}$$

Rearrangement of (4.108) yields

$$\frac{dG(x_1)/dx_1}{eZG(\partial\phi/\partial x_1)} = \frac{1}{mw_1}\frac{dF(w_1)}{dw_1}\frac{1}{F} \tag{4.109}$$

Each side of (4.109) depends only upon its own variable; therefore both sides must be equal to the same constant, say $-b$. The right side of

(4.109) then becomes

$$\frac{dF}{F} = -bmw_1\,dw_1$$

which may be integrated to

$$F = ae^{-b(mw_1^2/2)} \tag{4.110}$$

where a is a constant of integration. The left side of (4.109) becomes

$$\frac{1}{G}\left(\frac{dG}{dx_1}\right) = -\,beZ\,\frac{\partial\phi}{\partial x_1}$$

which integrates to become

$$G = e^{-beZ\phi} \tag{4.111}$$

Combination of (4.110) and (4.111) yields

$$f_1 = ae^{-b(\frac{1}{2}mw_1^2+Ze\phi)} \tag{4.112}$$

When $\phi \rightarrow 0$, one obtains the maxwellian distribution. This result, for $\partial\phi/\partial x \neq 0$, must correspond to equilibrium rather than a collisionless situation, because in the latter case all particles would accelerate in a direction parallel to the electric field.

In the other two directions, f_2 and f_3 are obviously maxwellian; thus,

$$f = ae^{-b(m/2)w_1^2-\frac{1}{2}(m/kT)(w_2^2+w_3^2)-bZe\phi(x_1)} \tag{4.113}$$

At the point at which $\phi = 0$, f must be maxwellian; thus $b = 1/kT$, and (4.113) becomes

$$f = n_0\left(\frac{m}{2\pi kT}\right)^{\frac{3}{2}} e^{-(mw^2/2kT)-eZ\phi/kT} \tag{4.114}$$

This result is obviously independent of the directions of the coordinate x_1; thus (4.114) applies when $\phi = \phi(\mathbf{x})$. In Sec. 4.17, this analysis is extended to include the magnetic case. Equation (4.114) can easily be extended to the gravitational field by replacing $eZ\phi$ by mgz.

4.13 DEBYE SHIELDING LENGTH[4]

In the vicinity of all surfaces in contact with a plasma, there are space-charge effects caused by the difference in thermal velocities of the charged species. These can be categorized by the type of surface: If the surface is a perfect insulator such that all electrons and all ions which collide with it are reflected, then the phenomenon is called *Debye shielding*. On the other hand, if the surface is a perfect electrical conductor such that all electrons which contact the surface are absorbed and all positive ions are neutralized, then the device is called a *probe*. A probe at a potential such that the net ion flow is just equal to the electron flow is not equivalent to the perfect insulator; the latter is probably a more realistic model for a real insulator, since deionization will occur at the surface of an insulator.

In addition to specifying the condition of the surface, two other parameters must be specified. The first is the ratio of the mean free path λ to the Debye length d. When λ/d is small, then the plasma may be considered in equilibrium and (4.114) may be used, with $0 < \mathbf{w} < \infty$. However, if λ/d is large, then no collisions occur within the space-charge region. Equation (4.114) may still be used, but there is now a limit on the lowest velocity because the smallest velocity may be greater than zero.

Finally, the magnitude of surface voltage ϕ_p must be considered; for $e\phi_p/kT_0$ either small or large, certain linearizations may be possible which simplify the problem. Note that when $\lambda/d \gg 1$ and $e\phi_p/kT \gg 1$, and when the surface is conducting, the resulting behavior is governed by Child's law. One could also distinguish between a positive surface potential and a negative surface potential, but owing to certain symmetries, this is not necessary.

The problem also depends on the shape of the surface: For Debye shielding, one is usually interested in a plane or spherically symmetric geometry, but for a probe, one is interested in a plane or cylindrical surface. In this section, the Debye shielding will be derived for several cases, and in subsequent sections probe theory and Child's law will be derived. In all these analyses, it is assumed that the number density of electrons is large so that the distribution function exists.

4.13.1 Debye Shielding, $\lambda/d \ll 1$. We consider first the classical Debye shielding in which the surface is plane, $e\phi_p/kT \ll 1$, and $\lambda/d \ll 1$, so that at all spatial points the entire velocity range exists.

(*a*) *Plane Nonconductor.* If the surface is positive with respect to the plasma, then the surface will attract electrons to the vicinity; these electrons will "shield" the plasma from the positive surface. The plasma is assumed to be in equilibrium, so that the distribution functions for electrons and ions, assumed to be uniformly charged, are:

$$f_e = n_{e_0}\left(\frac{m_e}{2\pi kT}\right)^{\frac{3}{2}} e^{-(\frac{1}{2}mw^2 - e\phi)/kT} \tag{4.115}$$

$$f_I = n_{I_0}\left(\frac{m_I}{2\pi kT}\right)^{\frac{3}{2}} e^{-(\frac{1}{2}mw^2 + Ze\phi)/kT} \tag{4.116}$$

where the zero subscript refers to conditions far from the surface. From (4.115) and (4.116), their respective number densities are obtained by integration over all velocities, from 0 to ∞.

$$\begin{aligned} n_e &= n_{e_0} e^{e\phi/kT} \\ n_I &= n_{I_0} e^{-Ze\phi/kT} \\ &= Z^{-1} n_{e_0} e^{-Ze\phi/kT} \end{aligned} \tag{4.117}$$

since $n_{e_0} = Zn_{I_0}$ in a neutral plasma. To solve the problem, an additional relation is required between the charge density and ϕ; this is obviously Poisson's equation,

$$\frac{\partial^2 \phi}{\partial x^2} = -\frac{\rho_e}{K_0} = -\frac{n_{e_0}e}{K_0}\left(e^{-Ze\phi/kT} - e^{e\phi/kT}\right) \tag{4.118}$$

where x is the distance normal to the surface. Let us also assume that $Ze\phi \ll kT$ so that the exponential functions in (4.118) may be expanded. Then (4.118) becomes

$$\frac{\partial^2 \phi}{\partial x^2} = -\frac{n_{e_0}e}{K_0}\left(1 - \frac{Ze\phi}{kT} - 1 - \frac{e\phi}{kT}\right)$$

or

$$\frac{\partial^2 \phi}{\partial x^2} - \frac{(Z+1)e^2 n_{e_0}}{K_0 kT}\phi = 0 \tag{4.119}$$

which has the solution

$$\phi = \phi_s e^{-[(Z+1)e^2 n_{e_0}/K_0 kT]^{\frac{1}{2}}x} = \phi_s e^{-\sqrt{Z+1}x/d} \tag{4.120}$$

where the constant d is given by

$$d = \left(\frac{e^2 n_{e_0}}{K_0 kT}\right)^{\frac{1}{2}} \tag{4.121}$$

If $Z = 1$, when $x = d$, the potential has fallen to one-fourth of the value at the surface. Thus d is a measure of the distance that a potential can extend in a plasma. This distance, which will be used often, is called the *Debye shielding length.* With $Z = 1$, this problem may be solved for arbitrary values of $e\phi/kT$. This is left as an exercise.

(*b*) *Spherical Shielding.* The analysis can be extended to a point charge Ze in a plasma. In spherical coordinates, Poisson's equation becomes

$$\frac{1}{r^2}\frac{\partial}{\partial r}r^2\frac{\partial \phi}{\partial r} = \frac{e^2 n_{e_0}(Z+1)}{K_0 kT}\phi \tag{4.122}$$

Before proceeding, one may normalize r with respect to d as follows: Let $\xi = r\sqrt{Z+1}/d$. Then (4.122) becomes

$$\xi^{-2}\frac{\partial}{\partial \xi}\left(\xi^2 \frac{\partial \phi}{\partial \xi}\right) - \phi = 0 \tag{4.123}$$

It is easily verified that the solution to (4.123) is [see Eq. (*l*), Sec. 2.6.1]

$$\phi = \frac{A}{\xi}e^{-\xi}$$

where A is a constant of integration, or

$$\phi = \frac{A'}{r}e^{-r\sqrt{Z+1}/d}$$

Near $r = 0$, ϕ must be $Ze/4\pi K_0 r$, which determines the constant A'. Thus, the potential is

$$\phi = \frac{Ze}{4\pi K_0 r} e^{-r\sqrt{Z+1}/d} \tag{4.124}$$

in the vicinity of a point charge Ze. For $e\phi/kT \gg 1$, linearization cannot be accomplished, and so the spherically symmetric problem is much more difficult. Thus, the matching to the inverse-r law in (4.124) is only approximated. Nevertheless, the coulombic field near the ion is essentially damped for $r > d$.

4.13.2 Debye Shielding, $\lambda/d \gg 1$. Next we consider the case when $\lambda/d \gg 1$; that is, charged particles experience no collisions in the space-charge region.

(*a*) *Plane Nonconductor.* Consider first the planar case with ϕ_p positive. As electrons approach the surface they will be accelerated, so that at any given point the minimum velocity in the $+x$ direction is $\sqrt{2e\phi/m_e}$; that is,

$$w_x > 0 \qquad \sqrt{\frac{2e\phi}{m_e}} < w_x < \infty$$

These electrons are then reflected by the surface according to the model, so that their velocity is reversed. Thus, there will be a large number of particles returning from the surface with $w_x < 0$; reflection requires that $w_x = -w_x$, so that the velocity range for negative velocities is

$$w_x < 0 \qquad -\infty < w_x < -\sqrt{\frac{2e\phi}{m_e}}$$

Thus, the number density of electrons is

$$n_e = n_{e_0}\left(\frac{m_e}{2\pi k T_0}\right)^{\frac{3}{2}} e^{+e\phi/kT}\left(\int_{-\infty}^{-\sqrt{2e\phi/m_e}} e^{-m_e w^2/2kT} d\mathrm{w} + \int_{\sqrt{2e\phi/m_e}}^{\infty} e^{-m_e w^2/2kT} d\mathrm{w}\right)$$

which integrates to

$$n_e = n_{e_0} e^{e\phi/kT} \operatorname{erfc} \sqrt{\frac{e\phi}{kT}}$$

On the other hand, the velocity range of positive ions is complete so that

$$n_I = n_{I_0} e^{-e\phi/kT}$$

where Z has been taken as unity. When $e\phi/kT \gg 1$, the ion density is therefore zero, and the problem reduces to Child's law except for a factor of 2 due to reflection (see Sec. 4.15).

For $e\phi/kT \ll 1$, the various terms may be expanded so that Poisson's equation becomes

$$-\frac{\partial^2\phi}{\partial x^2} = \frac{\rho_e}{K_0} = \frac{en_{e_0}}{K_0}\left(2\pi^{-\frac{1}{2}}\sqrt{\frac{e\phi}{kT}} - \frac{2e\phi}{kT}\right)$$

Now, with $e\phi/kT \ll 1$, the radical dominates the expression for the charge density; that is, the charge density near the surface is *positive* instead of negative. Thus, near the surface the electron density is depleted rather than enhanced, and Debye shielding will not occur within a distance d.

(*b*) *Spherical Shielding.* Actually, all the cases of Debye shielding which have been considered above are somewhat academic and rarely occur in practice; however, there is one case which is important: when $\lambda/d \gg 1$, and when the geometry is spherically symmetric. This corresponds to the region which surrounds a positive ion in a gas. Here, electron capture by the ion is a rare occurrence, so that the model of a perfect insulating surface is extremely good. However, as the electrons approach the ion, they are accelerated, and have a minimum value of $|\mathbf{w}|$. This minimum value of $|\mathbf{w}|$ corresponds to a minimum value of velocity when the electron is far from the ion. For such small values of $|\mathbf{w}|$, electron orbits around the ion are then *closed;* that is, the electron orbit is elliptical. For closed orbits, the minimum radial velocity at the apogee is zero; therefore the minimum radial velocity at $\mathbf{r}$ is $\sqrt{2e\phi(r)/m_e}$. The angle between the electron velocity and a radius vector from the ion depends on the initial angular momentum around the ion, and all angles are possible, but the minimum value of $|\mathbf{w}|$ is still $\sqrt{2e\phi/m_e}$. Thus, in velocity space, a sphere of radius $\sqrt{2e\phi/m_e}$ has no electrons in it. The number density of electrons near an ion is then

$$n_e = n_{e_0}e^{e\phi/kT}\left(\frac{m_e}{2\pi kT}\right)^{\frac{3}{2}}\int_{\sqrt{2e\phi/m_e}}^{\infty} 4\pi w^2 \exp\left(\frac{-m_e w^2}{2kT}\right) dw$$

which can be integrated to

$$n_e = n_{e_0}\left(2\pi^{-\frac{1}{2}}\sqrt{\frac{e\phi}{kT}} + \exp\frac{e\phi}{kT}\operatorname{erfc}\sqrt{\frac{e\phi}{kT}}\right)$$

In the region far from the ion, the exponential and the error function may be expanded. Retaining terms only up to $e\phi/kT$ to the first power, the result is

$$n_e = n_{e_0}\left(1 + \frac{e\phi}{kT}\right)$$

For ions, this depletion in velocity space does not occur; hence,

$$n_I = n_{I_0}e^{-Ze\phi/kT} \approx n_{I_0}\left(1 - \frac{Ze\phi}{kT}\right)$$

Combination of n_e and n_I in Poisson's equation gives exactly (4.122), so that the potential is of the form (4.124) for large r or small ϕ.

4.14 PLASMA PROBES

The plasma probe, sometimes called the *Langmuir probe*, is a convenient device for obtaining the properties of a plasma[5] (see Fig. 4.8). The probe can be a wire, a flat plate, or any other suitable shape, but should be kept cold so that no electrons are emitted from it, and therefore all electrons which flow to the probe are absorbed by it. Also, if the work function of the surface is less than the ionization potential of the gas, any neutral particles which strike the surface will be emitted as neutral particles, while any ions which strike the surface will be neutralized. Thus, the net current to the probe is the sum of the electron and ion currents.

The probe is connected to a variable voltage supply, and the current is measured as a function of the applied voltage. To measure the bulk plasma properties, it is necessary that the probe *not* disturb the plasma. For a high-temperature plasma, this means that the probe width or diameter be much smaller than a mean free path, so that the plasma in the immediate vicinity is not cooled by the probe. In the following sections, two common probes are analyzed: the flat probe and the circular probe.

4.14.1 Flat Probes. Consider a flat probe with $\lambda/d \gg 1$. If the probe is positive with respect to the plasma, the complete Knudsen flow of electrons will reach the probe, or $\frac{1}{4}n_e\langle c_e\rangle$ per unit area of the probe. On the other hand, not all ions will reach the probe; only those with an initial velocity greater than that required to overcome the potential barrier will reach the probe. Thus, the limits of integration for w_{I_1} are $\sqrt{2e\phi_p/m_I}$ and ∞, where it is assumed that the ions are singly ionized. Thus, the positive ion flux to the surface of the probe is equal to the flux

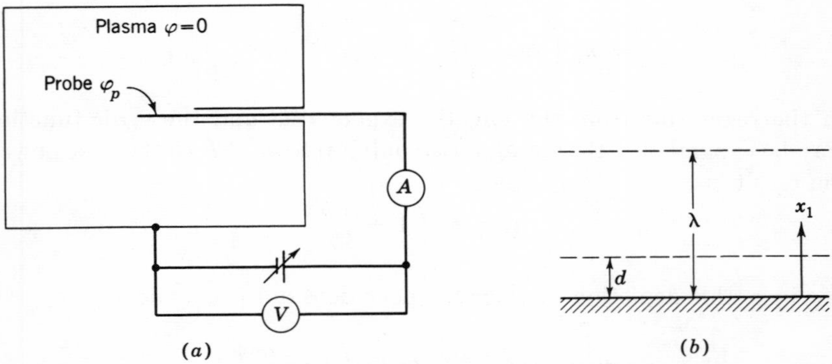

FIGURE 4.8 Plasma probes: (*a*) Probe circuit; (*b*) flat probe, $\lambda/d \gg 1$.

to the surface $x = d$, corrected by the limits of integration,

$$n_{I_0}\left(\frac{m_I}{2\pi kT_I}\right)^{\frac{3}{2}} \iint_{-\infty}^{\infty} \int_{\sqrt{2e\phi/m_I}}^{\infty} e^{-m_I w^2/2kT_I}\, d\mathbf{w} = \tfrac{1}{4} n_I \langle c\rangle_I e^{-e\phi_p/kT_I}$$

The total current to the probe is therefore

$$j = \tfrac{1}{4} n_{e_0} e[\langle c\rangle_I e^{-e\phi_p/kT_I} - \langle c\rangle_e] \tag{4.125}$$

If, on the other hand, $\lambda/d \ll 1$, then the ion current must be calculated at $x = 0$. For this case, the full range of ion velocities is present owing to collisions, but the distribution function at $x = 0$ has been changed because of the local wall potential. Thus, the positive ion flux is

$$n_I\left(\frac{m_I}{2\pi kT_I}\right)^{\frac{3}{2}} \iint_{-\infty}^{\infty} \int_0^{\infty} e^{-m_I W^2/2kT_I - e\phi_p/kT_I}\, d\mathbf{w} = \tfrac{1}{4} n_I \langle c\rangle_I e^{-e\phi_p/kT}$$

which is the same expression as previously derived. Thus, the probe performance is independent of the value of λ/d. In a similar manner, the probe current can be obtained when $\phi_p < 0$; the result is

$$j = \tfrac{1}{4} n_e e(\langle c\rangle_I - \langle c\rangle_e e^{e\phi_p/kT_e}) \qquad \phi_p < 0 \tag{4.126}$$

We have deliberately allowed the electron temperature to be different from the ion temperature, but have assumed that both distributions are maxwellian. Equations (4.125) and (4.126) are shown in Fig. 4.9. Note that at $\phi_p = 0$ a large electron current is drawn. In practice, it is difficult to determine the actual plasma potential. However, it is still possible to use the probe to determine the three unknowns, T_e, T_I, and n_I.

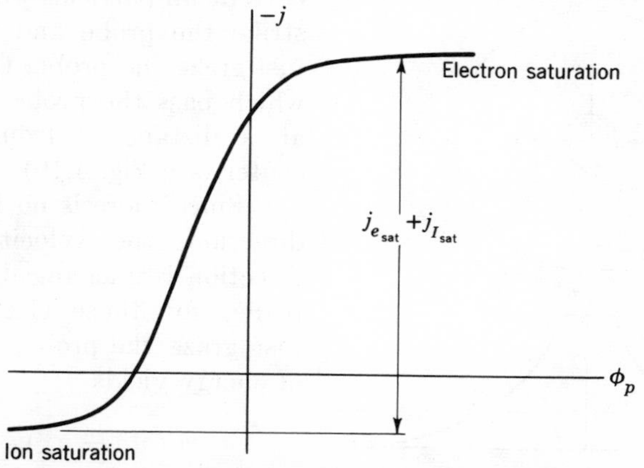

FIGURE 4.9 Characteristics of a single probe.

First, the sum of the two saturation currents is

$$j_{e_s} + j_{I_s} = \tfrac{1}{4} n_e e(\langle c_e \rangle + \langle c_I \rangle)$$

Second, the slope for $\phi_p > 0$ is

$$\frac{\partial j}{\partial \phi_p} = -\left(\frac{1}{4} n_e e^2 \frac{\langle c_I \rangle}{kT_I}\right) e^{-e\phi_p/kT_I} \tag{4.127}$$

while for $\phi_p < 0$,

$$\frac{\partial j}{\partial \phi_p} = -\left(\frac{1}{4} n_e e^2 \frac{\langle c_e \rangle}{kT_e}\right) e^{e\phi_p/kT_e} \tag{4.128}$$

These three relations provide, in theory, enough data to determine T_I, T_e, and n_I. Occasionally two probes connected through a variable voltage supply are used to bypass the difficulty of determining the plasma potential.

4.14.2 Circular Probes. Most plasma probes have a circular cross section. For this shape, the motion of the electrons and ions in the vicinity of the probe must be analyzed in more detail.[6] Consider a probe of radius a, of perfect electrical conductivity, oriented parallel to the z axis. Also, let its length be very large. We consider a region around the probe where the potential is different from the plasma potential. If $\lambda/d \ll 1$, the results of the previous section apply. If $\lambda/d \gg 1$, no collisions occur. Outside this region collisions may occur, and so the distribution function is maxwellian. As charged particles enter this region, they are deflected by the potential of the probe. If the probe is positive, electrons are attracted to the probe and positive ions are repelled. Only those charged particles which collide with the probe will contribute to the probe current. Following Langmuir, we will include in the probe current all particles which actually strike the probe and those which just graze the probe, that is, those which pass the probe tangentially at a distance a from the probe center (see Fig. 4.10).

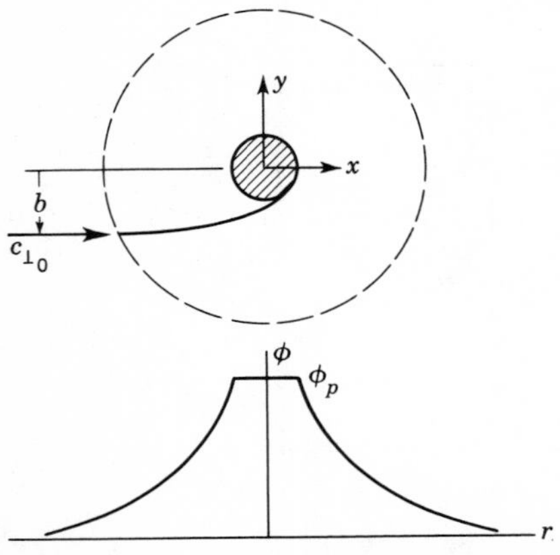

FIGURE 4.10 Cylindrical plasma probe.

Since there is no field in the z direction, the velocity in the z direction is unchanged. In the xy plane, for those electrons which just graze the probe, conservation of energy yields

$$\frac{m_e(c_\perp{}^2 - c_{\perp_0}^2)}{2} = e\phi_p$$

where $c_\perp = \sqrt{c_x^2 + c_y^2}$, and $c_{\perp_0}^2$ is the initial velocity of the electron as it enters the potential field. Conservation of angular momentum yields

$$bc_{\perp_0} = c_\perp a$$

at grazing incidence, where b is the impact parameter of the electron as it enters the region of the probe. Combination of these two relationships yields the following expression for the impact parameter for grazing incidence:

$$b = a\sqrt{1 + \frac{2e\phi_p}{c_{\perp_0}^2 m_e}}$$

For a given probe potential, electrons with initial velocities of $c_{\perp_0}$ must have an impact parameter less than b in order to collide with the probe. This critical impact parameter allows the problem to be treated in a manner similar to the collision frequency. Thus, the collision cylinder is $2bc_{\perp_0}L$, where L is the length of the probe; and the element of velocity volume is

$$d\mathbf{c} = 2\pi dc_z c_{\perp_0} dc_{\perp_0}$$

The collision frequency with the probe is thus

$$4\pi aL \int_{-\infty}^{\infty} \int_0^{\infty} \sqrt{1 + \frac{2e\phi_p}{m_e c_\perp^2}}\, c_\perp^2 f\, dc_z\, dc_\perp$$

where the subscript 0 has been dropped. The limits of integration for c are $-\infty$ to $+\infty$, but for $c_\perp$ are obviously 0 to ∞. The distribution function f is to be evaluated outside the region of influence of the probe and is therefore maxwellian, with ϕ taken as zero. Also, $2\pi aL$ is the probe area; the current density to the probe due to electrons is then

$$-j_e = 2en_{e_0}\left(\frac{m_e}{2\pi kT_0}\right)^{\frac{3}{2}} \int_{-\infty}^{\infty} e^{-m_e c_z^2/2kT_0}\, dc_z \int_0^{\infty} c_\perp^2 e^{-m_e c_\perp^2/2kT_0} \times \sqrt{1 + \frac{2e\phi_p}{m_e c_\perp^2}}\, dc_\perp$$

The first integral yields $(2\pi kT_0/m_e)^{\frac{1}{2}}$. To integrate the second integral requires expansion of the radical. For $e\phi_p/m_e c_\perp^2 \ll 1$, only the first two terms need be taken, so that this integral becomes

$$\begin{aligned} -j_e &= \frac{en_{e_0}m_e}{\pi kT_0} \int_0^{\infty} \left(c_\perp^2 + \frac{e\phi_p}{m_e}\right) e^{-m_e c_\perp^2/2kT_0}\, dc_\perp \\ &= \tfrac{1}{4} en_{e_0}\langle c\rangle_e \left(1 + \frac{e\phi_p}{kT_0}\right) \qquad \frac{e\phi_p}{kT} \ll 1 \qquad (a) \end{aligned}$$

Thus, for small positive values of the probe, the correction is small.

When $e\phi_p/kT_0 \gg 1$, the expansion of the radical becomes

$$\sqrt{\frac{2e\phi_p}{m_e}}\frac{1}{c_\perp}\sqrt{1+\frac{m_e c_\perp{}^2}{2e\phi_p}} \approx \sqrt{\frac{2e\phi_p}{m_e}}\left(\frac{1}{c_\perp}+\frac{m_e c_\perp}{4e\phi_p}\right)$$

Integration then yields

$$-j_e = \frac{en_{e_0}}{\pi}\left(\frac{2e\phi_p}{m_e}\right)^{\frac{1}{2}}\left(1+\frac{kT_0}{2e\phi_p}\right)$$

This result can be interpreted more easily by squaring the above expression, to obtain

$$j_e{}^2 = \frac{e^2 n_{e_0}^2}{\pi^2}\frac{2e\phi_p}{m_e}\left(1+\frac{kT_0}{e\phi_p}\right)$$

Rearrangement yields

$$j_e{}^2 = \frac{4}{\pi}\left(\frac{n_{e_0}\langle c\rangle_e}{4}\right)^2\left(1+\frac{e\phi_p}{kT_0}\right) \qquad \frac{e\phi_p}{kT_0} \gg 1 \tag{b}$$

This expression is actually quite close to (a), which can be written as

$$j_e{}^2 = \left(\frac{n_{e_0}\langle c\rangle_e}{4}\right)^2\left(1+\frac{2e\phi_p}{kT_0}\right)$$

Equation (b) states that as the probe is made more positive, no definite saturation is reached. Of course, if ϕ_p is made too positive, then secondary electrons may be emitted by the probe and the gas may break down.

When $e\phi_p/kT_0$ is large-positive, no positive ions reach the probe, so that (b) represents the complete current. When $e\phi_p/kT_0$ is small, there is a contribution from the positive ions. Conservation of energy and angular momentum for ions at grazing incidence yield

$$\tfrac{1}{2}m_I(c_\perp{}^2 - c_{\perp_0}^2) = -e\phi_p$$

$$c_\perp = \left(\frac{b}{a}\right)c_{\perp_0}$$

from which the critical impact parameter b is

$$b = a\sqrt{1-\frac{2e\phi_p}{m_I c_{\perp_0}^2}}$$

In this case, for an ion to graze the surface, $m_I c_{\perp_0}^2 > 2e\phi_p$. Thus the lower limit of integration for $c_\perp$ is $\sqrt{2e\phi_p/m_I}$. The ion current is then given by

$$j_I = Zen_{I_0}\frac{m_I}{\pi kT}\int_{\sqrt{2e\phi_p/m_I}}^{\infty}\sqrt{1-\frac{2e\phi_p}{m_I c_\perp{}^2}}\,c_\perp{}^2\,e^{-m_I c_\perp{}^2/2kT}\,dc_\perp$$

The radical can be expanded when $e\phi_p/m_I c_\perp^2 \ll 1$, and the integral evaluated. The result is

$$j_I = \tfrac{1}{4} n_{I_0} \langle c \rangle_I [(1 - 2\pi^{-\frac{1}{2}}\phi^*) \operatorname{erf} \phi^{*\frac{1}{2}} + 2\pi^{-\frac{1}{2}}\phi^{*\frac{1}{2}} \exp - \phi^*] eZ \qquad (4.129)$$

where $\phi^* = e\phi_p/kT$. Thus, as ϕ^* becomes large, the ion current rapidly becomes zero. When $\phi^* = 0$, the ordinary Knudsen diffusion result is obtained.

4.15 CHILD'S LAW[6,7]

In Sec. 4.13.1 the space-charge sheath in the vicinity of an insulator was considered; the result gave the Debye shielding length. A similar analysis can be performed for the potential distribution when a net current is flowing. For the special case of large positive values of $e\phi_p/kT_e$ and a large mean free path for electrons, the result is known as *Child's law*. In this section, Child's law, including thermal motion, is derived. It is assumed that the electrons which are accelerated toward the probe or positive surface come from a maxwellian distribution where the potential ϕ is zero. Elsewhere, the potential is positive. As before, it is assumed that the probe is flat. Since the region of $\phi > 0$ is collisionless, the minimum electron velocity toward the probe is $w_{1_{\min}} = \sqrt{2e\phi/m_e}$. The electron density is therefore

$$n_e = n_{e_0} \left(\frac{m_e}{2\pi k T_e} \right)^{\frac{1}{2}} e^{e\phi/kT_e} \int_{\sqrt{2e\phi/m_e}}^{\infty} e^{-m_e w_1^2/2kT_e} \, dw_1 \qquad (4.130)$$

which integrates to

$$n_e = \tfrac{1}{2} n_{e_0} e^{e\phi/kT_e} \left[1 - \operatorname{erf} \left(\frac{e\phi}{kT_e} \right)^{\frac{1}{2}} \right] \qquad (4.131)$$

For small values of ϕ, no solution can be obtained because the electron density decreases near the probe as in the corresponding case for Debye shielding. But for large values of $e\phi/kT_e$, Poisson's equation can be integrated by expanding the expression in brackets in (4.131) as follows:

$$n_e = \frac{n_{e_0}}{2\sqrt{\pi}\,(e\phi/kT)^{\frac{1}{2}}} \left(1 - \frac{kT_e}{2e\phi} + \cdots \right) \qquad (4.132)$$

The electron current is

$$-j_e = n_{e_0} e \left(\frac{m_e}{2\pi k T_e} \right)^{\frac{1}{2}} e^{e\phi/kT_e} \int_{\sqrt{2e\phi/m_e}}^{\infty} w_1 e^{-m_e w_1^2/2kT_e} \, dw_1$$
$$= n_{e_0} \left\langle \frac{c_e}{4} \right\rangle$$

as before. Thus,

$$n_e = \frac{j_e}{e}\left(\frac{m_e}{2e\phi}\right)^{\frac{1}{2}}\left(1 - \frac{kT_e}{2e\phi} + \cdots\right)$$

Because the voltage is highly positive, no positive ions will be present. Poisson's equation then becomes

$$\frac{d^2\phi}{dx^2} \equiv \frac{d}{d\phi}\frac{1}{2}\left(\frac{d\phi}{dx}\right)^2 = \frac{j_e}{K_0}\left(\frac{m_e}{2e\phi}\right)^{\frac{1}{2}}\left(1 - \frac{kT_e}{2e\phi}\right) \tag{4.133}$$

which can be integrated immediately to

$$\frac{1}{2}\left(\frac{d\phi}{dx}\right)^2 = \frac{j_e}{K_0}\left(\frac{m_e}{2e}\right)^{\frac{1}{2}}\left(2\phi^{\frac{1}{2}} + \frac{kT_e}{e}\,\phi^{-\frac{1}{2}}\right)$$

or

$$\frac{d\phi}{dx} = 2\sqrt{\frac{j_e}{K_0}\left(\frac{m_e}{2e}\right)^{\frac{1}{2}}\phi^{\frac{1}{2}}\left(1 + \frac{kT_e}{2e\phi}\right)}$$

For $kT_e/e\phi \ll 1$, the term $(1 + kT_e/2e\phi)^{\frac{1}{2}}$ can be written as $(1 + kT_e/e\phi)^{\frac{1}{4}}$. Hence,

$$\frac{d\phi}{dx} = 2\sqrt{\frac{j_e}{K_0}\left(\frac{m_e}{2e}\right)^{\frac{1}{2}}}\left(\phi + \frac{kT_e}{e}\right)^{\frac{1}{4}}$$

which integrates immediately to

$$\frac{4}{3}\left(\phi + \frac{kT_e}{e}\right)^{\frac{3}{4}} = 2\sqrt{\frac{j_e}{K_0}\left(\frac{m_e}{2e}\right)^{\frac{1}{2}}}\,(x - x_0)$$

where x_0 is the distance at which $\phi + kT_e/e = 0$. Rearrangement yields

$$j_e = \frac{4}{9}\sqrt{\frac{2e}{m_e}}(x - x_0)^{-2}\left(\phi + \frac{kT_e}{e}\right)^{\frac{3}{2}} K_0 \tag{4.134}$$

This is the usual form of Child's law. Since j_e is fixed by conditions in the plasma, (4.134) predicts that the voltage-affected region increases with the three-fourths power of the probe voltage. Rearrangement of (4.134) with the use of $j_e = \frac{1}{4}n_{e_0}e\langle c\rangle_e$ yields

$$x - x_0 = \frac{4}{3}\left(\frac{\pi}{4}\right)^{\frac{1}{4}} d\left[\frac{e\phi}{kT}\left(1 + \frac{kT_e}{e\phi}\right)\right]^{\frac{3}{4}}$$

where d is the Debye length, or

$$x - x_0 \approx d\left(\frac{e\phi}{kT_e}\right)^{\frac{3}{4}} \tag{4.135}$$

Thus, the affected region can be many times larger than the Debye length if the probe potential is large enough. For this analysis to be correct, x_0 must be smaller than the mean free path, and it is not sufficient to have only $d < \lambda$.

4.16 DISTRIBUTION FUNCTION IN A MAGNETIC FIELD

In the presence of a magnetic field, the charged particles will execute helical motion between collisions. Consider a uniform magnetic field, zero electric field, zero mean motion of the charged particles, and the charged particles in equilibrium. The steady-state Vlasov equation is then

$$eZ\mathbf{c} \times \mathbf{B} \cdot \nabla_c f = 0$$

Obviously, the only requirement on f is that $f = f(c^2)$ since $\nabla_c f = 2\mathbf{c}f'(c^2)$ and $\mathbf{c} \times \mathbf{B} \cdot \mathbf{c} = 0$. Specifically, if isotropy is again required, the distribution function is maxwellian, even though the vector velocity of each particle is continuously changing between collisions.

In the presence of both electric and magnetic fields, and if the charged particles are flowing, the distribution function becomes more complex. The following form for f may be assumed:

$$f = ae^{-b[|\mathbf{w}-\mathbf{v}|^2/2 - eZ(\mathbf{v}\cdot\mathbf{A})/m + eZ\phi/m]} \tag{4.136}$$

where $\mathbf{v}$ is the mean constant motion for the particular charged species. This may be substituted into (4.99) with $\partial f/\partial t = (\partial f/\partial t)_c = 0$. The various terms are:

$$\begin{aligned}
\nabla f &= beZm^{-1}[(\mathbf{v} \cdot \nabla)\mathbf{A} + \mathbf{v} \times (\nabla \times \mathbf{A}) - \nabla\phi]f \\
&= beZm^{-1}[(\mathbf{v} \cdot \nabla)\mathbf{A} + \mathbf{v} \times \mathbf{B} + \mathbf{E}]f \\
\nabla_{\mathbf{w}} f &= -b(\mathbf{w} - \mathbf{v})f
\end{aligned}$$

Substitution into (4.99) yields

$$\mathbf{w} \cdot (\mathbf{v} \cdot \nabla)\mathbf{A} - \mathbf{v} \cdot \mathbf{E} = 0 \tag{4.137}$$

as the condition which must be met in order for the plasma to be in equilibrium. Because $\mathbf{w}$ appears in the first term, it is not possible to satisfy this requirement in general. Therefore, both terms must be zero. The term $\mathbf{v} \cdot \mathbf{E} = 0$ requires that this species flow perpendicular to the electric field. The other term requires that $(\mathbf{v} \cdot \nabla)\mathbf{A} = 0$, which requires that $\mathbf{A}$ have no dependence on the direction of $\mathbf{v}$. Evaluation of the constants of (4.136) in terms of temperature and density finally yields

$$f = n_0\left(\frac{m}{2\pi kT}\right)^{\frac{3}{2}} \exp - \frac{m}{kT}\left(\frac{|\mathbf{w} - \mathbf{v}|^2}{2} - eZ\mathbf{v} \cdot \frac{\mathbf{A} - \mathbf{A}_0}{m} + eZ\,\frac{\phi - \phi_0}{m}\right) \tag{4.138}$$

where n_0 is the number density at a point where $\phi = \phi_0$ and $A = A_0$. From (4.138) the mean velocity $\mathbf{w}$ is obviously $\mathbf{v}$, and the number density is

$$n = n_0 \exp\left(eZ\mathbf{v} \cdot \frac{\mathbf{A} - \mathbf{A}_0}{kT} - eZ\,\frac{\phi - \phi_0}{kT}\right) \tag{4.139}$$

4.17 CLASSICAL PINCH[8]

In the classical pinch, a current is established in a plasma. As the current is increased, the magnetic field surrounding the plasma becomes appreciable and exerts a magnetic pressure on the plasma which confines it (see Fig. 4.11). This geometry possesses cylindrical symmetry; however it is difficult to analyze. To simplify the problem, we will consider a one-dimensional geometry which possesses most of the required features (see Fig. 4.12). Let $A_x(0) = \phi = 0$; the number density of electrons and ions (assumed singly ionized) is then

$$\begin{aligned} n_I &= n_0 \exp \frac{ev_I A_x}{kT} \\ n_e &= n_0 \exp \frac{-ev_e A_x}{kT} \end{aligned} \tag{4.140}$$

where n_0 is the number density of electrons at $x = 0$. We will also assume that $v_e = -v_I$ for this model. The equation for A_x becomes

$$\frac{\partial^2 A_x}{\partial z^2} = -\mu_0 j_x = \mu_0 e(n_e v_e - n_I v_I)$$

or, with (4.140),

$$\frac{\partial^2 A_x}{\partial z^2} = 2\mu_0 e n_0 v_e \exp \frac{-ev_e A_x}{kT} \tag{4.141}$$

As $z \to \infty$, B_y will become constant for this model; thus A_x must increase linearly with z. Thus the exponential in (4.141) cannot be expanded as in (4.119), and the complete equation must be solved. It is con-

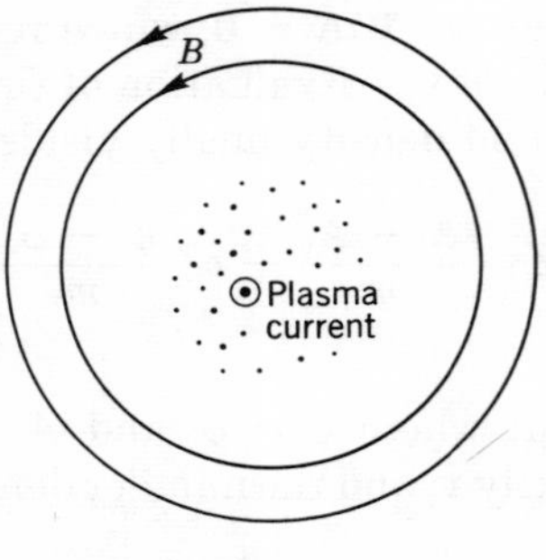

FIGURE 4.11 Classical pinch.

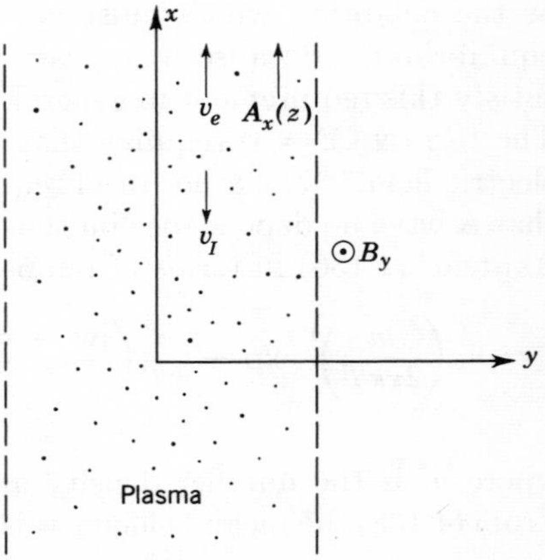

FIGURE 4.12 Sheet pinch.

venient to define the following nondimensional variables,

$$\begin{aligned} \zeta &= z\sqrt{2\mu_0 e^2 n_0 \frac{v_e^2}{kT}} = \sqrt{2}\, z \frac{v_e}{c_0 d} \\ A^* &= A_x e \frac{v_e}{kT} \end{aligned} \tag{4.142}$$

where c_0 is the speed of light, and d is the Debye length. Also,

$$\begin{aligned} \frac{\partial A^*}{\partial \zeta} &= (2\mu_0 n_0 kT)^{-\frac{1}{2}} \frac{\partial A_x}{\partial z} \\ &= \left(\frac{B_y^2}{2\mu_0 p_0}\right)^{\frac{1}{2}} \end{aligned} \tag{4.143}$$

where p_0 is the electron pressure $n_0 kT$ at $z = 0$. Equation (4.141) becomes

$$\frac{\partial^2 A^*}{\partial \zeta^2} \equiv \frac{1}{2} \frac{\partial}{\partial A^*} \left(\frac{\partial A^*}{\partial \zeta}\right)^2 = \exp(-A^*)$$

which can be integrated immediately to

$$\frac{\partial A^*}{\partial \zeta} = \sqrt{c - 2\exp(-A^*)}$$

where c is a constant of integration. From (4.143), as $z \to \infty$, the magnetic pressure must equal the gas pressure $p_e + p_I = 2p_0$. Thus $(\partial A^*/\partial \zeta)(\infty) = \sqrt{2}$, and therefore $c = 2$. Thus,

$$\frac{\partial A^*}{\partial \zeta} = 2^{\frac{1}{2}}[1 - \exp(-A^*)]^{\frac{1}{2}} \tag{4.144}$$

which can easily be integrated again by letting $\exp(-A^*) = \psi$. The result is

$$A^* = \ln \cosh^2\left(\frac{\zeta}{2^{\frac{1}{2}}}\right) \tag{4.145}$$

where at $z = 0$ the value of A^* has been chosen to be zero. Substitution of (4.145) into (4.144) yields the magnetic field,

$$B_y = \sqrt{2\mu_0 p_0}\, \frac{\partial A^*}{\partial \zeta} = 2\sqrt{\mu_0 p_0} \tanh \frac{\zeta}{2^{\frac{1}{2}}} \tag{4.146}$$

From (4.140) the number density is obtained:

$$n_e = n_0 e^{-A^*} = n_0 \cosh^{-2} \frac{\zeta}{2^{\frac{1}{2}}} \tag{4.147}$$

As can easily be verified, the sum of the pressure $2n_e kT$ and the magnetic pressure $B_y^2/2\mu_0$ remains constant. Equations (4.146) and (4.147) are

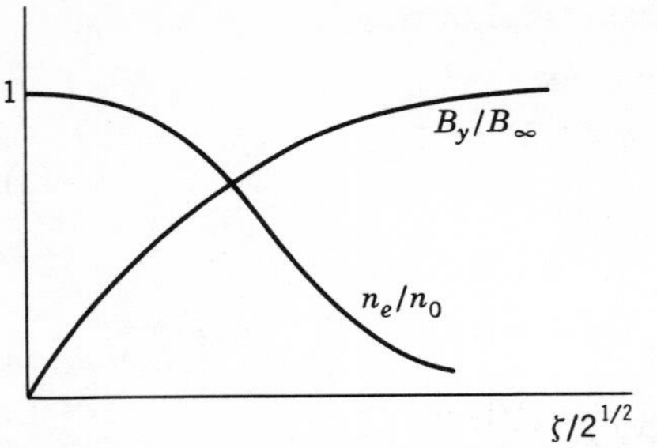

FIGURE 4.13 Density and magnetic field in a sheet pinch.

shown graphically in Fig. 4.13. This analysis verifies that such pinches are possible; that is, it is possible to use a self-excited magnetic field to contain a plasma. There are three faults with this analysis: First, these pinches become unstable for large currents. Second, an electric field is required to maintain the current; under these conditions, it is the rare case that the distribution function is a displaced maxwellian. Third, if electric fields are used to create the current, it is unlikely that $v_e = v_I$, because the mobility of the ions is usually much less than that of the electrons. This last defect is simple to remedy. Suppose it is assumed that $v_I = 0$. From (4.139),

$$\begin{aligned} n_e &= n_0 \exp\left[\frac{eZ}{kT}(-v_e A_x + \phi)\right] \\ n_I &= n_0 \exp\left(\frac{-eZ\phi}{kT}\right) \end{aligned} \tag{4.148}$$

The plasma must still be electrically neutral, which requires that $n_e \approx n_I$. From (4.148) this requires that $\phi = v_e A_x/2$, so that

$$n_e = n_0 \exp - \frac{1}{2}\frac{ev_e A_x}{kT}$$

and

$$j = -en_e v_e = -en_0 v_e \exp - \frac{1}{2}\frac{ev_e A_x}{kT}$$

This is used in (4.141); it is seen that the only required change is a factor of 2 in the definitions of ζ and A^*.

The scale distance is $d(c_0/v_e)$, from (4.142). Normally, the Debye length d is of the order of 10^{-4} to 1 mm. Thus, v_e must be quite large to have a reasonable scale height of about one centimeter.

In the cylindrical geometry, one may approximate the gradual change in density by a sharp decrease at radius r. From Chap. 2, the magnetic field is

$$B(r) = \frac{\mu_0 I}{2\pi r}$$

where I is the total current within a circle of radius r,

$$I = \int_0^r 2\pi r j(r)\, dr$$

The magnetic pressure at r must equal the hydrostatic pressure at the center; hence,

$$n_0kT = \frac{B^2(r)}{2\mu_0} = \frac{\mu_0 I^2}{8\pi^2 r^2}$$

so that the number of electrons (or ions) per unit length is

$$n_0\pi r^2 \approx \frac{\mu_0 I^2}{8\pi kT}$$

The confinement of particles is therefore proportional to the square of the current but inversely proportional to the temperature.

4.18 CONSERVATION EQUATIONS

In the previous sections, the distribution function and all properties were determined explicitly. However, there are very few problems which can be solved to this degree of completeness; for complex problems, the exact distribution function cannot be obtained. Thus, one must resort to simplifying the problem by considering only gross properties, such as density, velocity, and thermal energy. These quantities can be obtained not only directly from the distribution function but also from the conservation equations which deal only with these quantities, as explained below. The conservation equations bear the same relation to the Boltzmann equation as the latter does to single-particle orbit theory: the more complex the problem, the less detail which can be obtained concerning the motion of individual particles.

The conservation equations can be obtained from either continuum considerations or integration of the Boltzmann equation. To be consistent with our particle approach, we will choose the latter route; this also has the advantage of yielding the behavior of the individual species.

The conservation equations, as the name implies, indicate the manner in which the various average quantities in a flowing ionized gas are conserved. They are usually obtained only for those quantities which are conserved by the particles during collision; the usual quantities being mass, charge, momentum, and energy. We will neglect nuclear reactions in which a sizable amount of mass is converted into energy, and radiation in which energy and momenta are imparted to a photon which has considerably different properties than the usual particle. If no collisions occur, other conservation equations can also be written; these will be mentioned later.

The starting point is the Boltzmann equation, repeated below:

$$\frac{\partial f_s}{\partial t} + \mathbf{w} \cdot \nabla f_s + \frac{\mathbf{F}_s}{m_s} \cdot \nabla_w f_s = \left(\frac{\partial f_s}{\partial t}\right)_c$$

To obtain a conservation equation, multiply this equation by a molecular property Θ_s, which is conserved in a collision, and integrate over velocity space as follows:

$$\int \Theta_s \left(\frac{\partial f_s}{\partial t}\right) d\mathbf{w} + \int \Theta_s \mathbf{w} \cdot \nabla f_s \, d\mathbf{w} + \int \frac{\Theta_s \mathbf{F}_s}{m_s} \cdot \nabla_w f_s \, d\mathbf{w} = \int \Theta_s \left(\frac{\partial f_s}{\partial t}\right)_c d\mathbf{w} \tag{4.149}$$

The above equation is not convenient to use because average quantities are desired; thus f_s must not be within an operator. This may be accomplished for the first term as follows:

$$\int \Theta_s \left(\frac{\partial f_s}{\partial t}\right) d\mathbf{w} = \frac{\partial}{\partial t} \int \Theta_s f_s \, d\mathbf{w} = \frac{\partial}{\partial t} (n_s \langle \Theta \rangle_s) \tag{4.150}$$

because Θ_s will be chosen as charge, mass, momentum, or energy, which usually do not depend explicitly on either time or position. Similarly, the second term in (4.149) becomes

$$\int \Theta_s \mathbf{w} \cdot \nabla f_s = \nabla \cdot \int \Theta_s \mathbf{w} f_s \, d\mathbf{w} = \nabla \cdot n_s \langle \Theta \mathbf{w} \rangle_s \tag{4.151}$$

The third term in (4.149) may be integrated by parts as follows:

$$\int \Theta_s \frac{\mathbf{F}_s}{m_s} \cdot \nabla_w f_s \, d\mathbf{w} = -\int \frac{f_s}{m_s} \nabla_w \cdot (\Theta_s \mathbf{F}_s) \, d\mathbf{w}$$

since $f_s \to 0$ at $w = \pm\infty$. This may be simplified further by considering the form of $\mathbf{F}_s$: for electrical, magnetic, and even gravitational forces, $\mathbf{F}_s$ does not depend on the velocity parallel to $\mathbf{F}_s$. Thus,

$$\nabla_w \cdot (\Theta_s \mathbf{F}_s) = \mathbf{F}_s \cdot \nabla_w \Theta_s$$

and the force term then becomes

$$\int \frac{f_s}{m_s} \mathbf{F}_s \cdot \nabla_w \Theta_s \, d\mathbf{w} = \frac{n_s}{m_s} \langle \mathbf{F} \cdot \nabla_w \Theta \rangle_s \tag{4.152}$$

Substitution of (4.150) to (4.152) into (4.149) yields Maxwell's transport equation:

$$\frac{\partial}{\partial t} (n_s \langle \Theta \rangle_s) + \nabla \cdot (n_s \langle \Theta \mathbf{w} \rangle_s) - \frac{n_s}{m_s} \langle \mathbf{F}_s \cdot \nabla_w \Theta \rangle_s = \int \Theta_s \left(\frac{\partial f}{\partial t}\right)_c d\mathbf{w} \tag{4.153}$$

4.18.1 Conservation of Species. To obtain conservation of species, let $\Theta_s = m_s$. Substitution into the transport equation (4.153) yields

$$\frac{\partial}{\partial t} (n_s m_s) + \nabla \cdot (n_s m_s \langle \mathbf{w} \rangle_s) = \int m_s \left(\frac{\partial f_s}{\partial t}\right) d\mathbf{w} \tag{4.154}$$

The mass density of the s species is $\rho_s = n_s m_s$, and the average velocity of the s species is $\mathbf{v}_s = \langle \mathbf{w} \rangle_s$. The collision term becomes

$$\int m_s \left(\frac{\partial f_s}{\partial t}\right)_c d\mathbf{w} = m_s \left(\frac{\partial}{\partial t}\right)_c \int f_s \, d\mathbf{w} = m_s \left(\frac{\partial n_s}{\partial t}\right)_c$$
$$= m_s \dot{n}_s = \dot{\rho}_s$$

where $\dot{\rho}_s$ is the rate of formation of s mass density due to collisions. Obviously, s particles are formed by chemical reactions which are collision processes. With these substitutions, the conservation law for the s species becomes

$$\frac{\partial \rho_s}{\partial t} + \nabla \cdot (\rho_s \mathbf{v}_s) = \dot{\rho}_s \tag{4.155}$$

This can also be written in a slightly different form by using the diffusion velocity $\mathbf{V}_s = \mathbf{v}_s - \mathbf{v}$, where $\mathbf{v}$ is the mean mass velocity of the entire gas,

$$\frac{D\rho_s}{Dt} + \rho_s \nabla \cdot \mathbf{v} + \nabla \cdot (\rho_s \mathbf{V}_s) = \dot{\rho}_s \tag{4.156}$$

where $D/Dt = \mathbf{v} \cdot \nabla + \partial/\partial t$.

4.18.2 Global Conservation of Mass. This is obtained by summing (4.155) over all species. Since the overall density is $\rho = \sum_s \rho_s$, and the mass-averaged velocity is $\rho \mathbf{v} = \sum_s \rho_s \mathbf{v}_s$, there is obtained

$$\frac{\partial \rho}{\partial t} + \nabla \cdot \rho \mathbf{v} = 0 \tag{4.157}$$

The collision term $\sum_s \rho_s$ is zero because mass is essentially conserved in collisions involving chemical reactions.

4.18.3 Species Momentum. To obtain the momentum equation for a single species, let $\Theta = m_s \mathbf{w}_s$. The transport equation then becomes

$$\frac{\partial}{\partial t} (\rho_s \langle \mathbf{w} \rangle_s) + \nabla \cdot (\rho_s \langle \mathbf{ww} \rangle_s) - n_s \langle (\mathbf{F}_s \cdot \nabla_w) \mathbf{w} \rangle_s = \int m_s \mathbf{w} \left(\frac{\partial f_s}{\partial t}\right)_c d\mathbf{w} \tag{4.158}$$

The terms can be simplified as follows:

$$\begin{aligned}
\langle \mathbf{w} \rangle_s &= \mathbf{v}_s \\
\langle \mathbf{ww} \rangle_s &= \mathbf{vv} + \mathbf{vV}_s + \mathbf{V}_s\mathbf{v} + \langle \mathbf{cc} \rangle_s \\
\rho_s \langle \mathbf{cc} \rangle_s &= \mathbf{p}_s \\
\mathbf{F}_s \cdot \nabla_w \mathbf{w} &= \mathbf{F}_s \\
\langle \mathbf{F} \rangle_s &= eZ_s \langle \mathbf{E} + \mathbf{w} \times \mathbf{B} \rangle_s = eZ_s(\mathbf{E} + \mathbf{v} \times \mathbf{B}) + eZ_s \mathbf{V}_s \times \mathbf{B} \\
&= eZ_s(\mathbf{E}^* + \mathbf{V}_s \times \mathbf{B})
\end{aligned}$$

With these relations, (4.158) becomes

$$\frac{\partial}{\partial t}(\rho_s \mathbf{v}_s) + \nabla \cdot [\rho_s(\mathbf{v}\mathbf{V}_s + \mathbf{V}_s\mathbf{v})] + \nabla \cdot (\rho_s \mathbf{v}\mathbf{v}) + \nabla \cdot \mathsf{p}_s = \mathbf{P}_s(m\mathbf{w}) + n_s e Z_s(\mathbf{E}^* + \mathbf{V}_s \times \mathbf{B}) \quad (4.159)$$

Expressions for $\mathbf{P}_s$ for momentum transfer between particles will be derived in Sec. 5.8. Note that the definition of pressure as being the difference between the particle velocity and the mass-averaged velocity gives rise to two terms involving diffusion velocity. If the pressure tensor p_s' is defined as[9]

$$\mathsf{p}_s' = \rho_s\langle \mathbf{c}'\mathbf{c}' \rangle_s \quad (4.160)$$

where $\mathbf{c}_z' = \mathbf{w}_s - \mathbf{v}_s$, then the momentum equation does not contain these terms:

$$\frac{\partial}{\partial t}(\rho_s \mathbf{v}_s) + \nabla \cdot (\rho_s \mathbf{v}_s \mathbf{v}_s) + \nabla \cdot \mathsf{p}_s' = \mathbf{P}_s(m\mathbf{w}) + n_s e Z_s(\mathbf{E}^* + \mathbf{V}_s \times \mathbf{B}) \quad (4.161)$$

The question is, naturally, which expression, (4.24*b*) or (4.160), is the "real" pressure in a fluid. Normally, pressure is the momentum transfer to a surface which is moving at the mass-averaged velocity. The contribution from each species to this pressure depends on the difference between the particle velocity and the mass-averaged velocity; thus $\mathsf{p}_s = \rho_s\langle \mathbf{c}\mathbf{c} \rangle_s$ instead of $\rho_s\langle \mathbf{c}'\mathbf{c}' \rangle_s$. On the other hand, the pressure p_s' is that associated with only the mass motion of the s species; it is that which would be detected by a gauge moving at velocity $\mathbf{v}_s$ and which was sensitive *only* to the s species. The relation between these two pressure tensors, from their definitions, is

$$\mathsf{p}_s' = \mathsf{p} - \rho_s \mathbf{V}_s \mathbf{V}_s \quad (4.160a)$$

Unfortunately, the use of p_s in the momentum equation leads to contributions to the momentum from diffusion; that is, $\nabla \cdot (\rho_s \mathbf{v}\mathbf{V}_s)$ and $\nabla \cdot (\rho_s \mathbf{V}_s \mathbf{v})$. These are usually neglected, so that (4.159) and (4.161) are identical in form. Under these conditions, no distinction is made between p_s' and p_s.

4.18.4 Overall Momentum Equation. The overall momentum equation is obtained by summation over all species. Terms such as $\sum_s \rho_s \mathbf{V}_s$ are zero by definition. In addition, $\sum_s \mathbf{P}_s = 0$ due to conservation of momentum during each collision. In addition, the sum of the partial-pressure tensors is the total-pressure tensor p. Thus, the sum of equations (4.159) becomes

$$\frac{\partial}{\partial t}(\rho \mathbf{v}) + \nabla \cdot (\rho \mathbf{v}\mathbf{v}) + \nabla \cdot \mathsf{p} = \mathbf{E}^* \sum_s n_s e Z_s + \sum_s n_e e Z_s \mathbf{V}_s \times \mathbf{B} \quad (4.162)$$

The first term on the right contains the net charge since $\sum_s n_s e Z_s = \rho_e$. However, this is usually very small in a plasma and may be neglected. The second term on the right side of (4.162) contains the conduction current since $\mathbf{j} = \sum_s n_e e Z_s \mathbf{V}_s$.

On the left side of (4.162), the first two terms may be expanded as follows:

$$\rho\left(\frac{\partial \mathbf{v}}{\partial t}\right) + \mathbf{v}\left(\frac{\partial \rho}{\partial t}\right) + \rho(\mathbf{v}\cdot\nabla)\,\mathbf{v} + \mathbf{v}\nabla\cdot(\rho\mathbf{v}) = \rho\left[\frac{\partial \mathbf{v}}{\partial t} + (\mathbf{v}\cdot\nabla)\mathbf{v}\right] = \rho\frac{D\mathbf{v}}{Dt}$$

where use has been made of overall conservation of mass. Finally, the pressure tensor can be written in terms of the stress tensor $\boldsymbol{\tau}$ and the hydrostatic pressure p,

$$\mathsf{p} = \boldsymbol{\tau} + p\mathsf{I}$$

where $p = \frac{1}{3}\sum_i p_{ii}$.

With these simplifications, the overall momentum equation becomes

$$\rho\left(\frac{D\mathbf{v}}{Dt}\right) + \nabla\cdot\boldsymbol{\tau} + \nabla p = \rho_e(\mathbf{E} + \mathbf{v}\times\mathbf{B}) + \mathbf{j}\times\mathbf{B}$$

$$\equiv \rho_e\mathbf{E} + \mathbf{J}\times\mathbf{B} \tag{4.163}$$

Equation (4.163) contains only those forces which are due to the presence of free charge. In addition to these, there are also other electrical forces, due to the polarization and magnetic moments of particles.[10,11,12]

Even with the additional forces outlined above, the overall momentum equation is still not complete, because expressions for the total electrical conduction current $\mathbf{j}$ and the stress tensor $\boldsymbol{\tau}$ have not been given. The expression for conduction current will be derived in Chap. 5. To obtain the stress tensor, $\sum_s \rho_s\langle\mathbf{cc}\rangle_s - p\mathsf{I}$, one can let this be Θ_s and obtain a transport equation. In fact, this will be done for the trace of $\mathbf{cc}$ to obtain the energy equation. Unfortunately, the term $\langle\Theta\mathbf{w}\,\nabla f\rangle$ will generate a higher-order term, $\langle \mathbf{c}c^2\rangle$, in the transport equation. In fact, each moment of the Boltzmann equation will produce a term involving the next higher moment. Thus, this procedure cannot be used to obtain a closed set of equations which completely describe the gas.

This dilemma is resolved by returning to the Boltzmann equation and by approximating the collision term $(\partial f/\partial t)_c$ with an expression which involves only the distribution functions. This procedure yields N unknown distribution functions and N Boltzmann equations, one for each species. These equations, however, cannot be solved exactly. To obtain a solution, some additional assumptions must be made. One assumption is that all the distribution functions are close to maxwellian about a single temperature T. The distribution function is then expanded as follows:

$$f_s = f_{0_s} + \beta f_{1_s} + \beta^2 f_{2_s} + \cdots$$

where β is a small parameter and is linear in pressure gradients, forces, and concentration gradients, and f_{0_s} is maxwellian. This procedure will produce expressions for f_{1_s}, etc., from which all transport coefficients may be evaluated. The other procedure is to assume the form of f_s for all but one species, which permits the solution for not only f_{1_s}, f_{2_s}, etc., but also f_{0_s}. This latter procedure is convenient to use for a very slightly ionized gas to obtain the electron conduction current. The former procedure, however, is more general, and yields the following expression for the shear-stress tensor in the S region:

$$\tau_{ij} = -\eta\left(\frac{\partial v_i}{\partial x_j} + \frac{\partial v_j}{\partial x_i}\right) + \frac{2}{3}\eta\delta_{ij}\nabla \cdot \mathbf{v}$$

where η is the viscosity which depends on composition and temperature, and is given by a fairly complex expression.[13]

4.18.5 Species Energy Equation. The energy equation can be derived in a manner similar to that of the momentum equation, with Θ taken as the total energy of an individual particle ϵ, which is the sum of the particle translation kinetic energy plus internal energy due to rotation, vibration, electronic excitation, and chemical energy. In general, the internal energy of a given particle is not correlated with the particle velocity, but the average internal energy is a function of temperature in a gas at equilibrium. If the gas is close to equilibrium, that is, if the distribution function for velocities is close to maxwellian, we may still assume that the average internal energy of the particle depends only on the gas temperature.

The particle energy with respect to laboratory coordinates is (see Sec. 4.4.5)

$$\Theta_s = \epsilon = \tfrac{1}{2}m_s w^2 + \epsilon_{\text{int}} = \tfrac{1}{2}m_s \sum_k w_k w_k + \epsilon_{\text{int}} \tag{4.164}$$

where ϵ_{int} is the internal energy of a particular particle. We next evaluate the various terms in the transport equation. First, $\langle\Theta\rangle_s$ is given by

$$\langle\Theta\rangle_s = \langle\epsilon\rangle_s = \tfrac{1}{2}m_s \sum_k \langle(v_k + c_k)^2\rangle_s + \langle\epsilon_{\text{int}}\rangle_s$$

As before, the diffusion velocity is $\mathbf{V}_s = \langle\mathbf{c}\rangle_s$. In addition, the temperature of the s species is defined in a manner which is consistent with the definition of the partial pressure,

$$p_s = \tfrac{1}{3}n_s m_s \sum_k \langle c_k c_k\rangle_s = n_s k T_s$$

from which

$$\tfrac{3}{2}kT_s = \tfrac{1}{2}m_s\langle c_k c_k\rangle \equiv \langle\epsilon_{\text{tr}}\rangle_s \tag{4.165}$$

where $\langle\epsilon_{tr}\rangle_s$ is the average random translational energy. For a gas in equilibrium, the temperature of each species is the same, since the temperature is measured by a thermometer which moves with the mass-averaged velocity of the gas $\mathbf{v}$. If each species temperature were not identical, the thermometer would absorb energy from some species and transfer it to other species, which is contrary to the concept of equilibrium. It is also assumed that for a nonelectrically conducting gas, the temperatures must still be equal for the same reason. For an electrically conducting gas, this may not be true, since the charged species may absorb energy from the electric field and transfer this energy to the neutral particles. For this transfer to occur, the temperature of the charged species must be larger than the temperature of the neutral species. This will be derived later. With (4.165), $\langle\Theta\rangle_s$ becomes

$$\langle\Theta\rangle_s = \tfrac{1}{2}m_s v^2 + m_s \sum_k v_k V_k{}^s + \langle\epsilon\rangle_s \tag{4.166}$$

where $\langle\epsilon\rangle_s = \langle\epsilon_{tr}\rangle_s + \langle\epsilon_{int}\rangle$ is the "peculiar" energy of the species. Next, Θw_i becomes

$$\Theta w_i = \tfrac{1}{2}m_s w_k w_k w_i + w_i \epsilon^s_{int}$$

Substitution of $\mathbf{w} = \mathbf{v} + \mathbf{c}$ yields

$$\Theta w_i = \tfrac{1}{2}m_s[v_i v^2 + v_i c^2 + c_i v^2 + c_i c^2 + 2v_i(\mathbf{v}\cdot\mathbf{c}) + 2c_i(\mathbf{v}\cdot\mathbf{c})] + \epsilon^s_{int} w_i$$

Taking the average, there is obtained

$$\langle\Theta w_i\rangle_s = \tfrac{1}{2}m_s(v_i v^2 + v_i\langle c^2\rangle_s + V_i{}^s v^2 + \langle c_i c^2\rangle_s) + m_s[v_i(\mathbf{v}\cdot\mathbf{V}_s)] + m_s \sum_k v_k\langle c_i c_k\rangle_s + v_i\langle\epsilon_{int}\rangle_s + \langle\epsilon_{int} c_i\rangle_s$$

or, when rearranged,

$$\langle\Theta w_i\rangle_s = v_i(\tfrac{1}{2}m_s v^2 + \tfrac{1}{2}m_s\langle c^2\rangle_s + \langle\epsilon_{int}\rangle_s) + \langle c_i(\tfrac{1}{2}m_s c^2 + \epsilon_{int})\rangle_s + \tfrac{1}{2}m_s v^2 V_i{}^s + m_s v_i(\mathbf{v}\cdot\mathbf{V}_s) + m_s \sum_k v_k\langle c_i c_k\rangle_s \tag{4.167}$$

The sum of the terms $\frac{1}{2}m_s\langle c^2\rangle_s + \langle\epsilon_{int}\rangle_s$ is the peculiar energy of the s species $\langle\epsilon\rangle_s$. The term $\langle c_i(\frac{1}{2}m_s c^2 + \epsilon_{int})\rangle$ is therefore molecular transport of peculiar energy, which is the heat-flux vector $q_i{}^s/n_s$. Also, $n_s m_s\langle c_i c_k\rangle_s$ is the pressure tensor p^s_{ik}. Thus, (4.167) becomes

$$\langle\Theta w_i\rangle_s = v_i(\tfrac{1}{2}m_s v^2 + \langle\epsilon\rangle_s) + \frac{q_i{}^s}{n_s} + \tfrac{1}{2}m_s v^2 V_i{}^s + m_s v_i(\mathbf{v}\cdot\mathbf{V}_s) + \frac{v_k p_{ik}}{n_s} \tag{4.168}$$

Finally, the force term must be evaluated. With $\partial\Theta/\partial w_i = m_s w_i$, and $F_i = eZ(E_i + w_j B_k - w_j B_k)$,

$$\sum_i \frac{F_i}{m_s}\left(\frac{\partial\Theta}{\partial w_i}\right) = eZ_s(\mathbf{E} + \mathbf{w}\times\mathbf{B})\cdot\mathbf{w} = eZ_s\mathbf{E}\cdot\mathbf{w}$$

Hence,

$$\left\langle \sum \frac{F_i}{m_s}\left(\frac{\partial \Theta}{\partial w_i}\right)\right\rangle_s = eZ_s\mathbf{E}\cdot\langle \mathbf{w}\rangle_s = eZ_s\mathbf{E}\cdot\mathbf{v}_s \tag{4.169}$$

With the use of (4.166), (4.168), and (4.169), the species energy equation becomes

$$\begin{aligned}\frac{\partial}{\partial t}\left(\tfrac{1}{2}n_s m_s v^2 + n_s m_s \mathbf{v}\cdot\mathbf{V}_s + n_s\langle\epsilon\rangle_s\right) + \nabla\cdot\left[n_s\mathbf{v}\left(\tfrac{1}{2}m_s v^2 + \langle\epsilon\rangle_s\right)\right] + \nabla\cdot\mathbf{q}_s \\ + \nabla\cdot\left(\tfrac{1}{2}n_s m_s v^2\mathbf{V}_s\right) + \nabla\cdot\left[n_s m_s\mathbf{v}(\mathbf{v}\cdot\mathbf{V}_s)\right] + \nabla\cdot(\mathbf{v}\cdot\mathsf{p}_s) - \mathbf{E}\cdot\mathbf{J}_s \\ = \int \epsilon\left(\frac{\partial f}{\partial t}\right)_c d\mathbf{w}\end{aligned} \tag{4.170}$$

where $\mathbf{J}_s = n_s e Z_s \mathbf{v}_s$. Also note that $\rho_s = n_s m_s$. It is convenient to express the peculiar energy of a species on the basis of mass; thus let

$$e_s = \frac{\langle\epsilon\rangle_s}{m_s} \tag{4.171}$$

With these substitutions, (4.170) becomes

$$\begin{aligned}\frac{\partial}{\partial t}\rho_s\left(\tfrac{1}{2}v^2 + \mathbf{v}\cdot\mathbf{V}_s + e_s\right) + \nabla\cdot\rho_s\left(\tfrac{1}{2}v^2 + e_s\right)\mathbf{v} + \nabla\cdot\mathbf{q}_s \\ + \nabla\cdot\rho_s\left[\tfrac{1}{2}v^2\mathbf{V}_s + \mathbf{v}(\mathbf{v}\cdot\mathbf{V}_s)\right] + \nabla\cdot(\mathbf{v}\cdot\mathsf{p}_s) \\ = \mathbf{E}\cdot\mathbf{J}_s + \int \epsilon_t\left(\frac{\partial f}{\partial t}\right)_c d\mathbf{w}\end{aligned} \tag{4.172}$$

4.18.6 Alternate Form of Species Energy Equation. An alternate form of the energy equation can also be written in terms of the peculiar energy with respect to the velocity of the s species; that is, let $\epsilon_{\text{tr}} = \frac{1}{2}m_s c_s'^2$, instead of the previous definition $\epsilon_{\text{tr}} = \frac{1}{2}m_s c_s^2$. Then the energy equation becomes[9]

$$\begin{aligned}\frac{\partial}{\partial t}\rho_s\left(\tfrac{1}{2}v_s^2 + e_s'\right) + \nabla\cdot\rho_s\left(\tfrac{1}{2}v_s^2 + e_s'\right)\mathbf{v}_s + \nabla\cdot\mathbf{q}_s' + \nabla\cdot(\mathbf{v}_s\cdot\mathsf{p}_s') \\ = \mathbf{E}\cdot\mathbf{J}_s + \int \epsilon\left(\frac{\partial f}{\partial t}\right)_c d\mathbf{w}\end{aligned} \tag{4.173}$$

where $\mathbf{q}_s' = \frac{1}{2}\rho_s\langle\mathbf{c}'c'^2/2\rangle_s$, $\mathsf{p}_s = \rho_s\langle\mathbf{c}'\mathbf{c}'\rangle_s$, and $e_s' = m_s^{-1}\left(\frac{1}{2}m_s\langle c'^2\rangle_s + \langle\epsilon_{\text{int}}\rangle\right)$. This formulation has the advantage that the diffusion terms are not present in (4.173), but note that the total heat flux is *not* $\sum_s \mathbf{q}_s'$, and the total-pressure tensor is *not* $\sum_s \mathsf{p}_s'$. It is also common to take $\frac{1}{2}m_s\langle c'^2\rangle$ as $\frac{3}{2}kT_s'$; however, this is the temperature that a thermometer would measure if moving with velocity $\mathbf{v}_s$ and if it detected only the s species. It is sometimes assumed that all species have the same temperature T_s', but there is little justification for this. In spite of this, (4.173) is often used with no distinction between T_s' and T_s, $\mathbf{p}_s'$ and $\mathbf{p}_s$, and $\mathbf{q}_s'$ and $\mathbf{q}_s$. The relation between the pressures is given by (4.160*a*); the relation between T_s' and T_s is[9]

$$T_s' = T_s - \tfrac{1}{2}m_s V_s^2 \tag{4.174}$$

and for heat flux

$$q_{is}' = q_i^s - \tfrac{3}{2}p_s V_i^s - \sum_k p_{ik}^s V_k^s + \rho_s V_s^2 V_i^s \tag{4.175}$$

4.18.7 Overall Energy Equation. The overall energy equation is obtained by summation of (4.172) over all species, noting that $\Sigma \rho_s \mathbf{V}_s = 0$,

$$\frac{\partial}{\partial t}[\rho(\tfrac{1}{2}v^2 + e)] + \nabla \cdot [\rho(\tfrac{1}{2}v^2 + e)\mathbf{v}] + \nabla \cdot \mathbf{q} + \nabla \cdot (\mathbf{v} \cdot \mathbf{p}) = \mathbf{E} \cdot \mathbf{J} \tag{4.176}$$

since the sum of the collision terms is zero in the absence of radiation, and the average internal energy e is defined by $\rho e = \sum_s \rho_s e_s$. The internal energy of a species is given by

$$e_s = \int_{T_0}^{T_s} C_{v_s}\, dT_s + e_{\text{chem}}^s \tag{4.177}$$

provided that the distribution function is maxwellian or close to maxwellian. If the distribution function is not maxwellian, the contribution to the peculiar energy from the peculiar velocities can still be calculated as $\frac{1}{2}\langle c^2\rangle_s$, but there is no simple way of determining the distribution of such internal energy as rotation, vibration, and electronic excitation. In general, maxwellian distribution functions occur for all species only when all species temperatures are identical, in which case the total energy is

$$e = \sum_s \frac{\rho_s e_s}{\rho} = \sum_s \int_{T_0}^{T} \left(\frac{\rho_s}{\rho}\right) C_{v_s}\, dT + \sum_s \left(\frac{\rho_s}{\rho}\right) e_{\text{chem}}^s = \int_{T_0}^{T} \langle C_v \rangle\, dT + e_{\text{chem}} \tag{4.178}$$

where the average specific heat is defined by

$$\langle C_v \rangle = \sum_s \left(\frac{\rho_s}{\rho}\right) C_v^s \tag{4.179}$$

The heat-flux vector can be calculated from the distribution functions. For the special case of scalar properties (S region), and when all distribution functions are close to maxwellian about a single temperature T, the heat-flux vector is usually expressed as the sum of two terms by neglecting the heat conduction due to thermodiffusion, as follows:[13]

$$\mathbf{q} = -\mathcal{K}\,\nabla T + \sum_s \mathbf{V}_s \rho_s h_s \tag{4.180}$$

where h_s is the enthalpy, equal to $e_s + p_s/\rho_s$, and where $\mathcal{K}$ is the ordinary coefficient of thermal conductivity and is a function only of the local composition and temperature of the gas, but does *not* depend on the gradients of temperature or composition. Because of this dependence, $\mathcal{K}$ is sometimes called the "frozen" thermal conductivity. Under special conditions, the diffusion velocity depends only on gradients in composition of the gas, which in turn depend only on the temperature gradient. Under these special conditions, $\mathbf{q} = -\mathcal{K}' \nabla T$, but this relation is not general.

Conduction currents obviously give rise to heat transport. For example, the diffusion of electrons is $\mathbf{V}_e = -\mathbf{j}_e/n_e e$, and the enthalpy of electrons is $\frac{5}{2}kT_e/m_e$. Thus,

$$\mathbf{V}_e \rho_e h_e = -\frac{\frac{5}{2}\mathbf{j}_e k T_e}{e}$$

The expressions for $\mathcal{K}$ are extremely complex, but can be simplified somewhat because the electrons have very little influence on the distribution function of the heavy particles. Thus, $\mathcal{K}$ is separable into a thermal conductivity of the heavy particles $\mathcal{K}''$ and a separate contribution due to electrons. In calculating the latter, collisions of the electrons between themselves must be included as well as between electrons and the heavy particles. Thus, (4.180) becomes

$$\mathbf{q} = -\mathcal{K}'' \nabla T'' - \mathcal{K}_e \nabla T_e + \sum_s \mathbf{V}_s \rho_s h_s \tag{4.181}$$

where T'' is the average temperature of the heavy particles.

In the T' region, the coefficient of thermal conductivity becomes a tensor. However, if the Hall parameter for ions is much less than unity, only $\mathcal{K}_e$ is a tensor. The complete expressions for $\mathcal{K}_e$, including thermodiffusion, will be derived in Chap. 5.

4.18.8 Alternate Overall Energy Equation. Equation (4.176) is not a convenient form for the energy equation. It is more convenient to obtain explicit expressions for either the energy e or for the total enthalpy $H = \frac{1}{2}v^2 + e + p/\rho$. To obtain the form in terms of energy, the first two terms in (4.176) can be expanded as follows:

$$\rho\left(\frac{\partial}{\partial t}\right)(\tfrac{1}{2}v^2 + e) + (\tfrac{1}{2}v^2 + e)\left(\frac{\partial \rho}{\partial t}\right) + \rho\mathbf{v}\cdot\nabla(\tfrac{1}{2}v^2 + e) + (\tfrac{1}{2}v^2 + e)\,\nabla\cdot(\mathbf{v}\rho)$$

The sum of the second and fourth terms above is zero, from continuity. Also,

$$\begin{aligned}\nabla\cdot(\mathbf{v}\cdot\mathbf{p}) &= \sum_i\sum_k \frac{\partial}{\partial x_i} v_k p_{ik} = \sum_i\sum_k \frac{\partial}{\partial x_i}(v_k p \delta_{ik}) + \sum_i\sum_k \frac{\partial}{\partial x_i}(v_k \tau_{ik}) \\ &= \nabla\cdot p\mathbf{v} + \nabla\cdot(\mathbf{v}\cdot\boldsymbol{\tau})\end{aligned}$$

Thus, (4.176) can be written as

$$\rho\left[\left(\frac{\partial}{\partial t}\right)(\tfrac{1}{2}v^2 + e) + \mathbf{v}\cdot\nabla(\tfrac{1}{2}v^2 + e)\right] \equiv \rho\left(\frac{D}{Dt}\right)(\tfrac{1}{2}v^2 + e)$$
$$= -\nabla\cdot\mathbf{q} - \nabla\cdot(p\mathbf{v}) - \nabla\cdot(\mathbf{v}\cdot\boldsymbol{\tau}) + \mathbf{E}\cdot\mathbf{J} \quad (4.182)$$

The terms $\frac{1}{2}v^2$ are eliminated by carrying out the indicated operations in (4.182) and use of the overall momentum equation. The result is

$$\rho\left(\frac{De}{Dt}\right) + p\nabla\cdot\mathbf{v} = -\Phi - \nabla\cdot\mathbf{q} + \mathbf{E}\cdot\mathbf{j} - \mathbf{v}\cdot\mathbf{j}\times\mathbf{B}$$

where Φ is the well-known dissipation function $\sum_i\sum_j \tau_{ij}\left(\frac{\partial v_j}{\partial x_i}\right)$, and $\mathbf{j} = \sum_s n_s e Z_s \mathbf{V}_s$. The last two terms can be combined since

$$\mathbf{E}^* = \mathbf{E} + \mathbf{v}\times\mathbf{B}$$

Also, $\nabla\cdot\mathbf{v} = -\rho^{-1}(D\rho/Dt) = \rho D(\rho^{-1})/Dt$, from continuity. The energy equation then becomes

$$\rho\left(\frac{De}{Dt}\right) + \rho p\,\frac{D(\rho^{-1})}{Dt} = -\Phi - \nabla\cdot\mathbf{q} + \mathbf{E}^*\cdot\mathbf{j} \quad (4.183)$$

which is the familiar form, with the addition of $\mathbf{E}^*\cdot\mathbf{j}$, which is called the *ohmic heating*. If the conduction current $\mathbf{j}$ is linearly proportional to E^*, that is,

$$\mathbf{j} = \sigma\mathbf{E}^* \quad (4.184)$$

where σ is the electrical conductivity, then the ohmic heating becomes j^2/σ, which is the usual expression. However, in a plasma in a magnetic field, the electric current is a *tensor* function of the moving electric field. This can be written in two ways,

$$\mathbf{j} = \boldsymbol{\sigma}\cdot\mathbf{E}^*$$

or by means of the following vector equation (see Sec. 5.8),

$$\mathbf{j} = \sigma\left(\frac{\mathbf{B}}{B}\right)E_\parallel^* + \sigma\,\frac{(1+\beta)\mathbf{E}_\perp^* + \omega_e\tau_e(\mathbf{E}_\perp^*\times\mathbf{B})/B}{(1+\beta)^2 + \omega_e^2\tau_e^2} \quad (4.185)$$

where $E_\parallel^*$ is parallel to the magnetic field, $E_\perp^*$ is perpendicular, and $\beta = \omega_e\tau_e\omega_I\tau_I$. The ohmic heating is then given by

$$\mathbf{E}^*\cdot\mathbf{j} = \frac{1}{\sigma}\left[j_\parallel^2 + j_\perp^2(1 + \omega_e\tau_e\omega_I\tau_I)\right]$$
$$\equiv \frac{1}{\sigma}\left[j^2 + j_\perp^2(\omega_e\tau_e\omega_I\tau_I)\right] \quad (4.186)$$

where ω_e, ω_I are the electron and ion cyclotron frequencies, and τ_e, τ_I are the electron and ion mean collision times. Thus, the ohmic heating is not the square of the current divided by the scalar conductivity, but has an additional term due to the Hall effect and ion slip (see Chap. 5).

The other form of the energy equation is written in terms of total enthalpy $H = \frac{1}{2}v^2 + e + p/\rho$, or

$$\begin{aligned} H &= \tfrac{1}{2}v^2 + h \\ &= \tfrac{1}{2}v^2 + \sum_s \left(\frac{\rho_s}{\rho}\right) h_s \\ &= \tfrac{1}{2}v^2 + \sum \left(\frac{\rho_s}{\rho}\right)\left(\int C_{p_s}\,dT + h_s^\circ\right) \\ &= \tfrac{1}{2}v^2 + \int \langle C_p\rangle\,dT + \sum \left(\frac{\rho_s}{\rho}\right) h_s^\circ \end{aligned} \tag{4.187}$$

where $\langle C_p\rangle$ is $\sum \left(\frac{\rho_s}{\rho}\right) C_{p_s}$, the "frozen" specific heat, and h_s° is the enthalpy of formation. This form can be obtained from (4.182) by adding and subtracting p/ρ from the two terms on the left side. Thus, the following terms must be added to the right side,

$$\rho\left(\frac{\partial}{\partial t}\right)\left(\frac{p}{\rho}\right) + \rho\mathbf{v}\cdot\nabla\left(\frac{p}{\rho}\right) = \frac{\partial p}{\partial t} + \nabla\cdot(p\mathbf{v}) \tag{4.188}$$

where use has been made of the continuity equation. Then (4.182) becomes

$$\rho\frac{DH}{Dt} - \frac{\partial p}{\partial t} = -\nabla\cdot\mathbf{q} - \nabla\cdot(\mathbf{v}\cdot\boldsymbol{\tau}) + \mathbf{E}\cdot\mathbf{J} \tag{4.189}$$

Note that the stationary electric field and the *total* current appear in (4.189), in contrast to (4.183), which contains the moving electric field and the conduction current. The term $\mathbf{E}\cdot\mathbf{J}$ is the total electric energy which is added to the flow.

Finally, the entropy equation can be derived from the energy equation. The second law of thermodynamics is

$$T\,dS = de + p\,d(\rho^{-1})$$

which becomes

$$T\frac{DS}{Dt} = \frac{De}{Dt} + p\frac{D\rho^{-1}}{Dt} \tag{4.190}$$

Substitution of the energy equation for De/Dt yields the following form of the entropy equation:

$$\rho T\frac{DS}{Dt} = -\Phi - \nabla\cdot\mathbf{q} + \mathbf{E}^*\cdot\mathbf{j} \tag{4.191}$$

When $\mathbf{j} = \sigma\mathbf{E}^*$, the electrical term becomes j^2/σ. For a more complete discussion of the transport equations, see refs. 12 and 13.

4.18.9 Conservation of Charge. Conservation of charge or electricity can be derived by letting $\Theta_s = eZ_s$. For a single species, the result is obviously

$$\frac{\partial}{\partial t}(en_sZ_s) + \nabla \cdot (n_seZ_s\mathbf{v}_s) = eZ_s\dot{n}_s \tag{4.192}$$

where $\dot{n}_s$ is local rate of production of the charged species s by collisions. Letting $\rho_e{}^s = en_sZ_s$, the charge density of the s species, (4.192) becomes

$$\frac{\partial \rho_e{}^s}{\partial t} + \nabla \cdot \mathbf{J}_s = \dot{\rho}_e{}^s \tag{4.193}$$

The overall conservation of electricity is obtained by summation of (4.193) over all species,

$$\frac{\partial \rho_e}{\partial t} + \nabla \cdot \mathbf{J} = 0 \tag{4.194}$$

in agreement with classical theory.

REFERENCES CITED

1. Jeans, Sir J. H.: *An Introduction to the Kinetic Theory of Gases,* pp. 135–138, Cambridge University Press, London, 1952.
2. Linhart, J. G.: *Plasma Physics,* pp. 54–58, North Holland Publishing Company, Amsterdam, 1960.
3. Kornowski, E.: "On Some Unsteady Free-molecular Solutions to the Boltzmann Equation," *Gen. Elec. Rept.* R59SD463, November, 1959.
4. Debye, P., and E. Hückel: *Physik. Z.,* **24**:185 (1923).
5. Aisenberg, S.: "Modern Probe Techniques for Plasma Diagnosis," in N. W. Mather and G. W. Sutton (eds.), *Proc. 3d Symp. Eng. Aspects Magnetohydrodynamics,* Gordon and Breach, Science Publishers, Inc., New York, 1964.
6. Langmuir, I., and K. T. Compton: "Electrical Discharges in Gases: part II, Fundamental Phenomena in Electrical Discharges," *Rev. Mod. Phys.,* **3**:191–257 (1931).
7. Cobine, James: *Gaseous Conductors,* pp. 124–128, Dover Publications, Inc., New York, 1958.
8. Bennett, W. H.: *Phys. Rev.,* **45**:89 (1934).
9. Burgers, J. (ed.): "Statistical Plasma Mechanics," in F. H. Clauser (gen. ed.), *Symposium on Plasma Dynamics,* p. 131, Addison-Wesley Publishing Company, Inc., Reading, Mass., 1960.
10. Abraham, M., and R. Becker: *Electricity and Magnetism,* 2d ed., Hafner Publishing Company, Inc., New York, 1949.
11. Green, H. S.: "Ionic Theory of Plasmas and Magnetohydrodynamics," *Phys. Fluids,* **2**:341 (1959).

12. Chu, Boa-Teh: "Thermodynamics of Electrically Conducting Gases," *Phys. Fluids,* **2**:473 (1959).
13. Hirschfelder, J. O., C. F. Curtiss, and R. B. Bird: *Molecular Theory of Gases and Liquids,* John Wiley & Sons, Inc., New York, 1954.

GENERAL REFERENCES

Condon, E. U., and H. Odishaw (eds.): *Handbook of Physics,* McGraw-Hill Book Company, New York, 1958.

Cowling, T. G.: *Molecules in Motion,* Harper Torchbooks, Harper & Row, Publishers, Incorporated, New York, 1960.

Drummond, J. E.: *Plasma Physics,* McGraw-Hill Book Company, New York, 1961.

Grad, H.: "Principles of the Kinetic Theory of Gases," *Handbuch der Physik,* vol. XII, Springer-Verlag OHG, Berlin, 1958.

Guggenheim, E. A.: *Elements of the Kinetic Theory of Gases,* Pergamon Press, New York, 1960.

Hirschfelder, J. O., C. F. Curtiss, and R. B. Bird: *Molecular Theory of Gases and Liquids,* John Wiley & Sons, Inc., New York, 1954.

International Summer Course in Plasma Physics (Riso), Danish Atomic Energy Commission, 1960.

Jeans, Sir J. H.: *The Dynamical Theory of Gases,* reprinted by Dover Publications, Inc., New York, 1954.

Jeans, Sir J. H.: *An Introduction to the Kinetic Theory of Gases,* Cambridge University Press, London, 1952.

Spitzer, L.: *Physics of Fully Ionized Gases,* vol. 2, Interscience Publishers, Inc., New York, 1962.

5

CONDUCTION AND DIFFUSION IN IONIZED GASES

5.1 INTRODUCTION

In this chapter, the expressions for the electrical conduction current will be derived. It is assumed that the local composition of the ionized gas is calculable; hence at any point the number density of all species is known as well as the temperature of the heavy species. It is also assumed that electrical conduction occurs by diffusion of the charged species. Conduction can also occur by charge exchange between two particles during a collision, but this is usually unimportant. The conduction current is given by (4.22) as follows:

$$\mathbf{j} = \sum_s n_s e Z_s \mathbf{V}_s \tag{4.22}$$

where

$$n_s \mathbf{V}_s = \int \mathbf{c} f_s \, d\mathbf{c} \tag{4.16}$$

In order to calculate $\mathbf{V}_s$, the distribution function f_s must be known. Note that this cannot be maxwellian about a zero velocity, for then $\mathbf{V}_s = 0$. Nor can it be chosen as maxwellian about $\mathbf{V}_s$, for then (4.16) is merely an identity. Thus, it is necessary to obtain an expression for f_s in terms of the local densities, pressure, temperatures, electric fields, magnetic fields, etc., by direct solution of the Boltzmann equation. There are N such Boltzmann equations, one for each species in the gas. To obtain a solution, two steps must be taken. First, it is necessary to express the collision term $(\partial f_s/\partial t)_c$ in terms of the distribution functions $f_1, \ldots, f_2, \ldots, f_s, \ldots, f_N$. This results in N Boltzmann equations in N unknowns, and in principle each equation can be solved.

Unfortunately, this is not possible in practice, and one must therefore resort to some type of series solution. Because of this latter complication as well as some others, at present there is no complete exact theory for conduction in gases. Instead, a number of expressions can be derived with different assumptions and degrees of validity.

The simplest set of assumptions is called the *Lorentz model,* in which only the electron conduction is calculated by assuming that the electrons collide only with heavy species in binary elastic collisions. In the Lorentz approximation, the effects of electric and magnetic fields are considered in calculating the electron distribution function, while the distribution function for the heavy particles is taken to be maxwellian. This procedure results in an expression for the electron energy and conduction in terms of collision cross sections. These will be evaluated for an inverse-force law and for various cases, including collisions with ions for which additional assumptions are required. The relationship to the Fokker-Planck equation will also be given. The contribution of ion diffusion to the total conduction current will be evaluated on the basis of the three-fluid model.

In a partially ionized gas, the ponderomotive force $\mathbf{j} \times \mathbf{B}$ can cause appreciable pressure gradients, which, in addition to the effects of electric and magnetic fields, can also cause diffusion and electric currents. This will also be analyzed using the three-fluid model.

The three-fluid model is based on the Chapman-Enskog method, which is the basis for most calculations of the transport processes in gases. To utilize this approach, it is assumed that all species have a velocity distribution which is close to maxwellian about the *same* temperature. The resulting expression for the diffusion velocity of the various species is in terms of gradients of temperature, pressure, concentrations, and generalized forces on each species, and is taken as $\rho_e \mathbf{E} + eZ_s \mathbf{V}_s \times \mathbf{B}$. Although the resulting expression has broader application, the numerical results are less accurate because of the assumed form of the distribution functions. In addition, the Onsager form of irreversible thermodynamics states that the expression for the diffusion velocities must be explicit rather than implicit; thus the Chapman-Enskog method is incorrect in principle when applied to ionized gases. Finally, in the Chapman-Enskog method for evaluating the diffusion coefficients, the presence of electric and magnetic fields is neglected, in sharp contrast to the Lorentz gas. In spite of these deficiencies, this form is still of interest and will be presented.

5.2 COLLISION TERM IN BOLTZMANN'S EQUATION[1]

In Chap. 4, it was implied that the collision term of Boltzmann's equation, $(\partial f_s/\partial t)_c$, could be written in terms of the distribution functions only. This can be accomplished in two ways. The first is applicable if the particles are subject to individual binary collisions, in which case the collision term is calculated from the binary-collision frequency. This is the basis, for example, of the Chapman-Enskog method and the Lorentz model. The other method applies when the particle is subjected to the attractive or repulsive forces from many other particles simultaneously, and individual binary collisions do not exist. In this case the collision term of the Boltzmann equation is proportional to the first and higher derivatives of the distribution function; this is called the *Fokker-Planck equation.* We will first concentrate on the binary collisions; later we will derive the Fokker-Planck equation.

For binary collisions, the collision term in Boltzmann's equation is equal to the difference between the rate at which particles are added to the distribution function and the rate at which they are removed. If an r particle with velocity $\mathbf{w}$ collides with an s particle, after collision it will have some other velocity and will have been removed from the distribution function at $f_r(\mathbf{w})$. Thus, the rate of removal, $(\partial f_r/\partial t)\, d\mathbf{w}_r$, is proportional to the number of collisions per unit time which remove r particles from the velocity range between $\mathbf{w}$ and $\mathbf{w} + d\mathbf{w}_r$. The collision frequency of r particles in the velocity range $\mathbf{w}$ to $\mathbf{w} + d\mathbf{w}_r$ with s particles in the velocity range $\mathbf{w}$ to $\mathbf{w} + d\mathbf{w}_s$ is the number of each species in its velocity range multiplied by the relative collision volume. The number of r particles is $f_r\, d\mathbf{w}_r$ and the number of s particles is $f_s\, d\mathbf{w}_s$ in these velocity ranges. The collision volume in Sec. 4.8.2 had been taken as $g\pi R_{rs}^2$, where πR_{rs}^2 is the area of the base of the collision cylinder, and g is the relative speed. To be more general, we will consider an element of the base of the collision cylinder in cylindrical coordinates b and ϵ, where b is the radius or "impact parameter," and ϵ is the azimuthal angle (see Fig. 5.1). Therefore an element of the collision cylinder is $g(db)(b\, d\epsilon)$.

To obtain the total contribution due to collisions of this type, the impact parameter b is integrated from zero to $b_{\max}$, where $b_{\max}$ is the maximum impact parameter which results in a collision; ϵ is integrated from 0 to 2π; and collisions with all the s particles must be included so

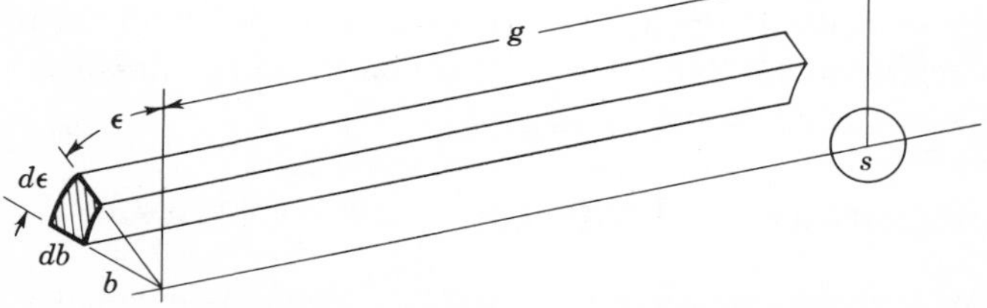

FIGURE 5.1 Element of collision cylinder, $g(db)(b\, d\epsilon)$.

that $\mathbf{w}_s$ is integrated over all values. Thus,

$$\left[\frac{\partial f_r}{\partial t}\right]_c^- d\mathbf{w}_r = -\left(\iiint f_s g b \, db \, d\epsilon \, d\mathbf{w}_s\right) f_r \, d\mathbf{w}_r \tag{5.1}$$

The parentheses in (5.1) contain just the expression for the collision frequency $\nu_r(\mathbf{w}_r)$ [see (4.56)]. Thus, the rate at which r particles in the velocity range $\mathbf{w}_r$ to $\mathbf{w}_r + d\mathbf{w}_r$ are removed from the distribution function $f_r(\mathbf{w}_r)$ is equal to $-\nu_r(\mathbf{w}_r)f_r(\mathbf{w}_r)$.†

Now, corresponding to (5.1), there are elastic collisions such that *after* the collision the particles will have velocities $\mathbf{w}_r$ and $\mathbf{w}_s$. These are called *inverse* collisions. Before the inverse collision, the particles had velocities $\mathbf{w}_r'$ and $\mathbf{w}_s'$. Thus the rate at which r particles are *added* to the distribution function is

$$\left[\frac{\partial f}{\partial t}\right]_c^+ d\mathbf{w}_r' = \iiint f_r(\mathbf{w}_r') f_s(\mathbf{w}_s') g' b \, db \, d\epsilon \, d\mathbf{w}_s' \, d\mathbf{w}_r' \tag{5.2}$$

where $\mathbf{w}_r'$ and $\mathbf{w}_s'$ must be such that *after* a collision the particles have velocities $\mathbf{w}_r$ and $\mathbf{w}_s$.

The total change is the sum of (5.1) and (5.2). However, it is convenient to express $d\mathbf{w}_s' \, d\mathbf{w}_r'$ in terms of $d\mathbf{w}_s \, d\mathbf{w}_r$. This can be done by means of the jacobian

$$d\mathbf{w}_s' \, d\mathbf{w}_r' = |J| \, d\mathbf{w}_s \, d\mathbf{w}_r$$

where $J = \partial(\mathbf{w}_s',\mathbf{w}_r')/\partial(\mathbf{w}_s,\mathbf{w}_r)$. For the inverse collisions, a jacobian J' can be similarly defined. Now, if the collisions are elastic, the dynamics of an inverse collision are exactly the same as for the direct collisions, except for an interchange of primed and unprimed velocities; hence $J' = J$. Furthermore, from the theory of jacobians, $JJ' = 1$. With this result, (5.1) and (5.2) can be summed to yield

$$\left(\frac{\partial f_r}{\partial t}\right)_c = \iiint [f_r(\mathbf{w}_r') f_s(\mathbf{w}_s') - f_r(\mathbf{w}_r) f_s(\mathbf{w}_s)] g b \, db \, d\epsilon \, d\mathbf{w}_s \tag{5.3}$$

Equation (5.3) should be summed over all species s, including r. Equation (5.3) is the basis for a rigorous derivation of the Maxwell-Boltzmann velocity distribution. In a gas in equilibrium with no spatial or time variations, $(\partial f_r/\partial t)_c = 0$. This condition requires that the integrand be zero for *all* values of $\mathbf{w}_r$ and $\mathbf{w}_s$, or

$$\ln f_r(\mathbf{w}_r) + \ln f_s(\mathbf{w}_s) = \ln f_r(\mathbf{w}_r') + \ln f_s(\mathbf{w}_s') \tag{a}$$

† Although f_r is a function of $\mathbf{x}$, $\mathbf{w}_r$, and t, for simplicity of notation it is shown only as $f_r(\mathbf{w}_r)$.

From (a), we see that the quantity $\ln f_r(\mathbf{w}_r)$ is conserved in a collision. For elastic collisions, momentum and energy are also conserved; that is,

$$\tfrac{1}{2}m_r w_r^2 + \tfrac{1}{2}m_s w_s^2 = \tfrac{1}{2}m_r w_r'^2 + \tfrac{1}{2}m_s w_s'^2$$
$$m_r w_k^r + m_s w_k^s = m_r w_k'^r + m_s w_k'^s \qquad k = 1, 2, 3 \qquad (b)$$

Thus, $\ln f_r$ must be a linear combination of the r particle's energy, momentum, and mass, or

$$\ln f_r(w_r) = a_0 \tfrac{1}{2} m_r w_r^2 + a_1 m_r w_1^r + a_2 m_r w_2^r + a_3 m_r w_3^r + a_4$$

which can be rearranged as follows, by evaluating the constants:

$$\ln f_r = -b[(w_1^r - v_1^r)^2 + (w_2^r - v_2^r)^2 + (w_3^r - v_3^r)^2] \qquad (5.4)$$

This is just the maxwellian distribution function.

5.3 LORENTZ APPROXIMATION IN A UNIFORM GAS[3]

If the gas is very slightly ionized so that very few electrons are present, then collisions between electrons and other electrons may be neglected. Also, because of the large mass ratio, the thermal motion of the heavy particles may be neglected in comparison to the thermal velocity of electrons; this is called the *Lorentz approximation*. Finally, the distribution function for s particles is taken as maxwellian, as follows: $f_s = a \exp(-b|\mathbf{w}_s - \mathbf{v}_s|^2)$. Because the distribution functions are usually in terms of the peculiar velocities, the collision integrals of (5.3) should be written in terms of $\mathbf{c}$ instead of $\mathbf{w}$. This is merely a shift of coordinates in velocity space. Thus Boltzmann's equation for electrons becomes

$$\frac{\partial f_e}{\partial t}(\mathbf{c}_e) + \mathbf{w}_e \cdot \nabla f_e(\mathbf{c}_e) - \frac{e}{m_e}(\mathbf{E} + \mathbf{w} \times \mathbf{B}) \cdot \nabla_w f_e(\mathbf{c}_e)$$
$$= \sum_{s \neq e} \iiint [f_e(\mathbf{c}_e')f_s(\mathbf{c}_s') - f_e(\mathbf{c}_e)f_s(\mathbf{c}_s)]gb\,db\,d\epsilon\,d\mathbf{c}_s \qquad (5.5)$$

Furthermore, we will assume that the gas is steady and uniform, although it is not possible to have an electric current in a magnetic field and have a uniform state of the gas [see (4.162)]. However, if the electron density is sufficiently small, the currents will also be small, and the state of the gas will be *almost* uniform. Thus, the first two terms in (5.5) are neglected. Finally, let $\mathbf{E} + \mathbf{w} \times \mathbf{B} = \mathbf{E}^* + \mathbf{c} \times \mathbf{B}$, and assume that there is only one scattering species s, so that (5.5) becomes

$$-\frac{e}{m_e}(\mathbf{E}^* + \mathbf{c} \times \mathbf{B}) \cdot \nabla_c f_e = \iint (f_e' f_s' - f_e f_s) gb\,db\,d\epsilon\,d\mathbf{c}_s \qquad (5.6)$$

Equation (5.6) is a nonlinear integrodifferential equation and cannot be solved in general. Now if $\mathbf{E}^*$ is zero, then we expect f_e to be maxwellian about the gas temperature T_s. For $\mathbf{E}^*$ small, we should expect f_e to be slightly perturbed from an isotropic distribution f_0, although f_0 may no longer be maxwellian. Furthermore, the perturbation from an isotropic distribution should be proportional to $\mathbf{E}^*$, since $\mathbf{E}^*$ is causing the perturbation. Assume that $\mathbf{E}^*$ is in the x_1 direction; then we may expect that $f_e = f_0(c^2) + E_1\tilde{f}_1$, where f_0 is isotropic and $\tilde{f}_1$ represents the perturbation. Now, the perturbation $\tilde{f}_1$ must be skewed; that is, $\tilde{f}_1$ must be a function of *odd* powers of the electron velocity in order for j_{e_1} to be nonzero. For example, the electric field will cause a current parallel to it; hence the simplest term in $\tilde{f}_1$ which will yield a current j_{e_1} is $c_1 f_1(c^2)$ where $f_1(c^2)$ is also isotropic. However, the presence of a magnetic field may cause currents in the other two directions; hence terms such as $c_2 h_1(c^2)$ and $c_3 g_1(c^2)$ are also required. Thus we may let

$$f_e = f_0 + E_1^*(c_1 f_1 + c_2 h_1 + c_3 g_1)$$

For convenience, the distribution function may be written in vector form as follows:

$$f_e = f_0 + \frac{e}{m}\left[(\mathbf{E}^* \cdot \mathbf{c}_e)f_1 + (\mathbf{B} \times \mathbf{E}^*) \cdot \mathbf{c}_e h_1 + \mathbf{B} \cdot \mathbf{c}_e(\mathbf{B} \cdot \mathbf{E}^*)g_1\right] \tag{5.7}$$

where f_0, f_1, h_1, and g_1 are isotropic. The first term in the brackets of (5.7) will yield the current in the direction of $\mathbf{E}^*$; the second term, in the direction normal to both $\mathbf{B}$ and $\mathbf{E}$; and the third term, in the direction of $\mathbf{B}$. For simplicity we will consider $\mathbf{B}$ perpendicular to $\mathbf{E}$; when $\mathbf{B}$ is not perpendicular to $\mathbf{E}$, the third term corresponding to g_1 is presented in Eqs. (5.84) to (5.89). In the remainder of this section, it is therefore assumed that $\mathbf{B} \cdot \mathbf{E} = 0$.

When (5.7), with $\mathbf{B} \cdot \mathbf{E} = 0$, is substituted into the Boltzmann equation (5.6), there will result terms whose coefficients are $|\mathbf{c}|$, c_1, c_2, c_1c_2, etc. Since $\mathbf{c}$ is an independent coordinate, all terms which are functions only of the magnitude of $\mathbf{c}$ may be equated separately, and likewise terms whose coefficients are c_1, c_2, c_1c_2, etc. Actually, terms involving the cross products c_ic_j $(i \neq j)$ are higher order and may be neglected. According to (5.7), the terms which depend on $|\mathbf{c}|$ will be scalar; terms involving c_1 will actually have the coefficient $\mathbf{E}^* \cdot \mathbf{c}_e$; terms involving c_2 will have the coefficient $\mathbf{B} \times \mathbf{E}^* \cdot \mathbf{c}_e$. All terms involving these three coefficients will be separately equated. The higher-order terms will have coefficients like $\mathbf{c}_e{}^\circ\mathbf{c}_e$ (traceless dyadic) or $(\mathbf{E}^* \cdot \mathbf{c}_e)(\mathbf{B} \times \mathbf{E}^*) \cdot \mathbf{c}_e$; these terms will be neglected.

To substitute (5.7) into (5.6), we must first calculate $\nabla_c f_e$ from (5.7) as follows:

$$\nabla_c f_e = \nabla_c f_0 + \frac{e}{m_e}\nabla_c[(\mathbf{E}^* \cdot \mathbf{c}_e)f_1] + \frac{e}{m_e}\nabla_c[(\mathbf{B} \times \mathbf{E}^*) \cdot \mathbf{c}_e h_1] \tag{5.8}$$

The first term in (5.8) is

$$\nabla_c f_0 = \left(\frac{\partial f_0}{\partial c}\right) \nabla_c c = f_0' \left[\mathbf{i} \left(\frac{\partial}{\partial c_x}\right) + \mathbf{j} \left(\frac{\partial}{\partial c_y}\right) + \mathbf{k} \left(\frac{\partial}{\partial c_z}\right) \right] (c_x^2 + c_y^2 + c_z^2)^{\frac{1}{2}} \tag{5.9}$$

Now $(\partial/\partial c_x)(c_x^2 + c_y^2 + c_z^2)^{\frac{1}{2}} = c_x(c_x^2 + c_y^2 + c_z^2)^{-\frac{1}{2}} = c_x/c$; and similar expressions are obtained for the other terms. Thus (5.9) becomes

$$\nabla_c f_0 = \frac{\mathbf{c}_e}{c_e} f_0' \tag{5.10}$$

For the second term of (5.8), one obtains

$$\nabla_c[(\mathbf{E}^* \cdot \mathbf{c}_e) f_1] = (\mathbf{E}^* \cdot \mathbf{c}_e) \frac{\mathbf{c}_e}{c_e} f_1' + f_1 \nabla_c(\mathbf{E}^* \cdot \mathbf{c}_e) \tag{5.11}$$

Now

$$\begin{aligned} \nabla_c(\mathbf{E}^* \cdot \mathbf{c}) &= \left[\mathbf{i} \left(\frac{\partial}{\partial c_x}\right) + \mathbf{j} \left(\frac{\partial}{\partial c_y}\right) + \mathbf{k} \left(\frac{\partial}{\partial c_z}\right) \right] (E_x^* c_x + E_y^* c_y + E_z^* c_z) \\ &= \mathbf{i} E_x^* + \mathbf{j} E_y^* + \mathbf{k} E_z^* = \mathbf{E}^* \end{aligned}$$

Thus, (5.11) becomes

$$\nabla_c[(\mathbf{E}^* \cdot \mathbf{c}_e) f_1] = (\mathbf{E}^* \cdot \mathbf{c}_e) \frac{\mathbf{c}_e}{c_e} f_1' + f_1 \mathbf{E}^* \tag{5.12}$$

The last term in (5.8) is similar to the second term, with $\mathbf{B} \times \mathbf{E}^*$ replacing $\mathbf{E}^*$; thus by substitution of $\mathbf{B} \times \mathbf{E}^*$ for $\mathbf{E}^*$ and h_1 for f_1 in (5.12), one obtains

$$\nabla_c(\mathbf{B} \times \mathbf{E}^* \cdot \mathbf{c}_e h_1) = (\mathbf{B} \times \mathbf{E}^* \cdot \mathbf{c}_e) \frac{\mathbf{c}_e}{c_e} h_1' + \mathbf{B} \times \mathbf{E}^* h_1 \tag{5.13}$$

We now obtain the left side of (5.6) with the use of (5.8) and (5.10) to (5.13):

$$\begin{aligned} -\frac{e}{m_e} \Bigg\{ & \mathbf{E}^* \cdot \frac{\mathbf{c}_e}{c_e} f_0' + \frac{e}{m_e c_e} (\mathbf{E}^* \cdot \mathbf{c}_e)^2 f_1' + \frac{e}{m_e} (\mathbf{E}^* \cdot \mathbf{E}^*) f_1 \\ & + \frac{e}{m_e c_e} (\mathbf{E}^* \cdot \mathbf{c}_e)(\mathbf{B} \times \mathbf{E}^* \cdot \mathbf{c}_e) h_1' + \frac{e}{m_e} \mathbf{E}^* \cdot (\mathbf{B} \times \mathbf{E}^*) h_1 \\ & + (\mathbf{c}_e \times \mathbf{B}) \cdot \frac{\mathbf{c}_e}{c_e} f_0' + \frac{e}{m_e c_e} (\mathbf{E}^* \cdot \mathbf{c}_e)(\mathbf{c}_e \times \mathbf{B}) \cdot \mathbf{c}_e f_1' + \frac{e}{m_e} (\mathbf{c}_e \times \mathbf{B}) \cdot \mathbf{E}^* f_1 \\ + \frac{e}{m_e c_e} & [(\mathbf{c}_e \times \mathbf{B}) \cdot \mathbf{c}_e][(\mathbf{B} \times \mathbf{E}^*) \cdot \mathbf{c}_e] h_1' + \frac{e}{m_e} (\mathbf{c}_e \times \mathbf{B}) \cdot (\mathbf{B} \times \mathbf{E}^*) h_1 \Bigg\} \end{aligned} \tag{5.14}$$

Next, (5.14) is simplified as follows: In (5.14), the fifth, sixth, seventh, and ninth terms are zero because $\mathbf{A} \times \mathbf{B} \cdot \mathbf{A} = 0$. The eighth term can be rearranged as follows:

$$\frac{e}{m_e} \mathbf{c}_e \times \mathbf{B} \cdot \mathbf{E}^* f_1 = \frac{e}{m_e} (\mathbf{B} \times \mathbf{E}^*) \cdot \mathbf{c}_e f_1 \tag{a}$$

The second term of (5.14) contains $(\mathbf{E}^* \cdot \mathbf{c}_e)^2$, which can be rearranged to contain the scalar product of the traceless dyadics and a scalar:

$$(\mathbf{E}^* \cdot \mathbf{c}_e)^2 = (\mathbf{E}^{*\circ}\mathbf{E}^*):(\mathbf{c}_e{}^\circ\mathbf{c}_e) + \tfrac{1}{3}E^{*2}c_e{}^2 \tag{b}$$

Finally, the scalar product in the last term of (5.14) can be rearranged as follows:

$$\begin{aligned}(\mathbf{c}_e \times \mathbf{B}) \cdot (\mathbf{B} \times \mathbf{E}^*) &= [\mathbf{B} \times (\mathbf{B} \times \mathbf{E})] \cdot \mathbf{c}_e \\ &= -(\mathbf{E}^* \cdot \mathbf{c}_e)B^2 + \mathbf{B}(\mathbf{B} \cdot \mathbf{E}^*) \cdot \mathbf{c}_e \end{aligned} \tag{c}$$

However, it was assumed that $(\mathbf{B} \cdot \mathbf{E}^*) = 0$. With the use of (*a*) to (*c*), (5.14) can be rearranged as follows:

$$\begin{aligned} -\frac{e}{m_e}\Bigg\{\frac{e}{m_e} E^{*2}(f_1 + \tfrac{1}{3}c_e f_1') &+ (\mathbf{E}^* \cdot \mathbf{c}_e)\left(c_e{}^{-1}f_0' - \frac{e}{m_e} B^2 h_1\right) \\ &+ \frac{e}{m_e}(\mathbf{B} \times \mathbf{E}^*) \cdot \mathbf{c}_e f_1 + \frac{e}{m_e c_e}(\mathbf{E}^{*\circ}\mathbf{E}^*):(\mathbf{c}_e{}^\circ\mathbf{c}_e)f_1' \\ &+ \frac{e}{m_e c_e}(\mathbf{E}^* \cdot \mathbf{c}_e)[(\mathbf{B} \times \mathbf{E}^*) \cdot \mathbf{c}_e]h_1'\Bigg\} \end{aligned} \tag{5.15}$$

The last two terms in (5.15) are of higher order and will be neglected. Equation (5.15) is the desired left side of Boltzmann's equation.

We obtain the right side of Boltzmann's equation by substitution of (5.7) into (5.6) as follows:

$$\begin{aligned} \left(\frac{\partial f_e}{\partial t}\right)_c = \iiint \Bigg\{ f_s(c_s')\left[f_0(c_e') + \frac{e}{m_e}(\mathbf{E}^* \cdot \mathbf{c}_e')f_1(c_e')\right. \\ \left. + \frac{e}{m_e}(\mathbf{B} \times \mathbf{E}^*) \cdot \mathbf{c}_e' h_1(c_e')\right] - f_s(c_s)\left[f_0(c_e) + \frac{e}{m_e}(\mathbf{E}^* \cdot \mathbf{c}_e)f_1(c_e)\right. \\ \left. + \frac{e}{m_e}(\mathbf{B} \times \mathbf{E}^*) \cdot \mathbf{c}_e h_1(c_e)\right]\Bigg\}\, gb\, db\, d\epsilon\, d\mathbf{c}_s \end{aligned} \tag{5.16}$$

Because (5.16) is linear in f_s, the terms with the desired coefficients appear very simply. Next, terms with like coefficients from (5.15) and (5.16) are equated, to obtain the following three equations for f_0, f_1, and h_1:

$$-\left(\frac{eE^*}{m_e}\right)^2(f_1 + \tfrac{1}{3}c_e f_1') = \iiint [f_s(c_s')f_0(c_e') - f_s(c_s)f_0(c_e)]gb\, db\, d\epsilon\, d\mathbf{c}_s \tag{5.17}$$

$$\begin{aligned} -\frac{e}{m_e c_e}(\mathbf{E}^* \cdot \mathbf{c}_e)\left(f_0' - \frac{ec_e}{m_e}B^2 h_1\right) = \frac{e}{m_e}\iiint [(\mathbf{E}^* \cdot \mathbf{c}_e')f_s(c_s')f_1(c_e') \\ - (\mathbf{E}^* \cdot \mathbf{c}_e)f_s(c_s)f_1(c_e)]gb\, db\, d\epsilon\, d\mathbf{c}_s \end{aligned} \tag{5.18}$$

$$\begin{aligned} -\left(\frac{e}{m_e}\right)^2(\mathbf{B} \times \mathbf{E}^*) \cdot \mathbf{c}_e f_1 = \frac{e}{m_e}\iiint [(\mathbf{B} \times \mathbf{E}^* \cdot \mathbf{c}_e')f_s(c_s')h_1(c_e') \\ - (\mathbf{B} \times \mathbf{E}^* \cdot \mathbf{c}_e)f_s(c_s)h_1(c_e)]gb\, db\, d\epsilon\, d\mathbf{c}_s \end{aligned} \tag{5.19}$$

Equations (5.17) to (5.19) constitute three coupled equations which are to be solved for the three unknowns, f_0, f_1, and h_1. First, the integrals on the right side must be evaluated. Consider (5.18), which is the simplest of the three equations. The thermal velocities of the electrons are much larger than those of the heavy particles, hence, in accordance with the Lorentz approximation, the relative velocity is essentially the electron velocity; thus $g = c_e$. Also, the heavy-particle velocity is essentially unchanged during a collision with an electron; thus $c_s' = c_s$. The magnitude of the electron velocity also is changed only slightly during a collision, so that $c_e' = c_e$. The major contribution to the integral of (5.18) comes from the change in *direction* of the electron velocity, $\mathbf{c}_e - \mathbf{c}_e'$. Thus, (5.18) becomes

$$-\mathbf{E}^* \cdot \left(\frac{\mathbf{c}_e}{c_e}\right)\left(f_0' - \frac{ec_e}{m_e} B^2 h_1\right) = -\mathbf{E}^* \cdot \int f_s \, d\mathbf{c}_s \int (\mathbf{c}_e - \mathbf{c}_e') f_1 c_e b \, db \, d\epsilon \quad (5.20)$$

Note that $\int f_s \, d\mathbf{c}_s = n_s$. To evaluate $\mathbf{c}_e'$, we must calculate the velocity after a collision with an s particle (see Fig. 5.2). Consider x, y, z coordinates where x is parallel to $\mathbf{c}_e$. Also, in the plane of the collision, let χ be the angle between $\mathbf{c}_e$ and $\mathbf{c}_e'$. Thus, neglecting motion of the s particle during the collision,

$$\begin{aligned} \mathbf{c}_e' &= \mathbf{i} c_e \cos \chi + \mathbf{j} c_e \sin \chi \cos \epsilon + \mathbf{k} c_e \sin \chi \sin \epsilon \\ &= \mathbf{c}_e \cos \chi + \mathbf{j} c_e \sin \chi \cos \epsilon + \mathbf{k} c_e \sin \chi \sin \epsilon \end{aligned} \quad (5.21)$$

With the use of (5.21), the second integral in (5.20) becomes

$$f_1 c_e \mathbf{c}_e \int_0^\infty (1 - \cos \chi) b \, db \int_0^{2\pi} d\epsilon - \mathbf{j} \int f_1 c_e^2 \sin \chi \, b \, db \int_0^{2\pi} \cos \epsilon \, d\epsilon - \mathbf{k} \int f_1 c_e^2 \sin \chi \int_0^{2\pi} \sin \epsilon \, d\epsilon$$

The last two terms are zero, while the integral in the first term becomes

$$\int_0^\infty \int_0^{2\pi} (1 - \cos \chi) b \, db \, d\epsilon \equiv Q_{es} \quad (5.22)$$

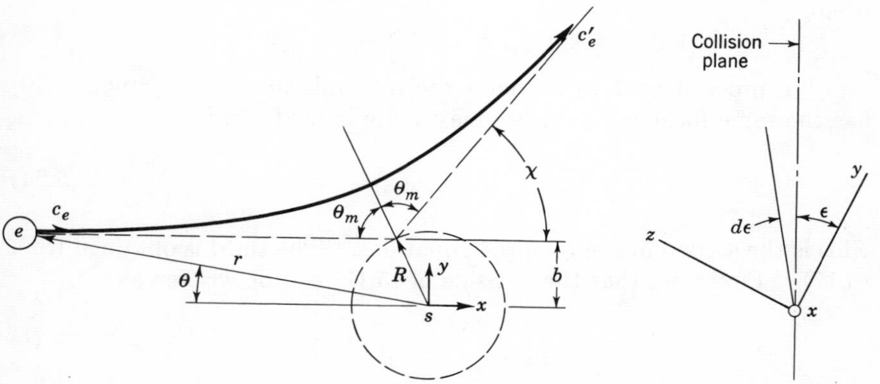

FIGURE 5.2 Geometry of a collision between an electron and a heavy particle.

This integral has a simple interpretation. Suppose that the electron and heavy particle were both elastic hard spheres. Then the electron would move in a straight line before and after collision, so that it would follow the asymptotic lines in Fig. 5.1. The distance of closest approach R would then be the sum of the radii of the two particles. The value of R is independent of θ, but may be a function of c_e. For a given value of c_e, the parameter b is

$$b = R \cos \theta \tag{d}$$

Hence,

$$db = -R \sin \theta \, d\theta \tag{e}$$

where $0 < \theta < \pi/2$. Also, $1 - \cos \chi = 2 \cos^2 \theta$. Substitution of (d) and (e) into (5.22) yields

$$\int\int (1 - \cos \chi) b \, db \, d\epsilon = \pi R^2 = Q_{es} \tag{f}$$

where Q_{es} is the classical collision cross section for hard-sphere electrons and particles. Note also that Q_{es} may be a function of c_e. Because of this simple interpretation, the integral in (f) will be designated Q_{es} in the succeeding derivations, but it is understood that Q_{es} will be calculated by means of (f). Finally, it is noted that this cross section, as defined by (f), applies only to the diffusion process under consideration.†

After substitution of (f) into (5.20) and elimination of the common factor, $\mathbf{E}^* \cdot \mathbf{c}_e$, (5.20) becomes

$$f_0' - \frac{ec_e}{m_e} B^2 h_1 = n_s c_e^2 Q_{es} f_1 \tag{g}$$

Finally, note that the collision frequency is $\nu_{es} = n_s c_e Q_{es}$. Thus, (g) becomes

$$f_0' - \frac{ec_e}{m_e} B^2 h_1 = \nu_{es}(c_e) f_1 c_e \tag{5.23}$$

where

$$\nu_{es}(c_e) = c_e n_s Q_{es} \equiv c_e n_s \int (1 - \cos \chi) b \, db \, d\epsilon$$

We proceed next to evaluate the integrals in (5.19). Since (5.19) has the same form as (5.18), we may write immediately

$$\frac{e}{m_e} f_1 = \nu_e(c_e) h_1 \tag{5.24}$$

This is the second of the required equations. The third is obtained from (5.17). First note that the left side of (5.17) can be written as

$$-\frac{1}{3} \left(\frac{eE^*}{m_e} \right)^2 c_e^{-2} \frac{d}{dc_e} (c_e^3 f_1) \tag{h}$$

† Cross sections for other processes are given in ref. 19, p. 525.

Because of this simple form, one should try to multiply (5.17) by $4\pi c_e^2\, dc_e \equiv d\mathbf{c}_e$ and integrate from zero to some velocity, say c_e^*. Then (5.17) becomes

$$-\frac{4\pi}{3}\left(\frac{eE^*}{m_e}\right)^2 c_e^{*3} f_1(c_e^*)$$
$$= \iint_0^{c_e*} f_s(c_s')f_0(c_e')gb\, db\, d\epsilon\, d\mathbf{c}_s\, d\mathbf{c}_e - \iint_0^{c_e*} f_s(c_s)f_0(c_e)gb\, db\, d\epsilon\, d\mathbf{c}_s\, d\mathbf{c}_e \quad (i)$$

In the first integral, when the electron velocity is c_e, the argument of f_0 is c_e', which differs from c_e by Δc_e, the change in c_e during a collision. Thus, integration with respect to c_e' is between the limits of 0 and $c_e'^*$. The lower limit remains zero, because the electron velocity having zero velocity will still have zero velocity after a collision with a heavy particle, neglecting the heavy-particle thermal motion. As before, we take $f_s(c_s') \approx f_s(c_s)$. Then the integrals in (i) become

$$\int_0^\infty f_s\, d\mathbf{c}_s \left[\int_0^{c_e*'} f_0(c_e)gb\, db\, d\epsilon\, d\mathbf{c}_e - \int_0^{c_e*} f_0(c_e)gb\, db\, d\epsilon\, d\mathbf{c}_e\right] \quad (j)$$

In (j), the electron velocities are dummies of integration, and the two integrals can be combined:

$$\int f_s\, d\mathbf{c}_s \int_{c_e*}^{c_e*'} f_0(c_e)gb\, db\, d\epsilon\, d\mathbf{c}_e \quad (k)$$

Next, $\Delta c_e \equiv c_e' - c_e$ must be calculated. In this calculation, the thermal motion of the heavy particle must be taken into account (see Fig. 5.3).

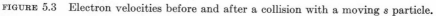

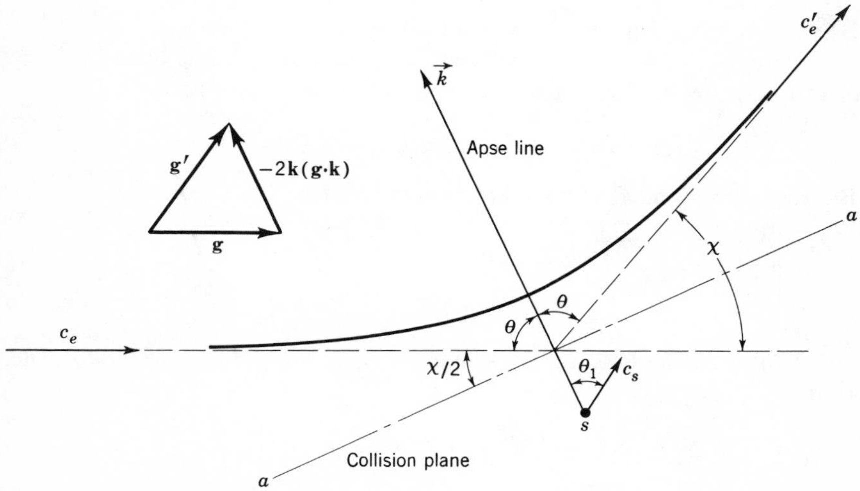

FIGURE 5.3 Electron velocities before and after a collision with a moving s particle.

We will assume that the mass of the heavy particle is so large that the collision of the electron with it will not change the velocity of the heavy particle; that is, $\mathbf{c}_s' = \mathbf{c}_s$. On the other hand, the thermal motion of the heavy particle will impart a change in the electron speed Δc_e. To obtain Δc_e, it is convenient to transform to coordinates which move with the heavy particle; this is accomplished by use of the relative velocities. The relative velocities before and after a collision are given by

$$\mathbf{g} = \mathbf{c}_e - \mathbf{c}_s \qquad \mathbf{g}' = \mathbf{c}_e' - \mathbf{c}_s \tag{l}$$

Then the relative velocities before and after the collision are given by

$$\mathbf{g}' = \mathbf{g} + 2\mathbf{k}g \sin\left(\tfrac{1}{2}\chi\right) = \mathbf{g} - 2(\mathbf{k} \cdot \mathbf{g})\mathbf{k} \tag{m}$$

where $\mathbf{k}$ is a unit vector is the direction of the apse line. From (l),

$$\mathbf{c}_e' = \mathbf{g}' + \mathbf{c}_s$$

Substitution of $\mathbf{g}'$ from (m) and $\mathbf{g}$ from (l) yields

$$\mathbf{c}_e' = \mathbf{c}_e - 2(\mathbf{k} \cdot \mathbf{c}_e)\mathbf{k} + 2(\mathbf{k} \cdot \mathbf{c}_s)\mathbf{k}$$

The above equation is next squared, and the term containing c_s^2 is neglected:

$$c_e'^2 \cong c_e^2 - 4(\mathbf{k} \cdot \mathbf{c}_e)(\mathbf{k} \cdot \mathbf{c}_s) \tag{n}$$

Upon taking the square root of (n), letting $\mathbf{k} \cdot \mathbf{c}_e \approx \sin\left(\frac{1}{2}\chi\right)$, and neglecting higher-order terms, one obtains

$$\Delta c_e \equiv c_e' - c_e = 2 \sin\left(\tfrac{1}{2}\chi\right)(\mathbf{c}_s \cdot \mathbf{k}) \tag{o}$$

Because $c_s \ll c_e$, Eq. (o) states that $\Delta c_e \ll c_e$.

Because Δc_e is so small, we may assume that $f_0(c_e)$ is linear between c_e and $c_e + \Delta c_e$, and accordingly expand f_0 in a Taylor series:

$$f_0(c_e) = f_0(c_e^*) + (c_e - c_e^*)f_0'(c_e^*) \tag{p}$$

Because $f_0(c_e^*)$ and $f_0'(c_e^*)$ are not functions of c_e, (k) becomes

$$f_0(c_e^*) \int f_s \, d\mathbf{c}_s \int_{c_e^*}^{c_e^*+\Delta c_e} gb \, db \, d\epsilon \, d\mathbf{c}_e + f_0'(c_e^*) \int f_s \, d\mathbf{c}_s \int_{c_e^*}^{c_e^*+\Delta c_e} gb \, db \, d\epsilon \, d\mathbf{c}_e \tag{q}$$

In the second integral of (q), let $g = c_e$ as before, and $d\mathbf{c}_e = 4\pi c_e^2 \, dc_e$; thus the integral becomes

$$4\pi f_0'(c_e^*) \int f_s \, d\mathbf{c}_s b \, db \, d\epsilon \int_{c_e^*}^{c_e^*+\Delta c_e} (c_e - c_e^*)c_e^3 \, dc_e = 2\pi(c_e^*)^3 f_0'(c_e^*) \int (\Delta c_e)^2 f_s b \, db \, d\epsilon \, d\mathbf{c}_s \tag{r}$$

Next, we may substitute Δc_e from (o), noting that $\mathbf{c}_s \cdot \mathbf{k} = c_s \cos \theta_1$. Also, $d\mathbf{c}_s = 2\pi \sin \theta_1 \, d\theta_1 c_s^2 \, dc_s$. Thus, (r) becomes

$$4\pi c_e^{*3} f_0'(c_e^*) \int 2 \sin^2 (\tfrac{1}{2}\chi) b \, db \, d\epsilon \cdot 2\pi \int f_s c_s^4 \cos^2 \theta_1 \sin \theta_1 \, dc_s \, d\theta_1 \qquad (s)$$

The last integral in (s) may be integrated over θ_1 from 0 to π, and becomes

$$2\pi \int_0^\infty \int_0^\pi f_s c_s^4 \cos^2 \theta_1 \sin \theta_1 \, dc_s \, d\theta_1 = \frac{kT_s}{m_s} \qquad (t)$$

Since $2 \sin^2 (\frac{1}{2}\chi) = 1 - \cos \chi$, the first integral in (s) is just the cross section Q_{es}. If we make use of (o), (s), and (t), then (i) becomes

$$-\tfrac{4}{3}\pi \left(\frac{eE^*}{m_e}\right)^2 c_e^{*3} f_1(c_e^*)$$
$$= f_0(c_e^*) \int_{c_e^*}^{c_e^*+\Delta c_e} f_s g b \, db \, d\epsilon \, dc_s \, dc_e + 4\pi \frac{kT_s}{m_s} c_e^{*3} f_0'(c_e^*) Q_{es} n_s \qquad (u)$$

Finally, the integral in the first term of (u) must be evaluated. To do this correctly requires the smaller terms of (n). However, the integral can be evaluated by a simpler method. When the electric field vanishes, the distribution function of electrons must become maxwellian, so that $f_e = f_0 =$ maxwellian; and $f_0'(c_e) = -f_0 m_e c_e / kT_s$, since the electron temperature will be equal to the gas temperature. Also, the integral in (u) is independent of E^*, so that when $E^* = 0$, the right side of (u) must be zero. With $\nu_{es} \equiv c_e n_s Q_{es}$, the integral becomes

$$\int_{c_e^*}^{c_e^*+\Delta c_e} f_s g b \, db \, d\epsilon \, dc_s \, dc_e = 4\pi c_e^{*3} \frac{m_e}{m_s} \nu_{es}(c_e^*) \qquad (v)$$

The integral is the same for finite E^*; thus (u) becomes

$$-\frac{1}{3}\left(\frac{eE^*}{m_e}\right)^2 f_1(c_e) = \frac{m_e}{m_s} \nu_{es}(c_e) f_0 + \frac{kT_s}{c_e m_s} \nu_{es}(c_e) f_0' \qquad (5.25)$$

Equations (5.23) to (5.25) are simpler to evaluate than (5.17) to (5.19). But it is first desirable to rearrange these equations. From (5.24),

$$h_1 = \frac{e}{m_e \nu_{es}} f_1 \qquad (5.26)$$

so that (5.23) becomes

$$f_1 = \frac{\nu_{es}}{c_e(\omega_e^2 + \nu_{es}^2)} \frac{df_0}{dc_e} \qquad (5.27)$$

where $\omega_e = eB/m_e$. Substitution of (5.27) into (5.26) yields

$$h_1 = \frac{e}{m_e c_e(\omega_e^2 + \nu_{es}^2)} \frac{df_0}{dc_e} \qquad (5.28)$$

Finally, substitution of (5.27) into (5.25) yields

$$-\left[\frac{1}{3}\left(\frac{eE^*}{m_e}\right)^2 \frac{1}{\omega_e{}^2 + \nu_{es}^2} + \frac{kT_s}{m_s}\right]\frac{df_0}{dc_e} = \frac{m_e}{m_s}\, c_e f_0(c_e) \tag{5.29}$$

Equations (5.27) to (5.29) describe the distribution function f_e within the Lorentz approximation. Actually, it is only necessary to determine f_0, since f_1 and h_1 follow immediately with the use of (5.29). The combination of (5.27) to (5.29) with (5.7) yields the following expression for f_e:

$$f_e = f_0 \left\{1 - \frac{e\nu_{es}\mathbf{E}^* \cdot \mathbf{c}_e + e\omega_e \mathbf{B} \times \mathbf{E}^* \cdot \mathbf{c}_e/B}{kT_s[(m_s/3kT_s)(eE^*/m_e)^2 + \omega_e{}^2 + \nu_{es}^2]}\right\} \tag{5.30}$$

To obtain f_0, (5.29) must be integrated, but this requires the function $\nu_{es}(c_e)$, which can be obtained only by knowledge of the cross section $Q_{es}(c_e) = \int\int (1 - \cos\chi) b\, db\, d\epsilon$.

In the formulation of the collision term in Boltzmann's equation, two effects were neglected by considering only binary *elastic* collisions. The first effect is that some collisions are *inelastic;* that is, some of the electron kinetic energy is converted into rotational, vibrational, or electronic excitation of the heavy particle, which is then interchanged with other heavy particles during a subsequent collision, or is discharged as radiation. The second effect is ionizing collisions by electrons, in which an electron interacts with an atom, molecule, or ion so that an additional electron is produced. In this case, neither the kinetic energy nor the momentum of the incident electron and heavy particle is preserved. To include this effect, additional terms are required for $(\partial f/\partial t)_c$.[7]

Fortunately, the excitation and ionization cross sections for most particles are much smaller than the cross section for elastic collisions, and these two effects change the distribution function only slightly. The net effect on the electrical conductivity of the gas is therefore small, but the effect on the electron temperature is large. This latter effect will be discussed in Sec. 5.5.

5.4 COLLISION CROSS SECTIONS

Most knowledge of the collision cross section for atoms and molecules comes from experiments; the collision integrals are actually used to deduce the force law from the experimental data rather than vice versa. Some typical cross sections for the elastic scattering of electrons are shown in Fig. 5.4, and the interparticle force law is quite complex. However, for two particles, namely, the simply polarizable particle and the ion, the force law is quite simple, and it is instructive to determine Q_{es} from (5.22). We will make this slightly more general by using an inverse-power-force law.[5] Since this law is spherically symmetric, (5.22) may be integrated

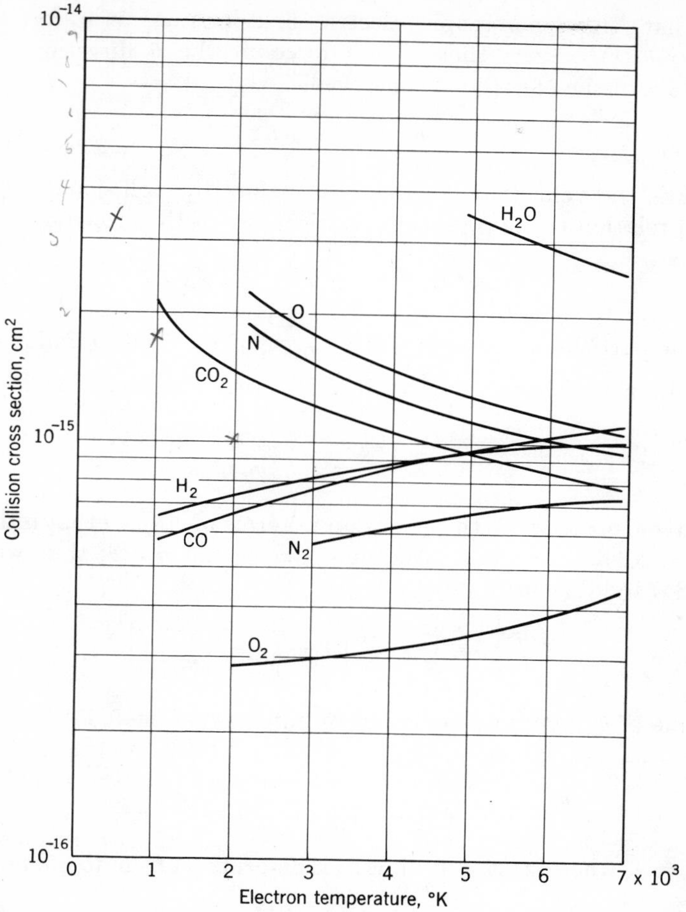

FIGURE 5.4 Collision cross sections for some atoms and molecules. (Data compiled by W. Chinitz, L. Eisen, and R. Gross, *ARS Preprint* 706-58.)

over the azimuthal angle ϵ from 0 to 2π to obtain

$$Q_{es} = 2\pi \int_0^\infty (1 - \cos \chi) b \, db \tag{5.31}$$

To obtain Q_{es}, it is necessary to determine the scattering angle $\chi(b)$, which is related to the polar angle θ_m as follows (see Fig. 5.2):

$$\chi = \pi - 2\theta_m(b)$$

where θ_m is the angle to the point r_m which is the closest approach distance; that is, θ_m is the angle to the apse line. To obtain θ_m we will assume only that the force field of the s particle is central and is much larger than the macroscopic electric field or magnetic forces; thus $\mathbf{F}_e = (\mathbf{r}/r)F_e(r)$. Since there is no force in the θ direction, angular momentum of the electron is conserved,

$$m_e r^2 \dot{\theta} = m_e c_e b \tag{5.32}$$

where c_e is the velocity of the electron before the collision. The other required relation is the conservation of energy of the electron,

$$\tfrac{1}{2}m_e(\dot{r}^2 + r^2\dot{\theta}^2) + u(r) = \tfrac{1}{2}m_e c_e^2 \tag{5.33}$$

where the particle potential is $u(r) = \int_0^\infty F(r)\,dr$. The angular velocity can be eliminated from (5.33) with (5.32); rearrangement yields

$$\frac{\dot{r}^2}{c_e^2} = 1 - \frac{b^2}{r^2} - \frac{u(r)}{\frac{1}{2}m_e c_e^2} \tag{5.34}$$

It is convenient to write this equation in terms of $r(\theta)$, so that integration will yield θ_m and hence χ. We note that $dr/d\theta = \dot{r}/\dot{\theta}$; thus we divide Eq. (5.34) by $\dot{\theta}^2$ from (5.32):

$$\left(\frac{dr}{d\theta}\right)^2 \equiv \frac{\dot{r}^2}{\dot{\theta}^2} = \frac{r^4}{b^2}\left[1 - \frac{b^2}{r^2} - \frac{u(r)}{\frac{1}{2}m_e c_e^2}\right] \tag{5.35}$$

The value of θ_m may now be found by integration of (5.35) from $r = \infty$ to $r = r_{\min}$:

$$\theta_m = \int_{r_m}^\infty \frac{b\,dr}{r^2[1 - (b^2/r^2) - u(r)/\frac{1}{2}m_e c_e^2]^{\frac{1}{2}}} \tag{5.36}$$

Now, $r = r_m$ when $dr/d\theta = 0$, thus r_m is determined from (5.35) as follows:

$$1 - \left(\frac{b}{r_m}\right)^2 - \frac{u(r_m)}{\frac{1}{2}m_e c_e^2} = 0 \tag{5.37}$$

Comparison with (5.36) shows that the integration starts when the denominator of the integrand is zero.

5.4.1 Inverse-power-force Law. To proceed further, $u(r)$ must be known. We shall select a simple force law between the electron and heavy particle as follows:

$$F_{es} = \alpha_{es} r^{-s} \tag{5.38}$$

where α_{es} is a constant of proportionality. When $s = 5$, the force law corresponds to a simple polarizable particle; this may be demonstrated as follows: Assume that the distance of separation of the negative-charge centroid from the positive-charge centroid varies directly as the local electric field due to the electron, and is collinear with the distance to the electron. Then the separation distance d is given as follows, where α is the constant of proportionality:

$$d = -\alpha E = \frac{\alpha e}{4\pi K_0 r^2} \tag{a}$$

The force on the electron due to the separated charges of the polarizable particle is

$$F_{es} = -\frac{e^2 Z}{4\pi K_0 (r - \frac{1}{2}d)^2} + \frac{e^2 Z}{4\pi K_0 (r + \frac{1}{2}d)^2} \tag{b}$$

where eZ is the separated charge. With $d \ll r$, the denominators in (b) may be expanded, from which

$$F_{es} = -\frac{Ze^2 d}{2\pi K_0 r^3} \tag{c}$$

Substitution of (a) for d yields

$$F_{es} = -\frac{2\alpha e^3 Z}{(4\pi K_0)^2 r^5} \tag{5.39}$$

Later it will be shown that the inverse fifth law possesses some unique properties. Finally, the hard-sphere interaction may be obtained by letting $\alpha_{es} = R_{es}^s$, substituting into (5.38), and letting $s \to \infty$. Thus, when the separation distance r is greater than R_{es}, the force on the electron is zero; but when $r < R_{es}$, the force is infinite.

From (5.38), the interparticle potential is

$$u(r) = \int_r^\infty F(r)\, dr = \frac{\alpha_{es} r^{1-s}}{s-1} \tag{5.40}$$

Substitution of (5.40) into (5.36) yields

$$\theta_m = -\int_\infty^{r_m} \left[\frac{r^4}{b^2} - r^2 \mp \frac{|\alpha_{es}| r^{5-s}}{\frac{1}{2} m_e c_e^2 (s-1) b^2}\right]^{-\frac{1}{2}} dr \tag{5.41}$$

where the $-$ sign applies if α_{es} is positive; e.g., the force on the electron is repulsive; and the $+$ sign is to be used if the force is attractive. Equation (5.41) can be simplified by the following change of variables:

$$\frac{r}{b} = \frac{1}{\beta} \tag{5.42}$$

Hence

$$d\left(\frac{r}{b}\right) = -\frac{d\beta}{\beta^2} \tag{5.43}$$

Also let

$$\beta_0 = b\left(\frac{m_e c_e^2}{|\alpha_{es}|}\right)^{1/(s-1)} \tag{5.44}$$

Then from (5.41) the deflection angle becomes

$$\chi = \pi + 2 \int_0^{\beta_m} \left[1 - \beta^2 \mp \frac{2}{s-1} \left(\frac{\beta}{\beta_0} \right)^{s-1} \right]^{-\frac{1}{2}} d\beta \tag{5.45}$$

Corresponding to the upper limit of integration, β_m is obtained from (5.37):

$$1 - \beta_m{}^2 \mp \frac{2}{s-1} \left(\frac{\beta_m}{\beta_0} \right)^{s-1} = 0 \tag{5.46}$$

From (5.44) to (5.46) it is seen that χ is a function only of β_0. Substitution of (5.44) into (5.31) yields

$$\begin{aligned} Q_{es}(c_e) &= 2\pi \left(\frac{m_e c_e{}^2}{|\alpha_{es}|} \right)^{2/(1-s)} \int_0^\infty [1 - \cos \chi(\beta_0)] \beta_0 \, d\beta_0 \\ &= 2\pi c_e{}^{-4/(s-1)} \left(\frac{|\alpha_{es}|}{m_e} \right)^{2/(s-1)} \int_0^\infty [1 - \cos \chi(\beta_0)] \beta_0 \, d\beta_0 \end{aligned} \tag{5.47}$$

The integral in (5.47) is a function only of s; it may be designated $A_1(s)$:

$$A_1(s) = \int_0^\infty [1 - \cos \chi(\beta_0)] \beta_0 \, d\beta_0 \tag{5.48}$$

Some typical values are shown below, for repulsive forces.[6]

s	$A_1(s)$
5	0.422
7	0.385
∞	0.500

Note that the velocity dependence of the cross section is given explicitly by (5.47); for example, for unshielded ions, $s = 2$, and the cross section varies inversely with the fourth power of the electron velocity. For $s = 5$, $Q_{es} \propto c_e{}^{-1}$, so that the collision frequency for electrons is independent of electron velocity. For hard spheres, $\alpha_{es} = r_0{}^s$ and $s \to \infty$, so that $Q_{e\infty} = \pi r_0{}^2$.

5.4.2 Inverse-square Law. For collisions of electrons with ions, the evaluation of A_1 is not so simple. In this case, $\alpha_{eI} = -e^2 Z_I (4\pi K_0)^{-1}$ with $s = 2$. From (5.45), the deflection angle is

$$\chi = \pi - 2 \int_0^{\beta_m} \left(1 - \beta^2 + 2 \frac{\beta}{\beta_0} \right)^{-\frac{1}{2}} d\beta \tag{5.49}$$

which integrates to

$$\chi = \pi - 2 \sin^{-1} \left[\frac{-\beta_0 \beta + 1}{(1 + \beta_0{}^2)^{\frac{1}{2}}} \right]_0^{\beta_m} \tag{5.50}$$

while the value of β_m from (5.46) is

$$\beta_m = \beta_0{}^{-1} \pm (\beta_0{}^{-2} + 1)^{\frac{1}{2}} \tag{5.51}$$

The upper limit of integration yields $\pi/2$, while the lower limit is $\sin^{-1}(1 + \beta_0^2)^{-\frac{1}{2}}$. The deflection angle obtained from (5.50) is then

$$\chi = 2 \sin^{-1}(1 + \beta_0^2)^{-\frac{1}{2}} \tag{5.52}$$

The value of $A_1(2)$ is next obtained from (5.48):

$$A_1(2) = \int \sin^2(\tfrac{1}{2}\chi)\, d(\beta_0^2) = \int_0^\infty \frac{d(\beta_0^2)}{1 + \beta_0^2} = \ln(1 + \beta_0^2)\Big]_0^\infty \tag{5.53}$$

If the upper limit of integration of (5.53) is taken as ∞, $A_1(2)$ diverges, which indicates that the cross section for a single ion is *infinite*. This dilemma may be resolved by noting that the potential about an ion in a plasma is shielded by the electrons which are attracted to its vicinity, as was shown in Sec. 4.13. The electric field potential near an ion with charge Z_I previously given by (4.124) may be generalized as follows for a gas which contains various species of ions, each with charge Z_s,

$$\phi = \frac{eZ_I}{4\pi K_0 r} e^{-\sqrt{2}\, r/d} \tag{5.54a}$$

where the Debye length is now taken as

$$d = \sqrt{\frac{2kK_0T}{\sum_s n_s e^2 Z_s^2}} \tag{5.54b}$$

As a first approximation to the shielded potential, the force on the electron may be taken as coulombic for $r < d$, and zero for $r > d$,[6] as follows:

$$F_{eI} = \frac{e^2 Z_I}{4\pi K_0 r^2} \qquad r < d$$
$$= 0 \qquad r > d$$

Then, in Eq. (5.53), the upper limit of integration of the impact parameter is $b = d$; or in terms of β_0, the upper limit is

$$\beta_{0_{\max}} = \frac{4\pi\, d m_e c_e^2 K_0}{e^2 Z_I} \tag{5.55}$$

With (5.55), then (5.53) becomes

$$A_1(2) = 2 \ln \sqrt{1 + \beta_{0_{\max}}^2} \tag{5.56}$$

and the cross section (5.47) becomes

$$Q_{eI} = \frac{4\pi e^4 Z_I^2}{m_e^2 c_e^4 (4\pi K_0)^2} \ln \sqrt{1 + \beta_{0_{\max}}^2} \tag{5.57}$$

Equations (5.55) and (5.57) have a simple interpretation: The radius r at which the electron kinetic energy is equal to its kinetic energy is given by

$$\tfrac{1}{2} m_e c_e^2 = \frac{e^2 Z_I}{4\pi K_0 r} \tag{a}$$

Let this value of r be designated b^*, that is, an average collision-impact parameter:

$$b^* = \frac{e^2 Z_I}{2\pi K_0 m_e c_e^2} \tag{b}$$

Then, from (5.55),

$$\beta_{0_{\max}} = \frac{2d}{b^*} \tag{5.58}$$

With (5.58), the cross section of (5.57) becomes

$$Q_{eI} = \pi b^{*2} \ln \sqrt{1 + \left(\frac{2d}{b^*}\right)^2} \tag{5.59}$$

If one were to think of the radius of an ion as the minimum impact parameter given by (b), then the corresponding cross section πb^{*2} must be multiplied by the logarithmic term in (5.59) to account for the long-range interactions between the electron and ion.

For the above theory to be valid, the repulsive field around the ion must be coulombic for most collisions; that is, $d/b^* \gg 1$. Then (5.59) simplifies to

$$Q_{eI} = \pi b^{*2} \ln \frac{2d}{b^*} \tag{5.60}$$

As an alternative to the Debye length, it has also been postulated that the maximum impact parameter should be the average distance L between electrons;[8] that is, let $b_{\max} = L = n_e^{-\frac{1}{3}}$. However (for a singly ionized gas),

$$\frac{d}{b^*} = \frac{(K_0 kT/e^2 n_e)^{\frac{1}{2}}}{b^*}$$

which, when multiplied by $e(2\pi K_0 m_e c_e^2)^{-\frac{1}{2}} = b^{*\frac{1}{2}}$, becomes

$$\frac{d}{b^*} = \left(\frac{kT_e}{2\pi m_e c_e^2}\right)^{\frac{1}{2}} n_e^{-\frac{1}{2}} b^{*-\frac{1}{2}}$$

For the *average* electron temperature, $m_e c_e^2 = 3kT_e$, so that

$$\frac{d}{b^*} = (6\pi)^{-\frac{1}{2}} \left(\frac{L}{b^*}\right)^{\frac{3}{2}} \tag{c}$$

and

$$\ln \frac{d}{b^*} = \tfrac{3}{2} \ln \frac{L}{b^*} - \tfrac{1}{2} \ln 6\pi \tag{d}$$

Thus, the difference between d/b^* or L/b^* is only a factor of $\frac{3}{2}$ in A_1.

The Debye shielding theory is applicable when the number of electrons in a Debye sphere is large so that the fluctuations of the Debye potential are small. This criterion may be written as

$$\tfrac{4}{3}\pi n_e d^3 \gg 1 \tag{e}$$

Substitution of (5.54*b*) for d, elimination of T_e by letting $m_e c_e{}^2 = 3kT_e$, and use of b^* from (*b*) to eliminate $c_e{}^2$ yield

$$\tfrac{4}{3}\pi n_e d^3 = \frac{2}{9}\frac{d}{b^*} \gg 1 \tag{f}$$

Thus, the requirement that the number of electrons within a Debye sphere be large is identical to the requirement that $d/b^* \gg 1$. These requirements are usually satisfied in ionized gases.

Finally, it is necessary to determine whether the collisions of the electron with the ion and its shielded potential may be regarded as binary. This criterion is that the ratio of the electron mean free path to the Debye length should be large. First, note that

$$\frac{\lambda_e}{b^*} = \left(n_e b^{*3}\pi \ln \frac{2d}{b^*}\right)^{-1} = \left(\frac{L}{b^*}\right)^3 \left(\pi \ln \frac{2d}{b^*}\right)^{-1}$$

Use of (*c*) yields

$$\frac{\lambda_e}{b^*} = 6\left(\frac{d}{b^*}\right)^2 \left(\ln \frac{2d}{b^*}\right)^{-1}$$

so that

$$\frac{\lambda_e}{d} = \frac{6d/b^*}{\ln (2d/b^*)} \tag{g}$$

Thus, if $d/b^* \gg 1$, then λ_e/d will also be much larger than unity, and the binary approximation may be used.

5.5 ELECTRON TEMPERATURE—LORENTZ APPROXIMATION

If the moving electric field E^* is zero, then (5.29) reduces to

$$-\frac{df_0}{dc_e} = \frac{f_0 c_e m_e}{kT_s} \tag{5.61}$$

which integrates immediately to the maxwellian velocity distribution function as follows:

$$f_0 = a \exp\left(-\frac{m_e c_e{}^2}{2kT_s}\right) \tag{5.62}$$

This result is not unexpected since it was assumed that when $E^* \to 0$, the electron distribution function is maxwellian. Note that this can be true only if the heavy particles also have a maxwellian distribution. Thus, when $E^* \to 0$, then $T_e = T_s$, as expected.

When $E^* > 0$, then (5.29) can be integrated as follows:

$$f_0(c_e) = a \exp\left\{-\int_0^{c_e} \frac{m_e c_e dc_e}{k[T_s + (m_s/3k)(eE^*/m_e)^2/(\omega_e{}^2 + \nu_{es}^2)]}\right\} \tag{5.63}$$

Under three conditions the denominator of (5.63) is a constant, and the zero-order velocity distribution function is maxwellian, but not necessarily about temperature T_s. These conditions are:

(i) ν_{es} = const; that is, the electrons are scattered by "maxwellian molecules."

(ii) $\omega_e \gg \nu_{es}$. (5.64)

(iii) $$\frac{m_s}{3kT_s}\left(\frac{eE^*}{m_e}\right)^2 \frac{1}{\omega_e^2 + \nu_{es}^2} \ll 1. \tag{5.65}$$

For these three conditions, Eq. (5.63) may be integrated to

$$f_0(c_e) = a \exp\left\{-\frac{m_e c_e^2}{2k[T_s + (m_s/3k)(eE^*/m_e)^2/(\omega_e^2 + \nu_{es}^2)]}\right\} \tag{5.66}$$

It is convenient to define a new variable $T^*(c_e)$ as follows:

$$T^*(c_e) = T_s + \frac{m_s}{3k}\left(\frac{eE^*}{m_e}\right)^2 \frac{1}{\omega_e^2 + \nu_{es}^2} \tag{5.67}$$

When any of the three conditions is met, T^* is constant; and (5.66) becomes simply

$$f_0(c_e) = ae^{-m_e c_e^2/2kT^*} \tag{5.68}$$

The constants of integration a and T^* are also given by substitution of (5.66) into (5.30) and integration of the resulting expression by means of (4.3) and (4.7). The result is that

$$a = n_e\left(\frac{m_e}{2\pi kT^*}\right)^{\frac{3}{2}} \tag{5.69}$$

as before, while the electron temperature is identically equal to T^*; that is,

$$T_e \equiv T^* = T_s + \frac{m_s}{3k}\left(\frac{eE^*}{m_e}\right)^2 \frac{1}{\omega_e^2 + \nu_{es}^2} \tag{5.70}$$

for the three conditions given by (5.65). Thus, if the electric field is sufficiently large, the electron temperature exceeds the gas temperature. This is a common effect in glow discharges. The increase in electron temperature (for $B = \omega_e = 0$) can be understood from simple arguments. Consider a 90° collision of an electron with a heavy particle which is initially at rest (see Fig. 5.5). Conservation of energy and momentum yield respectively

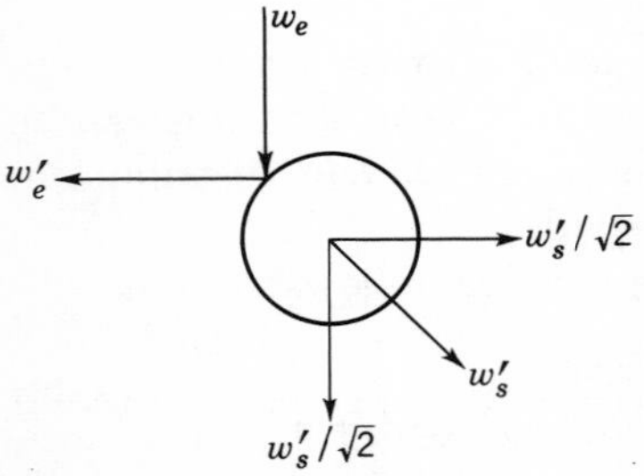

FIGURE 5.5 Collision of electron with heavy particles.

$$\tfrac{1}{2}m_e w_e^2 = \tfrac{1}{2}m_e w_e'^2 + \tfrac{1}{2}m_s w_s'^2 \tag{a}$$

$$m_e w_e = m_s w_s'/\sqrt{2} \tag{b}$$

Use of (*b*) to eliminate w'_s in (*a*) yields

$$\tfrac{1}{2}m_e w_e^2 - \tfrac{1}{2}m_e w_e'^2 = \frac{2m_e}{m_s}\frac{1}{2}m_e w_e^2 \tag{c}$$

Thus, the fraction of energy lost by the electron in one collision is twice the ratio of electron mass to heavy-particle mass. If the heavy particles have thermal energy, then (*c*) may be generalized as follows:

$$(\Delta\epsilon)_{\text{collision}} = \frac{2m_e}{m_s}\left(\tfrac{3}{2}kT_e - \tfrac{3}{2}kT_s\right) \tag{d}$$

On the other hand, the electron gains energy from the electric field equal to the distance it moves in the direction of the electric field: $\frac{1}{2}(eE/m_e)\tau^2$ times the force $-eE$ on the electron. In the steady state, these must be equal; thus,

$$\frac{1}{2}\frac{e^2E^2\tau^2}{m_e} = 3\frac{m_e}{m_s}k(T_e - T_s) \tag{e}$$

which agrees approximately with (5.70).

Of some historical interest is the Druyvesteyn distribution which is obtained from (5.63) by taking $T_s = \omega_e = 0$, and the cross section Q constant corresponding to $s \to \infty$. Then (5.63) becomes

$$f_0 = a \exp\left\{-3\left[m_s\left(\frac{eE}{m_e}\right)^2\lambda_e^2\right]^{-1}\int_0^{c_e} m_e c_e^3\, dc_e^2\right\}$$

where λ_e is the mean free path for electrons, equal to $(n_s Q_{es})^{-1}$, which is therefore also constant. This integrates to

$$f_0 = a \exp\left\{-\frac{3}{4}m_e c_e^4\left[m_s\left(\frac{eE}{m_e}\right)^2\lambda_e^2\right]^{-1}\right\} \tag{5.71}$$

The Druyvesteyn distribution predicts fewer electrons with high velocity than the maxwellian distribution corresponding to the same mean electron energy.[10]

For $T^*(c_e)$ given by (5.67), the complete electron distribution function, (5.30), can be written as

$$f_e = f_0\left(1 - \frac{e}{kT^*}\frac{\nu_{es}}{\omega_e^2 + \nu_{es}^2}\mathbf{E}^*\cdot\mathbf{c}_e - \frac{e}{kT^*}\frac{\omega_e}{\omega_e^2 + \nu_{es}^2}\frac{\mathbf{B}\times\mathbf{E}^*\cdot\mathbf{c}_e}{B}\right) \tag{5.72}$$

5.5.1 Effect of Inelastic Collisions. Equation (5.70) is approximately correct for heavy particles which are monatomic. For diatomic or polyatomic particles, (5.70) greatly overestimates the electron temperature, because electron collisions with these particles are not elastic; that is, some of the electron energy is absorbed by rotation or vibration of the molecule. Thus, the energy lost by an electron is not $2m_e/m_s$, but must be multiplied by a correction factor δ_s. Then (5.70) becomes

$$T_e \cong T_s + \frac{m_s}{3k\delta_s}\left(\frac{eE^*}{m_e}\right)^2 (\omega_e{}^2 + \nu_e{}^2)^{-1} \tag{5.73}$$

Figure 5.6 contains data on δ_s.

In experimental work the electron temperature is usually reported as a function of E/p, where p is the gas pressure. In terms of this parameter, (5.73) becomes

$$T_e \cong T_s \left[1 + \frac{\pi}{24\delta_s}\frac{T_s}{T_e}\frac{m_s}{m_e}\frac{e^2}{Q_{es}^2}\left(\frac{E}{p}\right)^2\right] \tag{5.74}$$

where Q_{es} is an average cross section at temperature T_e. If Q_{es} and δ_s are constant, (5.74) predicts that for small values of E/p, the electron tem-

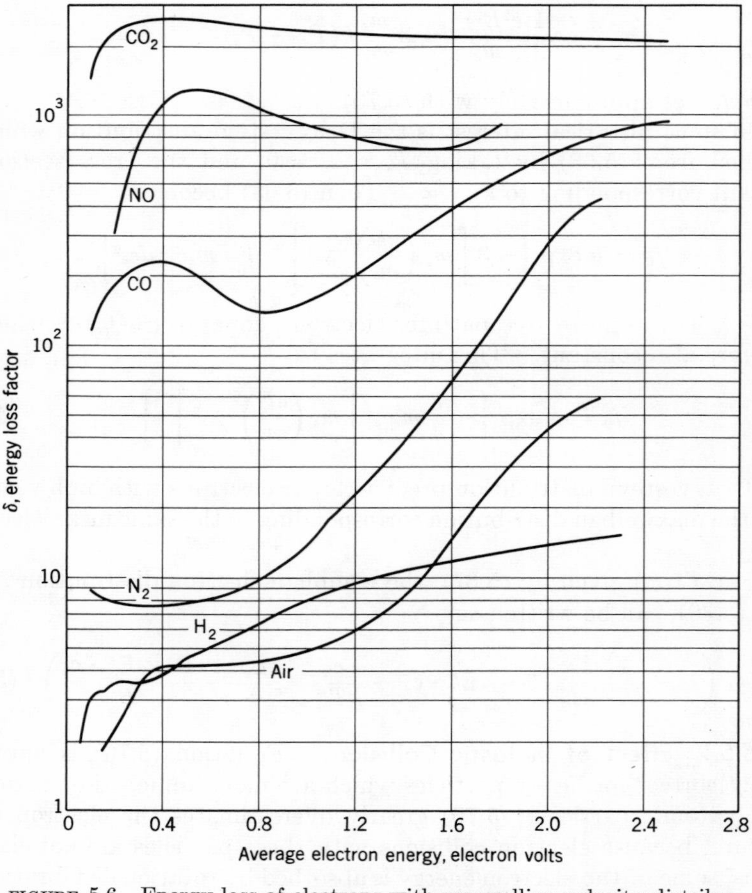

FIGURE 5.6 Energy loss of electrons with maxwellian velocity distribution with various gases. (Data compiled by H. Massey and J. D. Craggs, *Handbuch der Physik*, 37/1, pp. 314–415, 1959.)

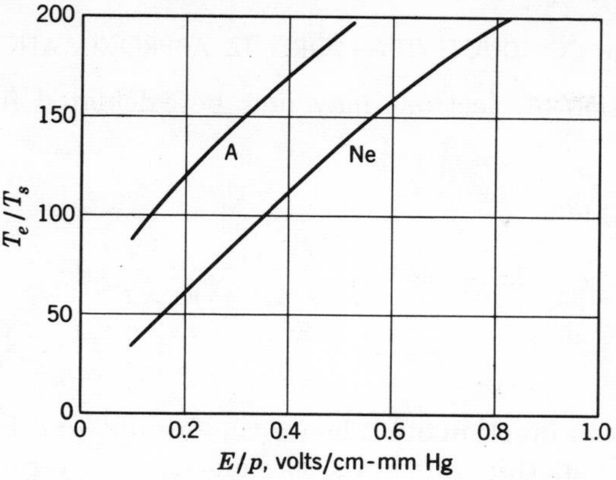

FIGURE 5.7 Electron temperature in argon and neon. (By permission from S. Brown, *Basic Data of Plasma Physics*, John Wiley & Sons, Inc., New York, 1959.)

perature increases quadratically with E/p, whereas at large electron temperatures, the electron temperature increases linearly with temperature. In actuality, neither δ nor Q_{es} is constant, so that (5.74) is only approximate. Note the extremely large differences in electron temperature between monatomic and diatomic gases (Figs. 5.7 and 5.8). These are caused by the large values of δ_s for diatomic gases (see Fig. 5.6).

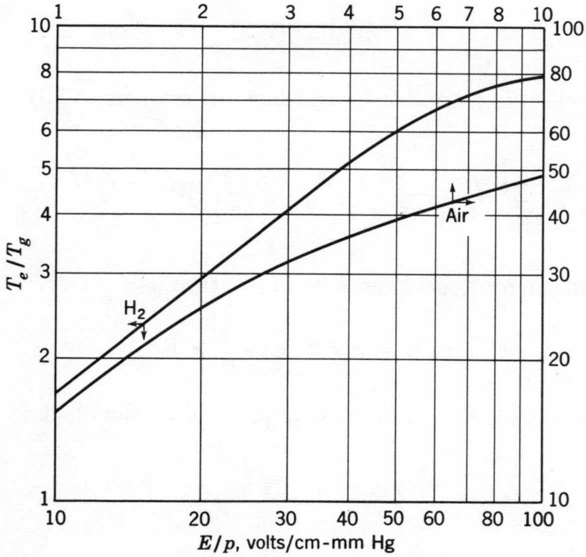

FIGURE 5.8 Electron temperature in hydrogen and air. (By permission from S. Brown, *Basic Data of Plasma Physics*, John Wiley & Sons, Inc., New York, 1959.)

5.6 ELECTRICAL CONDUCTIVITY—LORENTZ APPROXIMATION

The diffusion of electrons may now be calculated from (4.16) and (5.72):

$$\begin{aligned}\mathbf{V}_e &= n_e^{-1} \int \mathbf{c}_e f_e \, d\mathbf{c}_e \\ &= n_e^{-1} \left[\int_{-\infty}^{\infty} \mathbf{c}_e f_0 \, d\mathbf{c}_e - e\mathbf{E}^* \cdot \int_{-\infty}^{\infty} \frac{\mathbf{c}_e \mathbf{c}_e \nu_{es}}{\omega_e^2 + \nu_{es}^2} \frac{f_0}{kT^*} \, d\mathbf{c}_e \right. \\ &\qquad \left. - e \frac{(\mathbf{B} \times \mathbf{E}^*)}{B} \cdot \int_{-\infty}^{\infty} \frac{\mathbf{c}_e \mathbf{c}_e \omega_e}{\omega_e^2 + \nu_{es}^2} \frac{f_0}{kT^*} \, d\mathbf{c}_e \right]\end{aligned} \tag{5.75}$$

Now f_0 is an even function of c_e; hence the first integral in (5.75) is zero. In the second and third integrals, the off-diagonal terms in the diadic $\mathbf{c}_e\mathbf{c}_e$ are odd functions of $\mathbf{c}_e$, while f_0 is an even function, and therefore these terms will not contribute to these integrals. The remaining terms in the second integral of (5.75) are:

$$\begin{aligned}&-\mathbf{i}E_1^* e \int c_{e1}^2 \nu_{es} f_0 (\omega_e^2 + \nu_{es}^2)^{-1} (kT^*)^{-1} \, d\mathbf{c}_e \\ &-\mathbf{j}E_2^* e \int c_{e2}^2 \nu_{es} f_0 (\omega_e^2 + \nu_{es}^2)^{-1} (kT^*)^{-1} \, d\mathbf{c}_e \\ &-\mathbf{k}E_3^* e \int c_{e3}^2 \nu_{es} f_0 (\omega_e^2 + \nu_{es}^2)^{-1} (kT^*)^{-1} \, d\mathbf{c}_e\end{aligned} \tag{a}$$

Since f_0, ν_{es}^2, and T^* are even functions of $|\mathbf{c}_e|$, the three integrals in (*a*) are identical, and may be written as

$$\frac{e}{3k} \int c_e^2 \nu_{es} f_0 (\omega_e^2 + \nu_{es}^2)^{-1} T^{*-1} \, d\mathbf{c}_e \tag{b}$$

The same reasoning applies to the last integral in (5.75). Thus (5.75) becomes

$$\mathbf{V}_e = -\frac{1}{3} \frac{e}{n_e k} \left[\mathbf{E}^* \int_0^{\infty} \frac{c_e^2 \nu_{es} f_0 \, d\mathbf{c}_e}{(\omega_e^2 + \nu_{es}^2) T^*} + \frac{e}{m_e} (\mathbf{B} \times \mathbf{E}^*) \int_0^{\infty} \frac{c_e^2 f_0 \, d\mathbf{c}_e}{(\omega_e^2 + \nu_{es}^2) T^*} \right] \tag{5.76}$$

The electron current can therefore be written as

$$\mathbf{j}_e = \sigma_1 \mathbf{E}^* + \sigma_2 \frac{\mathbf{B}}{B} \times \mathbf{E}^* \tag{5.77}$$

where, from (5.76), the conductivity parallel to the electric field is given by

$$\sigma_1 = \frac{e^2}{3k} \int c_e^2 \nu_{es} f_0 (\omega_e^2 + \nu_{es}^2)^{-1} T^{*-1} \, d\mathbf{c}_e \tag{5.78}$$

But, in addition to the component of electron current which is parallel to the local moving electric field, there is a current which is perpendicular to both **B** and **E***. The conductivity for this component, σ_2, is given from (5.76) by

$$\sigma_2 = \frac{e^2\omega_e}{3k} \int c_e^2 f_0(\omega_e^2 + \nu_{es}^2)^{-1} T^{*-1} \, d\mathbf{c}_e \tag{5.79}$$

These two conductivities can also be written in an alternate form with the use of (5.29):

$$\sigma_1 = -\frac{1}{3}\frac{e^2}{m_e} \int c_e \nu_{es}(\omega_e^2 + \nu_{es}^2)^{-1} \frac{df_0}{dc_e} \, d\mathbf{c}_e \tag{5.80}$$

$$\sigma_2 = -\frac{1}{3}\frac{e^2}{m_e} \omega_e \int c_e(\omega_e^2 + \nu_{es}^2)^{-1} \frac{df_0}{dc_e} \, d\mathbf{c}_e \tag{5.81}$$

Note that the only difference between (5.80) and (5.81) is that the latter contains ω_e, the electron cyclotron frequency, while the former contains ν_{es}.

Another alternate form of (5.80) and (5.81) can be obtained by substitution of $d\mathbf{c}_e = 4\pi c_e^2 \, dc_e$ and then integration by parts. The result is

$$\sigma_1 = \frac{4\pi}{3}\frac{e^2}{m_e} \int f_0 \frac{d}{dc_e}\left(\frac{c_e^3 \tau_{es}}{1 + \omega_e^2 \tau_{es}^2}\right) dc_e \tag{5.82}$$

$$\sigma_2 = \frac{4\pi}{3}\frac{e^2}{m_e} \omega_e \int f_0 \frac{d}{dc_e}\left(\frac{c_e^3 \tau_{es}^2}{1 + \omega_e^2 \tau_{es}^2}\right) dc_e \tag{5.83}$$

where $\tau_{es} = \nu_{es}^{-1}(c_e)$.

When the electric field has a component $E_\parallel$ in the direction of the magnetic field, then (5.29) must be modified as follows:[11]

$$\frac{df_0}{dc_e} = -\frac{f_0 c_e m_e}{kT^*} \tag{5.84}$$

where T^* is now defined as

$$T^* = T_s + \frac{m_s}{\delta_s 3k}\left(\frac{e}{m_e \nu_{es}}\right)^2 \frac{E_\perp^{*2} + E_\parallel^2(1 + \omega_e^2 \tau_{es}^2)}{1 + \omega_e^2 \tau_{es}^2} \tag{5.85}$$

where $\mathbf{E}_\perp^*$ is the electric field perpendicular to **B**. For (5.76) there is an additional term in the direction of **B** given by

$$\mathbf{V}_{e_B} = -\frac{e}{n_e}\frac{\mathbf{B}}{B^2}\frac{(\mathbf{B} \cdot \mathbf{E})\omega_e^2}{3k} \int \frac{c_e^2}{\nu_{es}(\omega_e^2 + \nu_{es}^2)} \frac{f_0}{T^*} \, d\mathbf{c}_e \tag{5.86}$$

To obtain the total current in the direction of the magnetic field, the component from (5.76) must be added to (5.86). The result is

$$V_{e\parallel} = -\frac{eE_\parallel}{3kn_e} \int \frac{c_e^2 f_0}{\nu_{es} T^*} \, d\mathbf{c}_e \tag{5.87}$$

With (5.87), then (5.77) must be modified to become

$$\mathbf{j}_e = \sigma_1 \mathbf{E}_\perp^* + \sigma_2 \frac{\mathbf{B}}{B} \times \mathbf{E}_\perp^* + \sigma_3 \frac{\mathbf{B}}{B} E_\parallel \tag{5.88}$$

where, from (5.87),

$$\sigma_3 = \frac{e^2}{3k} \int \frac{c_e{}^2 f_0}{\nu_{es} T^*} \, d\mathbf{c}_e \tag{5.89}$$

Comparison of (5.89) with (5.78) shows that σ_3 is identical to σ_1 when σ_1 is evaluated in the absence of a magnetic field (except for the effects on f_0 and T^*).

Equation (5.88) can also be written in tensor form as follows:

$$j_{e_i} = \sum_j \sigma_{ij} E_j^* \tag{5.90}$$

From (5.88) the components of the electrical conductivity tensor with **B** in the z direction may be written as

$$\sigma_{ij} = \begin{bmatrix} \sigma_1 & -\sigma_2 & 0 \\ \sigma_2 & \sigma_1 & 0 \\ 0 & 0 & \sigma_3 \end{bmatrix} \tag{5.91}$$

Also, comparison of (5.78), (5.79), and (5.89) shows that the electrical conductivity tensor may be written as a single integral,

$$\sigma_{ij} = \frac{e^2}{3k} \int \frac{\Omega_{ij} c_e{}^2 f_0}{T^*} \, d\mathbf{c}_e \tag{5.91a}$$

where the collision-frequency tensor Ω_{ij} is defined as follows:

$$\Omega_{ij} = \begin{bmatrix} \dfrac{\nu_{es}}{\omega_e{}^2 + \nu_{es}^2} & -\dfrac{\omega_e}{\omega_e{}^2 + \nu_{es}^2} & 0 \\ \dfrac{\omega_e}{\omega_e{}^2 + \nu_{es}^2} & \dfrac{\nu_{es}}{\omega_e{}^2 + \nu_{es}^2} & 0 \\ 0 & 0 & \dfrac{1}{\nu_{es}} \end{bmatrix} \tag{5.92}$$

Equation (5.90) can also be inverted as follows:

$$E_i^* = \sum_j \eta_{ij} j_{e_j} \tag{5.90a}$$

where η_{ij} is the reciprocal of the conductivity tensor,

$$\eta_{ij} = [\sigma_{ij}]^{-1} = \frac{1}{\sigma_1{}^2 + \sigma_2{}^2} \begin{bmatrix} \sigma_1 & \sigma_2 & 0 \\ -\sigma_2 & \sigma_1 & 0 \\ 0 & 0 & \dfrac{\sigma_1{}^2 + \sigma_2{}^2}{\sigma_3} \end{bmatrix} \tag{5.93}$$

With knowledge of the electric field, the magnetic field, the cross section, and the loss factor δ_s, then f_0 may be calculated from (5.84) and (5.85), and the electrical conductivities from (5.82), (5.83), and (5.89). This is usually not done in practice, however. Instead, ν_{es} is evaluated for an average electron velocity, and then is taken as a constant so that it may be removed from the integral. This procedure is exact for maxwellian molecules for which ν_{es} is exactly constant. This will be shown in Sec. 5.6.3. In order to determine the extent of the possible error involved in this procedure, the integrals in (5.82), (5.83), and (5.89) will be calculated for the inverse-power law of Sec. 5.4. Two cases can be integrated explicitly: $\omega_e\tau_e \ll 1$, which will be covered in Sec. 5.6.1, and $\omega_e\tau_e \gg 1$, which is covered in Sec. 5.6.2, both cases for f_0 maxwellian. To assure this last condition, the electric fields are assumed small.

5.6.1 Inverse-power-force Law for $T_e = T^* = T_s$ and $\omega_e/\nu_e \ll 1$. In this section, it is assumed that the electric fields and magnetic fields are small so that $T^* = T_e = T_s$, and also that ω_e may be neglected in the various integrands. Since $T^* = T_s$, then f_0 is maxwellian about T_s. From (5.78),

$$\sigma_1 = \frac{4\pi n_e e^2}{3kT_s}\left(\frac{m_e}{2\pi kT_s}\right)^{\frac{3}{2}} \int \frac{c_e{}^4}{\nu_{es}} e^{-m_e c_e{}^2/2kT_s}\, dc_e$$

or, in terms of cross section,

$$\sigma_1 = \frac{4\pi}{3}\frac{n_e}{n_s}\frac{e^2}{kT_s}\left(\frac{m_e}{2\pi kT_s}\right)^{\frac{3}{2}} \int \frac{c_e{}^3}{Q_{es}} e^{-m_e c_e{}^2/2kT_s}\, dc_e$$

Substitution of Q_{es} from (5.47) with $A_1(s)$ taken constant yields

$$\sigma_1 = \frac{2}{3A_1(s)}\frac{n_e e^2}{n_s kT_s}\left(\frac{m_e}{2\pi kT_s}\right)^{\frac{3}{2}}\left(\frac{m_e}{\alpha_{es}}\right)^{2/(s-1)} \int_0^\infty c_e{}^{3+4/(s-1)} e^{-m_e c_e{}^2/2kT_s}\, dc_e \qquad (a)$$

The integral in (a) may be transformed to

$$\left(\frac{2kT_s}{m_e}\right)^{2s/(s-1)} \int_0^\infty e^{-\xi^2}\xi^{(3s+1)/(s-1)}\, d\xi \qquad (b)$$

where $\xi^2 = m_e c_e{}^2/2kT_s$. The integral in (b) can be evaluated from the definition of the Γ function,

$$\Gamma(n+1) = \int_0^\infty x^n e^{-x}\, dx \qquad (c)$$

Letting $x = \xi^2$, then (c) becomes

$$\tfrac{1}{2}\Gamma(n+1) = \int_0^\infty \xi^{2n+1} e^{-\xi^2}\, d\xi \qquad (d)$$

To relate this integral to our problem, we set

$$2n+1 = \frac{3s+1}{s-1} \qquad (e)$$

Addition of 1 to each side of (e) yields

$$2n + 2 = \frac{4s}{s - 1}$$

so that

$$n + 1 = \frac{2s}{s - 1}$$

and

$$\Gamma(n + 1) = \Gamma\left(\frac{2s}{s - 1}\right) \tag{f}$$

Substitution of (f), (d), and (b) into (a) yields

$$\sigma_1 = \frac{2}{3A_1(s)} \frac{e^2 n_e}{n_s \pi^{\frac{1}{2}} m_e} \left(\frac{m_e}{2kT_s}\right)^{\frac{1}{2}} \left(\frac{2kT_s}{\alpha_{es}}\right)^{2/(s-1)} \Gamma\left(\frac{2s}{s - 1}\right) \tag{5.94}$$

Equation (5.94) can be simplified by evaluation of the cross section at the mean thermal velocity. Thus, with $\langle c \rangle_e = (8kT_e/\pi m_e)^{\frac{1}{2}}$, this "average" cross section is

$$\langle Q_{es} \rangle = 2\pi A_1 \left(\frac{\alpha_{es}}{m_e}\right)^{2/(s-1)} \left(\frac{8kT_e}{\pi m_e}\right)^{-2/(s-1)} \tag{5.95}$$

With (5.95), then (5.94) becomes

$$\sigma_1 = \frac{8}{3\pi} \left(\frac{\pi}{4}\right)^{2/(s-1)} \Gamma\left(\frac{2s}{s - 1}\right) \frac{n_e e^2}{m_e \langle \nu_{es} \rangle} \tag{5.96}$$

where the "average" collision frequency is defined as

$$\langle \nu_{es} \rangle = n_s \langle c_e \rangle \langle Q_{es} \rangle \tag{5.97}$$

Now, the approximate procedure of evaluation of σ_1 is to consider ν_{es} at some average value, say $\langle \nu_{es} \rangle$, and integrate (5.78). The approximate result will be called σ_{1_0}, and is given by

$$\sigma_{1_0} = \frac{n_e e^2}{m_e \langle \nu_{es} \rangle} \tag{5.98}$$

Thus, the exact expression for the conductivity given by (5.93) differs from the approximate expression (5.98) by only the numerical factor

$$\frac{\sigma_1}{\sigma_{1_0}} = \frac{8}{3\pi} \left(\frac{\pi}{4}\right)^{2/(s-1)} \Gamma\left(\frac{2s}{s - 1}\right) \tag{5.99}$$

This factor is unity only for maxwellian molecules, for which $s = 5$. For electron-ion interactions, the factor is π, which is the largest error of the approximate formula. For hard spheres this factor is $8/3\pi = 0.85$. Thus, the approximate formula (5.98) appears to be adequate for most purposes. The special case of fully ionized gases will be discussed more fully in Sec. 5.6.4.

The general form of the expression for electrical conductivity can be obtained from very simple considerations. The drift velocity is the distance that an electron moves parallel to the electric field between collisions, divided by the collision time. The distance the electron moves parallel to E between collisions is $S \approx \frac{1}{2}(eE^*/m_e)\tau_e^2$. Thus $V_e \approx \frac{1}{2}eE^*/m_e\nu_e$, which agrees qualitatively with (5.98).

It is also of interest to compare the distribution function of (5.30) to a maxwellian distribution which has the same net electron diffusion. From (5.30),

$$f_e = f_0\left(1 - \frac{eE_1c_{e_1}}{\nu_{es}kT_e}\right) \tag{g}$$

where $B = 0$, and E is in the x_1 direction only. We will compare (g) to the displaced maxwellian,

$$f_e = ae^{-(m_e/2kT_e)[(c_{e_1}-V_{e_1})^2+c_{e_2}{}^2+c_{e_3}{}^3]} \tag{h}$$

where c_e is used since the heavy particles are assumed to have zero velocity. For small ratios of V_{e_1}/c_{e_1}, the exponent may be expanded, which yields

$$f_e = f_0\left(1 + \frac{m_ec_{e_1}V_{e_1}}{kT_e}\right) \tag{i}$$

Since $V_{e_1} \approx -eE_1/m_e\langle\nu_e\rangle$, then (i) becomes

$$f_e = f_0\left(1 - \frac{ec_{e_1}E_1}{kT_e\langle\nu_e\rangle}\right) \tag{j}$$

The only difference between (g) and (j) arises from the variation of the collision frequency ν_e with electron velocity. Thus, the exact distribution function (g) is a displaced maxwellian for constant collision frequency; otherwise it is skewed.

In a similar manner, the values of σ_2 may be evaluated from (5.79). In terms of σ_{1_0} and $\langle\nu_{es}\rangle$,

$$\sigma_2 = \tfrac{16}{3}\pi^{-\frac{3}{2}}\left(\frac{\pi}{4}\right)^{4(s-1)} \Gamma[\tfrac{3}{2} + 4(s-1)^{-1}]\frac{\omega_e\sigma_{1_0}}{\langle\nu_{es}\rangle} \tag{5.100}$$

The approximate evaluation of (5.79) in which ν_{es} is taken as $\langle\nu_{es}\rangle$ yields σ_{2_0}:

$$\sigma_{2_0} = \frac{\omega_e\sigma_{1_0}}{\langle\nu_{es}\rangle} \tag{5.100a}$$

The ratio of σ_2/σ_{2_0} is

$$\frac{\sigma_2}{\sigma_{2_0}} = \tfrac{16}{3}\pi^{-\frac{3}{2}}\left(\frac{\pi}{4}\right)^{4/(s-1)} \Gamma\left(\frac{3}{2} + \frac{4}{s-1}\right) \tag{5.101}$$

For $s = 5$, $\sigma_2 = \sigma_{2_0}$, of course, because ν_e is independent of c_e. For $s \to \infty$, $\sigma_2/\sigma_{2_0} \to 0.85$, which is only a small error. But for $s = 2$, the ratio of

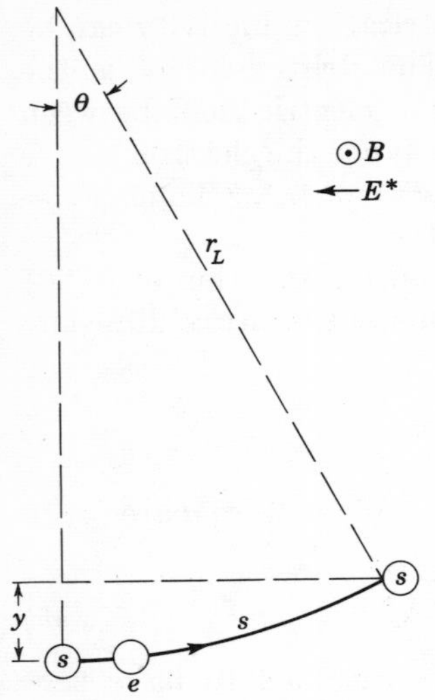

FIGURE 5.9 Electron motion in magnetic field for $\omega_e\tau_e < 1$.

σ_2/σ_{2_0} is 19! For $s = 3$, this has dropped to 1.96. Thus, the simplified equation (5.100*a*) is adequate for most gases, except for ions.

Equation (5.100*a*) can also be understood from simple considerations (see Fig. 5.9). In the direction transverse to the electric field, the particle moves the following distance between collisions:

$$y = r_L(1 - \cos\theta) \approx \tfrac{1}{2}r_L\theta^2 \qquad (k)$$

If the distance along the path between collisions is S, then $\theta = S/r_L$. As before, $S \cong \frac{1}{2}(eE/m_e)\tau_e^2$, while $r_L = v_\perp/\omega_e$, and the average value of $v_\perp$ is $\frac{1}{2}(eE/m_e)\tau_e$. The transverse drift velocity is y/τ_e, which with the use of (*k*) becomes

$$V_e = \frac{1}{4}\frac{eE}{m_e}\,\omega_e\tau_e^2 \qquad (l)$$

and the transverse conductivity is

$$\sigma_{2_0} = \frac{1}{4}\frac{n_e e^2\tau_e}{m_e}\,\omega_e\tau_e \cong \sigma_{1_0}\omega_e\tau_e \qquad (m)$$

which agrees qualitatively with (5.100*a*). Thus, the curvature of the electron trajectory in a magnetic field is responsible for the transverse current, which is usually referred to as the *Hall current;* this phenomenon is generally called the *Hall effect* and occurs in solids and liquid conductors as well as in ionized gases. From (5.100*a*) it is seen that this effect depends on the ratio of the electron cyclotron frequency to the electron collision frequency. This ratio can also be written as

$$\frac{\omega_e}{\nu_{es}} = \frac{\omega_e}{\langle c_e\rangle}\cdot\frac{1}{n_sQ_s} = \frac{\lambda_e}{r_L} \qquad (n)$$

where λ_e is the mean free path of the electrons, and r_L is the average Larmor radius. Note that ω_e/ν_{es} is the number of gyrations of an electron between collisions; thus the Hall effect depends on this quantity.

5.6.2 Inverse-power Law for $T_e = T^* = T_s$ and $\omega_e/\nu_e \gg 1$. When the magnetic field is large, ν_{es}^2 may be neglected in the denominators of (5.78) and (5.79). Then (5.78) may be integrated to yield

$$\sigma_1 = \frac{2}{3}\left(\frac{4}{\pi}\right)^{2/(s-1)}\Gamma\left(\frac{3s-5}{s-1}\right)\omega_e^{-2}\langle\nu_{es}\rangle^2\sigma_{1_0} \qquad (5.102)$$

where σ_{1_0} is given by (5.98). When $s = 5$, corresponding to maxwellian molecules, then $\sigma_1 = \omega_e^{-2}\langle\nu_e\rangle^2\sigma_{1_0}$; as before we will make this value of σ_1 our reference value to compare with (5.102) so that

$$\frac{\sigma_1(s)}{\sigma_1(5)} = \frac{2}{3}\left(\frac{4}{\pi}\right)^{2/(s-1)} \Gamma\left(\frac{3s-5}{s-1}\right) \qquad (5.103)$$

This ratio is $32/3\pi^2$ for $s = 2$ and $\frac{4}{3}$ for $s = \infty$. Thus, $\sigma_1(5)$ is a good approximation for σ_1 for the complete range of s.

For σ_2, then (5.79) becomes

$$\sigma_2 = \omega_e^{-1}\langle\nu_{es}\rangle\sigma_{1_0} = \frac{n_e e}{B} \qquad (5.104)$$

and is completely independent of the value of s.

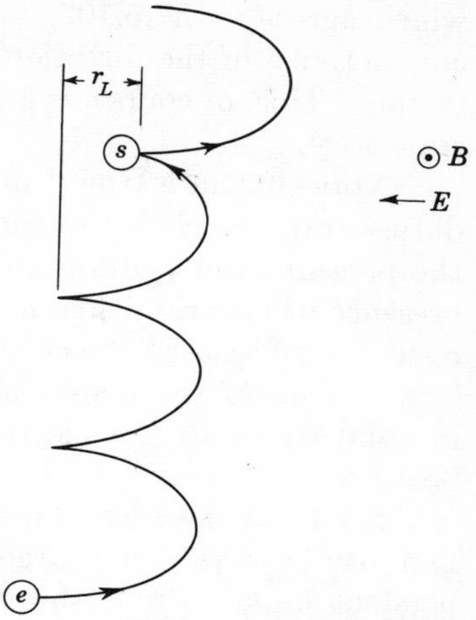

FIGURE 5.10. Electron motion for $\omega_e\tau_e \gg 1$.

The parallel and transverse conductivities for $\omega_e \gg \nu_{es}$ can also be understood from simple arguments. From Sec. 5.6.1, the value of $\omega_e\tau_e$ is simply the number of revolutions (in radians) of an electron between collisions. Thus when $\omega_e\tau_e$ is large, many such revolutions are made. Between collisions, the electron therefore drifts with velocity $\mathbf{E}^* \times \mathbf{B}/B^2$ [see (3.7)]. When a collision finally occurs, the electron will start on a new trajectory which is translated a distance of a Larmor radius in the direction $-\mathbf{E}$ (see Fig. 5.10). This affects the transverse drift little; thus the transverse current is

$$(j_e)_\perp = \frac{n_e e E}{B} = \frac{n_e e^2}{m_e \nu_e} \cdot \frac{m_e}{eB}\,\nu_e \cdot E = \sigma_{1_0}\frac{\nu_e}{\omega_e}E \qquad (a)$$

which agrees with (5.104). For the conduction parallel to $\mathbf{E}$, assume that the electrons initially have zero velocity. The average velocity during its trajectory will therefore be one-half the acceleration times the time for one gyration, or

$$c_e = \frac{1}{2}\frac{eE}{m_e}\frac{2\pi}{\omega_e} \approx \frac{\pi e E}{m_e \omega_e} \qquad (b)$$

The electron current parallel to E is then

$$j_e = n_e e V_d = \frac{n_e e r_L}{\tau_e} = \frac{n_e e c_e}{\omega_e \tau_e} \qquad (c)$$

Substitution of (c) into (b) then yields

$$j_e \cong \frac{\pi n_e e^2 \tau_e}{m_e} \cdot \frac{1}{{\omega_e}^2{\tau_e}^2} \cdot E \cong \frac{\sigma_{1_0} E}{{\omega_e}^2{\tau_e}^2} \qquad (d)$$

which agrees with (5.102). Furthermore, it is seen that the electrical conductivity in the direction of the electric field is decreased by a large factor. This, of course, is a direct result of the curvature of the electron trajectory.

Note that in a true "collisionless" plasma, charged particles cannot diffuse transversely into regions of lower magnetic field strength. From the present results, diffusion will occur whenever collisions occur in the presence of electric fields or any other type of gradient. The foregoing results have ignored the effect of ion currents. However, for sufficiently large values of the magnetic field, the ion current may be appreciable in comparison to the electron current. This is considered further in Sec. 5.8.

5.6.3 Maxwellian Particles ($s = 5$), $0 < \omega_e\tau_e < \infty$. For maxwellian particles ($s = 5$), large simplifications occur because ν_{e5} is independent of c_e. First, the distribution function is exactly maxwellian about T_e [see (5.68)]. Secondly, the expressions for σ_1, σ_2, and σ_3 in (5.78), (5.79), and (5.89) become

$$
\begin{aligned}
\sigma_1 &= \frac{n_e e^2}{m_e \nu_{e5}} \frac{1}{\omega_e{}^2\tau_{e5}^2 + 1} = \frac{\sigma_{1_0}}{\omega_e{}^2\tau_{e5}^2 + 1} \\
\sigma_2 &= \frac{\sigma_{1_0}\omega_e\tau_{e5}}{1 + \omega_e{}^2\tau_{e5}^2} \\
\sigma_3 &= \sigma_{1_0}
\end{aligned}
\tag{5.105}
$$

so that (5.88) becomes

$$
\mathbf{j}_e = \frac{\sigma_{1_0}\{\mathbf{E}^* + [(\mathbf{B}\times\mathbf{E}^*)/B]\omega_e\tau_{e5} + [\mathbf{B}(\mathbf{B}\cdot\mathbf{E}^*)/B^2]\omega_e{}^2\tau_{e5}^2\}}{1 + \omega_e{}^2\tau_{e5}^2} \tag{5.106}
$$

If $\mathbf{B}$ is chosen in the z direction, the components of σ_{ij} are

$$
\sigma_{ij} = \sigma_{1_0}\begin{bmatrix}
\dfrac{1}{1 + \omega_e{}^2\tau_{e5}^2} & \dfrac{-\omega_e\tau_{e5}}{1 + \omega_e{}^2\tau_{e5}^2} & 0 \\
\dfrac{\omega_e\tau_{e5}}{1 + \omega_e{}^2\tau_{e5}^2} & \dfrac{1}{1 + \omega_e{}^2\tau_{e5}^2} & 0 \\
0 & 0 & 1
\end{bmatrix} \tag{5.106a}
$$

In the plane normal to B, the angle between the electric field E^* and j_e is therefore given by $\tan\alpha = \omega_e\tau_{e5}$. This can be seen by choosing $\mathbf{E}^*$ in the x direction; then

$$
j_{e_x} = \frac{\sigma_{1_0}}{1 + \omega_e{}^2\tau_{e5}^2} E_x^* \qquad j_{e_y} = \frac{\sigma_{1_0}\omega_e\tau_e E_x^*}{1 + \omega_e{}^2\tau_{e5}^2} \tag{a}
$$

so that

$$
\frac{j_{e_y}}{j_{e_x}} = \tan\alpha = \omega_e\tau_{e5} \tag{b}
$$

From (a) and (b), the magnitude of the current in the plane normal to B is

$$|j_\perp| = \sigma_{1_0}|E_\perp^*| \cos \alpha$$
$$= |j_\perp|_{B=0} \cos \alpha \qquad (c)$$

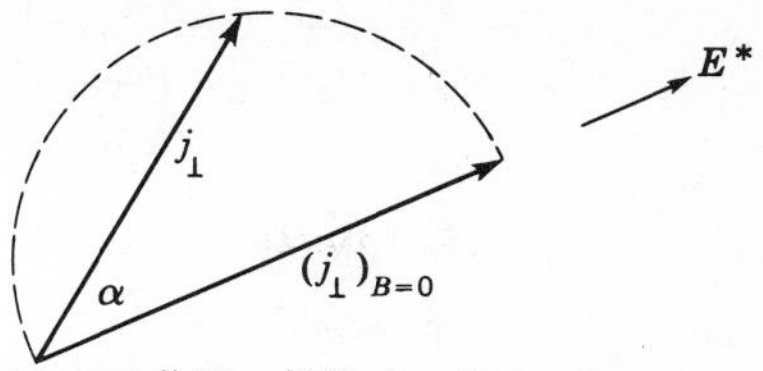

FIGURE 5.11 Effect of $\omega_e\tau_{e5}$ on the electron current where $\tan \alpha = \omega_e\tau_{e5}$.

This is merely the equation of a semicircle whose diameter is $j_\perp$ $(B = 0)$. Thus, as $\omega_e\tau_e$ increases, the electric current vector inscribes a semicircle (see Fig. 5.11). Finally, the component of $E_\perp^*$ in the direction of $j_\perp$ is

$$(E^*)_{j_\perp} = E_\perp^* \cos \alpha \qquad (d)$$

so that (c) becomes

$$|j_\perp| = \sigma_{1_0}(E_\perp^*)_{j_\perp} \qquad (e)$$

that is, the electrical conductivity is the *scalar* conductivity, when referred to the direction of $\mathbf{j}_e$. This is known as *Tonk's theorem*, but note that it is exact only for maxwellian molecules; for other molecules each of the terms in σ_{ij} will be multiplied by factors which depend on the interparticle potential and the value of $\omega_e\langle\tau_e\rangle$.

Equation (5.106) also has other interesting properties; if the scalar product with $\mathbf{E}^*$ is taken, this becomes

$$\mathbf{j} \cdot \mathbf{E}^* = \frac{j^2}{\sigma_{1_0}} \qquad (5.107)$$

for the term involving ohmic heating. This result is also valid only for maxwellian molecules. Finally, (5.106) can be vector-multiplied by $\mathbf{B}$ and the result used to eliminate $\mathbf{B} \times \mathbf{E}$ in (5.106). The result is

$$\mathbf{j}_e = \sigma_{1_0}\left(\mathbf{E}^* - \frac{\mathbf{j}_e \times \mathbf{B}}{n_e e}\right) \qquad (5.108)$$

Equation (5.108) is the usual form for the Hall current.[12] It may be understood by substitution on the right side for $\mathbf{j}_e = -\mathbf{V}_e n_e e$; then

$$\mathbf{j}_e = \sigma_{1_0}(\mathbf{E}^* + \mathbf{V}_e \times \mathbf{B}) = \sigma_{1_0}(\mathbf{E} + \mathbf{v}_e \times \mathbf{B}) \qquad (5.109)$$

Thus the "driving" force for electrons is the combined electric field and magnetic force on the electron gas.

For particles other than maxwellian molecules, Eq. (5.108) is only approximately correct. More generally, in the direction of $\mathbf{B}$, from (5.88),

$$(j_e)_B = \sigma_3 E_B \qquad (f)$$

where σ_3 is given by (5.89), and E_B is the component of **E** in the direction of B. In the other two directions,

$$\mathbf{j}_e = \sigma_1\left[1 + \left(\frac{\sigma_2}{\sigma_1}\right)^2\right]\mathbf{E}^* - \frac{\sigma_2}{\sigma_1}\frac{\mathbf{j}\times\mathbf{B}}{B} \tag{g}$$

or

$$\mathbf{j}_e = \sigma_1\left[1 + \left(\frac{\sigma_2}{\sigma_1}\right)^2\right]\left[\mathbf{E}^* - \frac{\sigma_2/\sigma_1^2}{1+(\sigma_2/\sigma_1)^2}\frac{\mathbf{j}\times\mathbf{B}}{B}\right] \tag{h}$$

Now $\sigma_1[1 + (\sigma_2/\sigma_1)^2]$ is usually close to σ_{1_0}, while $(\sigma_2/\sigma_1^2)B[1 + (\sigma_2/\sigma_1)^2]^{-1}$ is usually close to $(n_e e)^{-1}$. Thus (5.108) is a good approximation for a wide range of conditions.[13] This is discussed further at the end of the next section.

5.6.4 Lorentz Approximation—Fully Ionized Gas. The preceding results may also be extended to the case of a fully ionized gas, for small electric fields so that $T^* = T_s$. For ions with charge Z_I, from (5.56),

$$A_1(2) \cong 2 \ln \frac{2d}{b^*} \tag{a}$$

where

$$b^* = \frac{e^2 Z_I}{2\pi K_0 m_e c_e^2} \tag{b}$$

$$d = \sqrt{\frac{2K_0 kT}{\sum_s n_s e^2 Z_s^2}} \tag{c}$$

Now, in carrying out the integration of (5.78), the dependence of A_1 on c_e should be included; but since this is a logarithmic dependence which changes slowly, it is assumed that A_1 may be removed from the integrand, with c_e^2 replaced by its mean thermal value, $3kT/m_e$. Combination of (a), (b), and (c) then yields

$$A_1 = 2 \ln \Lambda \tag{d}$$

where

$$\Lambda = \frac{3}{2e^3 Z_I}\left[\frac{2(4\pi K_0 kT)^3}{\pi \sum_s n_s Z_s^2}\right]^{\frac{1}{2}} = \frac{1.2389 \times 10^4 T^{\frac{3}{2}}}{\sqrt{\frac{1}{2}\sum_s n_s Z_s^2}} \tag{5.110}$$

where T is in degrees Kelvin, and n_e is electrons per cubic centimeter. Λ is also equal to $\frac{9}{2}$ times the number of electrons in a spherical volume having a radius equal to the Debye length. Values of Λ have been given by Spitzer;[14] they are repeated in Table 5.1 for $Z_I = 1$. Note the blank spaces in Table 5.1; they correspond to values of d/b^* which are not sufficiently large to satisfy the assumptions.

Now the scalar electrical conductivity may be obtained from (5.78) with ω_e set equal to zero,

$$\sigma_1 = \frac{n_e(4\pi K_0)^2(2kT)^{\frac{3}{2}}}{\pi^{\frac{3}{2}} m_e^{\frac{1}{2}} e^2 \ln \Lambda \sum_{s\neq e} n_s Z_s^2} = \frac{2.83 \times 10^{-2} n_e T^{\frac{3}{2}}}{\ln \Lambda \sum_{s\neq e} n_s Z_s^2} \tag{5.111}$$

Table 5.1 Values of ln Λ

T, °K	n_e, electrons/cm³				
	10^6	10^9	10^{12}	10^{15}	10^{18}
10^2	9.43	5.97			
10^3	12.8	9.43	5.97		
10^4	16.3	12.8	9.43	5.97	
10^5	19.7	16.3	12.8	9.43	5.97
10^6	22.8	19.3	15.9	12.4	8.96

From L. Spitzer.[14]

when σ_1 is in ohm^{-1} m^{-1}, and T is measured in degrees Kelvin. Thus the electrical conductivity increases with approximately the three-halves power of temperature. The average cross section of an ion is obtained by substitution of $\alpha_{es} = -e^2 Z_I/4\pi K_0$ into (5.95),

$$\langle Q_{eI}\rangle = \frac{\pi^3 \ln \Lambda}{16}\left(\frac{e^2 Z_I}{4\pi K_0}\right)^2 \frac{1}{(kT)^2} \tag{5.112}$$

which decreases rapidly with increasing temperature.

In the Lorentz model, collisions between electrons were ignored, which is permissible only if the electron-electron collision frequency is small in comparison to the collision frequency of electrons with heavy particles. Now when Z_I is large, the number of electrons is Z_I times the number of ions, but from (5.112) the cross section of the ions increases as Z_I^2, so that the electron-electron collision frequency is small compared to the electron-ion collision frequency. But for Z_I equal to unity, this is no longer true, and the electron-electron collisions will affect the electron distribution function. This effect has been calculated by Spitzer and Härm[15] who found that for $Z_I = 1$, Eq. (5.111) must be multiplied by 0.582. Then (5.111) becomes, for singly ionized gas,

$$\sigma_1 = \frac{1.5085 \times 10^{-2} T^{\frac{3}{2}}}{\ln \Lambda} \qquad \text{mhos/m} \tag{5.113}$$

This reduction may be understood from the form of the distribution function [see (*g*), Sec. 5.6.1]. Because the collision frequency for electrons with ions varies as c_e^{-3}, the distribution function is highly skewed in the direction of the electric field when only electron-ion collisions are considered. On the other hand, if electron-electron collisions were more important than electron collisions with ions, the electron distribution function would be closer to maxwellian about the diffusion velocity V_e. The electrical conductivity for such an electron distribution function has also been calculated, and corresponds to the first approximation of the Chapman-Enskog method. This electrical conductivity is smaller by a factor of $32/3\pi = 3.396$ than the Lorentz approximation [see (5.160)]. For $Z_I = 1$, the number of electron-electron collisions is about equal to the number of electron-ion collisions; thus the actual distribution function will be between a displaced maxwellian and the highly skewed distribution function. Thus, the reduction should be about half of $32/3\pi$, or 1.7, whose reciprocal is 0.59, which agrees approximately with the more detailed calculation.

In terms of the mean cross section, for a singly ionized gas the scalar electrical conductivity is given by

$$\sigma = \frac{0.582\pi e^2}{m_e\langle c_e\rangle\langle Q_{eI}\rangle} \tag{e}$$

where, from (5.112),

$$\langle Q_{eI}\rangle = \frac{e^4 \ln \Lambda}{4\pi K_0{}^2 m_e{}^2 \langle c_e\rangle^4} \tag{f}$$

Values of $\langle Q_{eI}\rangle$ are shown in Fig. 5.12. By comparison with neutral particles, which have cross sections from 10^{-23} (argon at 2500°K) to 10^{-19} m², the cross section of ions is much larger.

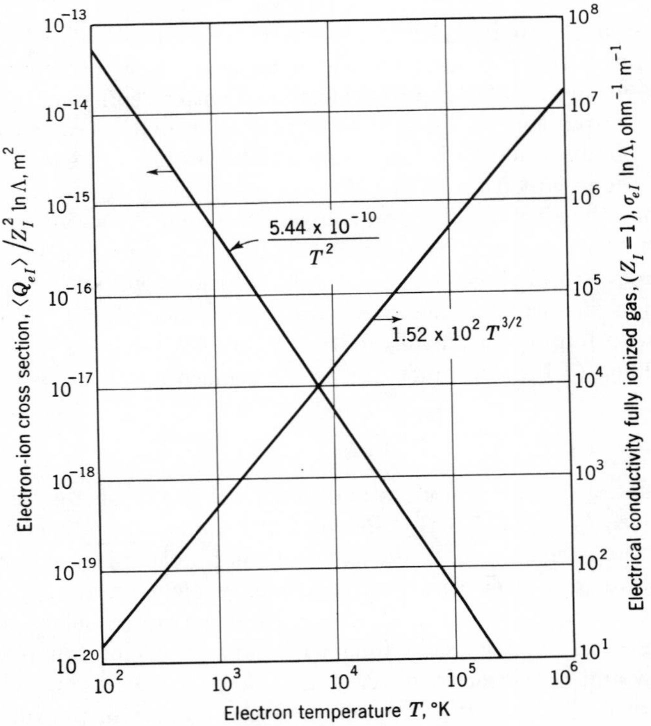

FIGURE 5.12 Electron-ion collision cross section for a fully ionized gas where $Z_I = 1$, $\sigma = 0.582\pi e^2/\langle c_e\rangle\langle Q_{eI}\rangle$.

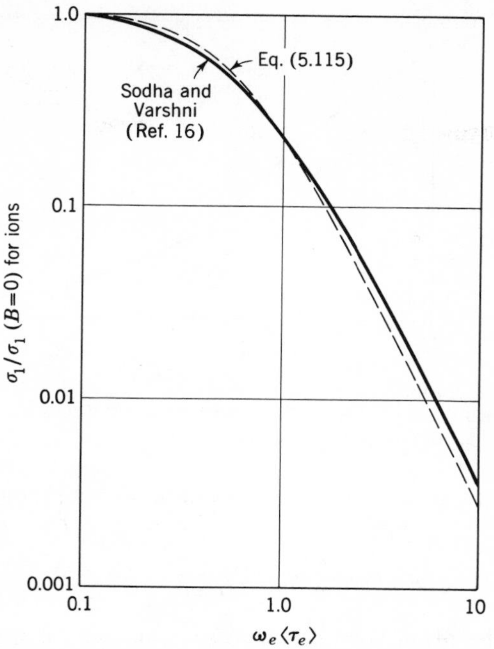

FIGURE 5.13 Reduction in σ_1 due to magnetic field for a fully ionized gas ($Z_I = 1$).

Also shown in Fig. 5.12 is the electrical conductivity of a fully ionized gas with $Z_I = 1$. This is the maximum electrical conductivity of a gas for small electric fields and cannot be exceeded, since any neutral particles or ions which are more than singly ionized act to decrease the electrical conductivity.

For strong magnetic fields, the results of Sec. 5.6.2 must be used. For σ_1 one then obtains

$$\sigma_1 = \frac{32}{3\pi^2} \frac{\sigma_{1_0}}{\omega_e^2\langle\tau_e\rangle^2} \tag{5.114}$$

Similarly, the transverse conductivity has been calculated for both weak and strong magnetic fields.[16] For weak magnetic fields, σ_2/σ_{2_0} is not 19 as given by (5.101), but is 4.05. For strong magnetic fields, σ_2 for the electron current is always $n_e e/B$ as given by (5.104), regardless of the distribution function.

For intermediate values of $\omega_e\langle\tau_{eI}\rangle$, Sodha and Varshni[16] have also calculated σ_1 and σ_2; these are shown in Figs. 5.13 and 5.14 as a function of $\omega_e\langle\tau_{eI}\rangle$, where $\langle\tau_{eI}\rangle$ is $\langle\nu_{eI}\rangle^{-1}$ as defined by (5.97). Also shown in Fig. 5.13 is the following approximate method of calculation of the reduction in

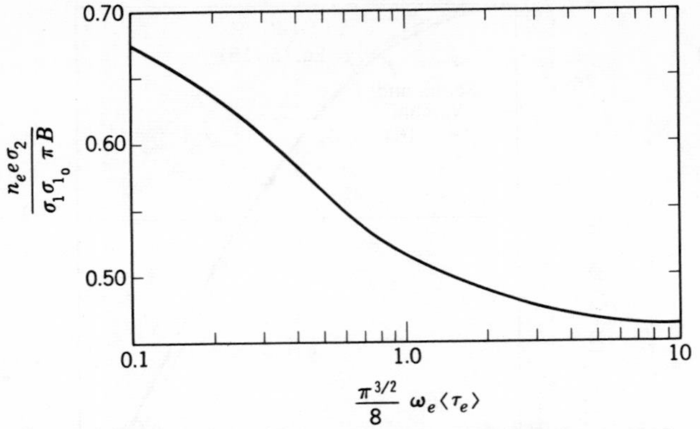

FIGURE 5.14 Variation in σ_2 with magnetic field for a fully ionized gas ($Z_I = 1$). (From ref. 16.)

σ_1 due to magnetic fields. Consider first maxwellian molecules; then from (5.105) and (5.98),

$$\sigma_1 = \frac{\sigma_{1_0}}{1 + (\sigma_{1_0} B/n_e e)^2} \qquad s = 5$$

For particles other than maxwellian, this may be modified as follows:

$$\sigma_1 = \frac{(\sigma_1)_{B=0}}{1 + [(\sigma_1)_{(B=0)} B/n_e e]^2}$$

Use of $\sigma_1 = 0.582\pi\sigma_{1_0}$, where σ_{1_0} is given by (5.98), yields

$$\frac{\sigma_1}{(\sigma_1)_{B=0}} = \frac{1}{1 + (0.582\pi)^2 \omega_e{}^2 \langle \tau_{eI} \rangle^2}$$

or

$$\frac{\sigma_1}{(\sigma_1)_{B=0}} = \frac{1}{1 + 3.35\omega_e{}^2 \langle \tau_{eI} \rangle^2} \tag{5.115}$$

Equation (5.115) is shown in Fig. 5.13 as the dashed line. The maximum error is about 25 per cent.

From Eq. (*h*), Sec. 5.6.3, with $(\mathbf{E}^* \cdot \mathbf{B}) = 0$, the current is given as follows:

$$\mathbf{j}_e = \sigma_1 \left\{ \left[1 + \left(\frac{\sigma_2}{\sigma_1} \right)^2 \right] \mathbf{E}^* + \frac{\sigma_2}{\sigma_1{}^2} \frac{\mathbf{j}_e \times \mathbf{B}}{B} \right\} \tag{g}$$

For strong magnetic fields, $\sigma_2 \gg \sigma_1$, and the above equation simplifies as follows:

$$\mathbf{j}_e = \frac{\sigma_2{}^2}{\sigma_1} \left(E^* - \frac{\mathbf{j}_e \times \mathbf{B}}{B\sigma_2} \right) \tag{h}$$

For strong magnetic fields, $\sigma_2 = n_e e/B$ always; and use of (5.114) and (5.98) yields

$$\mathbf{j}_e = \frac{3\pi^2}{32} \sigma_{1_0} \left(\mathbf{E}^* - \frac{\mathbf{j}_e \times \mathbf{B}}{n_e e} \right) \tag{i}$$

If the electron-electron collisions are neglected, then from (5.99), $(\sigma_1)_{B=0}$ for a fully ionized gas is $\pi\sigma_{1_0}$; thus the conductivity in the direction of the electric field in the presence of a magnetic field is reduced by a factor $3\pi/32$. But when electron-electron collisions are included, (5.114) should be reduced by a factor of 0.582, so that

$$\mathbf{j}_e = \frac{3\pi}{32(0.582)^2} 0.582\pi\sigma_{1_0}\left(\mathbf{E}^* - \frac{\mathbf{j}_e \times \mathbf{B}}{n_e e}\right) \qquad (j)$$

Thus, the reduction in the conductivity in the direction of the electric field is only 0.87.

5.6.5 Mixtures of Gases. The previous sections were based on the assumption of a single scattering species for electrons. In this section, the formulas will be extended to a mixture of several species, but where the electrons are still mainly responsible for electrical conduction. Thus, collisions between electrons are neglected, as are electromagnetic effects on the ion motion. The right side of Boltzmann's equation (5.3) must then be summed over all species s (except electrons). The modifications to (5.23), (5.24), and (5.25) are

$$f_0' - \frac{ec_e B^2 h_1}{m_e} = \nu_e(c_e)c_e f_1 \qquad (5.116)$$

$$\frac{ef_1}{m_e} = \nu_e(c_e)h_1 \qquad (5.117)$$

$$\frac{1}{3}\left(\frac{eE^*}{m_e}\right)^2 f_1 = m_e f_0 \sum_{s\neq e} \frac{\delta_s \nu_{es}}{m_s} + \frac{k}{c_e} f_0' \sum_{s\neq e} \frac{\delta_s \nu_{es} T_s}{m_s} \qquad (5.118)$$

where δ_s is the actual energy loss of an electron per collision with an s particle, divided by $2m_e/m_s$, and $\nu_e = \sum_{s\neq e} \nu_{es}$. In actual situations, the temperatures of the various species will be close to the average gas temperature T. Equations (5.116) to (5.118) can be rearranged as follows:

$$\frac{f_0'}{f_0} = -\frac{m_e c_e}{kT^*} \qquad (5.119)$$

$$f_1 = -\frac{\nu_e}{{\omega_e}^2 + {\nu_e}^2} \cdot \frac{m_e}{kT^*} f_0 \qquad (5.120)$$

$$h_1 = -\frac{e}{{\omega_e}^2 + {\nu_e}^2} \cdot \frac{f_0}{kT^*} \qquad (5.121)$$

where

$$T^* = T + \frac{1}{3}\left(\frac{eE^*}{m_e}\right)^2 \frac{\nu_e}{{\omega_e}^2 + {\nu_e}^2} \frac{1}{\sum_{s\neq e} \frac{\delta_s \nu_{es}}{m_s}} \qquad (5.122)$$

which are identical† in form to (5.27), (5.28), (5.65), and (5.67). Note the effect of δ_s in determining the electron temperature in (5.122). A

† If $\mathbf{E}^*$ has a component $E_\parallel$ parallel to $\mathbf{B}$, replace E^{*2} by $E_\perp^{*2} + E_\parallel^2(1 + {\omega_e}^2{\tau_e}^2)$.

small quantity of any species which has a large value of δ_s will dominate the term on the right and cause T^* to be close to T. Aside from this effect on T^*, the expressions for the electrical conductivity given by (5.78) to (5.89) remain identical except that ν_{es} must be replaced by

$$\nu_e = \sum_{s \neq e} \nu_{es} \tag{5.123}$$

For all maxwellian particles the conductivities become

$$\sigma_1 = \frac{n_e e^2 \nu_e}{m_e(\omega_e^2 + \nu_e^2)} = \frac{n_e e^2}{m_e \nu_e} \frac{1}{1 + \omega_e^2 \tau_e^2} \tag{5.124}$$

$$\sigma_2 = \frac{n_e e^2 \omega_e}{m_e(\omega_e^2 + \nu_e^2)} = \frac{n_e e^2}{m_e \nu_e} \frac{\omega_e \tau_e}{1 + \omega_e^2 \tau_e^2} \tag{5.125}$$

The value of σ_1 in the absence of a magnetic field may be written as

$$(\sigma_1)_{B=0} = \frac{n_e e^2}{m_e \sum\limits_{s \neq e} \nu_{es}} = \frac{1}{\sum\limits_{s \neq e} \dfrac{\nu_{es} m_e}{n_e e^2}} \tag{5.126}$$

The reciprocal of each term in the denominator of (5.126) may be regarded as the conductivity if only that particular species is present; thus (5.126) may be written as

$$(\sigma_1)_{B=0} = \frac{1}{\sum\limits_{s \neq e} \dfrac{1}{\sigma_{es}}} \tag{5.127}$$

where σ_{es} is σ_1 as defined by (5.78). An alternative viewpoint is that the *resistivities* are additive. Normally, (5.127) is broken up into only two terms, one for neutral particles (short-range forces) and one for ions (long-range forces), or

$$(\sigma_1)_{B=0} = \frac{n_e e^2}{m_e \left(\sum\limits_{s \neq e, I} \nu_{es} + \nu_{eI} \right)} \tag{5.128}$$

This may be written in the following alternative ways:

$$\sigma_1 = \frac{n_e e^2}{m_e \langle c_e \rangle (n_n \langle Q_{en} \rangle + n_I Q_{eI}^*)} \tag{5.129}$$

$$\sigma_1 = \frac{1}{1/\sigma_{en} + 1/\sigma_{eI}} \tag{5.130}$$

where $n_n = \sum\limits_{s \neq e, I} n_s$, that is, the total number of neutral particles, and $\langle Q_{en} \rangle$ is the average neutral cross section, given by

$$\langle Q_{en} \rangle = \sum_{s \neq e, I} \frac{n_s}{n_n} \langle Q_{es} \rangle \tag{5.131}$$

Also, σ_{eI} is given by (5.111). The cross sections in (5.129) are to be evaluated at the mean thermal velocity of electrons $\langle c_e \rangle$. To be correct in the limit as $n_n \to 0$, the cross section Q^*_{eI} in (5.129) should be related to $\langle Q_{eI} \rangle$ in (5.112) as follows (for $Z_I = 1$)[see Eq. (*e*), Sec. 5.6.4]:

$$Q^*_{eI} = \frac{\langle Q_{eI} \rangle}{0.582\pi} \tag{5.132}$$

Equations (5.129) and (5.130) are rigorous only if all particles are maxwellian. Sodha[17] has calculated σ_1 and σ_2 exactly for a mixture of electrons, ions, and maxwellian particles for $\omega_e \tau_e \ll 1$. The approximate formula (5.129) is compared to his calculation in Fig. 5.15. It is seen that use of (5.129) leads to an error of less than 2 per cent. For σ_2, the following formula may be used with less than 20 per cent error when $\omega_e \tau_e \ll 1$:

$$\sigma_2 = \frac{B\sigma_1^2}{n_e e} \tag{5.133}$$

In calculating the electrical conductivity of a partially ionized gas, it is easily seen that it is dominated by the species which has the greatest product of number density and cross section. Because the cross section of ions is very much larger than that of neutral particles (except at very

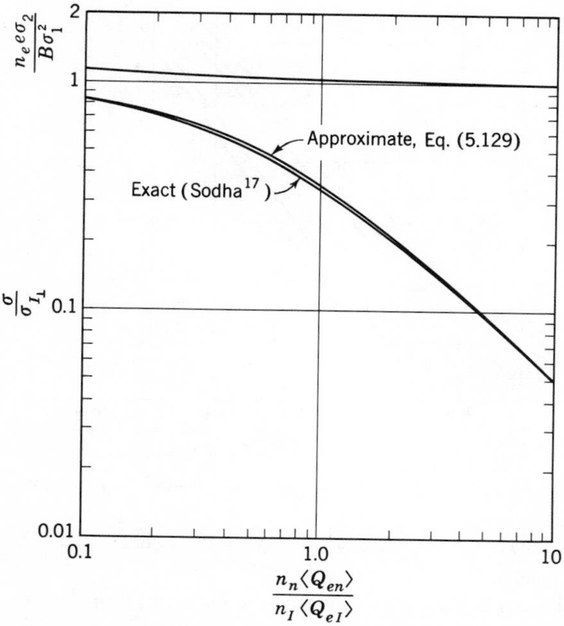

FIGURE 5.15 Variation of σ_1 and σ_2 with composition for a mixture of electrons, maxwellian particles, and ions ($Z_I = 1$) for $\omega_e \tau_e \ll 1$.

high temperatures), a small degree of ionization is sufficient for the ion cross section to dominate the collision frequency. The fraction of ionization where Q_{eI} begins to become important occurs when $n_n\langle Q_{en}\rangle = n_e\langle Q_{eI}\rangle$. At 5000°K, with $\langle Q_{en}\rangle = 10^{-21}$ m², these two terms are equal when $n_e/n_n \approx 2 \times 10^{-4}$, which is a very small degree of ionization. Thus, for a given gas mixture, as the temperature is increased from a low temperature, the electrical conductivity increases rapidly as the gas becomes ionized. But as soon as n_e/n_n exceeds $\langle Q_{en}\rangle/\langle Q_{eI}\rangle$, the conductivity increases only with the three-halves power of the temperature. At any given temperature, the maximum possible conductivity is that of a fully ionized gas at the same electron temperature. This conductivity and $\langle Q_{eI}\rangle$ are shown in Fig. 5-12.

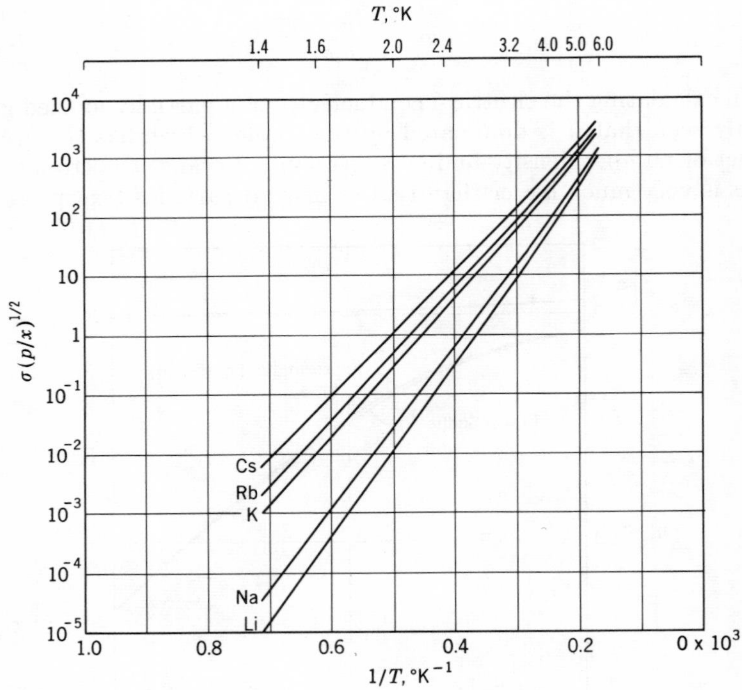

FIGURE 5.16 Electrical conductivity of seeded air, assuming that $\sum_s \left(\frac{n_s}{n}\right) Q_{es} = 10^{-11}$ cm²; effect of Q_I and Q_{seed} is neglected. Ionization of air is also neglected. Curve is therefore not valid for very small mole fraction of seed at high temperature. X = initial mole fraction of seed material; σ = electrical conductivity, ohm⁻¹ cm⁻¹; p = total pressure, atm. (From *Gen. Elec. Rept.* TIS R59SD459, by P. J. Friel, Dec. 1, 1959.)

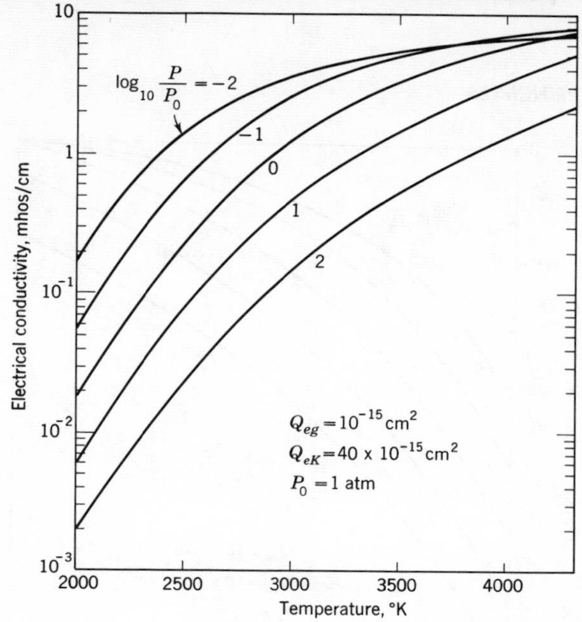

(*a*)

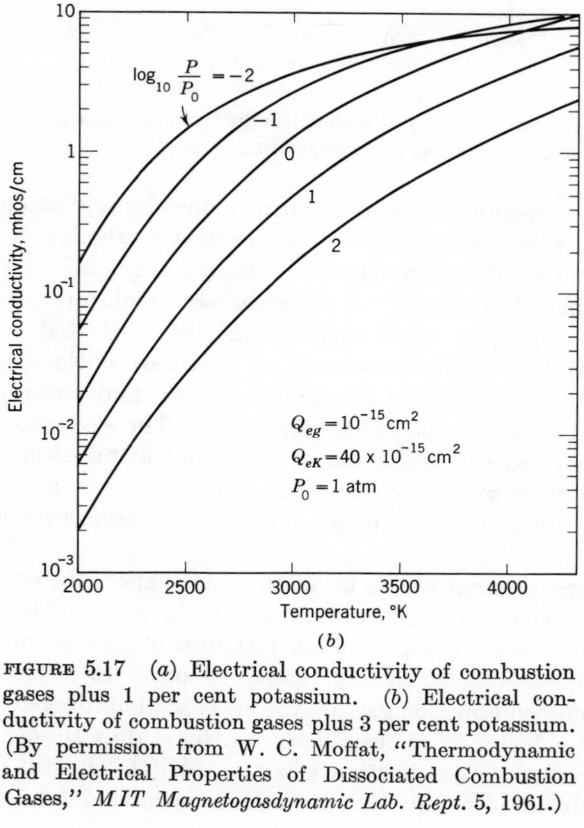

(*b*)

FIGURE 5.17 (*a*) Electrical conductivity of combustion gases plus 1 per cent potassium. (*b*) Electrical conductivity of combustion gases plus 3 per cent potassium. (By permission from W. C. Moffat, "Thermodynamic and Electrical Properties of Dissociated Combustion Gases," *MIT Magnetogasdynamic Lab. Rept.* 5, 1961.)

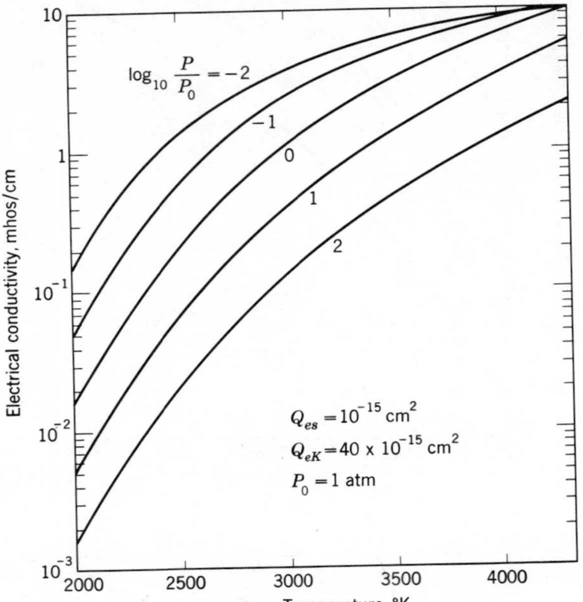

(c)

FIGURE 5.17 (*c*) **Electrical conductivity of combustion gases plus 10 per cent potassium.**

The cross sections for most neutral molecules and atoms vary only slightly with temperature; thus for approximate calculations, their cross sections may be taken as constant. Also, if the gas is only very slightly ionized so that electron-neutral collisions are much more frequent than electron-ion collisions, then $n_I\langle Q_{eI}\rangle$ may be neglected. Figure 5.16 shows the result of calculations based on these assumptions, for a mixture of various mole fractions of alkali metal vapor and air, where $\langle Q_{en}\rangle$ as given by (5.131) is assumed to be 10^{-15} cm². The electrons are assumed to be due only to the ionization of the alkali metal atoms. Actually, the electron cross section of the alkali metal atoms is much larger than 10^{-15} cm², so that Fig. 5.16 applies only for small concentrations of alkali metal.

For larger concentrations of alkali metal vapor, the cross section of the alkali metal atom must be included in the sum of (5.131). Such a calculation is shown in Fig. 5.17 for mixtures of potassium metal vapor and another gas with an average cross section of 10^{-15} cm². Although this is labeled "combustion gases," the cross section for combustion gases is larger by a factor of about 3 (see Fig. 5.4); thus these figures apply more to air than to combustion gases. Also $\langle Q_{eI}\rangle$ is still neglected, so that the calculated conductivities require correction for large ion con-

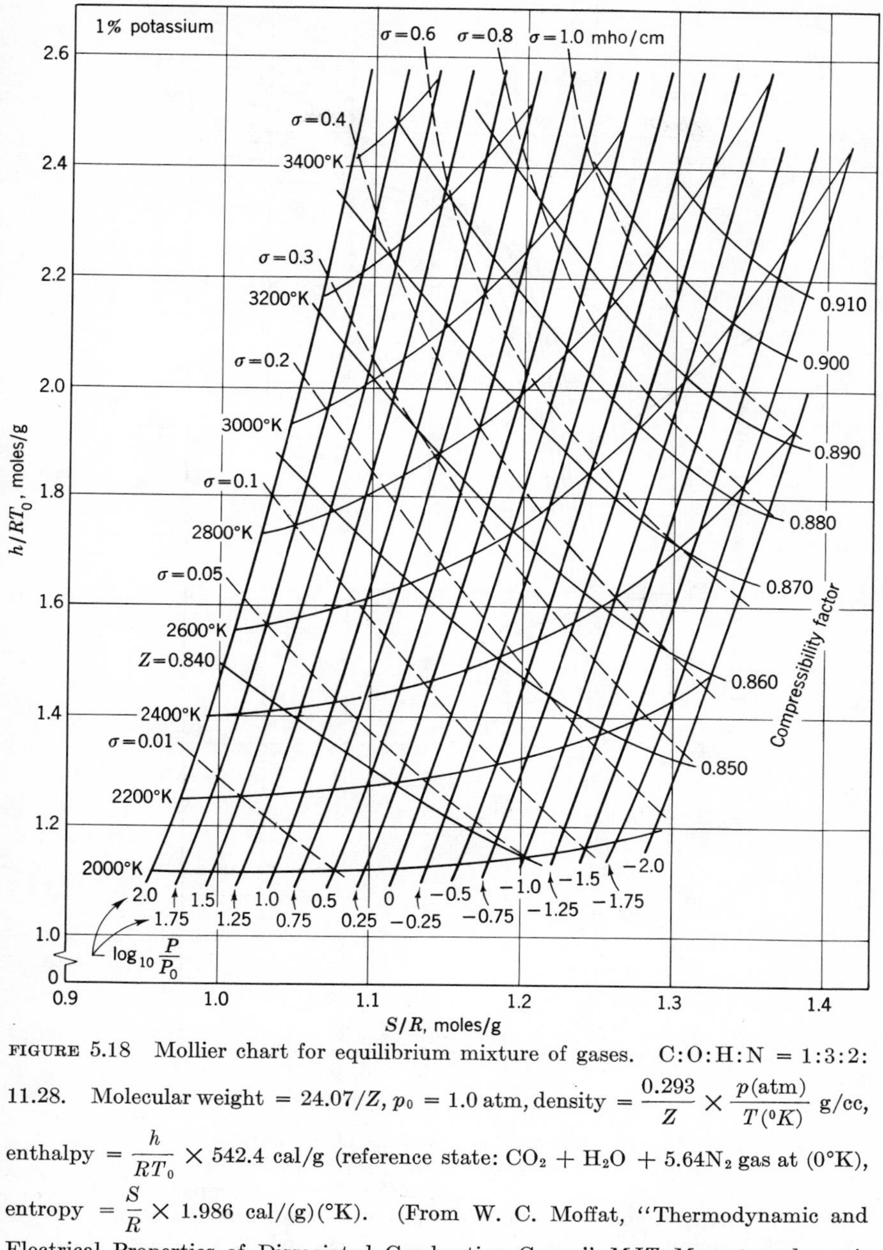

FIGURE 5.18 Mollier chart for equilibrium mixture of gases. C:O:H:N = 1:3:2:11.28. Molecular weight $= 24.07/Z$, $p_0 = 1.0$ atm, density $= \dfrac{0.293}{Z} \times \dfrac{p(\text{atm})}{T(^\circ\text{K})}$ g/cc, enthalpy $= \dfrac{h}{RT_0} \times 542.4$ cal/g (reference state: $CO_2 + H_2O + 5.64N_2$ gas at (0°K), entropy $= \dfrac{S}{R} \times 1.986$ cal/(g)(°K). (From W. C. Moffat, "Thermodynamic and Electrical Properties of Dissociated Combustion Gases," *MIT Magnetogasdynamic Lab. Rept.* 5, 1961.)

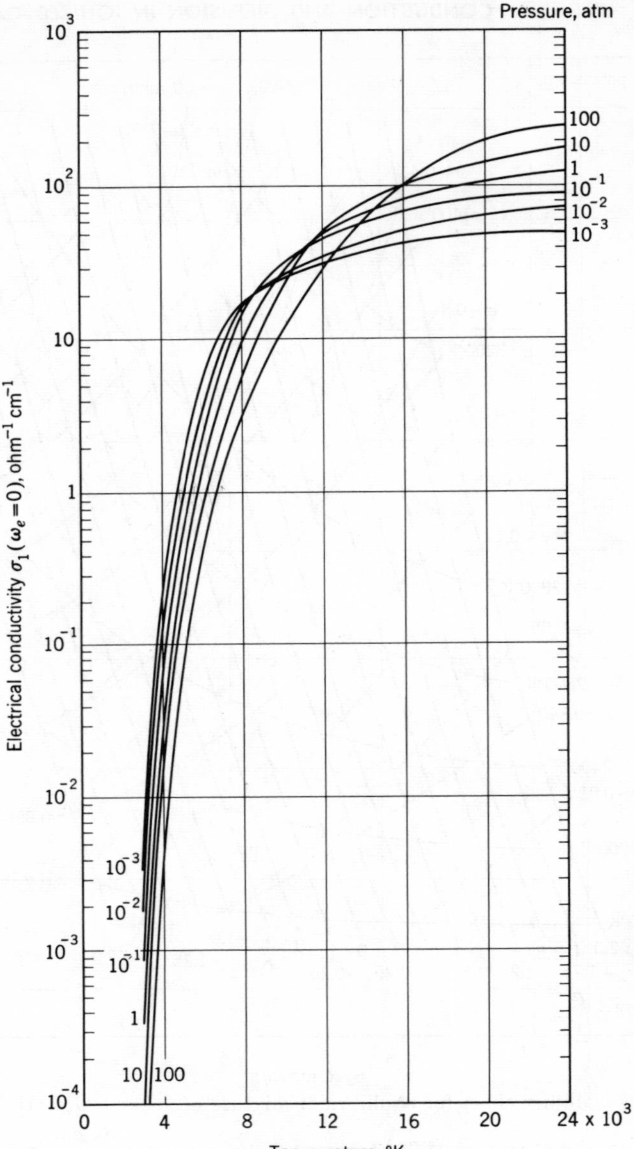

FIGURE 5.19 Electrical conductivity of equilibrium air, (1), constituents: N_2, NO, O_2, N, O, A, N_2^+, NO^+, O_2^+, O_2^+, N^+, O^+, O^-, A^+, N^{++}, O^{++}, A^{++}, N^{3+}, O^{3+}, e^-. Composition taken from (2). Cross sections based on mean thermal energy of electron. [(1) J. R. Viegas and T. C. Peng, "Electrical Conductivity of Ionized Air in Thermodynamic Equilibrium," *ARS J.* **31**:654 (1961).] [(2) G. Gilmore, "Equilibrium Composition and Thermodynamic Properties of Air to 24,000°K," *Rand Corp. Res. Mem.* 1543, August, 1955.]

centrations, corresponding to high temperature and low pressures. In Fig. 5.18, these approximate results have been superimposed on a Mollier chart for combustion gases.

A more realistic calculation takes into account the variation with temperature of the cross section of each chemical species, and the variation of chemical composition with temperature. Such a calculation is shown in Fig. 5.19 for air. The only approximations were as follows: (1) The cross sections of neutral particles were evaluated at the mean thermal electron energy, instead of by integration over the electron collision frequency; and (2) the additive rule of (5.130) has been extended to include doubly and triply ionized species instead of using the expression for σ_{eI} developed by Spitzer, which explicitly accounts for mixtures of multiply ionized ions. These errors, however, are less than 10 per cent.

5.7 THERMAL CONDUCTION AND DIFFUSION—LORENTZ APPROXIMATION[18]

In Sec. 5.4, the diffusion of electrons due to electric and magnetic fields was analyzed. But in addition to those two effects, temperature, concentration, and pressure gradients will cause electron diffusion. To obtain the effects of these additional gradients, it is necessary to retain the time and spatial terms in Boltzmann's equation as follows:

$$\frac{\partial f_e}{\partial t} + \mathbf{w}_e \cdot \nabla f_e - \frac{e}{m_e}(\mathbf{E}^* + \mathbf{c} \times \mathbf{B}) \cdot \nabla_w f_e = \int (f_e f_e - f'_e f'_e) gb\, db\, d\epsilon\, d\mathbf{c}_s$$
$$+ \sum_s \int (f_e f_s - f'_e f'_s) gb\, db\, d\epsilon\, d\mathbf{c}_s \qquad (5.134)$$

Collisions between electrons will be neglected. Before proceeding, the first two terms on the left should be transformed to mass-centered coordinates, to be consistent with the other terms. We therefore transform from the $\mathbf{w}_e$, $\mathbf{x}$, t coordinates to $\mathbf{c}_e$, $\mathbf{x}$, t, with $\mathbf{w}_e = \mathbf{v} + \mathbf{c}_e$, where $\mathbf{v}$ is the mass-centered velocity of the gas. Thus, $\nabla_w = \nabla_c$. Also,

$$\frac{\partial f}{\partial t} = \frac{\partial f}{\partial t} + \sum_i \frac{\partial f}{\partial c_i}\frac{\partial c_i}{\partial t} = -\nabla_c f \cdot \frac{\partial \mathbf{v}}{\partial t} + \frac{\partial f}{\partial t} \qquad (a)$$

Similarly,

$$\frac{\partial f}{\partial x_i} = \frac{\partial f}{\partial x_i} + \sum_j \frac{\partial f}{\partial c_j}\frac{\partial c_j}{\partial x_i} = \frac{\partial f}{\partial x_i} - \frac{\partial \mathbf{v}}{\partial x_i} \cdot \nabla_c f \qquad (b)$$

Substitution of (a) and (b) into (5.134) yields the following expression for the left side:

$$\frac{\partial f_e}{\partial t} - \frac{\partial \mathbf{v}}{\partial t} \cdot \nabla_c f_e + (\mathbf{c}_e + \mathbf{v}) \cdot \nabla f_e - \nabla_c f_e \cdot [(\mathbf{c}_e + \mathbf{v}) \cdot \nabla]\mathbf{v}$$
$$- \frac{e}{m_e}(\mathbf{E}^* + \mathbf{c}_e \times \mathbf{B}) \cdot \nabla_c f_e$$

Rearrangement and use of the tensor identity $\mathbf{a} \cdot (\mathbf{b} \cdot \nabla)\mathbf{c} = \mathbf{ab}:\nabla\mathbf{c}$ yields

$$\frac{Df_e}{Dt} + \mathbf{c} \cdot \nabla f_e - \left(\frac{D\mathbf{v}}{Dt} + \frac{e\mathbf{E}^*}{m_e}\right) \cdot \nabla_c f_e - \frac{e}{m_e}(\mathbf{c}_e \times \mathbf{B}) \cdot \nabla_c f_e - \nabla_c f_e \mathbf{c}_e : \nabla\mathbf{v} = \text{R.H.S.} \qquad (c)$$

The technique for solving this equation is the use of a series solution, as before. Thus, let

$$f_e = f_0 + (f_1)_E + (f_1)_\nabla + \cdots \qquad (d)$$

where f_0 is isotropic, $(f_1)_E$ is due only to electrical forces, and $(f_1)_\nabla$ is due to gradients. The heirarchy of equations is formed by substitution of (*d*) into (*c*) and equating similar terms. The equations for f_0 and $(f_1)_E$ are then given identically by (5.27) to (5.29). The remaining equations for $(f_1)_\nabla$ are contained in the rest of the terms. In the gradient terms, only the lowest order in f appears, as follows:

$$\frac{Df_0}{Dt} + \mathbf{c}_e \cdot \nabla f_0 - \frac{D\mathbf{v}}{Dt} \cdot \nabla_c f_0 - \nabla_c f_0 \mathbf{c}_e : \nabla\mathbf{v} = \sum_s \int f_s (f'_{1_\nabla} - f_{1_\nabla}) gb\, db\, d\epsilon\, d\mathbf{c}_s + \frac{e}{m_e}(\mathbf{c}_e \times \mathbf{B}) \cdot \nabla_c (f_1)_\nabla \qquad (e)$$

To proceed further, expressions are required for f_0 for the left side of (*e*). This can be obtained simply only if f_0 is maxwellian about the gas temperature T. Then,

$$\nabla f_0 = f_0 \left(\frac{\nabla n_e}{n_e} - \frac{3}{2}\frac{\nabla T}{T} + \frac{m_e c^2}{2kT^2}\nabla T\right) \qquad (f)$$

$$\nabla_c f_0 = -\frac{m_e \mathbf{c}_e}{kT} f_0 \qquad (g)$$

$$\frac{Df_0}{Dt} = f_0 \left(\frac{1}{n_e}\frac{Dn_e}{Dt} - \frac{3}{2T}\frac{DT}{Dt} + \frac{m_e c_e^2}{2kT^2}\frac{DT}{Dt}\right) \qquad (h)$$

The right side of (*h*) is still not in suitable form, and must be expressed in terms of gradients. This is accomplished by use of the Maxwell transport equations corresponding to an isotropic distribution function f_0. Thus, diffusion, heat conduction, and diagonal terms in the stress tensor are omitted. The resulting conservation equations are:

Number: $$\frac{Dn_e}{Dt} + n_e \nabla \cdot \mathbf{v} = 0 \qquad (i)$$

Global momentum: $$\rho \frac{Dv}{Dt} = \rho_e \mathbf{E}^* - \nabla p \qquad (j)$$

Global energy:

$$\frac{3}{2} kn \frac{DT}{Dt} = -p\nabla \cdot \mathbf{v} = -nkT\nabla \cdot \mathbf{v} \qquad (k)$$

In the momentum equation, the charge density is generally zero. In (*k*) it is assumed that the gas particles have zero internal energy so that the energy per particle is $\frac{3}{2}kT$. With the use of (*i*) and (*k*), (*h*) becomes

$$\frac{Df_0}{Dt} = -\frac{m_e c_e^2}{3kT} f_0 \nabla \cdot \mathbf{v} \qquad (h')$$

Then the left side of Boltzmann's equation (*e*) becomes†

$$f_0 \mathbf{c} \cdot \left[\frac{\nabla n_e}{n_e} + \left(\frac{m_e c_e^2}{2kT} - \frac{3}{2} \right) \frac{\nabla T}{T} - \frac{m_e}{\rho kT} \rho_e \mathbf{E}^* + \frac{m_e}{\rho kT} \nabla p \right] + \frac{m_e f_0}{kT} \mathbf{c}_e{}^\circ \mathbf{c}_e : \nabla \mathbf{v}$$
$$- \frac{e}{m_e} (\mathbf{c}_e \times \mathbf{B}) \cdot \nabla_c (f_1)_\nabla = \sum_s n_s c_e \int [(f_1)'_\nabla - (f_1)_\nabla] b\, db\, d\epsilon \qquad (l)$$

In (*l*), the off-diagonal terms of **cc** are small and may be neglected. Also, in the Lorentz approximation, g and $(f_1)_\nabla$ will not depend on c_s; thus $\int f_s\, d\mathbf{c}_s = n_s$ and $g = c_e$. Finally, use of the ideal gas and Dalton's law yields

$$\frac{\nabla n_e}{n_e} = \frac{n}{n_e} \nabla \frac{n_e}{n} + \frac{\nabla p}{p} - \frac{\nabla T}{T} \qquad (m)$$

Finally, let the "driving force" for Eq. (*l*) be defined as

$$\mathbf{G} = \frac{\nabla p}{p} + \frac{n}{n_e} \nabla \frac{n_e}{n} + \left(\frac{m_e c_e^2}{2kT} - \frac{5}{2} \right) \frac{\nabla T}{T} + \frac{m_e}{\langle m \rangle} \frac{\rho_e}{p} \mathbf{E}^* \qquad (n)$$

where the term involving $m_e/\rho kT$ has been neglected because of the small electron mass, and where $\langle m \rangle$ is the average particle mass in the gas. Then Eq. (*l*) may be written simply as

$$f_0 \mathbf{c}_e \cdot \mathbf{G} - \frac{e}{m_e} (\mathbf{c}_e \times \mathbf{B}) \cdot \nabla_c (f_1)_\nabla = \sum_s n_s c_e \int [(f_1)'_\nabla - (f_1)_\nabla] b\, db\, d\epsilon \qquad (o)$$

Comparison of (*o*) with (5.6) shows that they are identical if $\mathbf{E}^*$ is replaced by $kT\mathbf{G}/e$, and if the term involving $(e/m_e)\mathbf{E}^* \cdot \nabla_c f_1$ is omitted. In the previous analysis, the terms involving $\nabla_c f_1$ gave rise to (5.25). However, it is now necessary to take f_0 as maxwellian in order to obtain simple expressions for Df_0/Dt and ∇f_0. Substitution of a maxwellian distribution in the right side of (5.25) shows that this equation is satisfied if eE^*/m_e is sufficiently small; this then allows $(e/m_e)\mathbf{E}^* \cdot \nabla_c f_1$ to be omitted from the previous analysis. Thus, the distribution function is given by (5.7), (5.27), and (5.28), with $\mathbf{E}^*$ replaced by $\mathbf{E}^* + kT\mathbf{G}/e$, and f_0 taken as maxwellian. The result is

$$f_e = f_0 \left(1 - \mathbf{c}_e \cdot \mathbf{G}^* \frac{\nu_{es}}{\omega_e{}^2 + \nu_{es}^2} - \frac{\mathbf{B} \times \mathbf{G}^*}{B} \cdot \frac{\mathbf{c}_e \omega_e}{\omega_e{}^2 + \nu_{es}^2} \right) \qquad (5.135)$$

† Using $\mathbf{cc} = \mathbf{c}^0\mathbf{c} - \frac{1}{3}\mathbf{I}c^2$, and $\frac{1}{3}\mathbf{I} : \nabla \mathbf{v} = \frac{1}{3}\nabla \cdot \mathbf{v}$, where $\mathbf{c}^0\mathbf{c}$ is the traceless dyadic, and $\mathbf{I}$ is the unit dyadic δ_{ij}.

where, from (n),

$$\mathbf{G}^* = \mathbf{G} + \frac{e\mathbf{E}^*}{kT} = \frac{\nabla p}{p} + \frac{n}{n_e}\nabla\frac{n_e}{n} + \left(\frac{m_e c_e^2}{2kT} - \frac{5}{2}\right)\frac{\nabla T}{T} + \frac{e\mathbf{E}^*}{kT}\left(1 + \frac{m_e}{\rho}\sum_s n_s Z_s\right) \qquad (p)$$

In analogy with (5.76), the total electron diffusion can therefore be written as follows, with the use of the expression for $\mathbf{G}^*$ from (p):

$$\mathbf{V}_e = -\frac{1}{3n_e}\int\left[\frac{e\mathbf{E}^*}{kT}\left(1 + \frac{m_e}{\rho}\sum_s n_s Z_s\right) + \frac{\nabla p}{p} + \frac{n}{n_e}\nabla\frac{n_e}{n} + \left(\frac{m_e c_e^2}{2kT} - \frac{5}{2}\right)\frac{\nabla T}{T}\right]\cdot\frac{c_e^2 f_0 \nu_{es}}{(\omega_e^2 + \nu_{es}^2)}\,d\mathbf{c}_e - \frac{1}{3n_e}\frac{\mathbf{B}}{B}\times\int\left[\frac{e\mathbf{E}^*}{kT}\left(1 + \frac{m_e}{\rho}\sum_s n_s Z_s\right) + \frac{\nabla p}{p} + \frac{n}{n_e}\nabla\frac{n_e}{n} + \left(\frac{m_e c_e^2}{2kT} - \frac{5}{2}\right)\frac{\nabla T}{T}\right]\cdot\frac{c_e^2 f_0 \omega_e}{(\omega_e^2 + \nu_{es}^2)}\,d\mathbf{c}_e \qquad (5.136)$$

The first term in each integral is the electrical conduction due to $\mathbf{E}^*$; the other terms are pressure, concentration, and thermal diffusion, respectively. Note that the thermal-diffusion term is zero for maxwellian molecules, for which ν_{es} is a constant. In terms of the Ω_{ij} tensor given by (5.92), (5.136) can also be written as

$$\mathbf{V}_e = -\frac{4\pi}{3n_e}\int f_0 c_e^4(\mathbf{\Omega}\cdot\mathbf{G}^*)\,dc_e \qquad (5.136a)$$

In terms of diffusion coefficients, (5.136) can be rewritten as follows for a binary mixture of electrons and s particles:

$$V_{e_i} = \sum_j\left[\mu_{ij}E_j^*\left(1 + \frac{m_e}{\rho}\sum_s n_s Z_s\right) - \frac{m_s}{\langle m\rangle}(\mathfrak{D}_{es})_{ij}\frac{\partial}{\partial x_j}\left(\ln\frac{n_e}{n} + \ln p\right) - \frac{\alpha_{ij}}{n_e m_e}\frac{\partial}{\partial x_j}\ln T\right] \qquad (5.137)$$

The electron-mobility tensor μ_{ij} is simply related to the electrical conductivity tensor as follows:

$$\mu_{ij} = -\frac{\sigma_{ij}}{n_e e} \qquad (5.138)$$

The ordinary binary-diffusion coefficients are the tensor $(\mathfrak{D}_{es})_{ij}$ and are given by

$$(\mathfrak{D}_{es})_{ij} = -\frac{\langle m\rangle}{m_s}\frac{kT}{e}\mu_{ij} \approx -\frac{n_s}{n}\frac{kT}{e}\mu_{ij} \qquad (5.139)$$

where $\langle m\rangle$ is the average particle mass in the mixture, which in a binary mixture with electrons is essentially m_s. The α_{ij} are the thermal-diffusion coefficients. With the magnetic field taken in the z direction, the components of the thermal-diffusion tensor are as follows:

$$\alpha_{ij} = \frac{m_e}{3} \int \left(\frac{m_e c_e^2}{2kT} - \frac{5}{2} \right) c_e^2 \Omega_{ij} f_0 \, d\mathbf{c}_e \tag{5.140}$$

where Ω_{ij} is given by (5.92). The thermal-diffusion coefficient is very sensitive to the electron-particle force law in sharp contrast to electrical conductivity. For example, for

$$s = 2 \qquad \alpha_{33} = \frac{3\pi^2}{16} \frac{m_e n_e \langle c_e \rangle^2}{\langle \nu_e \rangle} \tag{q}$$

$$s = 5 \qquad \alpha_{33} = 0 \tag{r}$$

$$s = \infty \qquad \alpha_{33} = -\frac{1}{6} \frac{m_e n_e \langle c_e \rangle^2}{\langle \nu_e \rangle} \tag{s}$$

Note that the sign changes at $s = 5$, and that α_{33} is zero for maxwellian particles. Spitzer and Härm[15] have also calculated the correction to α_{33} due to electron-electron collisions. For $Z_I = 1$, Eq. (q) must be multiplied by 0.2727.

Equation (5.137) is actually quite simple, and is a result of neglecting the diffusion of all heavy particles and neglecting electron-electron collisions which tend to cause the electron distribution function to be somewhat closer to a displaced maxwellian than predicted by the Lorentz theory as developed above.[15] In spite of these restrictions, the theory is adequate for most purposes. Other theories have been developed to account for the diffusion of all particles, for example, the Chapman-Enskog method, and its extensions by Hirshfelder, Curtiss, and Bird.[19] However, this theory requires other assumptions and is not as accurate numerically for electrons (see Sec. 5.8).

In a similar manner, the heat conduction can be calculated as follows:

$$\mathbf{q}_e = \frac{m_e}{2} \int c_e^2 \mathbf{c}_e f_e \, d\mathbf{c}_e$$

where $f_e = f_0 + (f_1)_E + (f_1)_\nabla$. With the use of (5.135) and Eq. (p), the electron heat conduction is

$$\begin{aligned} \mathbf{q}_e = &-\frac{m_e}{6} \left(\mathbf{G}^{**} \int \frac{c_e^4 f_0 \nu_e}{\omega_e^2 + \nu_e^2} \, d\mathbf{c}_e + \frac{\mathbf{B}}{B} \times \mathbf{G}^{**} \int \frac{c_e^4 f_0 \omega_e}{\omega_e^2 + \nu_e^2} \, d\mathbf{c}_e \right) \\ &- \frac{m_e}{6} \left[\frac{\nabla T}{T} \int \left(\frac{m_e c_e^2}{2kT} - \frac{5}{2} \right) \frac{c_e^4 f_0 \nu_e}{\omega_e^2 + \nu_e^2} \, d\mathbf{c}_e \right. \\ &\left. + \frac{\mathbf{B}}{B} \times \frac{\nabla T}{T} \int \left(\frac{m_e c_e^2}{2kT} - \frac{5}{2} \right) \frac{c_e^4 f_0 \omega_e}{\omega_e^2 + \nu_e^2} \, d\mathbf{c}_e \right] \end{aligned} \tag{5.141}$$

where $\mathbf{G}^{**}$ is the driving force due to electric fields, pressure gradients, and electron-concentration gradients defined as follows:

$$\mathbf{G}^{**} = \frac{eE^*}{kT}\left(1 + \frac{m_e}{\rho}\sum n_s Z_s\right) + \frac{\nabla P}{p} + \frac{n}{n_e}\nabla\frac{n_e}{n} \tag{5.142}$$

Equation (5.141) can be written more conveniently in tensor form,

$$q_{e_i} = -\sum_j \left(\beta_{ij}G_j^{**} + \mathcal{K}_{ij}\frac{\partial T}{\partial x_j}\right) \tag{5.143}$$

where β_{ij} are the coefficients of heat conduction due to diffusion,

$$\beta_{ij} = \frac{m_e}{6}\int \Omega_{ij} f_0 c_e^{\,4}\, d\mathbf{c}_e \tag{5.144}$$

and $\mathcal{K}_{ij}$ are the coefficients of thermal conductivity,

$$\mathcal{K}_{ij} = \frac{m_e}{6T}\int \Omega_{ij}\left(\frac{m_e c_e^{\,2}}{2kT} - \frac{5}{2}\right) f_0 c_e^{\,4}\, d\mathbf{c}_e \tag{5.145}$$

where Ω_{ij} is given by (5.92) and $d\mathbf{c}_e = 4\pi c_e^{\,2}\, dc_e$. As with the components of σ_{ij} and α_{ij}, calculation of the components of $\mathcal{K}_{ij}$ other than $\mathcal{K}_{33}$ is complex. But for $\mathcal{K}_{33}$ with an inverse-power law for which the cross section is given by (5.47), the following is obtained:

$$\mathcal{K}_{33} = \frac{n_e k}{3\pi^{\frac{3}{2}} A_1 n_s}\left(\frac{m_e}{|\alpha_{es}|}\right)^{2/(s-1)}\left(\frac{2kT}{m_e}\right)^{(s+3)/2(s-1)}\left[\Gamma\left(\frac{4s-2}{s-1}\right) - \frac{5}{2}\Gamma\left(\frac{3s-1}{s-1}\right)\right] \tag{5.146}$$

Note that $\mathcal{K}_{33}$ is sensitive to the value of s: For $s = 2$, the thermal conductivity increases as the $\frac{5}{2}$ power of temperature; for $s = 5$, the thermal conductivity is directly proportional to temperature; while for $s = \infty$, it is proportional to the square root of temperature. This dependence on temperature is similar to that of electrical conductivity, except that the temperature exponent is increased by unity from that of electrical conductivity. But as with electrical conductivity, this temperature dependence is small compared with the temperature dependence of n_e, until n_e reaches the point at which electron-ion and electron-electron collisions are the dominant effect, after which $\mathcal{K}_{33} \sim T^{\frac{5}{2}}$. This, of course, occurs for very small ratios of n_e/n_n for most gases.

In terms of the average cross section given by (5.95), Eq. (5.146) can be written as

$$\mathcal{K}_{33} = \frac{n_e\langle c_e\rangle k}{3n_s\langle Q\rangle_{es}}\left(\frac{\pi}{4}\right)^{2/(s-1)}\left[\Gamma\left(\frac{4s-2}{s-1}\right) - \tfrac{5}{2}\Gamma\left(\frac{3s-1}{s-1}\right)\right]$$

The thermal conductivity of electrons can also be expressed in terms of the electrical conductivity (5.96), as follows:

$$\mathcal{K}_{33} = \sigma_1 \frac{k^2 T_e}{e^2} \left[\frac{2s}{s-1} \left(\frac{2s}{s-1} - \frac{3}{2} \right) \right]$$

The factors in the brackets is unity for $s = \infty$, and is $\frac{5}{2}$ for $s = 5$. Thus, as a general rule, the thermal conductivity is proportional to the product of the electrical conductivity and the electron temperature. This relation is known as the Wiedemann-Franz law.

For a fully ionized gas, or one in which charged-particle collisions are dominant, (5.146) must be corrected for electron-electron collisions by a factor[15] of 0.2252 for $Z_I = 1$. Thus, (5.146) becomes

$$\mathcal{K}_{33} \begin{pmatrix} Z_I = 1 \\ s = 2 \end{pmatrix} = (0.2252)(20) \left(\frac{2}{\pi} \right)^{\frac{3}{2}} \frac{(4\pi K_0)^2 (kT)^{\frac{5}{2}} k}{m_e^{\frac{1}{2}} e^4 \ln \Lambda} \tag{5.147}$$

Landshoff[20,21] has calculated $\mathcal{K}_{11} = \mathcal{K}_{22}$ and $\mathcal{K}_{12} = -\mathcal{K}_{21}$ for $\mathbf{B} \neq 0$ taking into account electron-electron collisions. These results are shown in Fig. 5.20. It is important to note that when $\nu_{eI} \gg \nu_{en}$, then (5.147) is the *complete* thermal conductivity of the gas, because electrons dominate the thermal conduction. When electrons are so few that this condition is not fulfilled, (5.146) only gives the contribution to the thermal conductivity due to electrons. To obtain the total thermal conductivity, the thermal conduction of the neutral particles must also be taken into account.

Returning to (5.143), two further simplifications are possible. First, β_{ij} are not independent coefficients, for comparison of (5.91*a*), (5.140), and (5.144) shows that

$$\beta_{ij} = \frac{kT}{m_e} \alpha_{ij} + \frac{5}{2} \left(\frac{kT}{e} \right)^2 \sigma_{ij} \tag{5.148}$$

Thus (5.143) can be written as

$$q_{e_i} = - \sum_j \left[\frac{kT}{m_e} \alpha_{ij} G_j^{**} + \frac{5}{2} \left(\frac{kT}{e} \right)^2 \sigma_{ij} G_j^{**} + \mathcal{K}_{ij} \frac{\partial T}{\partial x_j} \right] \tag{5.149}$$

Secondly, a temperature gradient causes thermal diffusion, and diffusion contributes to the energy-flux vector. To clearly separate these two effects, it is desirable to eliminate $\mathbf{G}^{**}$ from (5.143) with the use of the expression for $\mathbf{V}_e$. Now (5.137) may be written as follows, with the use of (5.138), (5.139), and (5.142):

$$V_{e_i} = - \sum_j \left(\frac{\sigma_{ij} kT}{n_e e^2} G_j^{**} + \frac{\alpha_{ij}}{n_e m_e T} \frac{\partial T}{\partial x_j} \right) \tag{5.150}$$

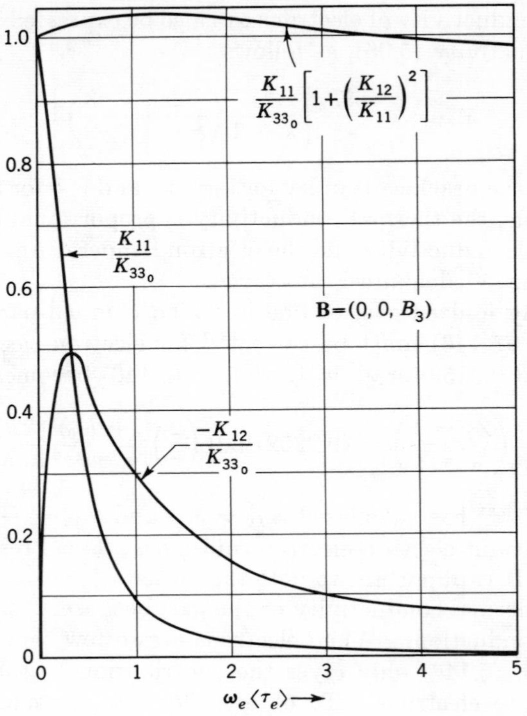

FIGURE 5.20 Thermal conductivity of a fully ionized gas, $Z_1 = 1$, when $E^* = 0$ and K_{33_0} refers to $B = 0$. [R. Landshoff, *Phys. Rev.*, 76:904 (1949).]

Thus, from (5.150),

$$-\sum_j \frac{kT}{e^2} \sigma_{ij} G_j^{**} = n_e V_{e_i} + \sum_j \frac{\alpha_{ij}}{m_e T} \frac{\partial T}{\partial x_j} \tag{t}$$

and, by matrix inversion,

$$-G_j^{**} = \frac{e^2}{kT} \sum_k (\sigma_{kj})^{-1} \left(n_e V_{e_k} + \sum_l \frac{\alpha_{kl}}{m_e T} \frac{\partial T}{\partial x_l} \right) \tag{u}$$

The reciprocal conductivity tensor is the resistivity tensor given by (5.93). Thus Eq. (*u*) becomes

$$-G_j^{**} = \sum_k \frac{e^2}{kT} \eta_{kj} \left(n_e V_{e_k} + \sum_l \frac{\alpha_{kl}}{m_e T} \frac{\partial T}{\partial x_l} \right) \tag{v}$$

Substitution of (t) and (u) into (5.149) with the use of (5.148) yields

$$q_{e_i} = \frac{5}{2} kTn_eV_{e_i} + \frac{n_e e^2}{m_e} \sum_{j,k} \alpha_{ij}\eta_{kj}V_{ek} - \sum_j \left(\mathcal{K}_{ij} - \frac{5}{2}\frac{k}{m_e}\alpha_{ij} - \frac{e^2}{m_e{}^2 T} \sum_{k,l} \alpha_{il}\eta_{kl}\alpha_{kj} \right) \frac{\partial T}{\partial x_j} \qquad (w)$$

The first and second terms within the parentheses can be combined using (5.140), (5.145). The result is

$$q_{e_i} = \frac{5}{2} kTn_eV_{e_i} + \frac{n_e e^2}{m_e} \sum_{j,k} \alpha_{ij}\eta_{kj}V_{ek} - \sum_j \left(\mathcal{K}^*_{ij} - \frac{e^2}{m_e{}^2 T} \sum_{k,l} \alpha_{il}\eta_{kl}\alpha_{kj} \right) \frac{\partial T}{\partial x_j} \qquad (5.151)$$

where

$$\mathcal{K}^*_{ij} = \mathcal{K}_{ij} - \frac{5}{2}\frac{k}{m_e}\alpha_{ij} = \frac{k}{3} \int \left(\frac{m_e c_e{}^2}{2kT} - \frac{5}{2} \right)^2 c_e{}^2 \Omega_{ij} f_0 \, d\mathbf{c}_e \qquad (x)$$

is the coefficient of thermal conductivity associated with the form of the heat flux given by (5.151). From this form, it is evident that $\mathcal{K}^*_{ij}$ is always positive. Since α_{ij} may be negative or positive, (x) is proof that $\mathcal{K}_{ij}$ is also always positive.

Equation (5.151) is somewhat complex and requires some explanation. First, when the magnetic field is zero, the off-diagonal components of all the transport properties are zero, and the diagonal components are equal to each other. Under these conditions, the expression in parentheses in (5.151) is called the *ordinary thermal conductivity*. Second, when the coefficients of thermal diffusion are zero, (5.151) reduces to a much simpler form. For this reason, in (5.151) it is usual to take the α_{ij} equal to zero, but they may still be retained in (5.150) to calculate the diffusion. Third, in the energy equation (k), Sec. 5.7, the energy of the electron was taken as $\frac{3}{2}kT$, to which another kT was later added to give a total of $\frac{5}{2}kT$ for the first term in (5.151). Now, $\frac{5}{2}kT/m_e$ is the enthalpy of electrons per unit mass; if the energy equation (k) had originally been written in terms of total energy, including chemical (that is, ionization) energy, then the first term in (5.151) would become

$$q_{e_i} = h_e n_e m_e V_{e_i} \qquad (y)$$

where h_e is the sensible enthalpy plus chemical enthalpy of the electrons. The generalization of (5.151) to include the contribution of heat conduction of all species but neglecting the contribution from thermal diffusion is[19]

$$\mathbf{q}_{\text{total}} = \sum_s \rho_s h_s \mathbf{V}_s - \mathcal{K}_{\text{total}} \cdot \nabla T \qquad (5.152)$$

5.8 ELECTRICAL CONDUCTION AND DIFFUSION IN PARTIALLY IONIZED GASES

In the previous sections, expressions for the electron conduction were derived by ignoring the ion current, which implies that the ion current is so small that it neither contributes to the total current nor affects the electron motion. These conditions are fulfilled either in a fully ionized gas, because the ion velocity is essentially equal to the gas velocity owing to the large mass ratio, or in a partially ionized gas because of the small ion mobility. However, the latter condition is correct only when the Hall parameter for electrons, $\omega_e\tau_e$, is small. For large values of the Hall parameter for electrons, the electron current is reduced, so that the ion current is no longer negligible in comparison to the electron current. It should be noted that the Hall parameter for ions, $\omega_I\tau_I$, is usually smaller than that for electrons, $\omega_e\tau_e$, because of larger ion mass.

To obtain the diffusion and electrical conduction in such a mixture of gases, including the effects of diffusion of all species, the Boltzmann equation should be solved simultaneously for all species. Because of its complexity, this solution can be obtained only approximately, and in addition few solutions exist at present which also include thermal diffusion and heat conduction in a magnetic field.[22] The approximation appears mainly in the calculation of the transport properties: They are calculated in the *absence* of the magnetic field. Thus, to consider the additional complexity of the ion current, again some sacrifice in accuracy must be made.

5.8.1 Species-momentum Transfer. To start on the multicomponent gas, we will use the species-momentum equation (4.159), instead of the Boltzmann equation, but with some simplifications. For a single species, the momentum terms on the left side are not independent of the overall momentum; in fact, if the diffusion velocities are small, then (4.159) may be written as follows for the rth species:

$$\frac{\rho_r}{\rho}\left(\frac{\partial \rho \mathbf{v}}{\partial t} + \nabla \cdot \rho \mathbf{v}\mathbf{v}\right) + \rho \mathbf{v}\left(\frac{D}{Dt}\frac{\rho_r}{\rho}\right) + \nabla \cdot \mathsf{p}_r = \mathbf{P}_r + n_r e Z_r(\mathbf{E}^* + \mathbf{V}_r \times \mathbf{B}) \tag{5.153}$$

Next, since the diagonal terms in the pressure tensor do not contribute to the diffusion, these will be neglected. Also, the second term above will be neglected, since this term is zero when $\mathbf{v}$ is zero. Then, with the use of overall conservation of mass, (5.153) becomes

$$\rho_r \frac{D\mathbf{v}}{Dt} + \nabla p_r = \mathbf{P}_r + n_r e Z_r(\mathbf{E}^* + \mathbf{V}_r \times \mathbf{B}) \tag{5.154}$$

where $\mathbf{P}_r$ is the momentum-exchange integral, given by (4.158),

$$\mathbf{P}_r = \int m_r \mathbf{w}_r \left(\frac{\partial f_r}{\partial t}\right)_c d\mathbf{w}_r + \int m_r \mathbf{w}_r \left(\frac{\partial f_r}{\partial t}\right)_{\text{inelastic}} d\mathbf{w}_r \qquad (a)$$

where
$$\left(\frac{\partial f_r}{\partial t}\right)_c = \sum_s \int (f_r' f_s' - f_r f_s) g b \, db \, d\epsilon \, d\mathbf{w}_s \qquad (b)$$

The first term in (a) accounts for the momentum change during elastic collisions, while the second term accounts for changes in momentum during inelastic collisions, the most important of which are chemical reactions. However, since in the present model it is assumed that all species share the total momentum in proportion to their relative mass density, this term may be neglected.

Combining (a) and (b),

$$\mathbf{P}_r = m_r \sum_s \int (\mathbf{w}_r f_r' f_s' - \mathbf{w}_r f_r f_s) g b \, db \, d\epsilon \, d\mathbf{w}_r \, d\mathbf{w}_s \qquad (c)$$

Since the integral of $\Theta f_r' f_s'$ is the same as for $\Theta' f_r f_s$, then (c) becomes

$$\mathbf{P}_r = m_r \sum_s \int (\mathbf{w}_r' - \mathbf{w}_r) f_r f_s g b \, db \, d\epsilon \, d\mathbf{w}_r \, d\mathbf{w}_s \qquad (d)$$

Equation (d) illustrates a basic difficulty when the transport equations are used, because the *form* of the distribution function in (d) must be assumed in order to evaluate the integral. Thus, it is usually assumed that the distribution function for each species is a *displaced* maxwellian about the mean velocity of that species; that is,

$$\mathbf{w}_r = \mathbf{v}_r + \mathbf{c}_r' \qquad (e)$$
$$f_r = a_r e^{-b_r c_r'^2} \qquad (f)$$

In order to evaluate (d), we may express $\mathbf{w}_r$ in terms of $\mathbf{g}$, and then $\mathbf{g}$ in terms of $\mathbf{c}_r'$, although other methods of substitution can be used. First, the center of mass velocity during a collision is given by

$$\mathbf{G} = \frac{m_s \mathbf{w}_s + m_r \mathbf{w}_r}{m_r + m_s} = \mathbf{G}' \qquad (g)$$

that is, the center of mass velocity before and after a collision is identical, owing to conservation of momentum. Next, the relative velocity between two particles is given by

$$\mathbf{g} = \mathbf{w}_r - \mathbf{w}_s \qquad (h)$$

Elimination of $\mathbf{w}_s$ between (g) and (h) yields

$$\mathbf{w}_r = \frac{m_s}{m_r + m_s} \mathbf{g} + \mathbf{G} \qquad (i)$$

before a collision, and

$$\mathbf{w}_r' = \frac{m_s}{m_r + m_s}\mathbf{g}' + \mathbf{G}' \qquad (j)$$

after a collision. Subtraction of (j) from (i) yields

$$\mathbf{w}_r' - \mathbf{w}_r = \frac{m_s}{m_r + m_s}(\mathbf{g}' - \mathbf{g}) \qquad (k)$$

In the direction of $\mathbf{g}$, then, $(\mathbf{g}' - \mathbf{g}) = -\mathbf{g}(1 - \cos\chi)$, where χ is angle of deflection of the relative velocity because of the collision. Also, the cross section for the collision is given by $Q_{rs} = \int(1 - \cos\chi)b\,db\,d\epsilon$; thus (d) becomes

$$\mathbf{P}_r = -\frac{m_r m_s}{m_r + m_s}\sum_s \int g\mathbf{g}Q_{rs}(g)f_r f_s\,d\mathbf{c}_r'\,d\mathbf{c}_s' \qquad (l)$$

since $d\mathbf{w}_r = d\mathbf{c}_r'$. Next, the g and Q_{rs} are to be expressed in terms of $\mathbf{c}_r'$, $\mathbf{c}_s'$, $\mathbf{v}_s$, and $\mathbf{v}_r$. First,

$$\mathbf{g}' = \mathbf{w}_r' - \mathbf{w}_s' = (\mathbf{c}_r' - \mathbf{c}_s') + (\mathbf{v}_r - \mathbf{v}_s) \qquad (m)$$

so that $$g' = \sqrt{\mathbf{g}'\cdot\mathbf{g}'} = [(\mathbf{c}_r' - \mathbf{c}_s')\cdot(\mathbf{c}_r' - \mathbf{c}_s') + 2(\mathbf{v}_r - \mathbf{v}_s)\cdot(\mathbf{c}_r' - \mathbf{c}_s') + (\mathbf{v}_r - \mathbf{v}_s)\cdot(\mathbf{v}_r - \mathbf{v}_s)]^{\frac{1}{2}} \qquad (n)$$

To simplify the radical, it is assumed that the r species is an electron and that s is a heavy particle; also that $\mathbf{v}_e$ and $\mathbf{v}_s$ are comparable to $\mathbf{c}_s'$, which is much smaller than $\mathbf{c}_e'$. Thus (n) can be simplified as follows:

$$g' = \sqrt{c_e'^2 - 2(\mathbf{c}_e\cdot\mathbf{c}_s) + 2(\mathbf{v}_e - \mathbf{v}_s)\cdot\mathbf{c}_e + \cdots}$$

and use of the binomial expansion yields

$$g \equiv g' = c_e' - \frac{\mathbf{c}_e'\cdot\mathbf{c}_s'}{c_e'} + \frac{(\mathbf{v}_e - \mathbf{v}_s)\cdot\mathbf{c}_e'}{c_e'} + \cdots \qquad (o)$$

Next, the cross section is evaluated in terms of c_e', by the following Taylor expansion:

$$Q_{es}(c_e') = Q_{es}(g) + \frac{dQ_{es}}{dc_e}(c_e' - g) \qquad (p)$$

Finally, substitution of (f), (m), (o), and (p) into (l) and integration by parts of terms containing dQ_{es}/dc_e' yield

$$\mathbf{P}_{es} = (\mathbf{v}_s - \mathbf{v}_e)\frac{n_s m_e}{3kT}\int Q_{es}(c_e')c_e'^3 f_e\,d\mathbf{c}_e' \qquad (5.155)$$

where higher-order terms are neglected, as can be m_e compared to m_s. Next, for f_e maxwellian, an average collision frequency ν_{es}^* can be defined by

$$\nu_{es}^{*} = \tfrac{4}{3}n_s\langle c_e\rangle \int_0^\infty e^{-\xi^2}\xi^5 Q_{es}\left(\sqrt{\frac{2kT}{m}}\,\xi\right)d\xi \tag{5.156}$$

so that (5.155) becomes

$$\mathbf{P}_e = m_e n_e \sum_s (\mathbf{v}_s - \mathbf{v}_e)\nu_{es}^{*} \tag{5.157}$$

If the gas contains only a single heavy species s, then (5.154) may be used to define an electrical conductivity in a manner similar to (5.108),

$$\mathbf{j} = \sigma_{es}(\mathbf{E}^{*} + \mathbf{V}_e \times \mathbf{B}) \tag{5.158}$$

where

$$\sigma_{es} = \frac{n_e e^2}{m_e \nu_{es}^{*}} = \frac{3}{4}\,\frac{n_e e^2}{m_e n_s\langle c_e\rangle \int_0^\infty e^{-\xi^2}\xi^5 Q_{es}\left(\sqrt{\frac{2kT}{m}}\,\xi\right)d\xi} \tag{5.159}$$

This procedure, based on the momentum equation instead of the Boltzmann equation, is generally called the *first approximation* of the Chapman-Enskog method. The results differ from the Lorentz model in several respects. First, only one electrical conductivity is defined instead of three, and this one is calculated independent of the magnetic field. Also, the integration over the distribution function appears in the denominator of (5.159) instead of in the numerator as in the Lorentz model. Because of these differences, it is not expected that (5.159) will yield exact values for the electrical conductivities; the utility of this method depends on the inclusion of ions. We can estimate the error in the use of (5.159) by use of an inverse-power law. With Q_{es} given by (5.47), integration of (5.159) yields

$$\sigma_{es} = \frac{3}{8\pi^{\frac{1}{2}}}\frac{n_e e^2}{m_e n_s}\left(\frac{2kT}{m}\right)^{(5-s)/2(s-1)}\left(\frac{m_e}{\alpha_{es}}\right)^{2/(s-1)}\frac{1}{A_1(s)\Gamma\left(\dfrac{3s-5}{s-1}\right)} \tag{5.160}$$

Compared to the Lorentz model, (5.94), $\sigma_{es} = \sigma_1$ only for $s = 5$. For $s = \infty$, σ_{e_∞} reduces to the following simple form:

$$\sigma_{e_\infty} = \frac{3}{4}\frac{n_e e^2}{m_e\langle c_e\rangle n_s Q_{es}} = \frac{3}{4}\frac{n_e e^2}{m_e \nu_{es}} \tag{5.160a}$$

This is sometimes used as the basis for multiplying the simple conductivity by $\frac{3}{4}$, or, alternately, multiplying the collision frequency by $\frac{4}{3}$. However, atoms and molecules are not hard spheres, and there is little justification for this numerical correction.

For $s = 2$, corresponding to a fully ionized gas with $Z_I = 1$, (5.94) gives a conductivity which is larger than (5.160) by a factor of $32/3\pi = 3.396$, which is the factor mentioned in Sec. 5.6.4. When the formula in (5.94) is corrected to account for electron-electron collisions which cause the distribution function to be more nearly maxwellian, the results of (5.160) are larger only by a factor of 1.7.

In general, to improve the accuracy of the first approximation further, it appears desirable to use the best available data on cross sections to evaluate ν_{es}^*; that is, let $\nu_{es}^* = n_s\langle c_e\rangle\langle Q_{es}\rangle$.

Equation (5.159) is exactly equivalent to that obtained from the complete Chapman-Enskog[23,24] method; the relation of the electron-diffusion coefficient to the scalar conductivity in the absence of a magnetic field is as follows:

$$\sigma = \frac{n_e e^2 m_2 n}{\rho kT}[\mathfrak{D}_{12}]_1 \approx \frac{n_e e^2 n}{kTn_2}[\mathfrak{D}_{12}]_1 \tag{5.161}$$

5.8.2 Generalization to Arbitrary Mass. To generalize the above results to particles of arbitrary mass, it is necessary to use only the "reduced" mass $m_r m_s/(m_r + m_s)$ instead of m_r. Thus, the dynamical friction (5.157) becomes

$$\mathbf{P}_r = \sum_s \frac{n_r m_r m_s}{m_r + m_s}\nu_{rs}^*(\mathbf{V}_s - \mathbf{V}_r) \tag{5.162}$$

or, in terms of $\tau_{rs}^* = \nu_{rs}^{*-1}$,

$$\mathbf{P}_r = \sum_s \frac{n_r m_r m_s}{m_r + m_s}\frac{\mathbf{V}_s - \mathbf{V}_r}{\tau_{rs}^*} \tag{5.163}$$

so that the momentum equation for the r species (5.154) becomes

$$\rho_r\frac{D\mathbf{v}}{Dt} + \nabla p_r = \sum_s \frac{n_r m_r m_s}{m_r + m_s}\frac{\mathbf{V}_s - \mathbf{V}_r}{\tau_{rs}^*} + n_r e Z_r(\mathbf{E}^* + \mathbf{V}_r \times \mathbf{B}) \tag{5.164}$$

An equation similar to (5.164) has been derived in the absence of velocity-dependent forces[25] and is given as follows:

$$\rho_r\frac{D\mathbf{v}}{Dt} + \nabla p_r = \sum_s \frac{n_r n_s kT}{n[\mathfrak{D}_{rs}]_1}(\mathbf{V}_s - \mathbf{V}_r) + n_r\mathbf{F}_r \tag{5.165}$$

where $\mathbf{F}_r$ is the force on the r particle. Equation (5.164) is identical to (5.165) if the force on the rth particle is taken as $eZ_r(\mathbf{E}^* + \mathbf{V}_r \times \mathbf{B})$, and if the collision time τ_{rs} is taken as

$$\tau_{rs}^* = \frac{nm_r m_s}{n_s(m_r + m_s)kT}[\mathfrak{D}_{rs}]_1 = \frac{3\pi^{\frac{1}{2}}}{8n_s}\sqrt{\frac{m_r m_s}{2kT(m_r + m_s)}}\,\frac{1}{\int_0^\infty e^{-\xi^2}\xi^5 Q\,d\xi} \tag{5.166}$$

5.8.3 Applications to Partially Ionized Gases. To proceed to the partially ionized gas, assume that the ions are only singly ionized and that the gas is electrically neutral, so that $n_e = n_I$. Also assume that the neutral species all have the same velocity with respect to laboratory coordinates $\mathbf{v}_n$. This implies also that their diffusion velocities $\mathbf{V}_n = \mathbf{v}_n - \mathbf{v}$ are also identical. Finally, it is assumed that the composition of the gas is constant. Our objective is to solve for the total conduction current $\mathbf{j} = n_e e(\mathbf{V}_I - \mathbf{V}_e)$ in terms of only electric and magnetic fields and the electron pressure. To do this, three equations must be used: the electron-momentum equation, the ion-momentum equation, and the overall momentum equation.

For the electron-momentum equation, the inertia may be neglected because the mass of the electron is so small. Then (5.164) becomes

$$\nabla p_e + n_e e(\mathbf{E}^* + \mathbf{V}_e \times \mathbf{B}) = n_e m_e\Big[(\mathbf{V}_n - \mathbf{V}_e) \sum_{s \neq I,e} \nu_{es}^* + \nu_{eI}^*(\mathbf{V}_I - \mathbf{V}_e)\Big] \quad (a)$$

where ν_{es}^* and ν_{eI}^* are defined by (5.156). The total electron collision frequency with neutral species is $\nu_{en}^* = \sum_{s \neq I,e} \nu_{es}^*$. Let the difference between diffusion velocities of ions and electrons be designated as $\mathbf{V}^*$ as follows:

$$\mathbf{V}^* = \mathbf{V}_e - \mathbf{V}_I \quad (b)$$

so that the total conduction current is

$$\mathbf{j} = n_e e(\mathbf{V}_I - \mathbf{V}_e) = -n_e e \mathbf{V}^* \quad (c)$$

It is also desirable to eliminate the neutral velocity by means of

$$m_e n_e \mathbf{V}_e + m_I n_I \mathbf{V}_I + \mathbf{V}_n \sum_{s \neq e,I} m_s n_s = 0 \quad (d)$$

Also, define the number density of neutral particles as $n_n = \sum_{s \neq e,I} n_s$, and the mass of the average neutral particle as

$$m_n = \frac{\sum_{s \neq e,I} m_s n_s}{n_n} \quad (e)$$

and let the ratio of the ion mass to the average neutral-particle mass be α. Equation (d) may be solved for $\mathbf{V}_n$, which becomes

$$\mathbf{V}_n = -\frac{m_e n_e \mathbf{V}_e + m_I n_I \mathbf{V}_I}{m_n n_n}$$

and use of (b) yields

$$\mathbf{V}_n = -\frac{m_e n_e \mathbf{V}^* + (m_e n_e + m_I n_I)\mathbf{V}_I}{m_n n_n}$$

or

$$\mathbf{V}_n \approx -\frac{m_e n_e}{m_n n_n}\mathbf{V}^* - \frac{\alpha n_e}{n_n}\mathbf{V}_I \quad (f)$$

since generally $m_e \ll m_I$. Use of (f) and (b) in (a) yields

$$\nabla p_e + n_e e(\mathbf{E}^* + \mathbf{V}_e \times \mathbf{B}) = -n_e m_e \frac{\mathbf{V}^*}{\tau_{eI}^*} - \frac{m_e n_e}{\tau_{en}^*}\left[\left(1 + \frac{m_e n_e}{m_n n_n}\right)\mathbf{V}^* + \mathbf{V}_I\left(1 + \frac{\alpha n_I}{n_n}\right)\right] \quad (g)$$

Use of the currents $\mathbf{j}$ and $\mathbf{j}_I$, where $\mathbf{j}_I = en_I\mathbf{V}_I$, and $\omega_e = eB/m_e$ on the right side of Eq. (g) yields

$$\nabla p_e + n_e e\mathbf{E}^* - (\mathbf{j} - \mathbf{j}_I) \times \mathbf{B} = \frac{\mathbf{j}B}{\omega_e \tau^*_{eI}} + \frac{\mathbf{j}B}{\omega_e \tau^*_{en}}\left(1 + \frac{m_e n_e}{m_n n_n}\right) - \frac{\mathbf{j}_I B}{\omega_e \tau^*_{en}}\left(1 + \frac{\alpha n_I}{n_n}\right) \qquad (h)$$

Note that $m_e n_e/m_n n_n$ is extremely small unless the number of neutral particles is very small, in which case τ^*_{en} becomes very large and that term need not be considered. For convenience, we use the following symbols:

$$K_{en} = (\omega_e \tau^*_{en})^{-1} \qquad K_{eI} = (\omega_e \tau^*_{eI})^{-1}$$

$$f = \frac{n_n m_n}{m_I n_I + m_n n_n} \qquad f^{-1} = 1 + \frac{\alpha n_I}{n_n} = 1 + \frac{\alpha n_e}{n_n}$$

Thus, f represents the mass fraction of atoms which are *not* ionized; when $n_I = 0$, $f = 1$; and when $n_n = 0$, $f = 0$; with these substitutions, (h) becomes

$$0 = -\nabla p_e - n_e e\mathbf{E}^* + (\mathbf{j} - \mathbf{j}_I) \times \mathbf{B} + B\mathbf{j}(K_{eI} + K_{en}) - B\mathbf{j}_I K_{en} f^{-1} \qquad (i)$$

In the same way, the momentum equation for ions is

$$\rho_I \frac{D\mathbf{v}}{Dt} = -\nabla p_I + n_I e(\mathbf{E}^* + \mathbf{V}_I \times \mathbf{B}) + n_e m_e \nu^*_{eI}(\mathbf{V}_e - \mathbf{V}_I) + n_I m_I \sum_{s \neq e,I} \nu^*_{Is} \frac{m_s}{m_I + m_s}(\mathbf{V}_n - \mathbf{V}_I) \qquad (j)$$

The term for the electron-ion interaction is obviously equal and opposite to the term in the electron equation (a). We also define an average collision frequency of ions with neutral particles as

$$\nu^*_{In} = \sum_{s \neq e,I} \nu^*_{Is} \frac{m_s}{m_I + m_s} = \tau^{*,-1}_{In} \qquad (k)$$

Then, with the use of (b), (f), and (k), Eq. (j) becomes

$$\rho_I \frac{D\mathbf{v}}{Dt} = -\nabla p_I + n_I e(\mathbf{E}^* + \mathbf{V}_I \times \mathbf{B}) + n_e m_e \nu^*_{eI}\mathbf{V}^* - n_e m_I \nu^*_{In}\left[\left(1 + \alpha\frac{n_e}{n_n}\right)\mathbf{V}_I + \frac{m_e n_e}{m_n n_n}\mathbf{V}^*\right]$$

In terms of currents and cyclotron frequencies this becomes

$$\rho_I \frac{D\mathbf{v}}{Dt} = -\nabla p_I + n_e e\mathbf{E}^* + \mathbf{j}_I \times \mathbf{B} - \frac{B\mathbf{j}}{\omega_e \tau^*_{eI}}\left(1 - \alpha\frac{n_e}{n_n}\frac{\tau^*_{eI}}{\tau^*_{In}}\right) - \frac{(1 + \alpha n_e/n_n)B}{\omega_I \tau^*_{In}}\mathbf{j}_I \qquad (l)$$

Finally, let $\omega_I \tau^*_{In} = K^{-1}_{In}$ and $\alpha n_e/n_n = (1 - f)/f$. Then (l) becomes

$$\rho_I \frac{D\mathbf{v}}{Dt} = -\nabla p_I + n_e e \mathbf{E}^* + \mathbf{j}_I \times \mathbf{B} + B\mathbf{j}K_{eI}\left(\frac{1-f}{f}\frac{\tau^*_{eI}}{\tau^*_{In}} - 1\right) - \frac{\mathbf{j}_I B K_{In}}{f} \tag{m}$$

To obtain the total current, $\mathbf{j}_I \times \mathbf{B}$, $D\mathbf{v}/Dt$, and then $\mathbf{j}_I$ must be eliminated between (i) and (m). We may eliminate $\mathbf{j}_I \times \mathbf{B}$ first by adding (i) and (m):

$$\rho_I \frac{D\mathbf{v}}{Dt} = -\nabla(p_I + p_e) + \mathbf{j} \times \mathbf{B} + B\mathbf{j}\left(K_{eI}\frac{1-f}{f}\frac{\tau^*_{eI}}{\tau^*_{In}} + K_{en}\right) - \frac{\mathbf{j}_I B(K_{en} + K_{In})}{f} \tag{n}$$

Next, $D\mathbf{v}/Dt$ is eliminated by the use of the overall momentum equation. Since viscous forces are omitted in (n), they are also neglected in the overall momentum equation. Thus,

$$\rho \frac{D\mathbf{v}}{Dt} + \nabla p - \mathbf{j} \times \mathbf{B} = 0 \tag{o}$$

Now

$$\frac{\rho_I}{\rho} = 1 - f$$

so that (o) becomes

$$\rho_I \frac{D\mathbf{v}}{Dt} = (1 - f)(-\nabla p + \mathbf{j} \times \mathbf{B}) \tag{p}$$

Substitution of (p) into (n) yields

$$0 = \nabla[(1 - f)p - p_I - p_e] + f\mathbf{j} \times \mathbf{B} + B\mathbf{j}K_{en}\left(1 + \frac{1-f}{f}\frac{\tau^*_{en}}{\tau^*_{In}}\right) - \mathbf{j}_I \frac{B(K_{en} + K_{In})}{f} \tag{q}$$

In Eq. (q), τ^*_{en}/τ^*_{In} may be neglected when $f \sim 1$. As $f \to 0$, the term $\mathbf{j}\tau^*_{en}/\tau^*_{In}$ is the same order of magnitude as $\mathbf{j}_I$, but because of the difference in cyclotron frequencies, $K_{en} \ll K_{In}$, and the term containing τ^*_{en}/τ^*_{In} may again be neglected. For this reason, $(1 - f)\tau^*_{en}/f\tau^*_{In}$ can be omitted with very little error.

The first term in (q) becomes

$$\nabla[-2fp_e + (1 - f)p_n] \tag{r}$$

Assuming equal temperatures, the perfect-gas law yields

$$\frac{p_n}{p_e} = \frac{n_n}{n_e} = \frac{\alpha f}{1 - f}$$

so that (r) becomes

$$\nabla f(\alpha - 2)p_e$$

For f constant (q) becomes

$$0 = f\nabla[(\alpha - 2)p_e] + f\mathbf{j} \times \mathbf{B} + B\mathbf{j}K_{en} - \mathbf{j}_I \frac{B(K_{en} + K_{In})}{f} \qquad (s)$$

Equation (s) is the required equation for $\mathbf{j}_I$, which is explicitly expressed as a function of ∇p_e and $\mathbf{j}$. Substitution of $\mathbf{j}_I$ from (s) into (i) yields the final desired relation,

$$\begin{aligned} 0 = -\nabla p_e - n_e e\mathbf{E}^* + \mathbf{j} \times \mathbf{B} + B\mathbf{j}(K_{eI} + K_{en}) \\ + \frac{f}{K_{en} + K_{In}} \{f[(\alpha - 2)\nabla p_e + \mathbf{j} \times \mathbf{B}] + B\mathbf{j}K_{en}\} \times \frac{\mathbf{B}}{B} \\ + \frac{K_{en}}{K_{en} + K_{In}} \{f[(\alpha - 2)\nabla p_e + \mathbf{j} \times \mathbf{B}] + B\mathbf{j}K_{en}\} \qquad (t) \end{aligned}$$

In most cases,

$$\frac{K_{en}}{K_{In}} = \frac{m_e}{m_I}\frac{\tau_{In}^*}{\tau_{en}^*} \ll 1$$

because the collision time of ions with neutrals is not greater than the collision time of electrons with neutrals. Thus, K_{en} may be neglected with respect to K_{In}, and (t) becomes

$$\begin{aligned} 0 = -\nabla p_e - en_e\mathbf{E}^* + \mathbf{j} \times \mathbf{B} + B\mathbf{j}(K_{eI} + K_{en}) \\ + \frac{f^2}{BK_{In}} [(\alpha - 2)\nabla p_e + \mathbf{j} \times \mathbf{B}] \times \mathbf{B} \qquad (u) \end{aligned}$$

Rearrangement of (u) yields

$$\begin{aligned} \mathbf{j} = \frac{n_e e^2}{m_e(\nu_{eI}^* + \nu_{en}^*)} \Big\{ \mathbf{E}^* + \frac{\nabla p_e}{n_e e} - \frac{\mathbf{j} \times \mathbf{B}}{n_e e} - \frac{f^2 \tau_{In}^*}{m_I n_e} [(2 - \alpha)\nabla p_e \times \mathbf{B} \\ + \mathbf{B} \times (\mathbf{j} \times \mathbf{B})] \Big\} \qquad (5.167) \end{aligned}$$

which is the desired equation for the total current $\mathbf{j}$ in terms of electric and magnetic fields, and electron pressure gradients. Equation (5.167) may also be written as[26]

$$\mathbf{j} = \sigma \left\{ \mathbf{E}^* + \frac{\nabla p_e}{n_e e} - \frac{\mathbf{j} \times \mathbf{B}}{n_e e} - \frac{f^2 \tau_{In}^*}{m_I n_e} [(2 - \alpha)\nabla p_e \times \mathbf{B} + \mathbf{B} \times (\mathbf{j} \times \mathbf{B})] \right\} \qquad (5.168)$$

where σ is the scalar electrical conductivity,

$$\sigma = \frac{n_e e^2}{m_e(\nu_{en}^* + \nu_{eI}^*)} \qquad (5.169)$$

in agreement with (5.128). The first term in (5.168) gives the effect of electric fields; the second term in the braces accounts for electron pressure gradients, the third term is the Hall effect, and the last term is "ion slip." The ion-slip term is obviously important for slightly ionized gases for which $f \sim 1$, when the magnetic fields are large.

Equation (5.168) can be reduced to a generalized Ohm's law by neglecting the electron pressure gradient. In terms of the mean electron collision time $\tau_e^* = (\nu_{en}^* + \nu_{eI}^*)^{-1}$, (5.168) becomes

$$\mathbf{j} = \sigma \mathbf{E}^* - \omega_e \tau_e^* \mathbf{j} \times \frac{\mathbf{B}}{B} + f^2 \omega_e \tau_e^* \omega_I \tau_{In}^* \left[\frac{\mathbf{B}}{B} \left(\frac{\mathbf{B}}{B} \cdot \mathbf{j} \right) - \mathbf{j} \right] \tag{5.170}$$

This is the final version of Ohm's law in a partially ionized gas, and we will next discuss some of its properties. If the gas is fully ionized, there are no neutral particles and f is zero; (5.170) then reduces to (5.108). If the gas is slightly ionized so that $f = 1$, then the last term can be neglected if

$$\omega_e \tau_e^* \omega_I \tau_{In}^* < 1$$

or

$$\omega_e^2 \tau_e^{*2} < \frac{m_I \tau_e^*}{m_e \tau_{In}^*} \tag{5.171}$$

Let us consider some possibilities as follows:

1. The gas is very slightly ionized so that $\tau_e^* = \tau_{en}^*$; furthermore the neutral particles are simply polarizable so that $\tau_{en}^* \approx \tau_{In}$. Then, to neglect ion slip, $\omega_e \tau_e < \sqrt{m_I/m_e}$, and very large values of $\omega_e \tau_e$ may be tolerated.

2. Again, the gas is very slightly ionized so that $\tau_e^* = \tau_{en}^*$; but let the neutral particles be hard spheres. Then (5.171) becomes

$$\omega_e^2 \tau_e^{*2} < \sqrt{\frac{m_I}{m_e}} \tag{5.172}$$

Large values of $\omega_e \tau_e^*$ may still be tolerated, but not as large as in case 1.

3. Again the gas is slightly ionized, but the ion density is sufficiently large ($>10^{-4}$) so that τ_e^* is dominated by electron-ion collisions; that is, $\tau_e^* = \tau_{eI}$. Then (5.171) becomes

$$\omega_e^2 \tau_e^{*2} < \frac{n_n}{n_I} \sqrt{\frac{m_I}{m_e}} \frac{\langle Q_{In} \rangle}{\langle Q_{eI} \rangle} \tag{5.173}$$

Depending on the ion and gas, Q_{In} is about the same size as Q_{en}, that is, from 10^{-15} to 10^{-14} cm^2; we assume the smaller value. With $\ln \Lambda$ about 10, from Fig. 5.12, $Q_{eI} \approx 10^{-11}$ cm^2 at 3000°K. Finally, for an ion of atomic weight of 20, (5.173) becomes

$$\omega_e^2 \tau_e^{*2} < 10^{-2} \frac{n_n}{n_e}$$

If $n_e = 10^{-4}n_n$, then $\omega_e\tau_e < 10^2$ to neglect ion slip; if $n_e = 10^{-3}n_n$, then $\omega_e\tau_e < 30$; etc. If we had chosen $Q_{In} = 10^{-14}$ cm^2, then $\omega_e\tau_e$ would be increased only by a factor of 3. If the ions were hydrogen, then $\omega_e\tau_e$ would be reduced further by $\sqrt{20}$. Thus, for slightly ionized gases where the electron motion is dominated by electron-ion collisions, ion slip becomes important at small values of $\omega_e\tau_e$.

Next, some of the properties of (5.170) are investigated. If we take the scalar product of (5.170) with **B**, then we obtain

$$j_B = \sigma E_B \tag{5.174}$$

and again the conductivity in the direction of the magnetic field is given by the scalar value. For the components of current in the other two directions (5.170) can be rearranged as follows:

$$(1 + \beta_1)\mathbf{j} = \sigma\mathbf{E}^* - \beta_2\mathbf{j} \times \frac{\mathbf{B}}{B} \tag{5.175}$$

where

$$\beta_1 = f^2\omega_e\tau_e^*\omega_I\tau_{In}^* \qquad \beta_2 = \omega_e\tau_e^* \tag{5.176}$$

To solve (5.175) explicitly for **j**, take its vector product with **B** and substitute for **j** × **B** back into it. The result is

$$[(1 + \beta_1)^2 + \beta_2^2]\mathbf{j} = (1 + \beta_1)\sigma\mathbf{E}^* - \beta_2\sigma\mathbf{E}^* \times \frac{\mathbf{B}}{B} \tag{5.177}$$

From (5.174) and (5.177) the tensor components of the conductivity become as follows, with the magnetic field taken in the z direction:

$$\sigma_{ij} = \sigma \begin{bmatrix} \dfrac{1 + \beta_1}{(1 + \beta_1)^2 + \beta_2^2} & -\dfrac{\beta_2}{(1 + \beta_1)^2 + \beta_2^2} & 0 \\ \dfrac{\beta_2}{(1 + \beta_1)^2 + \beta_2^2} & \dfrac{1 + \beta_1}{(1 + \beta_1)^2 + \beta_2^2} & 0 \\ 0 & 0 & 1 \end{bmatrix} \tag{5.178}$$

Next, we may check the validity of Tonk's theorem, by taking the scalar product of (5.175) with the current vector **j** to obtain

$$j_{\perp_B} = \frac{\sigma}{1 + \beta_1} E_{\parallel_j} \tag{5.179}$$

Thus, the presence of the ion-slip term reduces the effective conductivity by a factor of $1 + \beta_1$.

Equation (5.178) can be put in the same form as (5.106*a*). In terms of the present notation, (5.178) may be written as

$$\sigma_{ij} = \sigma' \begin{bmatrix} \dfrac{1}{1+\beta_2'^2} & -\dfrac{\beta_2'}{1+\beta_2'^2} & 0 \\ \dfrac{\beta_2'}{1+\beta_2'^2} & \dfrac{1}{1+\beta_2'^2} & 0 \\ 0 & 0 & 1 \end{bmatrix} \tag{5.180}$$

where

$$\sigma' = \frac{\sigma}{1+\beta_1} = \frac{n_e e^2 \tau_e^*}{m_e(1+\omega_e\tau_e^*\omega_I\tau_{In}^*)} \tag{5.181}$$

$$\tau_e^* = (\nu_{en}^* + \nu_{eI}^*)^{-1} \tag{5.182}$$

$$\beta_2' = \frac{\beta_2}{1+\beta_1} = \frac{\omega_e\tau_e^*}{1+\omega_e\tau_e^*\omega_I\tau_{In}^*} \tag{5.183}$$

When the magnetic field becomes very large, there will still be some current in the direction of the electric field, as long as the collision times do not vanish completely. At right angles to E and B, however, the electrons and ions will have the *same* drift velocity if $f \approx 1$; hence the Hall current will go to zero. Thus, if $f \approx 1$, σ_1/σ_2 will become very large as $\omega_e\tau_e^*$ becomes large, which is opposite to the case of $f = 0$, for which $\sigma_1/\sigma_2 = (\omega_e\tau_e)^{-1}$. This may be more easily seen by determining σ_1/σ_2 from (5.178).

$$\sigma_1 = \frac{\sigma(1+\beta_1)}{(1+\beta_1)^2+\beta_2^2} \tag{v}$$

$$\sigma_2 = \frac{\sigma(\beta_2)}{(1+\beta_1)^2+\beta_2^2} \tag{w}$$

from which

$$\frac{\sigma_1}{\sigma_2} = \frac{1+f^2\omega_e\tau_e^*\omega_I\tau_{In}^*}{\omega_e\tau_e^*} \tag{x}$$

For the completely ionized gas $f = 0$, and therefore $\sigma_1/\sigma_2 = (\omega_e\tau_e^*)^{-1}$ as before, but for the slightly ionized gas $f = 1$, and as $\omega_e\tau_e^*$ becomes very large, Eq. (x) becomes

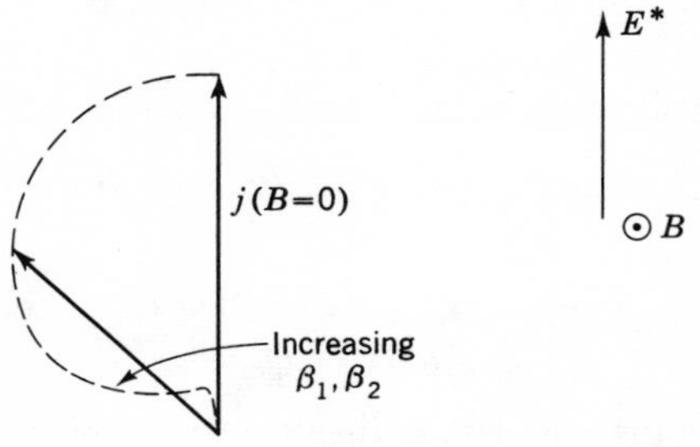

FIGURE 5.21 Electric current vector with ion slip.

$$\lim_{\omega_e\tau_e^* \to \infty} \left(\frac{\sigma_1}{\sigma_2}\right)_{f=1} = \omega_I \tau_{In}^* \tag{y}$$

The electric current polar diagram therefore appears in Fig. 5.21.

The fact that $\sigma_2/\sigma_1 \to 0$ as β_1 becomes larger than unity accounts for the small Hall coefficients measured in glow-discharge tubes at low pressures.

5.9 LARGE ELECTRON VELOCITIES AND RUNAWAY ELECTRONS

The collision term in the momentum equation for electrons may be regarded as damping or dynamical friction. For small electron drift velocities this term is linear in the electron velocity; that is, the damping force is directly proportional to the electron velocity. Thus, there will exist a steady-state electron drift in an electric field. However, this is a result of linearizing the electron velocity; that is, it was assumed that the drift velocity is much less than the mean thermal velocity and that the electron collision cross section is therefore independent of $\mathbf{V}_e$. However, if $|\mathbf{V}_e|$ is appreciable compared to $\langle c_e \rangle$, then this affects the collision frequency [see (4.81)]. Furthermore, if the cross section, and hence the collision frequency, decreases with increasing electron velocity, then the dynamical friction will not be linear with the drift velocity but may actually decrease. There may then be a maximum value of the electron drift velocity beyond which the dynamical friction may not be capable of balancing the electric field. For larger electric fields there will be no steady-state solution for the electron drift. This effect is most pronounced in fully ionized gases, which is the case considered in this section.

To formulate the problem, the expression for ν_{eI}^* must be calculated for arbitrary values of $\mathbf{v}_e$. We will consider the mean gas velocity, equal to the mean ion velocity, as zero; that is, $\mathbf{v}_I = \mathbf{v} = 0$; so that the electron average velocity is also the diffusion velocity. Neglecting $\mathbf{v}$ and electron-electron collisions, the momentum equation for electrons becomes

$$\rho_e \frac{D\mathbf{v}_e}{Dt} + \nabla p_e = -n_e e(\mathbf{E} + \mathbf{v}_e \times \mathbf{B}) + \mathbf{P}_{eI} \tag{5.184}$$

where the dynamical friction is given by

$$\mathbf{P}_{eI} = m_e \int f_e f_I (\mathbf{w}_e' - \mathbf{w}_e) |w_e| b\, db\, d\epsilon\, d\mathbf{c}_I\, d\mathbf{w}_e \tag{5.185}$$

As in Sec. (5.8),

$$\int (\mathbf{w}_e' - \mathbf{w}_e)\, d\epsilon \approx -2\pi \mathbf{w}_e (1 - \cos\chi) \tag{a}$$

and

$$2\pi \int (1 - \cos\chi) b\, db = Q_{es} \tag{b}$$

For electron-ion collisions, the collision cross section is given by (5.57):

$$Q_{eI} = \frac{e^4 \ln \Lambda}{4\pi K_0{}^2 m_e{}^2 w_e{}^4} \tag{c}$$

Also,

$$\int f_I \, d\mathbf{c}_I = n_I \tag{d}$$

Substitution of (a) through (d) into (5.185) yields the following expression for the dynamical friction:

$$\mathbf{P}_{eI} = \beta \int \frac{\mathbf{w}_e}{w_e{}^3} f_e \, d\mathbf{w}_e \tag{e}$$

where β is given by

$$\beta = -\frac{n_e e^4 \ln \Lambda}{4\pi K_0{}^2 m_e} \tag{f}$$

As before, Λ is considered as a constant during the integration and is given by (5.110). Now $\mathbf{w}_e/w_e{}^3 = -\nabla_{w_e}(w_e{}^{-1})$, so that (e) becomes

$$\mathbf{P}_{eI} = -\beta \int f_e \nabla_{w_e}\left(\frac{1}{w_e}\right) d\mathbf{w}_e \tag{g}$$

Equation (g) may be integrated by parts:

$$\mathbf{P}_{eI} = \beta \int \frac{1}{|w_e|} \nabla_{w_e} f_e d\mathbf{w}_e \tag{h}$$

Finally, we let $\mathbf{w}_e = \mathbf{v}_e + \mathbf{c}_e'$ as defined in (4.15), so that (h) may be written as

$$\mathbf{P}_{eI} = \beta \int \frac{1}{|\mathbf{c}_e - (-\mathbf{v}_e)|} \nabla_{c_e'} f_e \, d\mathbf{c}_e' \tag{i}$$

To integrate (i), it is simpler to convert (i) into a differential equation. This can be done by comparison to the magnetic potential $\mathbf{A}$, given by

$$\mathbf{A}(\mathbf{r}) = \frac{\mu_0}{4\pi} \int \frac{\mathbf{j}(\mathbf{r}') \, d\mathbf{r}'}{|\mathbf{r}' - \mathbf{r}|} \tag{j}$$

where $\mathbf{r} = \mathbf{i}x + \mathbf{j}y + \mathbf{k}z$. The corresponding differential equation for $\mathbf{A}$ is

$$\nabla^2 \mathbf{A}(\mathbf{r}) = -\mu_0 \mathbf{j}(\mathbf{r}) \tag{k}$$

Thus, the differential equation for (i) is

$$\nabla^2_{-v_e} \mathbf{P}_{eI} = -4\pi\beta \nabla_{-v_e} f_e(-v_e) \tag{l}$$

To proceed further, a distribution function for f_e must be assumed. Now, for large values of $\mathbf{v}_e$, that is, for $v_e > \langle c_e' \rangle$, the electron-ion collision cross section will be smaller than the electron-electron collision cross section, which is based on $\langle c_e' \rangle$. Electron-ion collisions cause f_e to be skewed, but electron-electron collisions cause f_e to be maxwellian, displaced by $\mathbf{v}_e$. Thus, if electron-electron collisions dominate, then the distribution function will be close to maxwellian. We will therefore assume that

$$f_e = a e^{-b c_e'^2} \tag{m}$$

With $\mathbf{r} = -b^{\frac{1}{2}}\mathbf{v}_e$, ($l$) can be written as

$$\nabla_r{}^2\mathbf{P}_{eI} = -4\pi\beta b^{-\frac{1}{2}}a\,\nabla_r e^{-r^2} \tag{n}$$

To solve Eq. (n), let $\mathbf{P}_{eI} = \nabla_r h$; then ($n$) may be integrated once to obtain

$$\nabla^2 h \equiv r^{-2}\frac{\partial}{\partial r}\left(r^2\frac{\partial h}{\partial r}\right) = -4\pi\beta b^{-\frac{1}{2}}ae^{-r^2} \tag{o}$$

Integration of (o) by parts, with $u = r$ and $dv = re^{-r^2}\,dr$, yields

$$\frac{\partial h}{\partial r} = -4\pi\beta b^{-\frac{1}{2}}a\left(\frac{1}{2r}e^{-r^2} + \frac{1}{2r^2}\int_0^r e^{-\xi^2}\,d\xi\right) \tag{p}$$

The terms in the parentheses in (p) can be written as a perfect differential,

$$-\frac{1}{2}\frac{d}{dr}\left(\frac{1}{r}\int_0^r e^{-r_1^2}\,dr_1\right)$$

so that $h(r)$ becomes

$$h = 2\pi\beta b^{-\frac{1}{2}}\frac{a}{r}\int_0^r e^{-r_1^2}\,dr_1 \tag{q}$$

and

$$\mathbf{P}_{eI} = \nabla_r h = \frac{\mathbf{r}}{r}\frac{\partial}{\partial r}h = 2\pi\beta b^{-\frac{1}{2}}a\frac{\partial}{\partial r}\left(\frac{1}{r}\int_0^r e^{-r_1^2}\,dr\right) \tag{r}$$

Substitution of β from (f), $a = n_e(m_e/2\pi kT)^{\frac{3}{2}}$, $b = m_e/2kT$ into (r) yields

$$\mathbf{P}_{eI} = -\frac{n_e{}^2e^4\ln\Lambda\,\mathbf{v}_e}{4\pi K_0{}^2|v_e|}\frac{m_e}{2kT}\frac{\partial}{\partial r}\left(\frac{1}{r}\frac{2}{\sqrt{\pi}}\int_0^r e^{-r_1^2}\,dr_1\right) \tag{5.186}$$

where

$$r = -\left(\frac{m_e}{2kT}\right)^{\frac{1}{2}}|\mathbf{v}_e| \tag{s}$$

Equation (5.186) gives the dynamical friction. We may check (5.186) for small values of r. Then

$$r \ll 1: \qquad \frac{\partial}{\partial r}\left(\frac{1}{r}\frac{2}{\sqrt{\pi}}\int_0^r e^{-r_1^2}\,dr_1\right) = \frac{4}{3\sqrt{\pi}}\left(\frac{m_e}{2kT}\right)^{\frac{1}{2}}|v_e| \tag{t}$$

for which a conductivity may be calculated from (5.184),

$$\sigma = -\frac{n_e e v_e}{E} = \frac{3}{16\pi^{\frac{1}{2}}}\frac{m_e(4\pi K_0)^2}{e^2\ln\Lambda}\left(\frac{2kT}{m_e}\right)^{\frac{3}{2}} \tag{u}$$

in agreement with the first approximation given by (5.160). But for larger values of $r = (m_e/2kT)^{\frac{1}{2}}v_e$, the term given by ($u$) is not simply linear with $|v_e|$; its value is shown in Fig. 5.22. It is seen that this term has a maximum when $|v_e|/(m_e/2kT)^{\frac{1}{2}}$ is unity; the value is 0.427, for which the critical electric field is

$$E\left[\frac{|v_e|}{(m_e/2kT)^{\frac{1}{2}}} = 1\right] = \frac{0.427n_e e^3\ln\Lambda}{4\pi K_0{}^2}\frac{m_e}{2kT} \tag{5.187}$$

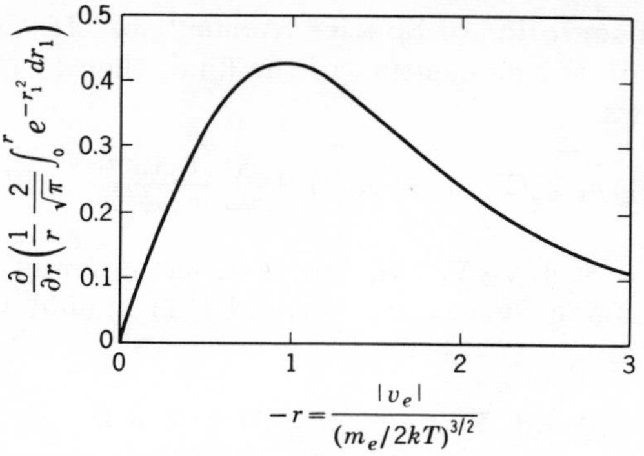

FIGURE 5.22 Dynamical friction factor for a fully ionized gas where $Z_i = 1$.

Values of the electric field larger than that given by (5.187) cannot be balanced by the dynamical friction term; instead the electron velocity will continue to increase. This phenomenon is known as *runaway*. To occur, the electric field must be larger than that which would cause the drift velocity of the electrons to be near their thermal velocity.

Thus, for sufficiently large electric fields or electron drift velocities in a fully ionized gas, only the electron inertia controls the electron motion. Since this is generally small, the electrical conductivity of the electrons becomes very large. For some applications this might be desirable, for example, in a gas-filled tube; but usually runaway is undesirable because it uncouples the electron motion from the rest of the gas so that the electrons interchange little momentum or energy with the rest of the gas. The electrons become essentially a free-electron gas, and the positive ions serve only to neutralize the space charge.

5.10 SPECIES–CONSERVATION EQUATIONS

In the gas dynamics of conducting gases, the gas is usually treated as a continuum with the transport properties calculated appropriately. However, in several cases, it is necessary to use the individual species-conservation equations, as in Secs. 5.7 and 5.8. For completeness, all the species-conservation equations will be repeated in this section, together with the collisional terms.

5.10.1 Conservation of Species. For conservation of species, Eq. (4.155) remains the same. In terms of the number density, this becomes

$$\frac{\partial n_s}{\partial t} + \nabla \cdot (n_s \mathbf{v}_s) = \dot{n}_s \tag{5.188}$$

where $\dot{n}_s$ is the number density rate of production of the s species by collisions, that is, chemical reactions, ionization, or deionization.

5.10.2 Conservation of Species Momentum. If it is assumed that all species *share* in the momentum of the fluid, then (5.164) can be generalized as follows,

$$\rho_s \frac{D\mathbf{v}}{Dt} + \nabla \cdot \mathbf{p}_s = n_s e Z_s(\mathbf{E}^* + \mathbf{V}_s \times \mathbf{B}) + \sum_r \frac{n_s m_s m_r}{m_r + m_s} \nu_{sr}^*(\mathbf{V}_r - \mathbf{V}_s) \quad (5.189)$$

where $D/Dt = \partial/\partial t + \mathbf{v} \cdot \nabla$. If, however, the different species acquire substantially different velocities, then (4.161) should be used, which becomes

$$\frac{\partial}{\partial t}(\rho_s \mathbf{v}_s) + \nabla \cdot (\rho_s \mathbf{v}_s \mathbf{v}_s) + \nabla \cdot \mathbf{p}_s' = n_s e Z_s(\mathbf{E} + \mathbf{v}_s \times \mathbf{B}) + \sum_r \frac{n_s m_s m_r}{m_r + m_s} \nu_{sr}^*(\mathbf{v}_r - \mathbf{v}_s) + \int m_s \mathbf{w} \left(\frac{\partial f_s}{\partial t}\right)_{\text{inelastic}} d\mathbf{w} \quad (5.190)$$

Whether (5.189) or (5.190) should be used depends upon the collision frequency, which in turn determines whether v_r is close to v_s. If $|\mathbf{v}_r - \mathbf{v}_s| \ll \langle c_s \rangle$, then (5.189) appears appropriate. But if the difference in velocities is comparable to the thermal velocities, then (5.190) should be used because the coupling between species is small. When the coupling is small, and the motion of each species is governed by the forces on it, then it appears desirable to reference the thermal motion of the species to its velocity $\mathbf{v}_s$. This allows each species to have a *different* temperature T_s, so that $p_s = n_s k T_s$. For the off-diagonal terms of the pressure tensor, there is no comparable simplification, and these terms are often omitted. Then with the use of (5.188), (5.190) may be written as

$$\rho_s \frac{D_s \mathbf{v}_s}{Dt} + \nabla p_s = n_s e Z_s(\mathbf{E} + \mathbf{v}_s \times \mathbf{B}) + \sum_r \frac{n_s m_s m_r}{m_s + m_r} \nu_{sr}^*(\mathbf{v}_r - \mathbf{v}_s) \quad (5.191)$$

where $D_s/Dt = \partial/\partial t + \mathbf{v}_s \cdot \nabla$, and inelastic collisions are neglected.

5.10.3 Species Energy Equation. To obtain the species energy equation, the energy loss term of (4.170) must be evaluated. For elastic collisions, this is given by

$$\sum_s \int \epsilon_t \left(\frac{\partial f_r}{\partial t}\right)_{c,s} d\mathbf{w}_r = \sum_s \int \frac{1}{2} m_r w_r^2 (f_r' f_s' - f_r f_s) gb\, db\, d\epsilon\, d\mathbf{w}_r\, d\mathbf{w}_s$$
$$= \sum_s \int \frac{1}{2} m_r (w_r'^2 - w_r^2) f_r f_s gb\, db\, d\epsilon\, d\mathbf{w}_r\, d\mathbf{w}_s \quad (5.192)$$

since the integral over $w_r^2 f_r' f_s'$ is identical to that over $w_r'^2 f_r f_s$.

From Eq. (*i*), Sec. 5.8.1, the velocity of an r particle, before a collision with an s particle, is given by

$$\mathbf{w}_r = \frac{m_s}{m_r + m_s} \mathbf{g} + \mathbf{G} \quad (a)$$

where $\mathbf{g}$ is the relative velocity before the collision,

$$\mathbf{g} = \mathbf{w}_r - \mathbf{w}_s = (\mathbf{c}_r - \mathbf{c}_s) + (\mathbf{v}_r - \mathbf{v}_s) \tag{b}$$

and $\mathbf{G}$ is the center of mass velocity which is not changed during a collision,

$$\mathbf{G} = \mathbf{G}' = \frac{m_r\mathbf{w}_r + m_s\mathbf{w}_s}{m_r + m_s} = \frac{m_r\mathbf{c}_r' + m_s\mathbf{c}_s'}{m_r + m_s} + \mathbf{v}_g \tag{c}$$

and where $\mathbf{v}_g$ is the average gas velocity of the two species,

$$\mathbf{v}_g = \frac{m_r\mathbf{v}_r + m_s\mathbf{v}_s}{m_r + m_s} \tag{d}$$

After the collision,

$$\mathbf{w}_r' = \frac{m_s}{m_r + m_s}\mathbf{g}' + \mathbf{G}' \tag{e}$$

The change in energy during a collision is thus

$$\tfrac{1}{2}m_r(w_r'^2 - w_r^2) = -\tfrac{1}{2}m_s(w_s'^2 - w_s^2) = \frac{m_r m_s}{m_r + m_s}(\mathbf{g}' - \mathbf{g}) \cdot \mathbf{G} \tag{f}$$

As before, in the direction of $\mathbf{g}$, $(\mathbf{g}' - \mathbf{g}) = -\mathbf{g}(1 - \cos\chi)$, and integration over $b\,db\,d\epsilon$ yields $-\mathbf{g}Q_{rs}(g)$. Thus, (5.192) becomes[27]

$$-\frac{m_r m_s}{m_r + m_s}\int \mathbf{g} \cdot \mathbf{G}gQ_{rs}(g)f_r f_s\,d\mathbf{c}_r'\,d\mathbf{c}_s' \tag{g}$$

To simplify the integration of (g), let species r be an electron, so that the expressions for $\mathbf{g}$, g, and $Q_{es}(g)$ from Sec. 5.8.1 may be used [Eqs. (m), (o), and (p)]. Also, assume that f_e and f_s are displaced maxwellians about the species average velocities $\mathbf{v}_e$ and $\mathbf{v}_s$, respectively. Integration of (g) over c_s' and integration by parts over c_e' yields

$$-\frac{m_e^2}{m_s}n_s\left(1 - \frac{T_s}{T_e}\right)\int Q_{es}c_e'^3 f_e\,d\mathbf{c}_e - m_e n_s(\mathbf{v}_e - \mathbf{v}_s) \cdot \mathbf{v}_g \int Q_{es}c_e' f_e\,d\mathbf{c}_e' \tag{h}$$

Terms like m_e/m_s have been neglected in comparison to unity. The first term in (h) represents the change in electron temperature due to differences between the electron temperature and heavy-particle temperature; the second term represents the "frictional" heating of the electrons due to differences in the electron gas velocity and heavy-particle gas. The first integral in (h) has been defined in terms of ν_{es}^* by (5.156) as follows:

$$\nu_{es}^* = \frac{n_s}{3n_e kT_e}\int Q_{es}c_e'^3 f_e\,d\mathbf{c}_e' \tag{i}$$

A slightly different collision frequency can be defined for the second integral in (h) as follows:

$$\nu_{es}^{**} = \frac{n_s}{n_e} \int Q_{es} c_e' f_e \, d\mathbf{c}_e' \qquad (j)$$

The energy loss term then becomes

$$n_e \sum_s \left(\frac{2m_e}{m_s}\right) (\tfrac{3}{2}kT_s - \tfrac{3}{2}kT_e)\nu_{es}^* + n_e m_e \sum_s (\mathbf{v}_s - \mathbf{v}_e) \cdot \mathbf{v}_g \nu_{es}^{**} \qquad (5.193)$$

To account for inelastic collisions, each term in the first expression of (5.193) should be multiplied by δ_s; in the second term $\mathbf{v}_g$ may be approximated by $\mathbf{v}_s$.

Equation (5.193) is to be used in conjunction with (4.172), but the latter contains a difficulty arising from the definition of $\mathbf{p}_e$. First, we will ignore the off-diagonal elements of the pressure tensor. Secondly, according to (5.193) the electron temperature may be *different* from the gas temperature. This temperature is defined as

$$\tfrac{3}{2}kT_e = \frac{m_e}{2}\left(\frac{n_e}{2\pi kT_e}\right)^{\frac{3}{2}} \int |\mathbf{w}_e - \mathbf{v}_e|^2 e^{-(m_e/2kT_e)|\mathbf{w}_e - \mathbf{v}_e|^2} \, d\mathbf{w}_e$$

To be consistent with this definition of temperature, the pressure must be similarly defined as $p_e = n_e kT_e$. Thus, in (4.172) the electron pressure is defined with respect to the average electron gas velocity $\mathbf{v}_e$.

In addition to the energy loss by elastic and inelastic collisions, additional electrons may also be created or destroyed. Then for (5.192) an additional term is required:

$$\int \epsilon \left(\frac{\partial f_e}{\partial t}\right)_{\text{chem}} d\mathbf{w}_e \qquad (k)$$

However, if the additional electrons are created by ionizing collisions by electrons, then each time such an electron collision occurs there will be an energy loss equal to the ionization energy. Thus for this special case, to (k) should be added a term

$$\dot{n}_e E_I \qquad (l)$$

With the use of (5.193), (k), and (l), then (4.172) becomes

$$\begin{aligned}\frac{\partial}{\partial t}\rho_e\left(\frac{1}{2}v_e^2 + \frac{3}{2}\frac{kT_e}{m_e}\right) &+ \nabla \cdot \rho_e \mathbf{v}_e \left(\frac{1}{2}v_e^2 + \frac{3}{2}\frac{kT_e}{m_e}\right) \\ &+ \nabla \cdot \mathbf{q}_e' + \nabla \cdot (\mathbf{v}_e p_e') = \mathbf{E} \cdot \mathbf{J}_e + n_e m_e \sum_s \nu_{es}^{**}(\mathbf{v}_s - \mathbf{v}_e) \cdot \mathbf{v}_s \\ + 2n_e m_e \sum_s \frac{\delta_s}{m_s}\nu_{es}^* &\left(\frac{3}{2}kT_s - \frac{3}{2}kT_e\right) - \dot{n}_e E_I + \int \epsilon \left(\frac{\partial f_e}{\partial t}\right)_{\text{chem}} d\mathbf{w}_e \end{aligned} \qquad (5.194)$$

The first and second terms on the right side of (5.194) can be combined by the following approximations: Let $\nu_{es}^{**} \approx \nu_{es}^{*}$, and let $\mathbf{v}_s \approx \mathbf{v}$. With the relations $\mathbf{J}_e = -n_e e\mathbf{v} + \mathbf{j}_e$, $\mathbf{E} = \mathbf{E}^* - \mathbf{v} \times \mathbf{B}$, those two terms become

$$\mathbf{E}^* \cdot \mathbf{j}_e + \mathbf{v} \cdot \left[-n_e e\mathbf{E}^* + \mathbf{j}_e \times \mathbf{B} + \sum_s n_e m_e \nu_{es}^*(\mathbf{V}_s - \mathbf{V}_e)\right] \qquad (m)$$

In the electron-momentum equation, the inertia terms in (5.191) may be neglected so that the expression in the brackets in (m) is equal to just ∇p_e; hence (m) becomes

$$\mathbf{E}^* \cdot \mathbf{j}_e + \mathbf{v} \cdot \nabla p_e \qquad (n)$$

In terms of total enthalpy of electrons, (5.194) then becomes

$$\rho_e \frac{D_e H_e}{Dt} + \nabla \cdot \mathbf{q}_e' + \nabla \cdot (\mathbf{v}_e p_e) - \frac{\partial p_e}{\partial t} + \dot{\rho}_e(\tfrac{1}{2}v_e^2 + \tfrac{3}{2}kT_e)$$
$$= \mathbf{E}^* \cdot \mathbf{j}_e + \mathbf{v} \cdot \nabla p_e - n_e \sum_s \frac{2m_e}{m_s} \delta_s \nu_{es}^* \tfrac{3}{2}k(T_e - T_s)$$
$$- \dot{n}_e E_I + \int \epsilon \left(\frac{\partial f_e}{\partial t}\right)_{\text{chem}} d\mathbf{w}_e \qquad (5.195)$$

In steady state and a homogeneous gas with zero gradients, (5.195) reduces to the result of Sec. 5.5. Equation (5.195) can also be written in terms of electron temperature directly, by neglecting the inertial term $\frac{1}{2}v_e^2$, with the following result:

$$n_e \frac{D_e}{Dt}(\tfrac{3}{2}kT_e) + \nabla \cdot \mathbf{q}_e' + p_e \nabla \cdot v_e + \dot{\rho}_e \frac{3}{2}\frac{k}{m_e} T_e$$
$$= \mathbf{E}^* \cdot \mathbf{j}_e + n_e \sum_s \frac{2m_e}{m_s} \delta_s \nu_{es}^* \tfrac{3}{2}k(T_s - T_e) - \mathbf{V}_e \cdot \nabla p_e - \dot{n}_e E_I$$
$$+ \int \epsilon \left(\frac{\partial f_e}{\partial t}\right)_{\text{chem}} d\mathbf{w}_e \qquad (5.196)$$

where off-diagonal terms in the electron-pressure tensor have been neglected.

An equation similar to (5.195) or (5.196) may be written for ions. However, because the ion mass is close to the neutral-particle mass, the ion temperature will generally be close to the neutral gas temperature. Also, the thermal conductivity of the ion gas is much smaller than that of the electron gas. Therefore, except for special situations, the ion gas need not be considered separately. Thus, the energy equation for gas (excluding electrons) is

$$\frac{\partial}{\partial t}\rho(\tfrac{1}{2}v^2 + e) + \nabla\cdot\rho(\tfrac{1}{2}v^2 + e)\mathbf{v} + \nabla\cdot\mathbf{q} + \nabla\cdot(\mathbf{v}\cdot\mathbf{p}) = \mathbf{E}\cdot\mathbf{J}_I + \sum_s \frac{\delta_s n_e m_e \nu_{se}^*}{m_s}\frac{3}{2}k(T_e - T_s) + n_e m_e \sum_s \mathbf{v}_s\cdot(\mathbf{V}_e - \mathbf{V}_s)\nu_{es}^* \quad (5.197)$$

where all properties are for the ion-neutral gas mixture.

The electron heat conduction q_e' is given by (5.151), which, neglecting the thermodiffusion effect, becomes

$$q_e' = \tfrac{5}{2}n_e kT_e\mathbf{V}_e - \mathbf{K}_e^*\cdot\nabla T_e \quad (5.198)$$

where $\mathbf{K}_e^*$ is the thermal conductivity tensor of electrons only, given by (x), Sec. 5.7. It is consistent to define the thermal conductivity tensor in terms of only the scalar thermal conductivity; thus with the magnetic field in the z direction, $\mathcal{K}_{ij} = \mathcal{K}\Omega_{ij}$, or

$$\mathcal{K}_{ij} = \mathcal{K}_e \begin{bmatrix} \frac{1}{1+\omega_e{}^2\tau^2} & \frac{\omega_e\tau}{1+\omega_e{}^2\tau^2} & 0 \\ \frac{\omega_e\tau}{1+\omega_e{}^2\tau^2} & \frac{1}{1+\omega_e{}^2\tau^2} & 0 \\ 0 & 0 & 1 \end{bmatrix} \quad (5.199)$$

where[28]

$$\tau = \frac{3}{5}\frac{\mathcal{K}_e m_e}{n_e k^2 T_e}$$

and $\mathcal{K}_e$ is the thermal conductivity of the electron gas having a maxwellian distribution function. For a fully singly ionized gas, this value of $\mathcal{K}_e$ is slightly smaller than $\mathcal{K}_{33}$ given by (5.147); that is,[29]

$$\mathcal{K}_e = \frac{75(4\pi K_0)^2 k(kT)^{\frac{5}{2}}}{32\pi^{\frac{1}{2}} m_e^{\frac{1}{2}} e^4 \ln\Lambda} \quad (5.200)$$

so that

$$\tau = \frac{1.64}{n_e\langle c_e\rangle\langle Q_{eI}\rangle} \quad (5.201)$$

5.11 AMBIPOLAR DIFFUSION

Ambipolar diffusion in ionized gases occurs when an electron pressure gradient exists in a partially ionized gas but when there is zero net current. We will derive the ambipolar diffusion coefficient for a singly ionized gas of a single species. As is the case for most plasmas, it is considered to be electrically neutral so that $n_e \approx n_I$. Thus, for zero current flow, $\mathbf{V}_e = \mathbf{V}_I$. We also consider the gas to be quiescent. Then (5.164) for electrons and ions becomes

$$\nabla p_e = \frac{n_e n_n kT}{n\mathfrak{D}_{en}}(\mathbf{V}_n - \mathbf{V}_e) - n_e e(\mathbf{E}^* + \mathbf{V}_e\times\mathbf{B}) \quad (a)$$

$$\nabla p_I = \frac{n_I n_n kT}{n\mathfrak{D}_{In}}(\mathbf{V}_n - \mathbf{V}_I) + n_I e(\mathbf{E}^* + \mathbf{V}_I\times\mathbf{B}) \quad (b)$$

Addition of (*a*) and (*b*), and use of $p_e \approx p_I$, $\mathbf{V}_e \approx \mathbf{V}_I$, $n_e \approx n_I$, yields

$$2\nabla p_I = \frac{n_I n_n kT}{n}\left(\frac{1}{\mathfrak{D}_{en}} + \frac{1}{\mathfrak{D}_{In}}\right)(\mathbf{V}_n - \mathbf{V}_I) \tag{c}$$

which can be arranged as follows:

$$\mathbf{V}_I - \mathbf{V}_n = \frac{n}{n_e n_n kT}\,\mathfrak{D}_a\,\nabla p_e \tag{5.202}$$

where $\mathfrak{D}_a$ is the ambipolar diffusion coefficient defined as

$$\mathfrak{D}_a = \frac{2\mathfrak{D}_{en}\mathfrak{D}_{In}}{\mathfrak{D}_{en} + \mathfrak{D}_{In}} \tag{5.203}$$

and where the binary diffusion coefficients are given by (5.166).

If the neutral particles can be considered as hard spheres, then $\mathfrak{D}_{en} \gg \mathfrak{D}_{In}$ and therefore $\mathfrak{D}_a \approx 2\mathfrak{D}_{In}$. Thus, the effective diffusion coefficient for ions is doubled. This can be understood from (*a*), where the electron pressure gradient causes an electric field, and this electric field acts on the ions exactly the same as the ion pressure gradient. Thus the effective ion pressure gradient is doubled.

5.12 FOKKER–PLANCK EQUATION

The preceding sections have used the assumptions of (1) elastic collisions between particles and (2) binary collisions, which means that an electron enters into only one force field of a scattering particle at a time, although this may be a "shielded" force field. This has been justified when a large number of electrons are within a sphere having the Debye length as a radius. However, there exists another point of view concerning electron-ion collisions, in which the force on an electron is calculated from the sum of the force fields of all other particles. If these forces are calculated in a self-consistent manner, all the properties of the plasma will be known. Furthermore, the force field of a single charged particle falls off very slowly with distance, and is very strong at short distances. Thus close collisions between charged particles, in which the velocity vector changes appreciably, are rare events; but long-range collisions in which the velocity vector changes only slightly with each collision are very frequent. Thus, a charged particle, when interacting with other charged particles, undergoes a large number of small deflections, and at any one time may be in the force field of many charged particles.

To analyze this situation, consider the Maxwell transport equation for a particle property Θ_s [see (4.149)]:

$$\int \Theta_s \frac{Df_s}{Dt}\,d\mathbf{w}_s = \sum_r \int (\Theta_s' - \Theta_s) f_r f_s g b\,db\,d\epsilon\,d\mathbf{w}_s\,d\mathbf{w}_r \tag{a}$$

Now, suppose the s particle during a "collision" has only a small change in velocity Δw_s. Then $\Theta' - \Theta$ may be expanded in a Taylor series as follows:[30]

$$\Theta(w_s') - \Theta(w_s) = \sum_{i=1}^{3} \Delta w_{s_i} \frac{\partial \Theta_s}{\partial w_{s_i}} + \sum_{i,j=1}^{3} \frac{1}{2} \Delta w_{s_i} \Delta w_{s_j} \frac{\partial^2 \Theta_s}{\partial w_{s_i}\, \partial w_{s_j}} + \cdots \tag{b}$$

Substitution of (b) into (a) and integration by parts over $\mathbf{w}_s$ yield

$$\int \Theta_s \frac{Df_s}{Dt}\, d\mathbf{w}_s = \sum_r \int \left[\sum_{i=1}^{3} \frac{\partial}{\partial w_{s_i}} (\Delta w_{s_i} f_s) + \frac{1}{2} \sum_{i,j=1}^{3} \frac{\partial^2 (\Delta w_{s_i} \Delta w_{s_j} f_s)}{\partial w_{s_i}\, \partial w_{s_j}} \right] \cdot \Theta_s f_r g b \, db\, d\epsilon\, d\mathbf{w}_r\, d\mathbf{w}_s \tag{c}$$

Next, define the average change in velocity of an s particle, integrated over all r particles, as follows:

$$\gamma_i = \sum_r \int \Delta w_{s_i} f_r g b\, db\, d\epsilon\, d\mathbf{w}_r \equiv \langle \Delta w_i \rangle_s \tag{d}$$

$$\gamma_{ij} = \sum_r \int \Delta w_{s_i} \Delta w_{s_j} f_r g b\, db\, d\epsilon\, d\mathbf{w}_r \equiv \langle \Delta w_i\, \Delta w_j \rangle_s \tag{e}$$

so that (c) becomes

$$\int \Theta_s \frac{Df_s}{Dt}\, d\mathbf{w}_s = \sum_r \int \Theta_s \left[- \sum_i \frac{\partial}{\partial w_{s_i}} (\gamma_i f_s) + \frac{1}{2} \sum_{i,j} \frac{\partial^2 (\gamma_{ij} f_s)}{\partial w_{s_i}\, \partial w_{s_j}} \right] d\mathbf{w}_s \tag{f}$$

The above equation must hold for any Θ; thus the integrands must be equal, or

$$\frac{Df_s}{Dt} = - \sum_i \frac{\partial}{\partial w_{s_i}} (\gamma_i f_s) + \sum_{ij} \frac{1}{2} \frac{\partial^2 (\gamma_{ij} f_s)}{\partial w_{s_i}\, \partial w_{s_j}} \tag{g}$$

This is known as the *Fokker-Planck equation*. The two terms in (g) are called the *dynamical friction* and the *diffusion* or *dispersion*, respectively. The above equation has also been derived by Chandrasekhar[31] from statistical arguments in which the γ_i, γ_{ij} are defined differently,

$$\gamma_i = \frac{1}{\Delta t} \int P\, \Delta w_i\, d(\Delta w_i)$$
$$\gamma_{ij} = \frac{1}{\Delta t} \int P\, \Delta w_i\, \Delta w_j\, d(\Delta w_j) \tag{h}$$

where $P = P(\mathbf{w},\Delta\mathbf{w})$ is the probability that an electron moving with velocity $\mathbf{w}$ will change its velocity by $\Delta\mathbf{w}$ in time Δt. The integrals in (h) are proportional to Δt; hence both γ_i and γ_{ij} may be calculated. But in the higher-order terms, the integrals will be proportional to $(\Delta t)^2$ or higher powers. Thus, if Δt is small, only the terms in (*g*) are important.

However, in most existing solutions, the γ's were calculated from (*d*) and (*e*) by considering the collision of a single *s* particle with the force field of an *r* particle.[32] Let us define

$$\begin{aligned} \{\Delta w_i\}_s &= \int \Delta w_{i_s} gb\, db\, d\epsilon \\ \{\Delta w_i\, \Delta w_j\}_s &= \int \Delta w_{i_s}\, \Delta w_{j_s} gb\, db\, d\epsilon \end{aligned} \tag{i}$$

so that

$$\begin{aligned} \gamma_i &= \sum_r \int f_r\, d\mathbf{w}_r \{\Delta w_i\}_s \\ \gamma_{ij} &= \sum_r \int f_r\, d\mathbf{w}_r \{\Delta w_i\, \Delta w_j\}_s \end{aligned} \tag{j}$$

Note that when a collision occurs, the center of mass velocity $\mathbf{G}$ remains the same, where

$$\mathbf{G} = \frac{m_s \mathbf{w}_s + m_r \mathbf{w}_r}{m_r + m_s} \tag{k}$$

so that

$$\mathbf{w}_s = \mathbf{G} + \frac{m_r}{m_r + m_s} \mathbf{g} \tag{l}$$

where $\mathbf{g}$ is the relative velocity $\mathbf{w}_s - \mathbf{w}_r$. Since the center of mass velocity remains constant during a collision,

$$\Delta \mathbf{w}_s = \frac{m_r}{m_s + m_r} \Delta \mathbf{g}$$

so that (*i*) becomes

$$\begin{aligned} \{\Delta w_i\}_s &= \frac{m_r}{m_s + m_r} \int \Delta g_i\, gb\, db\, d\epsilon = \frac{m_r}{m_s + m_r} \{\Delta g_i\} \\ \{\Delta w_i\, \Delta w_j\}_s &= \left(\frac{m_r}{m_s + m_r}\right)^2 \int \Delta g_i\, \Delta g_j\, gb\, db\, d\epsilon = \left(\frac{m_r}{m_s + m_r}\right)^2 \{\Delta g_i\, \Delta g_j\} \end{aligned} \tag{m}$$

Next, a local set of coordinates $X_\xi = (X_\mu, X_\nu, X_\sigma)$ is chosen so that X_μ lies along $\mathbf{g}$ prior to the collision. The change Δg_μ during a collision is next calculated in the local coordinates, using the fact that the relative velocity g is not changed during a collision. From (5.21)

$$\Delta g_\mu = g(1 - \cos \chi) \tag{n}$$

and

$$\{\Delta g_\mu\}_s = g^2 \int (1 - \cos \chi) b\, db\, d\epsilon = g^2 Q_{sr} \tag{o}$$

from the definition of the cross section. For charged particles, the cross section was given by Eq. (5.57), by the indicated integration. It was found that the integral diverged as $b \to \infty$, so that the upper limit of integration was chosen to be the Debye length. This same approximation is made here; thus the cross section is taken as

$$Q_{sr} = \frac{4\pi e^4 Z_r^2 Z_s^2}{m^{*2} g^4 (4\pi K_0)^2} \ln \Lambda \tag{p}$$

where the reduced mass is $m^* = m_r m_s/(m_r + m_s)$. Then

$$\{\Delta g_\mu\}_s = \frac{4\pi e^4 Z_r^2 Z_s^2}{m^{*2} g^2 (4\pi K_0)^2} \ln \Lambda \tag{q}$$

The quantities $\{\Delta g_\nu\}$, $\{\Delta g_\sigma\}$ which are normal to $\mathbf{g}$ are integrated in a similar fashion and are found to be zero, as in (5.21). In the same way, it is found that

$$\begin{aligned} \{\Delta g_\xi \Delta g_\eta\}_s &= 0 \qquad \xi \neq \eta \\ \{\Delta g_\mu \Delta g_\mu\}_s &= 0 \\ \{\Delta g_\nu \Delta g_\nu\}_s = \{\Delta g_\sigma \Delta g_\sigma\}_s &= \frac{4\pi e^4 Z_r^2 Z_s^2 \ln \Lambda}{m^{*2} g (4\pi K_0)^2} \end{aligned} \tag{r}$$

The expressions in (r) are transformed to laboratory coordinates by

$$\Delta g_i = (\mathbf{e}_i \cdot \mathbf{e}_\xi)\, \Delta g_\xi \tag{s}$$

where $\mathbf{e}_i \cdot \mathbf{e}_\xi$ is the direction cosine matrix. Finally (i), (m), (q), and (s) are combined to give

$$\{\Delta w_i\} = \frac{m_r}{m_s + m_r} \cdot \frac{4\pi Z_r^2 Z_s^2 e^4 \ln \Lambda}{m^{*2}(4\pi K_0)^2} \frac{g_i}{g^3} \tag{t}$$

Note that

$$\frac{g_i}{g^3} = \frac{\partial}{\partial g_i}\left(\frac{1}{g}\right) = \frac{m_r}{m_s + m_r} \frac{\partial}{\partial w_{i_s}} \left(\frac{1}{|\mathbf{w}_s - \mathbf{w}_r|}\right)$$

so that (t) becomes,

$$\{\Delta w_i\} = \Gamma_{sr} \left(\frac{m_s}{m^*}\right)^2 \frac{\partial}{\partial w_{s_i}} \frac{1}{|w_s - w_r|} \tag{u}$$

where

$$\Gamma_{sr} = \frac{m^{*2} e^4 Z_s^2 Z_r^2}{m_s^4 4\pi K_0^2} \ln \Lambda \tag{v}$$

In the same way, (i) becomes

$$\{\Delta w_i \Delta w_j\}_s = \Gamma_{sr} \frac{\partial^2 |\mathbf{w}_s - \mathbf{w}_r|}{\partial w_{s_i}\, \partial w_{s_j}} \tag{w}$$

Finally, $\langle \Delta w_i \rangle_s$, $\langle \Delta w_i \Delta w_j \rangle_s$ are calculated with the use of (d), (e), (i), (j), and (w),

$$\begin{aligned} \langle \Delta w_i \rangle_s &= \sum_r \Gamma_{sr} \frac{\partial h_{sr}}{\partial w_{i_s}} \\ \langle \Delta w_i \Delta w_j \rangle &= \sum \Gamma_{sr} \frac{\partial^2 g_{sr}}{\partial w_{i_s}\, \partial w_{j_s}} \end{aligned} \tag{x}$$

where

$$h_{sr} = \left(\frac{m_s}{m^*}\right)^2 \int \frac{f_r\, dw_r}{|\mathbf{w}_s - w_r|} \tag{y}$$

$$g_{sr} = \int f_r |\mathbf{w}_s - \mathbf{w}_r| dw_r \tag{z}$$

The Fokker-Planck equation (g) then becomes

$$\frac{Df_s}{Dt} = \sum_r \Gamma_{sr}\left[-\sum_i \frac{\partial}{\partial w_{s_i}}\left(f_s \frac{\partial h_{sr}}{\partial w_{s_i}}\right) + \frac{1}{2}\sum_{i,j} \frac{\partial^2}{\partial w_{s_i}\,\partial w_{s_j}}\left(f_s \frac{\partial^2 g_{sr}}{\partial w_{s_i}\,\partial w_{s_j}}\right)\right] \quad (5.204)$$

In the above form, terms containing like particles do not affect the momentum, and the second term also does not affect the momentum.

5.12.1 Electron Electrical Conductivity Using Fokker-Planck Equation. We will next use (5.204) to calculate the electron electrical conductivity of a fully ionized gas; thus s = electron. Multiplication of (5.204) by $m_e\mathbf{w}_e$ and integration over electron-velocity space yields

$$\rho_e\left[\frac{\partial \mathbf{v}_e}{\partial t} + (\mathbf{v}_e \cdot \nabla)\mathbf{v}_e\right] = -n_e e(\mathbf{E} + \mathbf{v}_e \times \mathbf{B}) - \nabla p_e = \mathbf{P}_{eI} \quad (5.205)$$

which is formally identical to (5.184), except that $\mathbf{P}_{eI}$ is now defined as

$$(P_{eI})_i = m_e\Gamma_{eI}\int w_{e_i}\sum_k \frac{\partial}{w_{e_k}}\left(f_e \frac{\partial h_{eI}}{\partial w_{e_k}}\right) d\mathbf{w}_e \quad (5.206)$$

Integration by parts yields

$$(P_{eI})_i = -m_e\Gamma_{eI}\int f_e\left(\frac{\partial h_{eI}}{\partial w_{e_i}}\right) d\mathbf{w}_e \quad (a)$$

From (y) of the previous section,

$$h_{eI} = \int \frac{f_I\, d\mathbf{w}_I}{|w_e - w_I|} \quad (b)$$

With a displaced maxwellian distribution for f_I given by

$$f_I = a_I e^{-b_I|\mathbf{w}_I - \mathbf{v}_I|^2} \quad (c)$$

h_{eI} becomes

$$h_{eI} = \frac{n_I \operatorname{erf}(b_I^{\frac{1}{2}}|\mathbf{w}_e - \mathbf{v}_I|)}{|\mathbf{w}_e - \mathbf{v}_I|} \quad (d)$$

where $b_I = m_I/2kT_I$. Since generally $w_e \gg \langle c\rangle_I$, the argument of the error function is large, and the error function becomes unity. Finally, the average ion motion is taken as zero, so that (d) becomes

$$h_{eI} = \frac{n_I}{|w_e|} \quad (e)$$

Substitution of (v) of Sec. 5.12 and (e) above into (a) yields

$$P_{eI} = \frac{n_I e^4 \ln \Lambda}{4\pi K_0{}^2}\int f_e \nabla \frac{1}{|w_e|}\, d\mathbf{w}_e \quad (f)$$

which is identical to (g) of Sec. 5.9. Thus, the resulting expressions for the electrical conductivity will be identical to those obtained in Sec. 5.9.

Thus, no new result is obtained by this procedure. The reason for these same results is that only binary collisions were computed when calculating $\langle \Delta w_e \rangle$, which resulted in the usual electron-ion cross section. The Fokker-Planck equation will give different results only when collective collisions are used. This however becomes a very difficult procedure, and a complete solution is not currently available. In summary, use of the Fokker-Planck equation in which the γ's are calculated using binary collisions will yield results which are similar to that obtained from the binary-collision integral.

REFERENCES CITED

1. Chapman, S., and T. G. Cowling: *The Mathematical Theory of Non-uniform Gases*, pp. 59–66, Cambridge University Press, London, 1953.
2. Jeans, Sir J. H.: *An Introduction to the Kinetic Theory of Gases*, p. 115, Cambridge University Press, London, 1952.
3. Ref. 1, pp. 354–355. Note that $\mathbf{F}_2 = \mathbf{E}^*/m_e$.
4. Ref. 1, p. 356.
5. Ref. 1, pp. 170–179.
6. Ref. 1, p. 172.
7. Spitzer, L.: *Physics of Fully Ionized Gases*, p. 72, Interscience Publishers, Inc., New York, 1956.
8. Ref. 1, p. 179.
9. Cobine, J.: *Gaseous Conductors*, pp. 205ff, Dover Publications, Inc., New York, 1958.
10. Druyvesteyn, M. J., and F. M. Penning: "The Mechanism of Electrical Discharges in Gases of Low Pressure," *Rev. Mod. Phys.*, **12**:87–174 (1940); **13**:72–73 (1941).
11. Wu, C. S.: "On the Distribution Function and Mean Energy of Electrons in a Slightly Ionized Gas in the Presence of Electric and Magnetic Fields," *Jet Propulsion Lab. CIT Rept.* 32-14, July 1, 1960.
12. Ref. 7, p. 23.
13. Sutton, G. W.: "Hall Effect in a Lorentz Gas," *Phys. Fluids*, **4**:1273–1274.
14. Ref. 7, p. 73.
15. Spitzer, L., and R. Härm: "Transport Phenomena in a Completely Ionized Gas," *Phys. Rev.*, **89**:977–981 (1953).
16. Sodha, M. S., and Y. P. Varshni: "Transport Phenomena in Completely Ionized Gas Considering Electron-Electron Scattering," *Phys. Rev.*, **111**: 1203–1205 (1958); "Dependence of Electron Mobility on Magnetic Field in a Fully Ionized Gas," *Phys. Rev.*, **114**:946–947 (1959).
17. Sodha, M. S.: "Electron Mobility in Partially Ionized Atomic Hydrogen," *Phys. Rev.*, **113**:1163–1164 (1959).
18. Ref. 1, pp. 338–345.
19. Hirshfelder, J. O., C. F. Curtiss, and R. B. Bird: *Molecular Theory of Gases and Liquids*, John Wiley & Sons, Inc., New York, 1954.
20. Landshoff, R.: "Transport Phenomena in a Completely Ionized Gas in Presence of a Magnetic Field," *Phys. Rev.*, **76**:904–909 (1949).

21. Landshoff, R.: "Convergence of the Chapman-Enskog Method for a Completely Ionized Gas," *Phys. Rev.*, **82**:442 (1951).
22. Wright, J. P.: "Effects of Neutral Particles on the Transport Properties of a Plasma in a Uniform Magnetic Field," *Phys. Fluids,* **4**:1341–1347 (1961).
23. Ref. 1, sec. 18.4.
24. Ref. 1, sec. 10.3.
25. Curtiss, C. F., and J. O. Hirschfelder: "Transport Properties of Multicomponent Gas Mixtures," *J. Chem. Phys.*, **17**:550–555 (1949).
26. Cowling, T. G.: *Magnetohydrodynamics*, pp. 105–108, Interscience Publishers, Inc., New York, 1957.
27. Petschek, H., and S. Byron: "Approach to Equilibrium Ionization behind Strong Shock Waves in Argon," *Ann. Phys.*, **1**:270–315 (1957).
28. Ref. 1, p. 337.
29. Ref. 1, p. 179.
30. Allis, W. P.: "Motion of Ions and Electrons," *Handbuch der Physik*, vol. XXI, Springer-Verlag OHG, Berlin, 1956.
31. Chandrasekhar, S.: "Stochastic Problems in Physics and Astronomy," *Rev. Mod. Phys.*, **15**:1–89 (1943).
32. Rosenbluth, M. N., W. M. McDonald, and D. L. Judd: "Fokker-Planck Equation for an Inverse-square Force," *Phys. Rev.*, **107**:1–6 (1957).

GENERAL REFERENCES

Allis, W. P.: "Motion of Ions and Electrons," *Handbuch der Physik*, vol. XXI, Springer-Verlag OHG, Berlin, 1956.

Chandrasekhar, S.: "Stochastic Problems in Physics and Astronomy," *Rev. Mod. Phys.*, **15**:1 (1943).

Chapman, S., and T. G. Cowling: *The Mathematical Theory of Non-uniform Gases*, Cambridge University Press, London, 1953.

Clauser, F. H. (gen. ed.): *Symposium on Plasma Dynamics*, Addison-Wesley Publishing Company, Inc., Reading, Mass., 1960.

Craggs, J. D., and H. S. W. Massey: "Collisions of Electrons with Molecules," *Handbuch der Physik*, vol. XXXVII/1, Atome III-Molekule 1, pp. 314–415, Springer-Verlag OHG, Berlin, 1959.

Delcroix, J. L.: *Introduction to the Theory of Ionized Gases*, translation by M. Clark, Jr., D. J. BenDaniel, and J. M. BenDaniel, Interscience Publishers, Inc., New York, 1960.

Drummond, James E. (ed.): *Plasma Physics*, McGraw-Hill Book Company, New York, 1961.

Ferraro, V. C. A., and C. Plumpton: *Magneto-fluid Mechanics*, Oxford University Press, Fair Lawn, N.J., 1961.

Hirschfelder, J. O., C. F. Curtiss, and R. B. Bird: *Molecular Theory of Gases and Liquids*, John Wiley & Sons, Inc., New York, 1954.

International Summer Course in Plasma Physics (Riso), Danish Atomic Energy Commission, 1960.

Linhart, J. G.: *Plasma Physics*, North Holland Publishing Company, Amsterdam, 1960.

Massey, H. S. W., and E. H. S. Burhop: *Electronic and Ionic Impact Phenomena*, Oxford University Press, Fair Lawn, N.J., 1952.

Menzel, D. H.: *Selected Papers on Physical Processes in Ionized Plasmas*, Dover Publications, Inc., New York, 1962.

Rose, D. J., and M. Clark: *Plasmas and Controlled Fusion*, John Wiley & Sons, Inc., New York, 1961.

Spitzer, L.: *Physics of Fully Ionized Gases*, Interscience Publishers, Inc., New York, 1956.

Theory of Neutral and Ionized Gases (Grenoble Université), John Wiley & Sons, Inc., New York, 1960.

Vlasov, A. A.: *Many-particle Theory and Its Application to Plasma*, Gordon & Breach, Science Publishers, Inc., New York, 1961.

Experimental Data on Electrical Conduction in Ionized Gases

Brown, S. C.: *Basic Data of Plasma Physics*, John Wiley & Sons, Inc., New York, 1959.

Cobine, J. D.: *Gaseous Conductors*, Dover Publications, Inc., New York, 1958.

Compton, K. T., and I. Langmuir: "Electrical Discharges in Gases, part I, Survey of Fundamental Processes," *Rev. Mod. Phys.*, **2**:123–242 (1930).

Compton, K. T., and I. Langmuir: "Electrical Discharges in Gases, part II, Fundamental Phenomena in Electrical Discharges," *Rev. Mod. Phys.*, **3**:191–257 (1931).

Druyvestyn, M. J., and F. M. Penning: "The Mechanism of Electrical Discharges in Gases of Low Pressure," *Rev. Mod. Phys.*, **12**:87–174 (1940); **13**:72 (1941).

Emeleus, K. G.: *The Conduction of Electricity through Gases*, Methuen & Co., Ltd., London, 1951.

Field, F. H.: *Electron Impact Phenomena and the Properties of Gaseous Ions*, Academic Press Inc., New York, 1957.

Guthrie, A., and R. K. Wakerling (eds.): *Characteristics of Electrical Discharges in Magnetic Fields*, McGraw-Hill Book Company, New York, 1949.

International Conference on Ionization Phenomena in Gases: N. R. Nilsson (ed.), *Proc. 4th Conf.*, 1960; H. Moecker (ed.), *Proc. 5th Conf.*, 1962; North Holland Publishing Company, Amsterdam.

Loeb, L. B.: *Basic Processes of Gaseous Electronics*, University of California Press, Berkeley, Calif., 1955.

Penning, F. M.: *Electrical Discharges in Gases*, The Macmillan Company, New York, 1957.

Thomson, J. J., and G. P. Thomson: *Conduction of Electricity through Gases*, Cambridge University Press, New York, 1933.

Von Engel, A.: *Ionized Gases*, Oxford University Press, Fair Lawn, N.J., 1955.

6

QUANTUM STATISTICS AND IONIZATION EQUILIBRIUM

6.1 INTRODUCTION

In the previous chapters it was assumed that there were n_e free electrons per cubic meter, without inquiry as to how they became separated from the atoms or molecules. This chapter presents some of the laws governing the formation of free electrons.

A neutral atom or molecule has Z electrons moving about it in more or less circular paths; the electric field due to the charge on the nucleus (screened by other electrons) balances the centrifugal force. These are called *bound electrons*. If a small amount of energy is given the electrons, one (or more) of them may change orbits so that the change in the sum of kinetic and potential energy equals the energy increment. If enough energy is supplied to one of the electrons, it may leave the force field of the nucleus completely, and its motion will be governed by the local electric and magnetic fields; that is, it becomes a free electron. The total energy in electron volts required to remove the first electron is called the *first ionization potential;* the incremental energy required to remove the second electron is called the *second ionization potential,* etc.

The required ionization energy may be supplied by a photon, by collision with an energetic atom or molecule, or by collision with an energetic electron. The ionization may proceed by stages; one collision may raise the energy of a bound electron, and a second collision may supply the additional energy required to remove the electron completely.

Ionization may also proceed by means of the Penning effect, which applies to mixtures of gases. One gas must have a possible excited state whose excitation energy exceeds or equals the ionization potential of the other gas. In addition, the time required for normal deexcitation must be long. Then, the excited particles will ionize the particles with the lower ionization potential upon collision. Deionization may proceed by the reverse process: An electron, ion, and some third particle (or surface) simultaneously collide; or an electron reattaches to an ion with a subsequent emission of a photon to carry away part of the ionization energy. Also, negative ions may be formed by the attachment of an electron to a neutral atom or molecule.

In principle, one may calculate the degree of ionization by calculating the rate of ionization and the rate of deionization. Each rate depends on the electron concentration; hence the electron density may be determined. Such a procedure is not usually possible, because of lack of adequate data on ionization and deionization. Some other method must therefore be found. Fortunately, for complete equilibrium, there is an entirely different method by which the number density of electrons may be found. This method is based on a very simple postulate: namely, the particles will arrange themselves among the accessible energy states, the arrangement or configuration being that which has the *highest* probability. The *accessible energy states* will be defined in Sec. 6.2.

Complete equilibrium is difficult to define. One possible definition is the final state of a mixture of gases in a volume whose boundaries also achieve a final static state. Another is that the distribution function for gas particles which obey Maxwell-Boltzmann statistics is maxwellian; however, we will show later that the maxwellian distribution function is a consequence of the assumption of equilibrium. Chemical reactions further complicate the problem. For example, a mixture of gaseous oxygen and hydrogen may remain such for years at room temperature, yet water is the equilibrium state. Under these conditions, there are possible quasi-equilibrium chemical states. Thus a definite statement concerning the chemical reactions to be included is required. An acceptable definition of equilibrium is that state where the particles have arranged themselves among the *accessible* energy states, the arrangement being that with the *highest* probability. In the previous example, if no water is formed, then water is *not* an accessible state. Equilibrium is achieved when the distribution function and all other quantities are static, and when diffusion is absent.

Unfortunately, we are interested in situations when the plasma or gas is *not* in such a state of equilibrium. However, it has been found, mostly from experience, that the properties are close to the equilibrium properties if the plasma or gas is not too far removed from equilibrium. For example, if the time rate of change of the plasma is small compared to the collision frequency; or if the diffusion velocities are small compared to the thermal velocities, then equilibrium properties may be used to a high degree of accuracy. We will examine other conditions later.

6.2 QUANTUM MECHANICS

Quantum or wave mechanics is based on a set of postulates concerning the motion of particles when their momentum or energy is very small. These postulates are in every sense similar to the postulation of Newton's laws of motion for large masses and small velocities; the postulates are acceptable because the results of calculations based on these postulates agree with experimental observation.

One of the consequences of the postulates is that associated with the momentum mw of any particle is a characteristic wavelength λ (as distinguished from the mean free path). This relation is

$$\lambda = \frac{h}{mw} \tag{6.1}$$

where h is the Planck constant of energy, which has been experimentally determined to be 6.625×10^{-33} joule-sec. We may use this concept to calculate the accessible energy levels of a single electron in motion about a nucleus of charge Ze. We may equate the coulombic force to the acceleration,

$$\frac{Ze^2}{4\pi K_0 r^2} = m_e r \omega^2 \tag{6.2}$$

where ω is the angular frequency of rotation. The total energy is

$$\epsilon = \tfrac{1}{2} m w_e{}^2 - \frac{Ze^2}{4\pi K_0 r} \tag{6.3}$$

Substitution of (6.2) yields

$$\epsilon = \tfrac{1}{2} m r^2 \omega^2 - m r^2 \omega^2 = -\tfrac{1}{2} m r^2 \omega^2 \tag{6.4}$$

It appears that this electron should be radiating away its energy, since it is being accelerated, but it is known that an electron in a stable orbit does not radiate. It is found that no radiation occurs if the orbit length is equal to n integer wavelengths,

$$2\pi r = n\lambda = n \frac{h}{m w_e} = \frac{nh}{m_e r \omega} \tag{6.5}$$

from which

$$\omega r^2 = n \frac{h}{2\pi m_e} \tag{6.6}$$

The total energy can also be written as

$$\epsilon = -\tfrac{1}{2} m_e \frac{r^3 \omega^2}{(r^2 \omega)^2} \tag{6.4a}$$

Substitution of (6.6) for $r^2\omega$ and (6.2) for $r^3\omega^2$ into (6.4a) yields

$$\epsilon_n = -\frac{1}{2} \frac{m_e Z^2 e^4 (2\pi)^2}{h^2} \frac{1}{n^2} \tag{6.7}$$

The particular value of n is called the *quantum number*. Consider next a change in electron energy level corresponding to n_1 to a state corresponding to n_2. The change in energy is

$$\Delta\epsilon = \tfrac{1}{2}m_e Z^2 e^4 \left(\frac{2\pi}{h}\right)^2 \left(\frac{1}{n_1^2} - \frac{1}{n_2^2}\right) \tag{6.8}$$

This energy appears as a photon with energy $h\nu$, where ν is the frequency of the associated radiation.

When a particle becomes ionized so that its electron is free to move about, this electron can still assume only certain values of momentum, as determined by (6.1). The components of momentum therefore are related to the following characteristic wavelengths in three orthogonal directions:

$$\begin{aligned} (mw_x)_e &= \frac{h}{\lambda_x} \\ (mw_y)_e &= \frac{h}{\lambda_y} \\ (mw_z)_e &= \frac{h}{\lambda_z} \end{aligned} \tag{6.9}$$

Thus, the total energy in translational motion of any particle is

$$\epsilon_s = \tfrac{1}{2}m_s(w_x^2 + w_y^2 + w_z^2) = \frac{h^2}{2m_s}\left(\frac{1}{\lambda_x^2} + \frac{1}{\lambda_y^2} + \frac{1}{\lambda_z^2}\right) \tag{6.10}$$

Consider the particle moving in a cube having a side L. As in the case of circular motion, the length L is postulated to be an integral number of wavelengths,

$$\lambda_i = \frac{2L}{n_i} \tag{6.11}$$

The factor of 2 arises by considering $n = 1$; the amplitude of the associated wave is repetitive at half wavelengths. Substitution of (6.11) into (6.10) yields the following expression for the accessible energy levels in translation:

$$\epsilon_s = \frac{h^2}{8mL^2}(n_x^2 + n_y^2 + n_z^2) \tag{6.12}$$

where n_x, n_y, n_z are the quantum numbers and may independently assume any integer values. Thus, the energy of a particle is not a continuous function of velocity; the energy can have only *certain discrete values*. We will next determine which combination of energy levels has the highest probability for occupation.

6.3 STATISTICS[1]

Let us consider three identical particles, A, B, and C. Assume also that they have access to only four energy states or levels which are integer multiples of some energy ϵ_0. A particle can therefore have an energy of 0, ϵ_0, $2\epsilon_0$, or $3\epsilon_0$. In addition, we must specify the total energy which is to be divided among the three particles: for simplicity, let the total energy be $3\epsilon_0$. Thus, one particle may have energy $3\epsilon_0$, and the other two zero energy; or one particle may have energy $2\epsilon_0$, another ϵ_0, and the third zero, etc. A table can therefore be made which shows the possible energy states (see Table 6.1).

Since the particles are identical, the first three columns are essentially identical. This is therefore called configuration I, and there are three possible ways of arranging the particles in this configuration. Similarly, there are six ways of arranging the particles in configuration II, but only one way that the particles can be arranged in configuration III. Now, each arrangement in each configuration is equally probable. Hence the probability of the particles being in configuration I is $\frac{3}{10}$, II is $\frac{6}{10}$, and III is $\frac{1}{10}$. Since the basic postulate is that the particles will be in the configuration with the highest probability, the particles will have configuration II.

Ordinarily, we will deal with a much larger number of particles, say N, and energy levels $\epsilon_0, \epsilon_1, \epsilon_2, \ldots$, with N_0 particles in energy level ϵ_0, N_1 particles in energy level ϵ_1, N_2 particles in energy level ϵ_2, etc. The probability of a given configuration ω_i is therefore

$$\omega_i = \frac{N!/N_0!N_1!N_2! \cdots}{\sum \dfrac{N!}{N_0!N_1!N_2! \cdots}} = \frac{N!/\Pi N_i!}{\sum \dfrac{N!}{\Pi N_i!}} \tag{6.13}$$

where the numerator is the number of possible arrangements in the ith configuration, and the denominator is the sum over all possible arrangements. For example, let us examine a single configuration, say II, in

Table 6.1 Possible Location of Particles among Energy Levels

Energy level	Possible configurations: I	II	III
$3\epsilon_0$	A B C		
$2\epsilon_0$		A A B B C C	
ϵ_0		B C A C A B	ABC
0	BC AC AB	C B C A B A	

which there is only one particle in each level. The number of ways of arranging N particles in the energy levels is $N!$ However, as is the case of I or II, if N_i particles are in the ith energy level, then these N_i particles can be arranged in that energy level $N_i!$ different ways. This reduces the total number of ways of arranging the particles by $N_i!$ Finally, to obtain the probability, one must divide by the total number of ways of arranging the particles; hence the denominator of (6.13). For the previous example, we have

Configuration I: $N_1 = N_2 = 0; N_3 = 1; N_0 = 2; N = 3$

$$\frac{N!}{\Pi N_i!} = \frac{6}{2} = 3$$

Configuration II: $N_0 = N_1 = N_2 = 1; N_3 = 0; N = 3$

$$\frac{N!}{\Pi N_i!} = 6$$

Configuration III: $N_0 = N_2 = N_3 = 0; N_1 = 3; N = 3$

$$\frac{N!}{\Pi N_i!} = 1$$

The sum of the ways of arranging the particles is 10; hence $\omega_{\mathrm{I}} = 0.3$, $\omega_{\mathrm{II}} = 0.6$, $\omega_{\mathrm{III}} = 0.1$.

The most probable state is designated $\overline{N_i}(\epsilon_i)$, that is, $\overline{N_0}$ particles have energy ϵ_0, $\overline{N_1}$ particles have energy ϵ_1, etc. For our example, the most probable state is $\overline{N_0} = 1$, $\overline{N_1} = 1$, $\overline{N_2} = 1$, $\overline{N_3} = 0$.

Thus, the problem of determining the most probable configuration is reduced to maximizing ω_i. Since we will specify the total number of particles N, we will therefore maximize with respect to $N_0, N_1, N_2, \ldots$, etc. However, two constraints must be observed:

$$\Sigma N_i = N \tag{6.14}$$

$$\Sigma N_i \epsilon_i = E \tag{6.15}$$

Equation (6.14) is a consequence of specifying the total number of particles; (6.15) is caused by specifying the total energy available to all N particles.

Instead of maximizing ω_i, we need only minimize $\Pi N_i!$ in the denominator of (6.13); or taking the logarithm, we must minimize the function F where

$$F = \Sigma \ln N_i! \tag{6.16}$$

subject to the constraints given by (6.14) and (6.15). Thus,

$$G = -\Sigma N_i + N = 0 \tag{6.17}$$

$$H = -\Sigma \epsilon_i N_i + E = 0 \tag{6.18}$$

According to the calculus of variations, it is necessary to set the variation δ of $F - \alpha G - \beta H$ equal to zero, where α and β are the *lagrangian multipliers* and are to be determined later. Thus the problem reduces to

$$\delta \left(\sum_i \ln N_i! + \alpha \sum N_i - \alpha N + \beta \sum N_i \epsilon_i - \beta E \right) = 0 \qquad (6.19)$$

The variations of N and E are zero since they are specified; in fact, the only variable is the number of particles in each energy level N_i. The first term of (6.19) is therefore

$$\sum \frac{\partial}{\partial N_i} (\ln N_i!)\, \delta N_i \qquad (6.20)$$

If N_i is a large integer, the derivative may be approximated by

$$\begin{aligned} \frac{d}{dN_i} \ln N_i! &= \ln (N_i!) - \ln (N_i - 1)! \\ &= \ln \frac{N_i!}{(N_i - 1)!} = \ln \frac{N_i(N_i - 1)!}{(N_i - 1)!} \\ &= \ln N_i \end{aligned} \qquad (6.21)$$

which is Stirling's approximation for large numbers.

The variation of ΣN_i is obviously $\Sigma\, \delta N_i$, while the variation of $\Sigma N_i \epsilon_i$ is obviously $\Sigma \epsilon_i\, \delta N_i$. Equation (6.19) with the use of (6.20) and (6.21) therefore becomes

$$\sum_i (\ln N_i + \alpha + \beta \epsilon_i)\, \delta N_i = 0 \qquad (6.22)$$

Since the variation δN_i is arbitrary, the brackets for each energy level must be individually equal to zero, which yields

$$\ln N_i + \alpha + \beta \epsilon_i = 0$$

or, for species s,

$$N_i^s = \lambda_s e^{-\beta \epsilon_i^s} = \lambda_s \theta^{\epsilon_i^s} \qquad (6.23)$$

where λ_s is a new constant equal to $e^{-\alpha}$, and $\theta = e^{-\beta}$. The subscript s indicates that it is a constant for only one species.

Sometimes there are $\bar{\omega}_i$ physical arrangements which have the same energy level ϵ_i; this energy level is called $\bar{\omega}_i$ degenerate, and (6.23) must be modified as follows:

$$N_i = \bar{\omega}_i^s \lambda_s \theta^{\epsilon_i^s} \qquad (6.24)$$

The total number of particles is given by the sum over all i, or

$$N_s = \sum_i N_i^s = \lambda_s \sum_i \bar{\omega}_i^s \theta^{\epsilon_i^s} \qquad (6.25)$$

6.4 PARTITION FUNCTION

The sum $\sum_i \bar{\omega}_i \theta^{\epsilon_i^s}$ is called the *partition function* for the s species; it is usually designated as f or Q. Since we have already used these symbols, we will depart from convention and designate the partition function by P_s,

$$P_s = \sum_i \bar{\omega}_i^s \theta^{\epsilon_i^s} \equiv \frac{N_s}{\lambda_s} \tag{6.26}$$

from (6.25). The fraction of particles in a given energy level is therefore

$$\frac{N_i^s}{N_s} = \frac{\bar{\omega}_i^s \lambda_s \theta^{\epsilon_i^s}}{\lambda_s P_s} = \frac{\bar{\omega}_i \theta^{\epsilon_i^s}}{P_s} \tag{6.27}$$

The partition function has some other interesting properties. For example, the total energy of the s species is given by

$$E_s = \sum_i N_i \epsilon_i^s = \lambda_s \sum_i \bar{\omega}_i \epsilon_i^s \theta^{\epsilon_i^s} \tag{6.28}$$

This can be written as

$$E_s = \lambda_s \theta \frac{\partial}{\partial \theta} \sum_i \bar{\omega}_i^s \theta^{\epsilon_i^s}$$

or

$$E_s = \lambda_s \frac{\partial P^s}{\partial \ln \theta} \tag{6.29}$$

Actually, the average energy per particle is usually specified, so that (6.29) becomes

$$\bar{\epsilon} = \frac{E_s}{N_s} = \frac{1}{P_s} \frac{\partial P_s}{\partial \ln \theta}$$

or

$$\bar{\epsilon} = \frac{\partial \ln P_s}{\partial \ln \theta} \tag{6.30}$$

Thus, if we can relate θ to temperature, and P_s to the particle energy levels, (6.30) is a convenient method of finding the average energy per particle as a function of temperature. However, the consequences are much more far reaching, as we shall see later.

6.5 RELATION TO THERMODYNAMICS

The first law of thermodynamics is as follows: The thermal and mechanical energy which is supplied to a fixed mass of substance increases its internal energy, or

$$dQ + dW = dE \tag{6.31}$$

where Q is the thermal energy, and W is the mechanical energy. We may also define an entropy S such that $dS = dQ/T$, so that (6.31) becomes

$$T\,dS + dW = dE \tag{6.32}$$

Consider a fixed mass on which no work is done and which is held at constant temperature. Then (6.32) becomes

$$d(TS) = dE \qquad \text{or} \qquad d(E - TS) = 0 \qquad \text{or} \qquad dA = 0 \tag{6.33}$$

where the Helmholtz *free energy* is defined as

$$A = E - TS \tag{6.34}$$

When a system is in chemical and thermal equilibrium, the criterion is that $dA = 0$, from (6.33). We will use this criterion later. Next, let us examine the manner in which the free energy A varies as the configuration is changed or as the number density n_s of each type of molecule shifts owing to chemical reactions. The change in total free energy is

$$\begin{aligned} dA &= d(E - TS) \\ &= dE - S\,dT - T\,dS \end{aligned} \tag{6.35}$$

Now the energy is a function of at most three variables: Let these be the entropy, the generalized geometric coordinates† x_i, and the number of particles of each species N_s. Thus, (6.35) becomes

$$dA = \frac{\partial E}{\partial S}\,dS + \sum_i \frac{\partial E}{\partial x_i}\,dx_i + \sum_s \frac{\partial E}{\partial N_s}\,dN_s - S\,dT - T\,dS \tag{6.36}$$

From the first law (6.32), if the geometric factors do not change so that dW is zero, then $\partial E/\partial S = T$, and the first and last terms of (6.36) cancel each other. The term $-\partial E/\partial x_i$ is called the *generalized force* X_i, and the term $\partial E/\partial N_s$ is called the *chemical potential* μ_s,

$$\frac{\partial E}{\partial x_i} = -X_i = \frac{\partial A}{\partial x_i} \tag{6.37}$$

$$\frac{\partial E}{\partial N_s} = \mu_s = \frac{\partial A}{\partial N_s} \tag{6.38}$$

so that (6.36) becomes

$$dA = -S\,dT - \sum_i X_i\,dx_i + \sum_s \mu_s\,dN_s \tag{6.39}$$

If we consider chemical equilibrium in a fixed volume at constant temperature, since $dT = 0$, the criterion for equilibrium is simply

$$\sum_s \mu_s\,dN_s = 0 \tag{6.40}$$

† For example, the dimensions of the volume containing all the particles.

We must next find a way to relate the chemical potential of classical thermodynamics to the partition function. Let us differentiate the function A/T,

$$d\left(\frac{A}{T}\right) = \frac{dA}{T} - \frac{A}{T^2}\,dT$$

$$= -\frac{S\,dT}{T} - \frac{\Sigma X_i\,dx_i}{T} + \frac{\Sigma \mu_s\,dN_s}{T} - \frac{E - TS}{T^2}\,dT \tag{6.41}$$

or $$d\left(\frac{A}{T}\right) = -\frac{E}{T^2}\,dT - \frac{1}{T}\sum X_i\,dx_i + \frac{1}{T}\sum \mu_s\,dN_s \tag{6.42}$$

To relate this to the partition function, let us differentiate the function $A_s \ln \theta$; then

$$d(A_s \ln \theta) = \frac{\partial}{\partial \ln \theta}(A_s \ln \theta)\,d(\ln \theta) + \ln \theta \sum_i \frac{\partial A_s}{\partial X_i}\,dX_i$$

$$+ \ln \theta \sum \frac{\partial A}{\partial N_s}\,dN_s + \ln \theta\,\frac{\partial A}{\partial \lambda_s}\,d\lambda_s \tag{6.43}$$

Let us tentatively consider the function $A_s \ln \theta$ to be given as follows:

$$A_s \ln \theta = N_s - N_s \ln N_s + N_s \ln P_s(\theta) \tag{6.44}$$

Differentiation of (6.44), with θ and λ_s independent, yields

$$\ln \theta\,\frac{\partial A_s}{\partial \lambda_s} = 0 \tag{6.45}$$

so that the coefficient of the last term of (6.43) is zero. Since there is no variation of $A_s \ln \theta$ with λ_s, then λ_s may be regarded as a constant.

The first coefficient of (6.43) is as follows, from (6.44), (6.26), and (6.29):

$$\frac{\partial A_s \ln \theta}{\partial \ln \theta} = \frac{N_s}{P_s}\frac{\partial P_s}{\partial \ln \theta} = E_s \tag{6.46}$$

Similarly, $$\frac{\partial A_s}{\partial N_s} = -\frac{\ln \lambda_s}{\ln \theta} \tag{6.47}$$

Substitution of (6.46) and (6.47) into (6.43) yields

$$d(A_s \ln \theta) = E_s\,d(\ln \theta) + \ln \theta \sum \frac{\partial A_s}{\partial x_i}\,dx_i - \ln \lambda_s\,dN_s \tag{6.48}$$

Finally, sum (6.48) over all s, with θ not a function of s,

$$d(\ln \theta \sum_s A_s) = \sum_s E_s\,d(\ln \theta) - \ln \theta \sum_s \sum_i X_i^s\,dx_i - \sum_s \ln \lambda_s\,dN_s \tag{6.49}$$

where $X_i^s = -\partial A_s/\partial x_i$ by analogy with (6.37). Comparison of (6.49) and (6.42) shows that they are identical if

$$\ln \theta = -\frac{1}{kT} \tag{6.50a}$$

$$A = \sum_s A_s \tag{6.50b}$$

$$E = \sum_s E_s \tag{6.50c}$$

$$X_i = \sum_s X_i^s \tag{6.50d}$$

$$\mu_s = kT \ln \lambda_s \tag{6.50e}$$

With the identifications of (6.50), the free energy of the s species (6.44) becomes

$$A_s = -N_s kT(\ln P_s - \ln N_s + 1) \tag{6.51}$$

Also, from (6.26),

$$\ln \lambda_s = -\ln P_s + \ln N_s \tag{6.52}$$

so that the chemical potential (6.50e) becomes

$$\mu_s = kT \ln \frac{N_s}{P_s} \tag{6.53}$$

or directly from (6.51) since $\mu_s = \partial A_s/\partial N_s$. The generalized force from (6.51) is

$$X_i^s = -\frac{\partial A_s}{\partial x_i} = N_s kT \frac{\partial}{\partial x_i} \ln P_s \tag{6.54}$$

and the entropy is similarly obtained,

$$S_s = \frac{\partial A_s}{\partial T} = -N_s k \frac{\partial}{\partial T} T(\ln P_s - \ln N_s + 1) \tag{6.55}$$

From (6.42) the energy is given by

$$E_s = -T^2 \frac{\partial}{\partial T}\left(\frac{A_s}{T}\right) = T^2 N_s k \frac{\partial}{\partial T} \ln P_s \tag{6.56}$$

This result could also be obtained directly from (6.29). The specific heat at constant volume is $C_{v_s} = N_s^{-1}\, \partial E_s/\partial T$, or

$$C_{v_s} = \frac{\partial}{\partial T}\left(\frac{E_s}{N_s}\right) = k \frac{\partial}{\partial T}\left(T^2 \frac{\partial}{\partial T} \ln P_s\right) \tag{6.57}$$

Thus it is possible to evaluate all equilibrium thermodynamic properties in terms of the partition function.

Finally, with the use of (6.50a), the partition function of (6.26) becomes

$$P_s = \sum_i \bar{\omega}_i^s e^{-\epsilon_i^s/kT} \tag{6.58}$$

6.6 PROPERTIES OF THE PARTITION FUNCTION

When evaluating the partition function, we must take into account the separate contribution to the energy levels. For example, a molecule has translational energy levels ϵ_i, rotational energy levels ϵ_j, vibrational energy levels ϵ_k, electronic excitation energy levels ϵ_l, and chemical energy states ϵ_0. The total energy is $\epsilon_i + \epsilon_j + \epsilon_k + \epsilon_l + \epsilon_0$; thus the partition function is

$$P_s = \sum_i \sum_k \sum_l \sum_j \bar{\omega}_i{}^s \bar{\omega}_j{}^s \bar{\omega}_k{}^s \bar{\omega}_l{}^s e^{-(\epsilon_i+\epsilon_j+\epsilon_k+\epsilon_l+\epsilon_0)/kT} \tag{6.59}$$

which can be represented as a multiple product,

$$P_s = \Big(\sum_i \bar{\omega}_i{}^s e^{-\epsilon_i{}^s/kT}\Big) \cdot \Big(\sum_j \bar{\omega}_j{}^s e^{-\epsilon_j{}^s/kT}\Big) \cdots \tag{6.60}$$

or

$$P_s = P_i{}^s P_j{}^s P_k{}^s P_l{}^s P_0{}^s \tag{6.61}$$

The rotational (j), vibrational (k), electronic (l), and chemical (0) are sometimes called the *internal* partition functions P_{int}. The average energy $\bar{E}^s$ is therefore

$$\bar{E}^s = \frac{\partial \ln P^s}{\partial \ln \theta} = kT^2 \frac{\partial \ln P_s}{\partial T} = kT^2 \left(\frac{\partial \ln P_i{}^s}{\partial T} + \frac{\partial \ln P_j{}^s}{\partial T} + \cdots \right) \tag{6.62}$$

If we define an average energy for each mode of excitation as

$$E_i{}^s = \frac{\partial \ln P_i{}^s}{\partial \ln \theta} \tag{6.63}$$

Eq. (6.62) becomes

$$E^s = E_i{}^s + E_j{}^s + E_k{}^s + E_l{}^s + E_0{}^s \tag{6.64}$$

6.6.1 Translational Partition Function. Let us next evaluate the translational partition function. Use of (6.12) in (6.58) yields

$$P_{s\,\text{trans}} = \sum_{n_x=1}^{\infty} \sum_{n_y=1}^{\infty} \sum_{n_z=1}^{\infty} e^{(-h^2/8m_sL^2kT)(n_x{}^2+n_y{}^2+n_z{}^2)} \tag{6.65}$$

which is separable according to (6.60):

$$P_{s\,\text{trans}} = \sum_{n_x=1}^{\infty} e^{(-h^2n_x{}^2/8m_sL^2kT)} \sum_{n_y=1}^{\infty} e^{(-h^2n_y{}^2/8m_sL^2kT)} \sum_{n_z=1}^{\infty} e^{(-h^2n_z{}^2/8m_sL^2kT)}$$

Since n_x, n_y, n_z are merely dummies of summation, this can be written as

$$P^s_{\text{trans}} = \Big(\sum_{n=1}^{\infty} e^{(-h^2n^2/8m_sL^2kT)} \Big)^3$$

Except at very low temperatures, $h^2/3m_sL^2kT \ll 1$; hence the summation may be replaced by an integral:

$$P^s_{\text{trans}} = \left(\int_0^\infty e^{(-h^2n^2/8m_sL^2kT)}\,dn\right)^3 = \left(\frac{2\pi m_s kT}{h^2}\right)^{\frac{3}{2}} L^3 \tag{6.66}$$

The term L^3 is normally regarded as the volume. The total partition function is therefore

$$P_s = \left(\frac{2\pi m_s kT}{h^2}\right)^{\frac{3}{2}} \mathcal{V} P^s_{\text{int}} \tag{6.67}$$

so that the free energy of the s species, from (6.51), is

$$A_s = -N_s kT \left[\ln\left(\frac{2\pi m_s kT}{h^2}\mathcal{V}\right)^{\frac{3}{2}} - \ln N_s + 1\right] - kTN_s \ln P^s_{\text{int}} \tag{6.68}$$

where $\mathcal{V} = L^3$ is the volume occupied by the N_s particles.

6.6.2 Pressure, Energy, and Velocities. We can calculate the pressure from (6.68) by considering the generalized geometric factor as the volume $\mathcal{V}$, and the generalized force as p_s. Then,

$$p_s = -\frac{\partial A_s}{\partial \mathcal{V}} = -\frac{kTN_s}{\mathcal{V}} = n_s kT \tag{6.69}$$

in agreement with kinetic theory. We may also calculate the translational energy from (6.56),

$$E_s{}^i = \tfrac{3}{2}N_s kT \tag{6.70}$$

which again agrees with kinetic theory. Finally, it is of interest to calculate the distribution function. From (6.24), the number having energies in the x direction is

$$N_{ix} = \frac{\bar{\omega}_i{}^s N_s e^{-\epsilon_i/kT}}{P_{xi}{}^s} = \frac{\bar{\omega}_i{}^s N_s e^{-\frac{1}{2}mw_x{}^2/kT}}{(2\pi m_s kT/h^2)^{\frac{1}{2}} L} \tag{6.71}$$

The velocities are related to the quantum number by (6.9) and (6.11):

$$n_x = \frac{2Lm_s w_x}{h} \tag{6.72}$$

The number of energy levels for a given velocity increment is therefore

$$dn_x = \frac{2Lm_s}{h}\,dw_x \tag{6.73}$$

Thus, the degeneracy is given by $\bar{\omega}_i = dn_x$, and (6.71) becomes

$$N_{ix} = \frac{2Lm_s N_s e^{-\frac{1}{2}m_s w_x{}^2/kT}/h}{(2\pi m_s kT/h^2)^{\frac{1}{2}}}\,dw_x \tag{6.74}$$

In defining the wavelength, no distinction was made as to whether the velocity was in the $+x$ or $-x$ direction; this leads to an additional degeneracy factor of 2 in (6.74). Actually, we later distinguish between $w_x < 0$ and $w_x > 0$; hence the factor of 2 may be dropped. Similar expressions are found for the y and z directions. The final result is

$$N = \frac{N_s}{L^3}\left(\frac{m_s}{2\pi kT}\right)^{\frac{3}{2}} e^{-\frac{1}{2}(m_s/kT)(w_x{}^2+w_y{}^2+w_z{}^2)}\,dw_x\,dw_y\,dw_z \tag{6.74a}$$

where N_s/L^3 is the number density of s particles. Thus, the partition function predicts the maxwellian velocity distribution.

6.7 CHEMICAL AND IONIZATION EQUILIBRIUM

We may now use (6.40) to predict the equilibrium composition of a mixture of several species. Consider the following chemical reaction:

$$\sum_a \nu_s \rightleftharpoons \sum_b \nu_s \tag{6.75}$$

where a refers to reactants, b to products, s to the species, and the ν's are the stoichiometric ratios. For example, the water reaction is

$$(O_2) + 2(H_2) \rightarrow 2(H_2O)$$

so that $\nu_{O_2} = 1$, $\nu_{H_2} = 2$, $\nu_{H_2O} = 2$. For convenience, select $(\nu_{s_1})_a$ to be unity. For an incremental change in the number of a_1 particles dN_{a_1}, then

$$\begin{aligned}(dN_s)_a &= \nu_{s,a}\,dN_{a_1} \\ (dN_s)_b &= -\nu_{s,b}\,dN_{a_1}\end{aligned} \tag{6.76}$$

Then the equation for chemical equilibrium, (6.40), becomes

$$\sum_a \mu_s\nu_s = \sum_b \mu_s\nu_s \tag{6.77}$$

From (6.50e) and (6.52), the chemical potential of the s species is given by

$$\mu_s = kT \ln \frac{P_s}{N_s} \tag{6.78}$$

It is more convenient to express P_s as the product $P^s_{\text{trans}} \cdot P^s_{\text{int}} \cdot P^s_{\text{chem}}$. Use of P^s_{trans} from (6.67) yields

$$\mu_s = kT \ln \frac{(2\pi m_s kT/h^2)^{\frac{3}{2}} \cdot P^s_{\text{int}} P^s_{\text{chem}}}{n_s} \tag{6.79}$$

By definition $P^s_{\text{chem}} = \theta^{-\epsilon_0} = e^{-\epsilon_0{}^s/kT}$ where $\epsilon_0{}^s$ is the chemical energy of the s species. Thus, (6.79) may be written as

$$\mu_s = -\epsilon_0{}^s + kT \ln\left[\left(\frac{2\pi mkT}{h^2}\right)^{\frac{3}{2}} P^s_{\text{int}}\right] \tag{6.80}$$

Substitution of (6.80) into (6.77) yields

$$-\sum_a \left\{\frac{\nu_s \epsilon_0{}^s}{kT} + \nu_s \ln\left[\left(\frac{2\pi m_s kT}{h^2}\right)^{\frac{3}{2}} \frac{P^s_{\text{int}}}{n_s}\right]\right\} = -\left\{\sum_b \frac{\nu_s \epsilon_0{}^s}{kT} + \nu_s \ln\left[\left(\frac{2\pi m_s kT}{h^2}\right)^{\frac{3}{2}} \frac{P^s_{\text{int}}}{n_s}\right]\right\}$$

from which we obtain

$$\frac{\prod_b n_s{}^{\nu_s}}{\prod_a n_s{}^{\nu_s}} = \frac{\prod_b [(2\pi m_s kT/h^2)^{\frac{3}{2}} P^s_{\text{int}}]^{\nu_s}}{\prod_a [(2\pi m_s kT/h^2)^{\frac{3}{2}} P^s_{\text{int}}]^{\nu_s}} \exp\left(\frac{\sum_a \nu_s \epsilon_0{}^s - \sum_b \nu_s \epsilon_0{}^s}{kT}\right) = K(T) \tag{6.81}$$

where $K(T)$ is called the *equilibrium constant.* Note that N_s is proportional to P_s [see (6.26)].

6.7.1 Ionization Equilibrium. Consider the following ionization reaction,

$$A_n \rightleftharpoons A_I + e \tag{6.82}$$

so that $\nu_n = \nu_e = \nu_I = 1$, and the first ionization energy ϵ_I is assigned only to the electron. Then (6.81) becomes

$$\frac{n_e n_I}{n_n} = \frac{P_e{}^{\text{int}} P_I{}^{\text{int}}}{P_n{}^{\text{int}}} e^{-\epsilon_I/kT} \left(\frac{2\pi m_e kT}{h^2}\right)^{\frac{3}{2}} = 2G(2.4137) \times 10^{15} T^{\frac{3}{2}} e^{-\epsilon_I/kT} \tag{6.83}$$

where T is in degrees Kelvin and n in cm^{-3}. This is known as *Saha's equation.*[2] In (6.83), the translational partition functions for ions and neutral particles are equal, since the masses are essentially identical. The internal structure of an electron consists only of spin, but the spin vector may be parallel or antiparallel to the applied electric field; hence the degeneracy of the electron is 2 and $P_e{}^{\text{int}} = 2$. For a polyatomic or diatomic molecule, the internal partition functions of the ion and molecule can be quite different; for alkali metals such as sodium, potassium, or cesium, the internal partition function of the neutral particle is twice that of the ion at zero temperature; this again is caused by the spin degeneracy of the outer electron. For these vapors, the coefficient $(P_e{}^{\text{int}} P_I{}^{\text{int}}/P_n{}^{\text{int}})$ is usually unity. The ratio $(P_I{}^{\text{int}}/P_n{}^{\text{int}})$ is sometimes called the *statistical weight G.* The internal partition functions for metal atoms and ions are shown in Table 6.2.

In using (6.83), care must be exercised with regard to n_n; these are the neutral particles of only those species which are ionized. A separate equation is required for each chemical species. On the other hand, n_e is the *total* electron concentration without regard to the source of electrons.

Table 6.2 Internal Partition Functions P_{int} of Various Neutral and Singly Ionized Seeding Elements

Element	Q^i at ground state, $T = 0°K$	2000°K	3000°K	4000°K	5000°K	6000°K	7000°K
Li	2	2.0000	2.0000	2.0579	2.0840	2.1716	2.2950
Li^+	1	1	1	1	1	1	1
Na	2	2.0000	2.0018	2.0141	2.1468	2.1052	2.2134
Na^+	1	1	1	1	1	1	1
K	2	2.0000	2.0000	2.0568	2.2421	2.3516	2.6074
K^+	1	1	1	1	1	1	1
Rb	2	2.0000	2.0089	2.0630	2.1967	2.4043	2.6700
Rb^+	1	1	1	1	1	1	1
Cs	2	2.0000	2.0245	2.1516	2.3950	2.7962	3.2898
Cs^+	1	1	1	1	1	1	1
Ca	1	1.0000	1.0000	1.0340	1.1482	1.3272	1.5970
Ca^+	2	2.0000	2.0087	2.0748	2.1992	2.3917	2.6439
Sr	1	1.0000	1.0000	1.0511	1.2411	1.5226	1.9371
Sr^+	2	2	2	2	2	2	2
Ba	1	1.0000	1.1970	1.7008	2.4901	3.4752	4.5980
Ba^+	2	2.2252	2.7920	3.4866	4.1732	4.8370	5.4324
Al	2	5.692	5.792	5.843	5.874	5.895	5.947
Al^+	1	1	1	1	1	1	1

By permission from Robert S. Buchanan, "Study of a Seeded Plasma," University of Michigan Report ARL 62-310, Contract 33(616)-8126, March, 1962.

For double ionization, an equation similar to (6.83) can be written. The reaction is

$$A^+ \rightleftharpoons e + A^{++} \tag{6.84}$$

so the equivalent equilibrium equation is

$$\frac{n_e n_s{}^{++}}{n_s{}^+} = \frac{2P_{\text{int}}^{++}}{P_{\text{int}}^{+}} e^{-\epsilon_{\text{II}}/kT} \left(\frac{2\pi m_e kT}{h^2}\right)^{\frac{3}{2}} \tag{6.85}$$

where ϵ_{II} is the second ionization potential.

In a mixture of gases containing electrons, some neutral particles have an affinity for electrons, in particular the halogens, since they only require one more electron to complete their outer shell; also O_2 and OH have electron affinities. The equilibrium is then

$$A + e \rightleftharpoons A^- \tag{6.86}$$

or

$$A^- \rightleftharpoons A + e$$

The proper form of the equilibrium equation is then

$$\frac{n_e n_n{}^s}{n_-{}^s} = \frac{2P_n{}^{\text{int}}}{P_-{}^{\text{int}}} e^{-\epsilon_-/kT} \left(\frac{2\pi m_e kT}{h^2}\right)^{\frac{3}{2}} \tag{6.87}$$

where ϵ_- is the electron affinity energy.

The ionization equation (6.83) is also written in terms of the degree of ionization α, where α is given by

$$\alpha = \frac{n_e}{n_I{}^s + n_n{}^s} \tag{6.88}$$

from which

$$n_I{}^s = n_e = \frac{\alpha}{1-\alpha} n_n{}^s \tag{6.89}$$

Hence the total number density associated with the ionization is

$$n = n_e + n_I{}^s + n_n{}^s = \frac{\alpha + 1}{1-\alpha} n_n \tag{6.90}$$

Substitution of (6.89) for n_e, n_I and (6.90) for n_n in the left side of (6.83) yields

$$\frac{n_e n_I}{n_n} = \frac{\alpha^2}{1-\alpha^2} n = \frac{2P_I{}^{\text{int}}}{P_n{}^{\text{int}}} \left(\frac{2\pi m_e kT}{h^2}\right)^{\frac{3}{2}} e^{-\epsilon_I/kT} \tag{6.91}$$

Extreme care must be used in the case of (6.91). Only one ionizable species can be present in the gas, and $n = 2n_e + n_n{}^s$ where s is the ionizable species. One can also let a partial pressure be defined as

$$p_s = nkT = (2n_e + n_n{}^s)kT \tag{6.92}$$

but this partial pressure changes with the degree of ionization. If the gas consists only of s neutral particles, singly ionized particles, and electrons, then (6.92) defines the total pressure, and (6.91) can be rewritten as

$$\frac{\alpha^2}{1-\alpha^2} = \frac{2P^I_{\text{int}}}{P^n_{\text{int}}} \frac{kT}{p} \left(\frac{2\pi m_e kT}{n^2}\right)^{\frac{3}{2}} e^{-\epsilon_I/kT} \tag{6.93}$$

Finally, if α is small, (6.93) becomes

$$\alpha = \left(\frac{2P^I_{\text{int}}}{P^n_{\text{int}}}\right)^{\frac{1}{2}} \frac{(kT)^{\frac{5}{4}}}{p^{\frac{1}{2}}} \left(\frac{2\pi m_e}{h^2}\right)^{\frac{3}{4}} e^{-\epsilon_I/2kT} \tag{6.93a}$$

If, on the other hand, an ionizable gas s is mixed with other non-ionizable gases r, so that $(n_s{}^I + n_s{}^n)/n_t = \beta$, and if the total pressure is p_t, and if n_e/n_s is small, then the degree of ionization of the s particles is given by

$$\alpha_s = \left(\frac{2P^I_{\text{int}}}{P^n_{\text{int}}}\right)^{\frac{1}{2}}_s \frac{(kT)^{\frac{5}{4}}}{\beta^{\frac{1}{2}} p_t{}^{\frac{1}{2}}} \left(\frac{2\pi m_e}{h^2}\right)^{\frac{3}{4}} e^{-\epsilon_I{}^s/2kT} \tag{6.94}$$

but the degree of ionization of the total mixture $\alpha' = n_e/n_t$ is given by

$$\alpha' = \frac{n_e}{n_t} = \frac{n_e}{n_s} \cdot \frac{n_s}{n} = \alpha \cdot \beta \tag{6.95}$$

or

$$\alpha' = \left(\frac{2P^I_{\text{int}}}{P^n_{\text{int}}}\right)^{\frac{1}{2}} \frac{(kT)^{\frac{5}{4}}}{p_t{}^{\frac{1}{2}}} \left(\frac{2\pi m_e}{h^2}\right)^{\frac{3}{4}} e^{-\epsilon_I{}^s/2kT} \beta^{\frac{1}{2}} \tag{6.96}$$

Thus, for p_t, T fixed, and α small compared to unity, then α' varies only as $\beta^{\frac{1}{2}}$, for $\alpha_s \ll 1$.

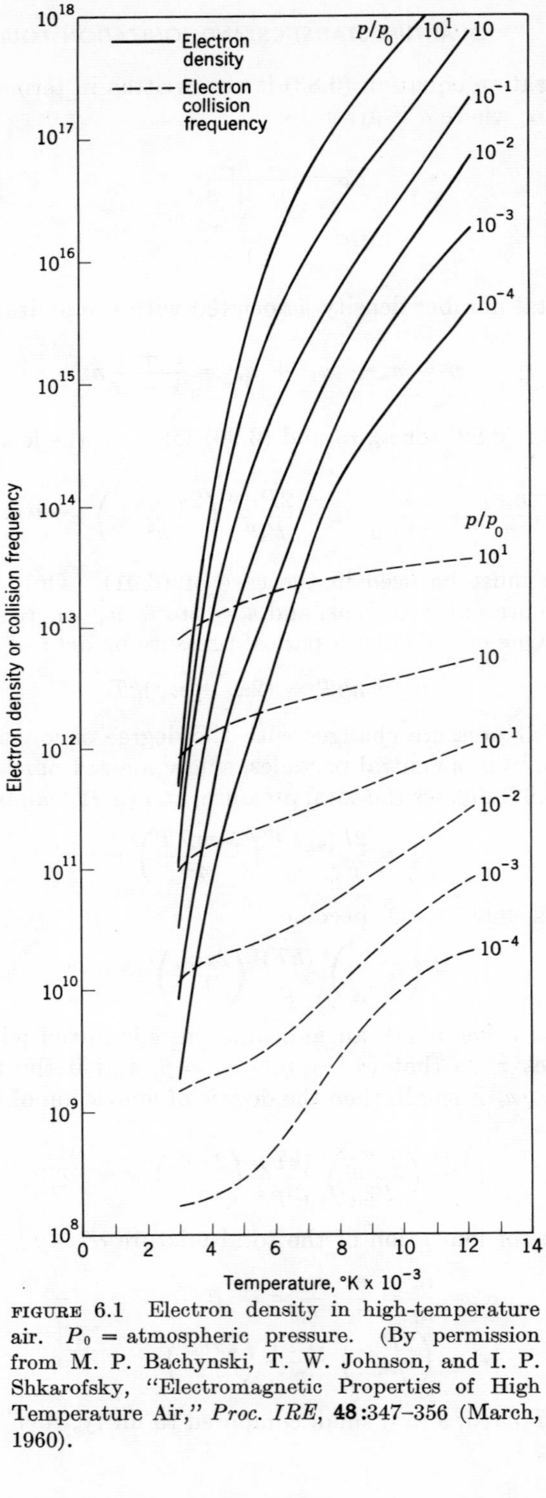

FIGURE 6.1 Electron density in high-temperature air. P_0 = atmospheric pressure. (By permission from M. P. Bachynski, T. W. Johnson, and I. P. Shkarofsky, "Electromagnetic Properties of High Temperature Air," *Proc. IRE*, **48**:347–356 (March, 1960).

Ionization potentials are shown in Table 6.3. Examination of these data shows that the ionization potentials of most gases are quite high, the lowest being 9.5 ev for NO. At high temperatures, NO is an important constituent of air, and up to about 8000°K, is primarily responsible for the ionization of air. The ionization of equilibrium air is shown in Fig. 6.1.

On the other hand, the ionization potentials of alkali metal vapors are quite low. Thus, if highly ionized air or combustion gases are desired, a small amount of alkali metal vapor may be added. This can be in the form of either pure metal vapor or a salt. The ionization of such vapors is shown in Figs. 6.2 to 6.5. Note that the mole fraction of liquid vapor is that of atomic species only, and does not include those atoms which are

Table 6.3 Molecular Weight and Ionization Potentials

Gas	Molecular weight	Ionization potential, ev	
		I	II
Noble gases			
Helium	4.03	24.46	54.14
Neon	21.83	21.47	40.9
Argon	39.4	15.68	27.76
Krypton	83.7	13.93	26.4
Xenon	130.2	12.08	21.1
Common gases			
H	1.008	13.53	
H_2	2.016	15.6	
N	14.008	14.48	29.47
N_2	28.016	15.51	
O	16.000	13.55	34.93
O_2	32.000	15.51	
CO	28.01	14.1	
CO_2	40.02	14.4	
NO	30.008	9.5	
Metal vapors (atoms)			
Lithium	6.940	5.363	75.26
Sodium	23.00	5.12	47.06
Aluminum	26.97	5.96	18.74
Potassium	39.10	4.318	31.66
Calcium	40.8	6.09	11.82
Rubidium	85.48	4.16	27.36
Cesium	132.91	3.87	14.8
Barium	137.36	5.19	9.95
Mercury	200.61	10.39	18.65

From *Handbook of Chemistry and Physics*, 33d ed., Chemical Rubber Publishing Company, Cleveland, Ohio, 1951.

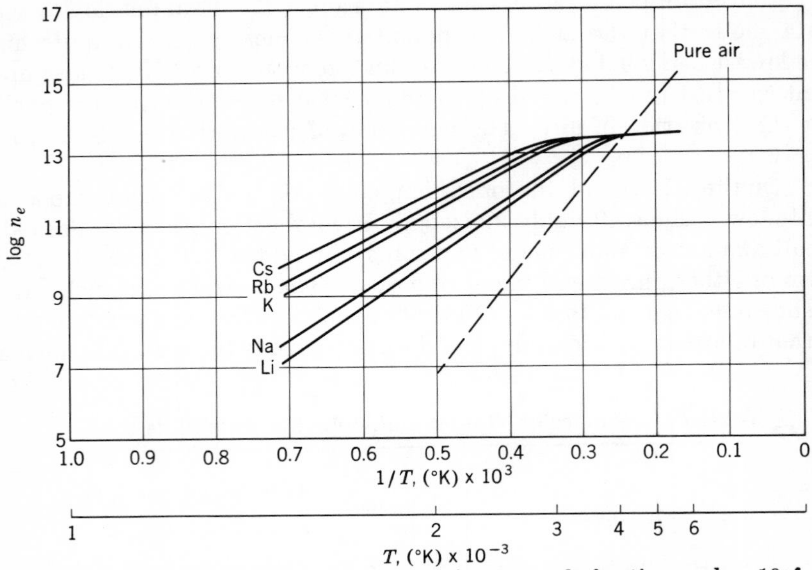

FIGURE 6.2 Electron density per cubic centimeter, mole fraction seed = 10^{-6} Cs, Rb, K, Na, Li, atmospheric density.

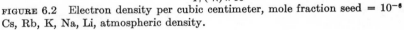

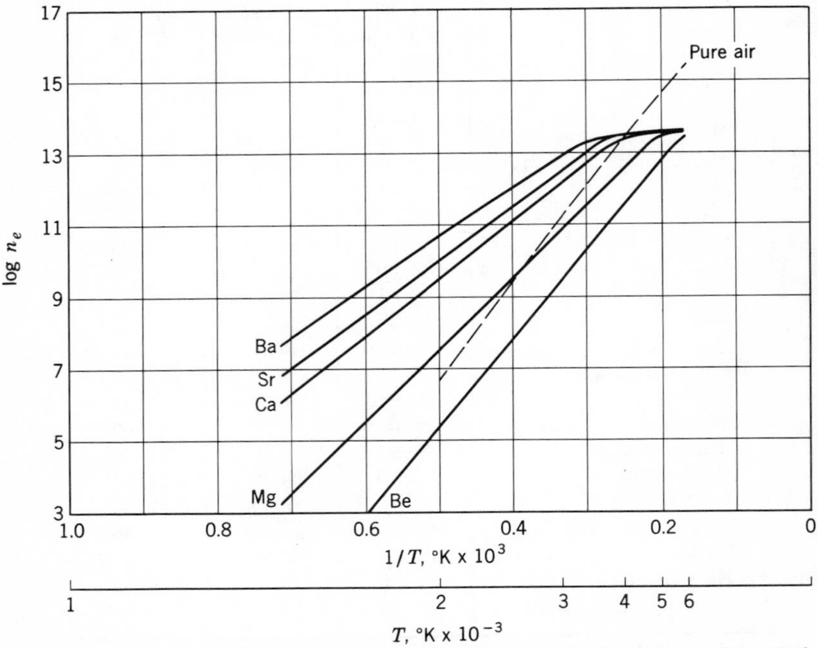

FIGURE 6.3 Electron density per cubic centimeter, mole fraction seed = 10^{-6} Ba, Sr, Ca, Mg, Be, atmospheric density.

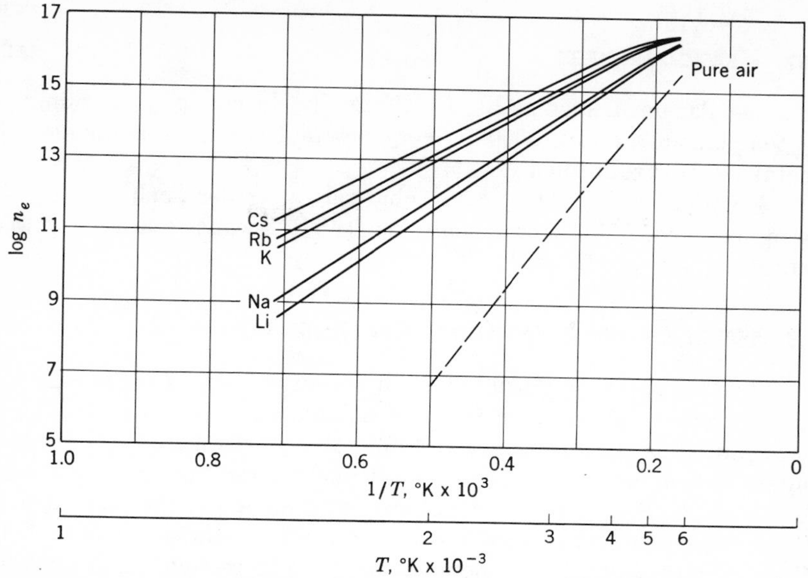

FIGURE 6.4 Electron density per cubic centimeter, mole fraction seed = 10^{-3} Cs, Rb, K, Na, Li, atmospheric density.

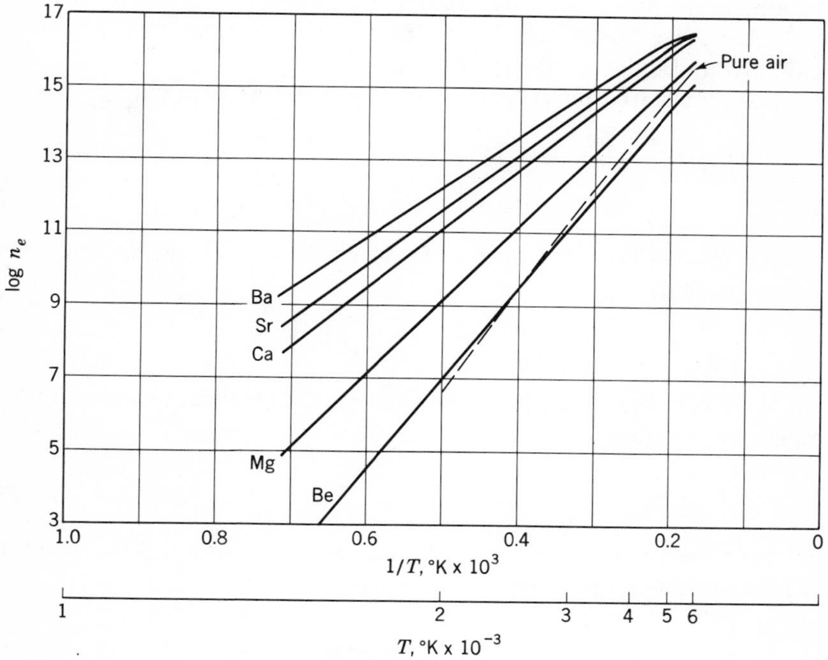

FIGURE 6.5 Electron density per cubic centimeter, mole fraction seed = 10^{-3} Ba, Sr, Ca, Mg, Be, atmospheric density. (By permission from P. J. Friel, "Electron Density and Electrical Conductivity of High Temperature Air Seeded with the Alkali and Alkali Earth Metals," *Gen. Elec. Rept.* R59SD459, December, 1959.)

in molecular form, such as K_2, KOH, etc., in the case of potassium. But at temperatures above 3000°K, very few molecular compounds of alkali metal vapors are formed.

Finally, in the noble gases, charged molecules such as He_2^+ have been observed. These are usually neglected, because relatively few such molecular ions are formed.

6.8 EFFECT OF DEBYE SHIELDING ON IONIZATION[3-6]

The ionization potential was previously defined as the energy necessary to remove an electron from an isolated particle. This energy may be regarded as that necessary to remove an electron from the coulombic potential field created by the particle's nucleus and surrounding electrons. However, in Sec. 4.13 it was shown that in a plasma, the positively charged particle will attract free electrons and shield the coulombic field. The net effect is that less energy is required to remove an electron from such a particle; that is, the apparent ionization potential in a plasma is less than that of a single particle. In this section, the depression of the ionization potential is calculated from classical theory by adding to the particle free energy the electrostatic energy associated with the Debye field surrounding each charged particle.

For an isolated particle, the ionization energy is given by

$$\begin{aligned}\epsilon_I &= e\int_{r_0}^{\infty} E\,dr = -e\int_{r_0}^{\infty}\frac{\partial\phi}{\partial r}\,dr \\ &= e[\phi(r_0) - \phi(\infty)] = e\phi(r_0)\end{aligned} \tag{6.97}$$

where r_0 is the bound position of the electron. For a coulombic field (singly ionized),

$$\phi(r) = \frac{e}{4\pi K_0 r} \tag{6.98}$$

and therefore, from Eqs. (6.97) and (6.98), the classical expression for the ionization potential is†

$$\epsilon_I = \frac{e^2}{4\pi K_0 r_0} \tag{6.99}$$

However, in a plasma, we have shown that the potential surrounding a single charge is more closely given by [see (4.124)]

$$\phi'(r) = \frac{e}{4\pi K r}\, e^{-\sqrt{2}r/d} \tag{6.100}$$

where d is the Debye shielding length. The effect of this shielding of

† This same result is obtained if the electron kinetic energy is included as in (6.4), except the equilibrium radius of the bound electron becomes $\frac{1}{2}r_0$.

the ion is that it requires less energy to remove the electron than the ionization potential ϵ_I. This has the effect of reducing the ionization potential.

For a gas of arbitrary ionization, where different ions may have different values of Z_s, it is easily shown that the shielded potential around a charged particle is

$$\phi_i(r) = \frac{eZ_i}{4\pi K r} e^{-r/D} \tag{6.101}$$

where

$$D^2 = \frac{K_0 kT}{\sum_s n_s e^2 Z_s^2} = \frac{\mathcal{V} K_0 kT}{\sum_s N_s e^2 Z_s^2} \tag{6.101a}$$

where the summation s is to be taken over all ions and electrons. Equation (6.101) is simplified by expanding the exponential and keeping only the first two terms. This is valid because r_0 in (6.103) is of order of magnitude of the radius of the orbit of the bound electrons, which is usually much smaller than the Debye length. Then (6.101) becomes

$$\phi_i(r) = \frac{eZ_i}{4\pi K_0 r} - \frac{e^2 Z_i \left(\sum_s Z_s^2 n_s\right)^{\frac{1}{2}}}{4\pi K_0 (K_0 kT)^{\frac{1}{2}}} \tag{6.102}$$

The electrostatic field energy associated with the potential field of the charged particle is obtained by integration of (6.102) with respect to all charges eZ, from zero to eZ_s, varying the charge on each particle simultaneously. The result is

$$e \int_0^{eZ_s} \phi_i(r_0)\, dZ = \frac{e^2 Z_s^2}{2 \cdot 4\pi K_0 r} - \frac{e^2 Z_s^2}{3 \cdot 4\pi K_0 D} \tag{6.103}$$

The first term in (6.103) corresponds to the ordinary ionization potential (half is assigned to the electron and half to the ion). The second term is the reduction due to the Debye shielding. The additional Helmholtz free energy A_{el} caused by shielding is obtained by multiplying the second term in (6.103) by N_s, and summing over all ionized species s:[7]

$$A_{\text{el}} = -\frac{\left(\sum_s n_s e^2 Z_s^2\right)^{\frac{3}{2}} \mathcal{V}}{3 \cdot 4\pi K_0 (K_0 kT)^{\frac{1}{2}}} \tag{6.104}$$

The additional contribution to the chemical potential for the s species is obtained from (6.38) and (6.104) as follows:

$$\begin{aligned} \mu_{\text{el}_s} = \frac{\partial A_{\text{el}}}{\partial N_s} &= -\frac{1}{2} \frac{e^2 Z_s^2 \left(\sum_r n_r e^2 Z_r^2\right)^{\frac{1}{2}}}{4\pi K_0 (K_0 kT)^{\frac{1}{2}}} \\ &= -\frac{1}{2} \frac{e^2 Z_s^2}{4\pi K_0 D} \end{aligned} \tag{6.105}$$

This addition to the chemical potential is sometimes referred to as $kT \ln \gamma_s$, where γ_s is the *chemical activity*. It represents the deviation from the ideal chemical potential caused by the mutual attraction between particles. The ionization equilibrium must be corrected by (6.105) for each species. Thus, for a given element r, with ions Z^r_{s+1}, $Z_s{}^r$, the ionization is given by

$$\frac{n_e n^r_{s+1}}{n_s{}^r} = \frac{2P^{\text{int}}_{r,s+1}}{P^{\text{int}}_{r,s}} \left(\frac{2\pi m_e kT}{h^2}\right)^{\frac{3}{2}} e^{-\epsilon^r{}_{s+1}/kT} e^{e^2(1+Z^2{}_{s+1}-Z_s{}^2)/2\cdot 4\pi K_0 kT}$$

which, with $Z_{s+1} = s + 1$, $Z_s = s$, simplifies to

$$\frac{n_e n^r_{s+1}}{n_s{}^r} = 2G \left(\frac{2\pi m_e kT}{h^2}\right)^{\frac{3}{2}} e^{-\epsilon^r{}_{s+1}/kT} e^{(s+1)e^2/4\pi K_0 DkT} \tag{6.106}$$

For singly ionized species, the correction factor due to Debye shielding in (6.106) is $e^2/4\pi K_0 D$. The significance can be more easily understood by multiplying numerator and denominator by $\sum\limits_s n_s Z_s{}^2$, the weighted number density of charged particles,

$$\frac{(s+1)e^2}{4\pi K_0 DkT} \cdot \frac{\sum\limits_s n_s Z_s{}^2}{\sum\limits_s n_s Z_s{}^2} = \frac{s+1}{4\pi D^3 \Sigma n_s Z_s{}^2} = \frac{s+1}{3N_z} \tag{6.107}$$

where $N_z = (4\pi/3)D^3 \Sigma n_s Z_s{}^2$ is the average weighted charge number in a sphere of radius equal to the Debye length D. In a weakly ionized gas, N_z is usually large so that the correction is small. However, at elevated temperatures and large pressures, this can become small, causing an appreciable correction, (see Fig. 6.6).

The Debye correction also changes the total pressure.[8] From (6.54),

$$p_{\text{el}} = -\left(\frac{\partial A_{\text{el}}}{\partial \mathcal{V}}\right)_{N_s} = \frac{\partial}{\partial \mathcal{V}} \left[\frac{\left(\sum\limits_s N_s e^2 Z_s{}^2\right)^{\frac{3}{2}}}{\mathcal{V}^{\frac{1}{2}} 3 \cdot 4\pi K_0 (K_0 kT)^{\frac{1}{2}}}\right] \tag{6.108}$$

Differentiation of (6.108) yields

$$p_{\text{el}} = -\frac{\Sigma n_s Z_s{}^2 e^2}{6 \cdot 4\pi K_0 D} = -\frac{kT}{24\pi D^3} \tag{6.109}$$

In terms of N_z, this becomes

$$p_{\text{el}} = -\frac{\sum\limits_s n_s Z_s{}^2 kT}{18 N_z} \tag{6.110}$$

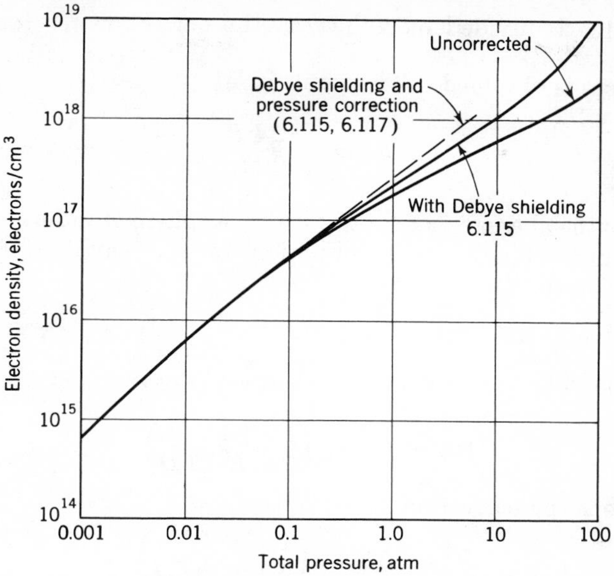

FIGURE 6.6 Effect of electrostatic interactions on electron density, sodium at $\frac{1}{2}$ ev (5807°K). (By permission from H. Meyers, J. H. Buss, and S. W. Benson, "Thermodynamics of Ionized Gases," *Douglas Eng. Paper* 611, January, 1960.)

Thus, if N_z is small, the reduction in pressure can be appreciable. In the same way, the reduction in entropy can be calculated. From (6.55),

$$S_{\text{el}} = -\frac{\partial A_{\text{el}}}{\partial T} = -\frac{1}{6T}\frac{\sum_s N_s e^2 Z_s{}^2}{4\pi K_0 D} = -\frac{k\mathcal{V}}{24D^3} \tag{6.111}$$

From (6.56), (6.111), and (6.104), the correction in the total energy can be calculated,

$$E_{\text{el}} = A_{\text{el}} + TS_{\text{el}} = -\frac{\sum_s N_s Z_s e^2}{2 \cdot 4\pi K_0 D} = -\frac{kT\mathcal{V}}{8\pi D^3} \tag{6.112}$$

where $\mathcal{V}$ is the total volume. The correction to the total enthalpy is

$$H_{\text{el}} = E_{\text{el}} + p_{\text{el}}\mathcal{V} = -\frac{2}{3}\frac{\sum_s N_s Z_s{}^2 e^2}{4\pi K_0 D}$$

or

$$H_{\text{el}} = -\frac{2k\mathcal{V}T}{3 \cdot 4\pi D^3} \tag{6.113}$$

When (6.113) is divided by $\mathcal{V} \sum_s n_s m_s$, the correction for the enthalpy per unit mass is obtained. The result is

$$h_{\text{el}} = -\frac{2}{9}\frac{kT}{M_z} \tag{6.114}$$

where M_z is the average mass of gas within a sphere of radius equal to the Debye length. Finally, the correction to the partition function is obtained from (6.78):

$$P_{s_{\text{el}}} = N_s e^{-\mu_{s_{\text{el}}}/kT} \tag{6.115}$$

From (6.105), the correction for electrons is

$$P_{e_{\text{el}}} = N_e \exp\left(\frac{1}{2}\frac{e^2}{4\pi K_0 kTD}\right) \tag{6.116}$$

while for ions the correction is

$$P_{s_{\text{el}}} = N_s \exp\left(\frac{1}{2}\frac{e^2 Z_s^2}{4\pi K_0 kTD}\right) \tag{6.117}$$

From (6.106) it is seen that n_s is still proportional to its partition function, as it should be from (6.26).

6.9 NONEQUILIBRIUM IONIZATION

Nonequilibrium ionization refers to any state of an ionized gas in which the electron and ion densities are different from those in an equilibrium plasma at the same temperature and total density. Two important classes of nonequilibrium ionization are (1) ionization and deionization processes, and (2) the effect of electric fields. These are treated separately below.

6.9.1 Ionization and Deionization. At temperatures less than several electron volts, ionization is mainly by electron impact, rather than by the heavy particles, since a charged particle affects the bound electrons by coulombic action; and the electron, because of its higher velocity, is more likely to resonate with the outer bound electrons. Thus, our model will be that electrons will ionize a neutral particle if the combined electron energy and particle energy relative to the motion of the center of mass $\mathbf{G}$ exceeds the ionization potential ϵ_I,

$$\tfrac{1}{2}m_e|\mathbf{c}_e - \mathbf{G}|^2 + \tfrac{1}{2}m_n|\mathbf{c}_n - \mathbf{G}|^2 > \epsilon_I \tag{6.118}$$

where the motion of the center of mass $\mathbf{G}$ is given by

$$(m_e + m_n)\mathbf{G} = m_e\mathbf{c}_e + m_n\mathbf{c}_n \tag{6.119}$$

Substitution of (6.119) into (6.118) yields the following criterion for ionization:

$$\frac{1}{2}\frac{m_e m_n}{m_e + m_n}|\mathbf{c}_e - \mathbf{c}_n|^2 > \epsilon_I \tag{6.120}$$

The quantity $m_e m_n/(m_e + m_n)$ is called the *reduced mass*. Since $m_e \ll m_n$, the reduced mass is equal to the electron mass; and also $\mathbf{c}_e - \mathbf{c}_n \approx c_e$. Thus the criterion for ionization by a single collision is that

$$\tfrac{1}{2}m_e c_e^2 > \epsilon_I \tag{6.120a}$$

Next consider electrons with velocities between $\mathbf{c}_e$ and $\mathbf{c}_e + d\mathbf{c}_e$, and neutral particles with velocities between $\mathbf{c}_n$ and $\mathbf{c}_n + d\mathbf{c}_n$. The total number of collisions per unit time per unit volume between these electrons and neutral particles is

$$\nu_{en}(c_e,c_n)\, d\mathbf{c}_e\, d\mathbf{c}_n = f_e f_n g Q_{en}\, d\mathbf{c}_n\, d\mathbf{c}_e \tag{6.121}$$

where Q_{en} is the total collision cross section. Let us assume that even if $\frac{1}{2}m_e c_e^2 > \epsilon_I$, only a fraction α of those collisions cause ionization. Thus, the number of electrons produced per unit time per unit volume is $\alpha\nu_{en}$:

$$d\dot{n}_e^+ = \alpha\nu_{en}\, dc_e\, dc_n = f_e f_n g\alpha Q_{en}\, d\mathbf{c}_n\, d\mathbf{c}_e \tag{6.122}$$

It is common to call αQ_{en} the cross section for ionization by electrons, or Q_e^+. The total number of electrons produced per unit time per unit volume is obtained by integration of (6.122). The integration is taken over all $\mathbf{c}_n$, but for $\mathbf{c}_e$, we must use (6.120) as the lower limit of integration. Taking Q_e^+ constant, and $g \approx c_e$, (6.122) becomes

$$\dot{n}_e^+ = Q_e^+ \int f_n\, d\mathbf{c}_n \int_{\sqrt{2\epsilon_I/m_e}}^{\infty} f_e|\mathbf{c}_e|\, d\mathbf{c}_e \tag{6.123}$$

It is necessary of course that the correct distribution function be used for (6.123), especially if $\epsilon_I \gg kT_e$, in which case only the tail of the distribution function causes ionization; the number of particles in this tail is very sensitive to the form of f_e. However, we will assume that f_e is maxwellian about T_e; this is true for sufficiently high electron densities, and if $Q_e^+ \ll Q_{en}$. Substitution of the maxwellian distribution

$$f_e = n_e\left(\frac{m_e}{2\pi kT_e}\right)^{\frac{3}{2}} \exp\left(-\frac{m_e c_e^2}{2kT}\right)$$

into (6.123) and integration yield[9]

$$\dot{n}_e^+ = n_e n_n Q_e^+ \langle c_e\rangle e^{-\epsilon_I/kT_e}\left(\frac{\epsilon}{kT_e} + 1\right) \approx k_I(T_e) n_e n_n \tag{6.124}$$

Thus, the rate of formation of new electrons is proportional to the number density of electrons and neutral particles, and is strongly dependent on the electron temperature. Actually, Q_e^+ is very sensitive to the electron energy; therefore (6.124) is to be regarded only as a crude approximation.

Also, impacts with electrons having energies less than the ionization energy but greater than the excitation energy may excite the neutral particle to an electronic state above the ground state. A subsequent collision with an energetic electron may raise the excitation level still further or actually complete the ionization. Such a process, called *multi-stage ionization*, is most likely to occur when the time between electron impacts is short compared with the spontaneous deexcitation or radiation time of the neutral particle. This generally requires a high electron density.

Deionization also occurs by collisions. These are either three-body collisions or two-body collisions with radiative decay of the excess energy. The deionization rate is proportional to the number of electrons and ions; thus,

$$\dot{n}_e^- = k_r n_e n_e = k_r n_e^2 \tag{6.125}$$

Since no energy is required for deionization, k_r is proportional to the electron-ion collision frequency. Although ν_{eI} varies strongly with electron temperature, as a first approximation we may take k_r as a constant.

When a gas is suddenly heated to a high translational temperature, the ionization will generally lag. This can be estimated by solving (6.124) and (6.125) for the gas in question. If few electrons were initially present, the initial ionization occurs by collisions of heavy particles; this is normally a long period and is called the *induction period.* Free electrons that are created by this process normally have a low translational energy initially, owing to the large energy of ionization. Before they are able to cause additional ionization by (6.124), they must be heated up to the gas temperature by collisions with the heavier gas particles. Because of the small electron mass, this heating process may also be lengthy in time. This time constitutes another induction period.

Even when the electrons are heated, there is a third induction period, caused by the low initial electron density, since (dn_e/dt) is proportional to n_e. This can be seen by solving (6.124) and (6.125) simultaneously, assuming n_n, k_r, and k_I constant. The result is shown below:

$$\frac{n_e}{n_{e_\infty}} = \frac{1}{1 + n_{e_\infty}/n_{e_0}e^{tk_I}} \tag{6.126}$$

where n_{e_∞} is the final number density of electrons, and n_{e_0} is the number density after the end of the second induction period. This third induction period for ionization is clearly shown on the left of Fig. 6.7.

Equation (6.126) may be simplified for large times as follows:

$$\frac{n_e}{n_{e_\infty}} = 1 - \frac{n_{e_\infty}}{n_{e_0}} e^{-tk_I} \qquad (6.127)$$

It would therefore appear that the time constant for ionization is $\tau_I = k_I^{-1}$. This amounts to using only (6.124) without (6.125), and underestimates the ionization time. A more realistic value of the ionization time is the time to reach 63.7 per cent of the final equilibrium electron number density.

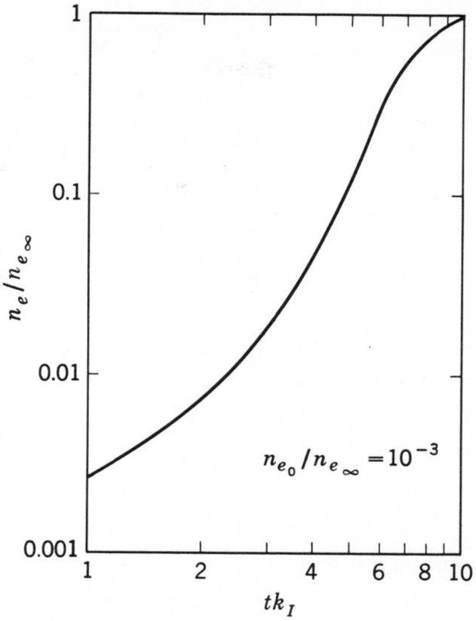

FIGURE 6.7 Third induction period for ionization.

Finally, there is a zeroth induction time, which actually precedes the other three. This is the time required to form the molecular compounds or atoms in the gas which will later be ionized. For example, if an alkali metal salt is added to a high-temperature flame, very little ionization will occur until either free alkali metal atoms or other alkali metal compounds with low ionization potentials are available. Another example is the ionization of air. At temperatures below 10,000°K, it is mainly NO that is responsible for the electrons. Thus, first O_2 must be dissociated, then N_2, and finally NO is formed. In theoretical studies of ionization in air,[10] it has been shown that at temperatures below 10,000°K, the ionization follows the NO formation closely, so that the ionization time depends on the zeroth induction period. Calculations of the ionization times have also been made; these are shown in Fig. 6.8. In these calculations, it was assumed that the temperature of the air is rapidly raised to some other constant temperature. It is seen that the ionization time decreases with increasing temperature, and increasing number density, as predicted by (6.124).

Ionization and deionization can also occur on surfaces. Surface ionization is of special importance in certain devices such as ion rockets. This depends on the difference between the work function of the surface and the ionization potential of the surface. If the surface work function is larger than the ionization potential, neutral particles which touch the surface will lose an electron to the surface. Photoionization is another method of ionization, but it is not important in most magnetohydrodynamic applications.

Finally, nonequilibrium ionization will occur when an ionized gas is suddenly cooled. Here also, because of the small mass of the electron,

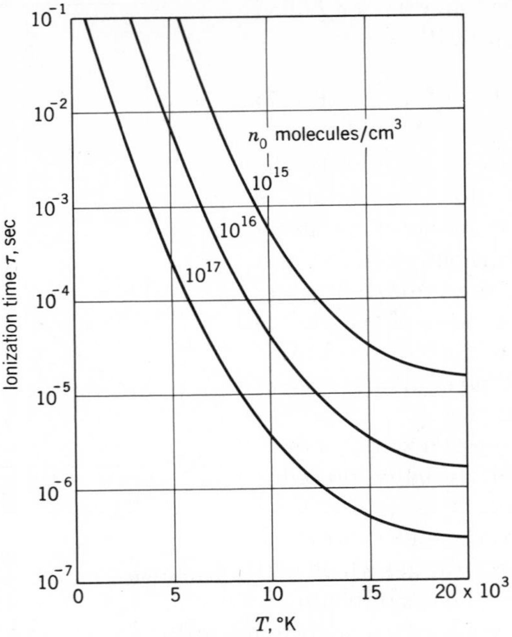

FIGURE 6.8 Ionization times for air. (M. H. Bortner, "The Effect of Temperature on Calculated Non-equilibrium Electron Densities," *Gen. Elec. Rept.* R61SD24, August, 1961.)

many collisions are required for the electron to lose its thermal energy. In addition, the deionization time is finite. This process permits a larger amount of ionization in an expanding flow than predicted by Saha's equation at the local static temperature.[11,12]

6.9.2 Nonthermal Ionization. Another important method of ionization in gases consists in heating the electrons to a temperature which is higher than that of the gas. These heated electrons are then capable of causing additional ionization.

The mechanism for heating electrons has been described in detail in Secs. 5.5 and 5.10. This argument is repeated below in a somewhat simplified fashion. Consider an ionized gas moving at velocity $\mathbf{v}$ in an electric and magnetic field. The electric field that the electrons "feel" is $\mathbf{E}^* = \mathbf{E} + \mathbf{v} \times \mathbf{B}$, on the average. This moving electric field will cause an electron current flow $\mathbf{j}_e$. The electric field energy absorbed by the electrons per unit volume is $\mathbf{j}_e \cdot \mathbf{E}^*$. Now, the electrons lose energy to the heavy particles in the gas by elastic and inelastic collisions. In elastic collisions, the energy loss during one collision is $(2m_e/m_s)\frac{3}{2}k(T_e - T_s)$, on the average. To obtain the energy loss to the s species of heavy particles, this must be multiplied by the number density of electrons and the electron collision frequency with the s particles ν_{es}. To account for inelastic collisions, this must be multiplied by the energy-loss factor δ_s, and finally summed over all s. In steady state, the energy gained by the electrons must equal the energy loss; thus,

$$\mathbf{j}_e \cdot \mathbf{E}^* = 3n_e k \sum \nu_{es} \frac{m_e}{m_s} \delta_s(T_e - T_s) \tag{6.128}$$

Usually, all the s particles will have the same temperature T. Thus (6.128) becomes

$$\mathbf{j}_e \cdot \mathbf{E}^* = 3n_e m_e k(T_e - T) \sum \nu_{es} \frac{\delta_s}{m_s} \tag{6.129}$$

which determines the electron temperature. Thus, if $\mathbf{j}_e$ or $\mathbf{E}^*$ is sufficiently large, the electron temperature may exceed the gas temperature, and additional ionization may occur. This occurs in ordinary glow discharges, but note that the degree of ionization is extremely sensitive to the electron distribution function.[13] However, if the number density of electrons is large, so that the collision frequency for electron-electron collisions is larger than that for inelastic electron–heavy-particle collisions, the electrons will acquire a maxwellian distribution. This leads to a considerable simplification for gases which are ionized mainly by electron collisions,

$$e + \mathrm{N} \rightleftharpoons \mathrm{N}^+ + 2e \tag{6.130}$$

because the equilibrium ionization then depends on the electron temperature only. If (6.130) is the only mechanism, then the degree of ionization will be given by Saha's equation based on the electron temperature.

In addition to (6.130), there is another important ionization and deionization mechanism, due to resonant radiation:

$$h\nu + \mathrm{N} \rightleftharpoons e + \mathrm{N}^+$$

If the resonant radiation is trapped so that none escapes from the gas, then the ionization will still be determined by Saha's equation based on the electron temperature. But if the resonant radiation is not trapped, this constitutes an important loss of energy from the electrons. Detailed calculations of the resulting degree of ionization have been made for various trappings of radiation.[14] The results show that Saha's equation (6.83) based on the electron temperature is valid for electron temperatures which are greater than about 4000°K, for a total number particle density greater than 10^{14} per cm^3 and dimensions greater than 1 cm.

Next, a relationship for the electron current is required. This is obtained from (5.177) and Eq. (s) of Sec. 5.8.3,

$$\mathbf{j}_e = \frac{\sigma[(1 + (\tau_e^*/\tau_{en}^*)\omega_I{}^2\tau_{In}^{*2}f]\mathbf{E}^* - \omega_e\tau_e^*(1 + \omega_I{}^2\tau_{In}^{*2})(\mathbf{E}^* \times \mathbf{B}/B)]}{(1 + \omega_e\tau_e^*\omega_I\tau_{In}^*)^2 + \omega_e{}^2\tau_e^{*2}} \tag{6.131}$$

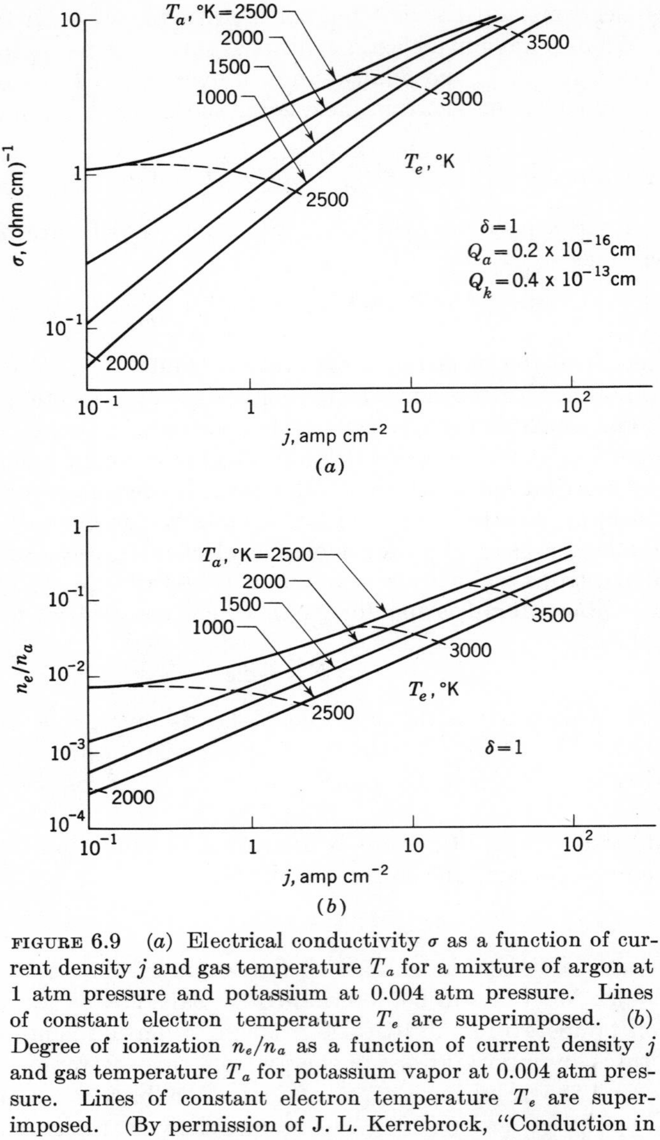

FIGURE 6.9 (*a*) Electrical conductivity σ as a function of current density j and gas temperature T_a for a mixture of argon at 1 atm pressure and potassium at 0.004 atm pressure. Lines of constant electron temperature T_e are superimposed. (*b*) Degree of ionization n_e/n_a as a function of current density j and gas temperature T_a for potassium vapor at 0.004 atm pressure. Lines of constant electron temperature T_e are superimposed. (By permission of J. L. Kerrebrock, "Conduction in Gases with Elevated Electron Temperature," *Engineering Aspects of Magnetohydrodynamics*, Columbia University Press, New York, 1962.)

where σ is given by (5.130). For most practical cases, $\omega_I \tau_{In} \ll 1$, and may be neglected in (6.131), so that the electron current is essentially given by the Lorentz approximation (Sec. 5.6.5). Equations (6.131) or (5.90) and (5.92), with (6.129) and (6.83), may then be used to calculate the electron temperature, degree of ionization, and electrical conductivity as a function of either the electric current or electric field. These calculations have been performed for a mixture of argon and potassium[14] (see Fig. 6.9), without a magnetic field, and have also been essentially verified experimentally.[14,15] The result is that electrical conductivities can be obtained at reasonable current densities which are much larger than the electrical conductivity at equilibrium at the same gas temperature. This is somewhat different from a glow discharge in that the gas temperature is higher; and consequently the gas density may be higher and the electron temperature much lower than in the usual glow discharge.

The use of elevated electron temperatures to produce ionization is most practical in gases with small loss factors δ. Thus, it may be used in monatomic gases, air, and hydrogen, but probably not in combustion gases (see Fig. 5.6).

6.10 THERMIONIC EMISSION

In many applications of magnetohydrodynamics, it is necessary to allow a current to flow through the plasma by means of electrodes which are connected to an external circuit. It is therefore necessary to exchange charged particles with a solid (or liquid) conductor. At an anode, electrons which collide with the surface can be absorbed by the surface. Also, if the work function of the anode is less than the ionization potential, neutral particles which collide with the anode surface have a probability of losing an electron to the surface.

At the cathode, positive ions can be neutralized in the same way, and there is a net electron flow from the cathode. In a gas, the ion collision frequency with a surface is equal to $n_I\langle c_I\rangle/4$; and generally this is too small to allow an appreciable current flow. It is more desirable to have free electrons leave the surface directly. The most common method of accomplishing this is by thermally heating the surface until electrons "boil off"; this process is known as *thermionic emission*. This can also be predicted by statistical methods. We will apply this method to a metal electrode in a gaseous plasma.

In a metal, there are usually as many free electrons as atoms. If the metal is cool, one might expect a large number of electrons to occupy low energy levels. This, however, is not the case, because of the Pauli exclusion principle, which states that in each energy level there can be at most only two electrons (corresponding to the two spin states). The result is that at low electron energies, the number of electrons with those energies is

$$\frac{\epsilon_i}{kT} \ll 1: \qquad N_i = \bar{\omega}_i \tag{6.132}$$

where the degeneracy factor of 2 is included in the total degeneracy $\bar{\omega}_i$. The number of electrons with large energies is small; thus,

$$\frac{\epsilon_i}{kT} \gg 1: \qquad N_i = \bar{\omega}_i \lambda e^{-\epsilon_i/kT} \tag{6.133}$$

[see (6.24)]. We can construct the following expression for N_i which satisfies both (6.132) and (6.133):

$$N_i = \frac{\bar{\omega}_i \lambda e^{-\epsilon_i/kT}}{1 + \lambda e^{-\epsilon_i/kT}} \tag{6.134}$$

Systems which obey (6.134) are said to obey *Fermi-Dirac statistics*, and the particles which obey (6.134) are called *fermions;* obviously electrons are fermions. Of course, (6.134) can be derived more rigorously.

The degeneracy for the velocity in one direction was given by (6.73); the total degeneracy is

$$\bar{\omega}_i = 2 dn_x\, dn_y\, dn_z = 2 \left(\frac{2Lm_e}{h}\right)^3 dw_x\, dw_y\, dw_z \tag{6.135}$$

for w_x, w_y, $w_z > 0$. The factor of 2 accounts for the two spin states of the electron. The element of volume $dw_x\, dw_y\, dw_z$ can be converted into a volume in spherical coordinates, equal to a spherical shell of radius w and thickness dw, $4\pi w^2\, dw$. The requirement that the velocities be positive causes us to consider only one quadrant of the spherical shell; thus,

$$dw_x\, dw_y\, dw_z = \tfrac{1}{8} 4\pi w^2\, dw \tag{6.136}$$

so that (6.135) becomes

$$\bar{\omega}_i = \pi \left(\frac{2Lm_e}{h}\right)^3 w^2\, dw \tag{6.137}$$

Finally, because the partition function is defined in terms of energy, the particle velocities in (6.137) are converted to energies by means of the following relations:

$$\epsilon = \tfrac{1}{2} m_e w^2 \qquad \left(\frac{2\epsilon}{m_e}\right)^{\frac{1}{2}} = w \qquad d\epsilon = m_e w\, dw \tag{6.138}$$

Substitution of (6.138) into (6.137) yields

$$\bar{\omega}_i = \frac{\pi}{2} \left(\frac{8m_e}{h^2}\right)^{\frac{3}{2}} \mathcal{V} \epsilon_i^{\frac{1}{2}}\, d\epsilon_i \tag{6.139}$$

where $\mathcal{V}$ is the volume, equal to L^3. With (6.134) and (6.139), the partition function for the electrons becomes

$$P_e = \sum_i \frac{\bar{\omega}_i e^{-\epsilon_i/kT}}{1 + \lambda e^{-\epsilon_i/kT}}$$

$$= \frac{1}{\lambda} \sum_i \frac{\bar{\omega}_i}{1 + e^{\epsilon_i/kT}/\lambda}$$

$$= \frac{\pi}{2\lambda} \left(\frac{8m_e}{h^2}\right)^{\frac{3}{2}} \mathcal{V} \int_0^\infty \frac{\epsilon^{\frac{1}{2}}\, d\epsilon}{1 + e^{\epsilon/kT}/\lambda} \tag{6.140}$$

where the sum has been replaced by an integral. By letting $\epsilon/kT = \xi$, the partition function for electrons becomes

$$P_e = \frac{\pi}{2\lambda} \left(\frac{8m_e kT}{h^2}\right)^{\frac{3}{2}} \mathcal{V} \int_0^\infty \frac{\xi^{\frac{1}{2}}\, d\xi}{1 + e^{\xi}/\lambda} \tag{6.141}$$

The integrand of (6.141) is shown in Fig. 6.10 and is compared to $\xi^{\frac{1}{2}}$. It is seen that the two shaded areas are approximately equal when $e^\xi = \lambda$, or $\xi = \ln \lambda$. Thus, the integral is approximated by

$$\int_0^{\ln \lambda} \xi^{\frac{1}{2}}\, d\xi = \tfrac{2}{3}(\ln \lambda)^{\frac{3}{2}} \tag{1.142}$$

The number of electrons N_e, from (6.20), is

$$N_e = \frac{\pi}{2} \left(\frac{8m_e kT}{h^2}\right)^{\frac{3}{2}} \mathcal{V}\tfrac{2}{3}(\ln \lambda)^{\frac{3}{2}} \tag{6.143}$$

It is convenient to replace λ by some other term. Since the total number of accessible states is greater than the number of electrons, we can define an energy ϵ^* such that the number of energy states with $\epsilon_i < \epsilon^*$ is equal to the number of electrons. From (6.139) the number of states with

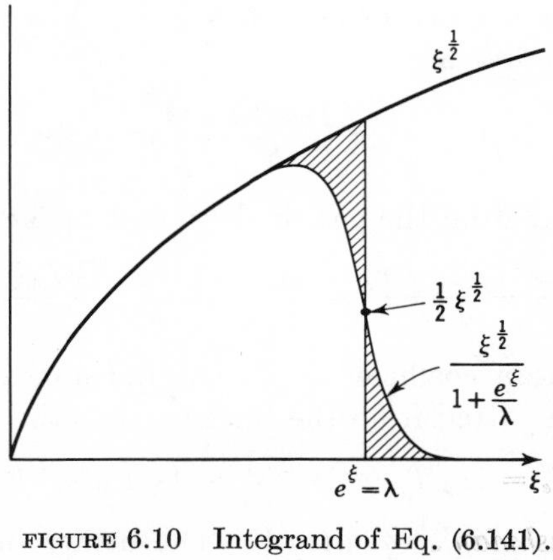

FIGURE 6.10 Integrand of Eq. (6.141).

energies less than ϵ^* is given by

$$N_e = \sum_{\epsilon=0}^{\epsilon_1=\epsilon^*} \bar{\omega}_i = \frac{\pi}{2}\left(\frac{8m_e}{h^2}\right)^{\frac{3}{2}} \mathcal{V} \int_0^{\epsilon^*} \epsilon_i^{\frac{1}{2}}\, d\epsilon_i$$

$$= \frac{\pi}{3}\left(\frac{8m_e}{h^2}\right) \mathcal{V}\epsilon^{*\frac{3}{2}} \tag{6.144}$$

where the summation has been replaced by an integral. Equating (6.143) and (6.144),

$$\ln \lambda = \frac{\epsilon^*}{kT} \tag{6.145}$$

which defines λ. For an electron to leave a metal it must climb a potential barrier χ_0 which is due to the coulombic attraction of the surrounding positive metal ions. Thus, an electron inside a metal has a potential energy $-\chi_0$. The chemical potential of the electrons in the metal then becomes

$$(\mu_e)_M = kT\left(\ln \lambda - \frac{\chi_0}{kT}\right) \tag{6.146}$$

With the use of (6.145), this becomes

$$(\mu_e)_M = -\chi_0 + \epsilon^* = -\chi_M \tag{6.147}$$

where χ_M is called the *work function* of the metal. When the electrons in the metal are in equilibrium with the electrons in the gas, $T_e = T_M$, where T_M is the metal temperature, and

$$(\mu_e)_M = (\mu_e)_{\text{gas}} \tag{6.148}$$

Substitution of (6.147) for $(\mu_e)_M$ and use of (6.66) yields

$$-\chi_M = kT_M \ln\left[\frac{(N_e)_{\text{gas}}}{\mathcal{V}} \frac{h^3}{2(2\pi m_e kT_M)^{\frac{3}{2}}}\right] \tag{6.149}$$

so that the number density of electrons in the gas phase which are in equilibrium with the metal is

$$(n_e)_{\text{gas}} = 2\left(\frac{2\pi m_e kT_M}{h^2}\right)^{\frac{3}{2}} e^{-\chi_M/kT_M} \tag{6.150}$$

The electron current from the gas to the metal surface is given by

$$j_e = -\frac{n_e e\langle c_e\rangle(1-r)}{4} = \frac{(1-r)4\pi e m_e(kT_M)^2}{h^3} e^{-\chi_M/kT_M} \tag{6.151}$$

where r is a reflection coefficient. In equilibrium, an electron current equal to (6.151) is emitted from the surface; thus the emission current is

$$j_e = A_M T_M{}^2 e^{-\chi_M/kT_M} = A_M T_M{}^2 e^{-b/T_M} \tag{6.152}$$

which is called *Dushman's equation.*[17] The utility of (6.152) is that it predicts the emission current even when the surface of the metal is in

Table 6.3 Thermionic Emission Constants in Vacuum

$$j = A_M T_M^2 \exp(-b/T)$$

Material	A_M, amp/(cm²)(°K)²	χ_M, ev	Temperature of measurement, °K	Reference
Carbon	46	3.96	2335	1
Cesium	162	1.81	500	2
Columbium	29	4.02	1438–1980	3
Hafnium	14.5	3.53	....	2
Iridium	35	5.33	....	7
Molybdenum	55	4.20	2500	4
Nickel	1,380	5.02	1400–1500	5
Platinum	170	5.40	1600–1800	6
Rhenium	95	5.07	....	7
Rhodium	33	4.81	....	8
Tantalum	55	4.19	1400–1700	9
	81	4.17		7
Thorium	60.2	3.89	1600	2, 10
Tungsten	46	4.54	....	7
Tungsten (etched)	39	5.25	....	12
Thorium on tungsten	2.79	3.04	<1600	10
BaO	2.88	1.95	....	10
CuO	1.55	2.05	1673	10
SrO	4.07	2.16	1200	10
ThO_2	5.7	3.69	2000	10
$ZrC_{0.90}$–$UC_{0.10}$	120	3.94	1750	11

References for Table 6.3

1. Ivey, H. F.: *Phys. Rev.*, **76**:567 (1949).
2. Cobine, James D.: *Gaseous Conductors*, Dover Publications, Inc., New York, 1958.
3. Reimann, A. L., and C. Kerr Grant: *Phil. Mag.*, **22**:34, (1936).
4. Wright, R. W.: *Phys. Rev.*, **60**:465 (1941).
5. Fox, G. W., and R. M. Bowie: *Phys. Rev.*, **44**:345 (1933).
6. Van Velzer, H. L.: *Phys. Rev.*, **44**:831 (1933).
7. Gust, W. H.: 22*d Annual Conference on Physical Electronics*, p. 142, March, 1962.
8. Wahlin, H. B., and L. V. Whitney: *J. Chem. Phys.*, **6**:594 (1938).
9. Fiske, M. D.: *Phys. Rev.*, **61**:513 (1942).
10. *International Critical Tables*, vol. 6, McGraw-Hill Book Company, New York, 1929.
11. Pidd, Robert W.: "Carbide Cathode Performance," *Proc. Round Table Discussion on Cathode Emission Invests. and Exptl. Techs. for Fabricating and Operating Thermionic Cells*, Power Information Center, University of Pennsylvania, June 1–2, 1961.
12. Hughes, Levinstine, and Kaplan: *Phys. Rev.*, **113**:1023–1028 (1959).

contact with a high vacuum, because the electrons inside the metal are not aware of the conditions outside of the metal. The current given by (6.152) is therefore the *maximum* thermionic electron current that can be drawn from a cathode. Since χ_M is of the order of 4 ev, while T_M is usually less than 0.3 ev, most of the variation of the thermionic emission current is due to the exponential term and far overshadows the effect of the T^2. Except for this effect, the form of (6.152) has been well verified by experiments. The theoretical value of A_M is given by

$$4\pi e m_e k^2/h^3 = 120.4 \text{ amp}/(\text{cm}^2)(°\text{K})^2$$

Values of A_M and χ_M for some solids are shown in Table 6.3 for vacuum conditions. A compilation of data for all elements is also available.[18]

When a cathode is in contact with a gas, some of the constituents of the gas may chemically combine with the cathode or may be chemisorbed on the surface. This will cause a net change in the surface work function.

One of the most interesting examples of this effect is a tungsten cathode in an atmosphere of cesium vapor. The cesium vapor partially deposits on the tungsten surface, lowering the work function (see Fig. 6.11). The solid lines represent extrapolations[19] of earlier data;[20] while the points represent recent experimental results.

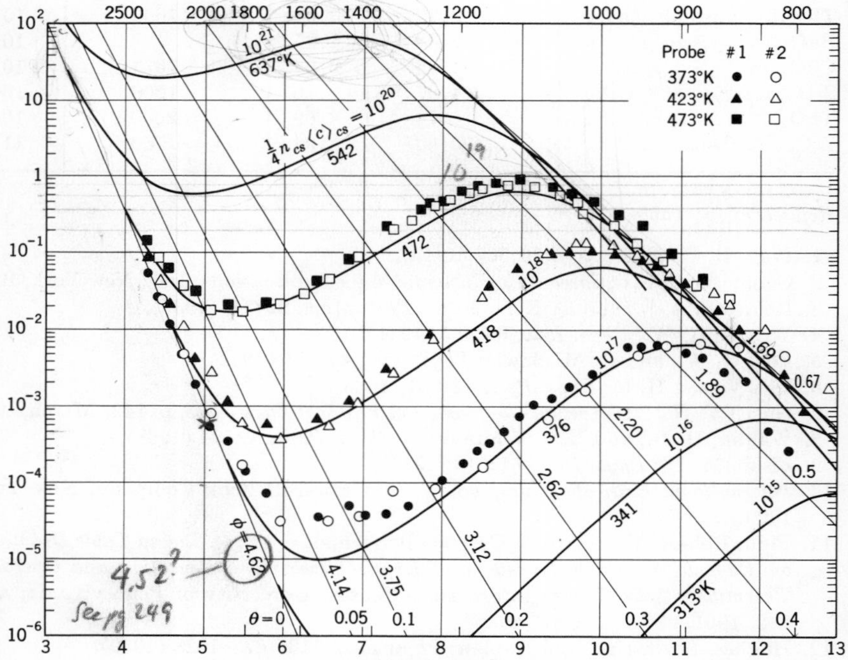

FIGURE 6.11 Thermionic emission from tungsten in the presence of cesium. (By permission from J. M. Houston and H. F. Webster, "Thermionic Energy Conversion," *Advances in Electronics and Electron Physics*, vol. 17, Pergamon Press, New York, 1962.)

Consider a given number density of cesium, with the cathode temperature low. The chemisorbed cesium lowers the work function of tungsten from its normal value of 4.52 to 1.69 ev. As the cathode temperature increases, the current follows the Dushman equation for 1.69 ev. With increasing temperature, some of the cesium is boiled off the tungsten surface, which increases the work function. The net effect is to produce a local maximum in the emission current. Further increases in the cathode temperature drive off more cesium, increasing the work function even further, so that the emission current decreases. Finally, when most of the cesium has been removed from the surface, the work function becomes equal to that of tungsten, and further increases in the cathode temperature cause the emission current to increase again. Thus, for a given number density of cesium in the gas phase, there is a local maximum current which occurs at a temperature which is much lower than the corresponding temperature for pure tungsten.

Experiments have also been performed with tungsten cathodes in potassium and rubidium vapor at very low pressures,[21] and more recently with other refractory metals in cesium vapor at very low pressure.[19] The results indicate that at the peak emission point of the S curve, the maximum emission is obtained from tungsten; rhenium is about 70 per cent of that of tungsten, molybdenum is about 60 per cent, Ta about 25 per cent, and columbium about 3 per cent.

It must be emphasized that the values may be changed considerably in the presence of working fluids in magnetohydrodynamic devices, but data on the effects are not yet available. In a magnetohydrodynamic device, there are, of course, other phenomena which can cause high emission. These include the formation of cathode spots, field emission, and the use of hollow cathode arcs.

REFERENCES CITED

1. Fay, James J.: Class notes, Cornell University, Ithaca, N.Y.
2. Saha, M. N.: *Phil. Mag.*, **40**:472 (1920).
3. Myers, H., J. H. Buss, and S. W. Benson: "Thermodynamics of Ionized Gases," *Proc. Conf. on Phys. Chem. in Aerodynamics and Space Flight*, Pergamon Press, New York, September, 1959.
4. Kidder, R. E., and H. E. Dewitt: "Application of a Modified Debye-Hückel Theory to a Fully Ionized Gas," *J. Nucl. Energy*, part C, 2, p. 218, 1961.
5. Harris, G. M., and J. Trulio: "Equilibrium Properties of a Partially Ionized Plasma," *J. Nucl. Energy*, part C, 2, p. 224, 1961.
6. Ecker, G., and W. Kroll: "Lowering of the Ionization Energy for a Plasma in Thermodynamic Equilibrium," *Phys. Fluids*, **6**:62–69 (1963).
7. Hill, T. L.: *Statistical Thermodynamics*, p. 331, Addison-Wesley Publishing Company, Inc., Reading, Mass., 1960.
8. Bienkowski, G. K.: "The Equation of State of an Ionized Gas," *MIT Naval Supersonic Lab. Rept.* 398, September, 1959.

9. Fowler, R. H., and E. A. Guggenheim: *Statistical Thermodynamics,* chap. 12, Cambridge University Press, London, 1956.
10. Bortner, M. H.: "The Effect of Temperature on Calculated Non-equilibrium Electron Densities," *Gen. Elec.* TIS *Rept.* R61SD24, 1961, and list of references.
11. Barger, R. L.: "Ionization and Deionization Processes in Low Density Plasma Flows," *NASA Tech. Note* D-740, April, 1961.
12. Eschenroeder, A. Q.: "Ionization Non-equilibrium in Expanding Flows," *ARS J.,* **32**:196–203 (February, 1962).
13. Dewan, E. M.: "Generalization of the Saha Equation," *Phys. Fluids,* **4**:759–764 (1961).
14. BenDaniel, D. J., and S. Tamor: "Non Equilibrium Ionization in Magnetohydrodynamic Generators," *Gen. Elec. Res. Lab. Rept.* 62-RL (2922E), January, 1962.
15. Kerrebrock, J. L.: "Conduction in Gases with Elevated Electron Temperature," in C. Mannal and N. W. Mather (eds.), *Proc. 2d Symp. Eng. Aspects Magnetohydrodynamics,* pp. 327–346, Columbia University Press, New York, 1962.
16. Robben, F.: "Non Equilibrium Ionization in a Magnetohydrodynamic Generator," *Phys. Fluids,* **5**:1308–1309 (1962).
17. Dushman, S.: "Thermionic Emission," *Rev. Mod. Phys.,* **2**:381–476 (1930); see pp. 458–459.
18. Michaelson, H. B.: "Work Functions of the Elements," *J. Appl. Phys.,* **21**:536–540 (1950).
19. Houston, J. M.: "Thermionic Emission of Refractory Metals in Cesium Vapor," *Proc. Round Table Discussion on Cathode Emission Invests. and Exptl. Techs. for Fabricating and Operating Thermionic Cells,* Power Information Center, University of Pennsylvania, June 1–2, 1961.
20. Taylor, J. B., and I. Langmuir: "The Evaporation of Atoms, Ions, and Electrons from Caesium Films on Tungsten," *Phys. Rev.,* **44**:423–453 (1933).
21. Killian, T. J.: "Thermionic Phenomena Caused by Vapors of Rubidium and Potassium," *Phys. Rev.,* **27**:578–587 (1926).

GENERAL REFERENCES

Fowler, R. H., and E. A. Guggenheim: *Statistical Thermodynamics,* Cambridge University Press, London, 1956.

Hill, T. L.: *Statistical Thermodynamics,* Addison-Wesley Publishing Company, Inc., Reading, Mass., 1960.

Lindsay, Robert B.: *Introduction to Physical Statistics,* John Wiley & Sons, Inc., New York, 1941.

Saha, M. N., and B. N. Srivastava: *Treatise on Heat,* The Indian Press, Allahabad, Calcutta, 1958.

7

ELECTROMAGNETIC WAVES AND RADIATION IN PLASMAS

7.1 INTRODUCTION

So far our discussion has been limited to the fundamentals of plasma physics and magnetohydrodynamics. In this chapter we will, for the first time, consider plasma motion in its simplest form: that is, wave motion. Despite the simplicity of the flow problem, a bewildering variety of wave motions are possible, and so only the simplest are investigated here. Throughout the discussion, the multifluid nature of the plasma will be apparent, although some wave motions can be studied within the framework of the one-fluid theory. This latter topic (Alfvén waves) will be deferred until Chap. 9, since all the discussion in Part II pertains essentially to the one-fluid theory of magnetohydrodynamic flow problems.

Before studying wave motions, two new radiation mechanisms that can arise because of the existence of charged particles in the gas are discussed. They are bremsstrahlung and cyclotron radiation. Next, the general question of wave motions is taken up. Because of the multitude of wave motions possible in a plasma in the presence of a magnetic field, no attempt is made to consider them all. Rather, attention is generally focused on two of the simplest, which are the longitudinal and transverse waves. In the former, the electric field lies in the direction of wave propagation, any induced magnetic field is negligible, and charge inequality is an essential feature. In the latter, the electric and magnetic fields are both normal to the direction of wave propagation, and charge inequality is negligible.

The first wave motions treated are forced oscillations, in which collisions dominate the situation, and the applied frequency is low enough so that any effects due to excess charge can be neglected. For this type of oscillation, neglecting excess charge amounts to the neglect of any spatial variation, so that the electric field and current simply vary in time. The simplest case of this type of electron oscillation in the absence of a magnetic field is treated first. Then, electron and ion cyclotron resonances are investigated by assuming an applied magnetic field normal to the applied electric field.

In the next section, free longitudinal oscillations are studied by allowing for charge inequality—in other words, high-frequency oscillations. First, both collisions and electron thermal motion are neglected, so that only a standing wave exists at the plasma frequency. The inclusion of thermal motion is shown to permit a traveling wave. Finally, damping due to a small but finite number of collisions is included.

Continuing, transverse oscillations are treated at first with no applied magnetic field. Then the addition of a magnetic field in the direction of propagation leads to the extraordinary wave.

Completing the chapter, the question of damping in collisionless plasmas (Landau damping) is taken up. Up to this point, a two-fluid theory, in which collisions are accounted for approximately, with the assumption of a constant mean free time between collisions, has been used and has proved adequate. In this theory, however, the so-called "damping" due to phase mixing has been neglected, since to study it one must analyze the velocity distribution. That is, a study of the plasma oscillation from the point of view of the Boltzmann equation is necessary. First, the concept of free-streaming motion in a collisionless plasma is introduced by analyzing the two-stream instability. This is then extended to a realistic plasma including collisions. Based on this then, it is shown that Landau damping does exist, and that when collisions are considered, they always dominate the situation. Thus, Landau damping is found to be of importance only in collision-free plasmas, and then only for wavelengths as short as or shorter than the Debye length in the plasma. In conclusion, ion cyclotron resonance is restudied, now within the framework of the Boltzmann equation analysis.

7.2 RADIATION FROM HOT PLASMAS

Most of this chapter will be concerned with electromagnetic waves in a plasma. Before considering this complex topic, however, we will first discuss, briefly, radiation from a plasma. In the absence of charged particles (electrons, ions) in a gas, radiation can be emitted only when electronically, vibrationally, or rotationally excited atoms or molecules are deexcited. In the case of an ionized gas, additional radiation occurs owing to the acceleration of charged particles. When a charged particle collides with another particle, it is deflected, and this deflection constitutes an acceleration or deceleration. This type of radiation is referred to as *bremsstrahlung*. The second type of radiation which we will consider here is called *cyclotron* radiation. It arises when a magnetic field is applied to the plasma, since a charged particle will gyrate in the presence of a magnetic field and experience a radial acceleration.

In the following treatment, each type of radiation will be calculated for a single particle and then summed over all particles. It is of course understood that a plasma contains many charged particles, so that the collective effect of the particles and radiation should be studied. This study of the collective effect is, however, only in its infancy at the present time.

7.2.1 Cyclotron Radiation. The constant radial acceleration which gives rise to cyclotron radiation is given by the following expression for a single species s:

$$\dot{w}_\perp = \frac{w_\perp^2}{r_L} = \omega w_\perp = \frac{eZ_s B w_\perp}{m_s} \tag{7.1}$$

where $w_\perp$ is the particle velocity perpendicular to the magnetic field. The rate at which energy is radiated by a charged particle with acceleration $\dot{w}_\perp$ has been calculated in Chap. 2 and is given in Eq. (2.105). Using this relation, the power radiated by a gyrating particle is

$$P_s = \frac{2}{3}\frac{e^4 Z_s^4 B^2 w_\perp^2}{4\pi K_0 c_0^3 m_s^2} \tag{7.2}$$

Here it is seen that the radiated power increases very rapidly as either the particle charge Z_s increases or mass m_s decreases. Because of the former, it is essential to eliminate impurities (high Z_s) from very high temperature plasmas in order to prevent self-cooling. Since $w_\perp^2$ is related to the electron temperature in the plasma, it is also important to keep this low. Both these considerations are important in thermonuclear research.

Neglecting reabsorption, the total radiated power is derived by multiplying Eq. (7.2) by the distribution function for the particular species in question and integrating over velocity space. Thus,

$$P_s = \frac{2}{3}\frac{e^4 Z_s^4 B^2}{4\pi K_0 c_0^3 m_s^3} p_{\perp s} \tag{7.3}$$

where $p_{\perp s} = \int m_s w_\perp^2 f \, d\mathbf{w}$. If there are several species of charged particles, the total power radiated is simply the sum of these separate contributions.

When $w_\perp$ increases to very large values, the analysis should include particle displacement and relativistic effects. This will give rise to higher harmonics and line broadening of each of these, both of which will greatly increase the radiated power.[1]

7.2.2 Bremsstrahlung. Although radiation will be emitted by any moving charged particle deflected by another particle, our principle interest will be in the deflection of an electron by an ion or atom. The collisions between free like particles will not be an important source of bremsstrahlung, since the acceleration of each will be equal and opposite, and there will be no net acceleration, to first approximation. For example, collisions between two free electrons will be neglected. The difference due to the collision of an electron with an ion or an atom (or molecule) is a result of the fact that the atomic nucleus is shielded by a cloud of electrons. Depending on conditions, the principle bremsstrahlung radiation generally occurs because of electrons passing very close to the atomic nucleus, so that screening due to the bound electrons is usually unimportant. Thus, a reasonable estimate of the total bremsstrahlung radiation can be made if we consider only the coulombic collision between an electron and a heavy particle of positive charge eZ. In order to accurately calculate this radiation, it would be necessary to employ the theory of quantum mechanics. Such a treatment is beyond the scope of this book, and so an approximate classical calculation will be carried out here. The reader interested in the more involved aspects of the theory should refer to the monograph by Heitler.[2]

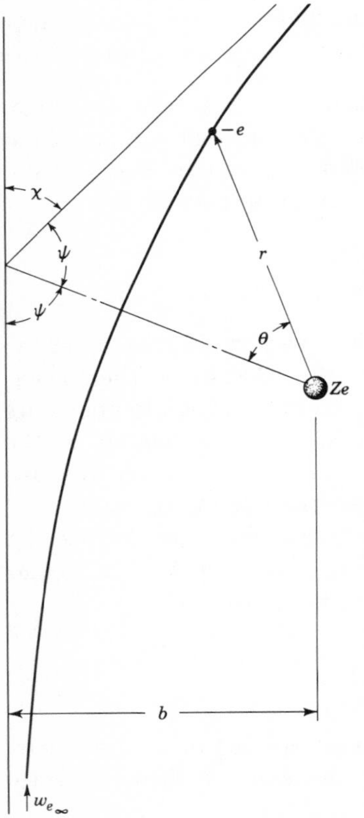

FIGURE 7.1 Path of an electron near an ion.

First, the acceleration of an electron as it approaches a positive charge eZ must be calculated. The radiation due to this acceleration can then be computed, based on Eq. (2.105) as before. The electron approaches the ion along a path initially a distance b, called the *impact parameter*, from the ion. It is deflected by a total angle χ (see Fig. 7.1). Since the ion mass is very much greater than the electron mass, it is assumed that the ion motion is not affected by the electron. The power radiated by the electron for one collision is given by

$$P = \frac{2}{3}\frac{e^2}{4\pi K_0 c_0{}^3}\int_{-\infty}^{\infty} \dot{w}_e{}^2\, dt \qquad (7.4)$$

and the acceleration of the electron is given by the ratio of the electrostatic force to the electron mass,

$$\dot{w}_e = \frac{e^2 Z}{4\pi K_0 m_e r^2} \tag{7.5}$$

The integration with respect to time in Eq. (7.4) is not convenient. This can be changed to integration with respect to θ by considering the conservation of angular momentum,

$$m_e r^2 \frac{d\theta}{dt} = m_e b w_{e_\infty} \tag{7.6}$$

Substitution of Eqs. (7.5) and (7.6) into Eq. (7.4) yields

$$P = \frac{2e^6 Z^2}{3(4\pi K_0)^3 c_0{}^3 m_e{}^2 b w_{e_\infty}} \int_{-(\pi-\psi)}^{\pi-\psi} r^{-2}\, d\theta \tag{7.7}$$

To proceed further, an expression for $r = r(\theta)$ is required. To obtain such an expression, the motion of a particle in an inverse-square force field must be obtained. The equation of motion in polar coordinates can be written simply as

$$m_e\left(\frac{d^2r}{dt^2} - r\dot{\theta}^2\right) = -\frac{Ze^2}{4\pi K_0 r^2} \tag{7.8}$$

Now

$$\frac{dr}{dt} = \frac{dr}{d\theta}\frac{d\theta}{dt} = \frac{dr}{d\theta}\dot{\theta}$$

and

$$\frac{d}{dt}\left(\frac{dr}{dt}\right) = \dot{\theta}\frac{d}{d\theta}\left(\frac{dr}{dt}\right) = \dot{\theta}\frac{d}{d\theta}\left(\frac{dr}{d\theta}\dot{\theta}\right)$$

or

$$\frac{d^2r}{dt^2} = \dot{\theta}^2\frac{d^2r}{d\theta^2} + \dot{\theta}\frac{dr}{d\theta}\frac{d\dot{\theta}}{d\theta} \tag{7.9}$$

Since $r^2\dot{\theta} = \text{const}$, differentiation of it with respect to θ yields

$$2r\frac{dr}{d\theta}\dot{\theta} + r^2\frac{d\dot{\theta}}{d\theta} = 0$$

or

$$\frac{d\dot{\theta}}{d\theta} = -\frac{2}{r}\frac{dr}{d\theta}\dot{\theta} \tag{7.10}$$

Combination of Eqs. (7.9) and (7.10) and substitution into (7.8) yield

$$\dot{\theta}^2\frac{d^2r}{d\theta^2} + \dot{\theta}^2\frac{dr}{d\theta}\left(-\frac{2}{r}\frac{dr}{d\theta}\right) - \dot{\theta}^2 r = -\frac{Ze^2}{4\pi K_0 r^2 m_e} \tag{7.11}$$

Finally, $\dot{\theta}$ is eliminated by use of the angular momentum from Eq. (7.6).

$$\frac{1}{r^2}\frac{d^2r}{d\theta^2} - \frac{2}{r^3}\left(\frac{dr}{d\theta}\right)^2 - \frac{1}{r} = -\frac{Ze^2}{4\pi K_0 b^2 w_{e_\infty}^2 m_e} \tag{7.12}$$

Equation (7.12) is still not in convenient form for solution. Let $r = u^{-1}$; then

$$\frac{dr}{d\theta} = \frac{d}{d\theta}\left(\frac{1}{u}\right) = -\frac{1}{u^2}\frac{du}{d\theta} = -r^2\frac{du}{d\theta} \tag{7.13}$$

$$\frac{d^2r}{d\theta^2} = -2r\frac{dr}{d\theta}\frac{du}{d\theta} - r^2\frac{d^2u}{d\theta^2}$$

or

$$\frac{d^2r}{d\theta^2} = 2r^3\left(\frac{du}{d\theta}\right)^2 - r^2\frac{d^2u}{d\theta^2} \tag{7.14}$$

Substitution of Eqs. (7.13) and (7.14) into Eq. (7.12) yields

$$\frac{d^2u}{d\theta^2} + u = \frac{e^2Z}{4\pi K_0 b^2 w_{e_\infty}^2 m_e} \tag{7.15}$$

The solution is simply

$$u = \frac{1}{r} = A\cos\theta + B\sin\theta + \frac{Ze^2}{4\pi K_0 b^2 w_{e_\infty}^2 m_e} \tag{7.16}$$

To evaluate the constants, take d/dt of Eq. (7.16):

$$-\frac{\dot{r}}{r^2} = (-A\sin\theta + B\cos\theta)\dot{\theta}$$

Now when $\theta = 0$, $\dot{r}$ is also zero, and we must put $B = 0$. Thus,

$$\frac{\dot{r}}{r^2} = (A\sin\theta)\dot{\theta}$$

Next, we know that when the electron is at ∞, we have $\dot{r} = w_{e_\infty}$ and $\theta = \pi - \psi$. Then, recalling again that $r^2\dot{\theta} = bw_{e_\infty}$, the constant A becomes

$$A = \frac{w_{e_\infty}}{bw_{e_\infty}\sin(\pi - \psi)} = (b\sin\psi)^{-1}$$

The solution is now

$$\frac{1}{r} = \frac{\cos\theta}{b\sin\psi} + \frac{Ze^2}{4\pi K_0 b^2 w_{e_\infty}^2 m_e} \tag{7.17}$$

Finally, this may be simplified further by obtaining the relationship between ψ and the particle properties and other collision conditions. Thus, when $r \to \infty$ and $\theta \to \pi - \psi$, Eq. (7.17) yields

$$\frac{\cos\psi}{b\sin\psi} = \frac{Ze^2}{4\pi K_0 b^2 w_{e_\infty}^2 m_e} \tag{7.18}$$

Using this to replace the last term in Eq. (7.17) gives

$$\frac{1}{r} = \frac{(\cos\theta/\cos\psi) + 1}{b\tan\psi} \tag{7.19}$$

With this expression for $r = r(\theta)$, the integral in Eq. (7.7) can now be evaluated. It becomes

$$I = \int_{-(\pi-\psi)}^{\pi-\psi} r^{-2}\,d\theta = \frac{1}{b^2\tan^2\psi}\int_{-(\pi-\psi)}^{\pi-\psi}\left(1+\frac{\cos\theta}{\cos\psi}\right)^2 d\theta$$

$$= \frac{1}{b^2\tan^2\psi}\left[2(\pi-\psi) + \frac{2\sin\theta}{\cos\psi}\Big|_{-\pi+\psi}^{\pi-\psi} + \frac{\frac{1}{2}\theta + \frac{1}{2}\sin\theta\cos\theta}{\cos^2\psi}\Big|_{-\pi+\psi}^{\pi-\psi}\right]$$

$$= \frac{1}{b^2}\left[(\pi-\psi)\left(\frac{2}{\tan^2\psi}+\csc^2\psi\right)+\frac{3}{\tan\psi}\right]$$

With the identity $\csc^2\psi = 1 + \cot^2\psi$, we obtain

$$I = \frac{1}{b^2}\left[(\pi-\psi)\left(1+\frac{3}{\tan^2\psi}\right)+\frac{3}{\tan\psi}\right] \tag{7.20}$$

In general, the average scattering angle of an electron by a single heavy particle is 90°, so that $\chi \cong \pi/2$ and $\psi \cong \pi/4$. This yields a value for I of $3(\pi + 1)/b^2$. On the other hand, in a fully ionized gas the average scattering angle is small, owing to the long-range Coulomb forces, so that $\chi \cong 0$ and $\psi \cong \pi/2$. Now $I \cong \pi/2b^2$. Since bremsstrahlung will be of principal interest for essentially fully ionized gases, we will use the latter value. It should be remembered, however, that this radiation will be an order of magnitude larger if the scattering is done primarily by neutral particles in the gas. Substitution of $I = \pi/2b^2$ into Eq. (7.7) then gives

$$P = \frac{\pi}{3}\frac{e^6Z^2}{(4\pi K_0)^3 c_0{}^3 m_e{}^2 b^3 w_{e_\infty}} \tag{7.21}$$

The sum over all such "collisions" having various values of b must now be taken. The number of electrons which approach the ion per second through the differential annular area $(2\pi b\,db)$ is equal to the number density times the volume, whose base is obviously $(2\pi b\,db)$. The height of the volume is obviously w_{e_∞}, since electrons which are further away than w_{e_∞} will not come sufficiently close to the ion to be deflected during the 1-sec time interval. Thus,

$$P_T = \int_{b_{\min}}^{\infty} n_e w_{e_\infty} P(2\pi b\,db) \tag{7.22}$$

Substitution of P from Eq. (7.21) into (7.22) and integration over b yield

$$P_T = \frac{2}{3}\frac{\pi^2 n_e Z^2 e^6}{(4\pi K_0)^3 c_0{}^3 m_e{}^2 b_{\min}} \tag{7.23}$$

If the minimum impact parameter $b_{\min}$ were zero, Eq. (7.23) would predict an infinite amount of power radiated, corresponding to an infinite acceleration of the electron as $r \to 0$. This singularity is removed by considering the basic postulate of quantum mechanics, namely, that the minimum value of angular momentum is equal to Planck's constant h, or

$$m_e b_{\min} w_{e_\infty} = h \tag{7.24}$$

In addition, Eq. (7.23) is for one ion: This must be multiplied by n_I to obtain the radiation per unit volume. Thus, the total radiation per unit volume for each ion species is

$$P_T = \frac{2}{3}\frac{\pi^2 n_e n_I e^6 Z^2 \langle w_e \rangle}{(4\pi K_0)^3 c_0{}^3 m_e h} \tag{7.25}$$

where $\langle w_e \rangle$ represents the mean electron velocity in the plasma. If desired, the electron temperature can be introduced by

$$\tfrac{1}{2} m_e (\langle w_e \rangle)^2 \cong \tfrac{3}{2} k T_e$$

As can be readily seen from Eq. (7.25), impurity ions with high Z in a plasma will increase the bremsstrahlung radiation considerably. Also, if the scattering medium is a solid (i.e., thin metal film), the radiation arising from the passage of an electron beam through the solid will be larger than that from an ion beam, since the mass of the scattered particle appears in the denominator of Eq. (7.25).

7.3 FORCED PLASMA OSCILLATIONS

At this point the question of time-varying fields and currents will be taken up. A convenient physical model upon which to base the discussion is shown in Fig. 7.2. When an electric field is applied to a conducting gas, a current will flow. If the direction of the applied field reverses, so will the current, and at low frequencies they will be in phase. As the frequency is raised, they will tend to be partially out of phase. It is to the study of these phase differences, as well as resonances occurring in the presence of an applied magnetic field, that this section is devoted. For simplicity, only time variations will be considered initially in an essentially collision-dominated plasma.

Very early it was recognized that if the maximum amplitude of the applied electric field were made large enough, some sort of discharge would occur. That is, ionization in the gas could be increased above its

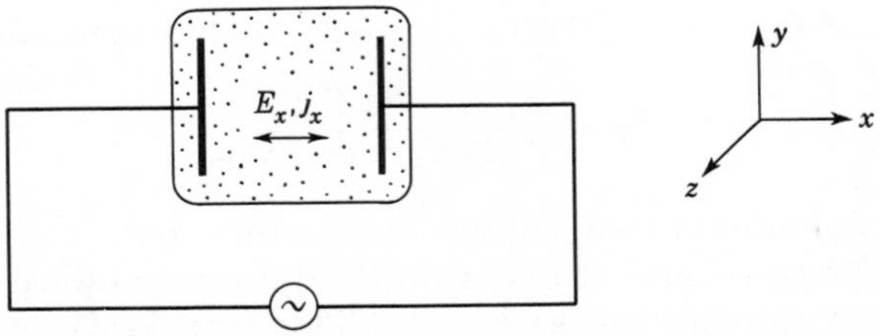

FIGURE 7.2 A-C plasma conductivity experiment.

thermal level. As a result, a great deal of research has been done on high-frequency discharges. In the present discussion, only small-amplitude oscillations will be considered, and so all discharge phenomena will be neglected.[3] Also, if the oscillation frequency is low enough, excess charge can be neglected and the plasma treated as if it were electrically neutral.† In this case spatial variations can be omitted. The discussion of the higher-frequency discharge will be deferred to Sec. 7.4, where it will be shown that *free* longitudinal oscillations are possible at the "plasma frequency."

The principle area of application of the results will be in plasma diagnostics. That is, one could, if desired, obtain some estimates of plasma properties by measuring the current phase shift at a given frequency. Another possible application exists if a magnetic field is applied perpendicular to the electric field. In this case resonances occur at the electron and ion cyclotron frequencies, which may make it possible to add energy to the plasma in an efficient way.

7.3.1 Time-varying Applied Electric Field. To analyze the problems of the present section, the transfer equations for electron- and ion-momentum conservation will be used, where the collision term is expressed as a function of a collision frequency ν_e. Initially, let us neglect ion motion, all spatial variations, and assume that no applied magnetic field exists. Then Eq. (5.165) becomes

$$\frac{d\mathbf{v}_e}{dt} = -\frac{e\mathbf{E}}{m_e} - \nu_e \mathbf{v}_e \tag{7.26}$$

Let us also assume that $\mathbf{v}_e$ and $\mathbf{E}$ are both in the x direction so that

$$\frac{dv_e}{dt} = -\frac{eE}{m_e} - \nu_e v_e \tag{7.27}$$

Next, let us assume that E varies sinusoidally with time at a frequency ω and amplitude E_0. Then

$$\frac{dv_e}{dt} = -\frac{eE_0}{m_e}\cos \omega t - \nu_e v_e \tag{7.28}$$

which has the solution

$$v_e = -\frac{eE_0}{m_e}\frac{\cos(\omega t - \beta)}{\sqrt{\nu_e^2 + \omega^2}} \tag{7.29}$$

where β is the phase angle with which the electric field $\mathbf{E}$ lags $\mathbf{v}_e$. It is given by

$$\tan \beta = \frac{\omega}{\nu_e}$$

† Charge conservation requires that $\nabla \cdot \mathbf{j} = -\partial\rho_e/\partial t$. For low-frequency oscillations, however, the displacement current can be neglected and $\mathbf{j} = \nabla \times \mathbf{B}$ shows that $\nabla \cdot \mathbf{j} = 0$. Thus, in this case ρ_e is constant or zero.

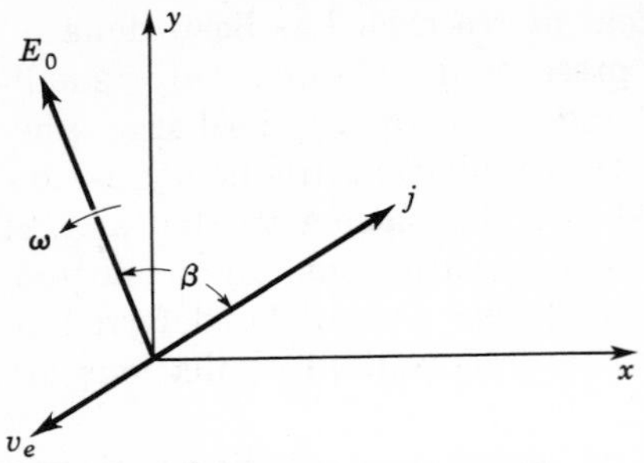

FIGURE 7.3 Rotating vector representation of alternating electric field and current density.

Since the current density $\mathbf{j} = -n_e e \mathbf{v}_e$, it is found from Eq. (7.29) to be

$$j = \frac{e^2 E_0}{m_e} \frac{n_e}{\nu_e} \frac{\cos(\omega t - \beta)}{\sqrt{1 + (\omega/\nu_e)^2}} \tag{7.30}$$

or recognizing that the scalar conductivity is $\sigma_0 = n_e e^2/m_e \nu_e$, this becomes

$$j = \frac{\sigma_0 E_0}{\sqrt{1 + (\omega/\nu_e)^2}} \cos(\omega t - \beta) \tag{7.31}$$

In order to visualize this situation more clearly, let us consider the electric field as a constant vector rotating about the z axis with an angular speed of ω. In this case the actual electric field magnitude is simply the projection of this constant vector on the x axis. The behavior of the various quantities discussed above can now be shown in Fig. 7.3. Here the phase-lag angle β of $\mathbf{j}$ as compared to $\mathbf{E}$ can be clearly seen. It should also be noted that the part of the electric current which is in phase with the electric field can be described in terms of an a-c conductivity, defined as

$$\sigma_{AC} = \frac{\sigma_0}{1 + (\omega \tau_e)^2} \tag{7.32}$$

where we have put $\nu_e = \tau_e^{-1}$. It is interesting to see that this is of precisely the same form as the reduced d-c conductivity in the presence of an applied magnetic field. In that case ω represented the electron cyclotron frequency, whereas now it is the frequency of oscillation of the electric field. The reason for the similarity is obvious. In the previous case electrons were constrained to gyrate around magnetic field lines, whereas now they must oscillate about a fixed position in space, by virtue of the oscillating electric field.

Finally, from Eq. (7.31) and the definition of β, we observe that for $\omega \sim 0$, the conductivity is essentially unchanged, and the electric field and current are in phase. As ω increases to larger values, the conductivity is reduced, and the current lags behind the electric field. In the limit of very large ω, the conductivity approaches zero, and the current is 90° out of phase. It must be cautioned, however, that ω must not be so large that the displacement current must be accounted for and the assumption of charge neutrality is violated, for in that case the analysis used is not valid. Further progress must then be made by means of a more detailed analysis (see Sec. 7.4).

7.3.2 Electron Cyclotron Resonance. If, in addition to an applied electric field, a static magnetic field is applied in the z direction (see Fig. 7.2), the above analysis must be modified and, as will be seen, a resonance

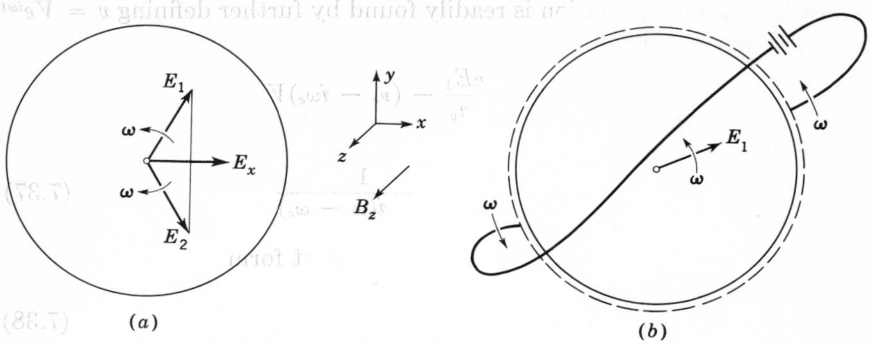

FIGURE 7.4 Counterrotating E vectors.

at the electron cyclotron frequency will be found. For this problem the appropriate equation is the electron-momentum equation (7.26), with the Lorentz force term due to the applied magnetic field added,

$$\frac{d\mathbf{v}_e}{dt} = -\left(\frac{e\mathbf{E}}{m_e} + \mathbf{v}_e \times \boldsymbol{\omega}_e\right) - \nu_e \mathbf{v}_e \tag{7.33}$$

where $\boldsymbol{\omega}_e \equiv e\mathbf{B}/m_e$ is the electron cyclotron frequency.

Now, an analysis of the case in which the electric field lies in the x direction alone will be rather complex. A more convenient mode of analysis will be to decompose the time-varying E_x into the sum of two counterrotating constant-magnitude E vectors as shown in Fig. 7.4a. In order to fix the physical concepts involved, a practical method of creating such a rotating constant E field is shown in Fig. 7.4b. Here a direct voltage is applied, via a pair of rotating brushes, to a set of electrodes arranged in the fashion of a commutator.

The problem which will be considered then has a constant B field in the z direction, and a constant electric field vector rotating in space about the z axis. If we wish the solution to the original problem, we then change the sign of ω and add the resulting solution to the one to be found presently.

First, we decompose Eq. (7.33) into x and y components,

$$\frac{dv_{e_x}}{dt} = -\frac{eE_x}{m_e} - v_{e_y}\omega_e - \nu_e v_{e_x} \tag{7.34}$$

$$\frac{dv_{e_y}}{dt} = -\frac{eE_y}{m_e} + v_{e_x}\omega_e - \nu_e v_{e_y} \tag{7.35}$$

and it should be noted that $\boldsymbol{\omega}_e$ is for the present taken to lie in the $+z$ direction. Next, define $v = v_{e_x} + iv_{e_y}$ and $E = E_x + iE_y$ so that Eqs. (7.34) and (7.35) can be combined to give

$$\frac{dv}{dt} = -\frac{eE}{m_e} - (\nu_e - i\omega_e)v \tag{7.36}$$

The solution of this relation is readily found by further defining $v = Ve^{i\omega t}$ and $E = E_1 e^{i\omega t}$. Then

$$Vi\omega = -\frac{eE_1}{m_e} - (\nu_e - i\omega_e)V$$

or, solving for V,

$$V = -\frac{eE_1}{m_e}\frac{1}{\nu_e + i(\omega - \omega_e)} \tag{7.37}$$

which can now be put into the more convenient form

$$V = -\frac{eE_1}{m_e}\frac{\nu_e - i(\omega - \omega_e)}{\nu_e^2 + (\omega - \omega_e)^2} \tag{7.38}$$

The solution for v is then found from $v = Ve^{i\omega t} = (V_R + iV_I)(\cos \omega t + i \sin \omega t)$. It is

$$v = \frac{-eE_1}{m_e}\frac{\nu_e \cos \omega t + (\omega - \omega_e)\sin \omega t + i[\nu_e \sin \omega t - (\omega - \omega_e)\cos \omega t]}{\nu_e^2 + (\omega - \omega_e)^2} \tag{7.39}$$

The real and imaginary parts of this expression are respectively v_{e_x} and v_{e_y}. Thus,

$$v_{e_x} = -\frac{eE_1}{m_e}\frac{\nu_e \cos \omega t + (\omega - \omega_e)\sin \omega t}{\nu_e^2 + (\omega - \omega_e)^2} \tag{7.40}$$

and

$$v_{e_y} = -\frac{eE_1}{m_e}\frac{\nu_e \sin \omega t - (\omega - \omega_e)\cos \omega t}{\nu_e^2 + (\omega - \omega_e)^2} \tag{7.41}$$

completing the solution of the problem. Clearly, since $E_x = E_1 \cos \omega t$ and $E_y = E_1 \sin \omega t$, the electron motion in either the x or y direction is out of phase with the applied electric field. In fact, Eqs. (7.40) and (7.41) can also be written in terms of the phase angle,

$$v_{e_x} = -\frac{eE_1}{m_e}\cos(\omega t - \beta) \tag{7.42}$$

$$v_{e_y} = \frac{eE_1}{m_e}\sin(\omega t - \beta) \tag{7.43}$$

where $\tan \beta = (\omega - \omega_e)/\nu_e$. This shows that, as might have been expected, v_{e_y} and v_{e_x} are 90° out of phase and of constant magnitude. Thus, electrons tend to move in circular paths.

Since resonance will occur with E_1 of Fig. 7.4 only when B_z is in the positive direction, we will calculate the energy input into the plasma for this case. The current flux in the x direction is found from $j_x = -n_e e v_{e_x}$ as

$$j_x = \sigma_0 E_1 \frac{\cos \omega t + [(\omega - \omega_e)/\nu_e]\sin \omega t}{1 + (\omega - \omega_e)^2/\nu_e^2} \tag{7.44}$$

The only portion of this that contributes to the power input is the part in phase with E_x. The average power input per unit volume is thus

$$P = j_x E_x = \tfrac{1}{2}\sigma_0 E_1{}^2 \left[1 + \frac{(\omega - \omega_e)^2}{\nu_e{}^2}\right]^{-1} \tag{7.45}$$

The maximum power input occurs when $\omega = \omega_e$, at which frequency it equals $\frac{1}{2}\sigma_0 E_1{}^2$. This is the electron cyclotron resonance anticipated earlier. Physically it arises because the electrons tend to gyrate as a result of the interaction between the applied electric and magnetic fields. When their gyration frequency equals the electron cyclotron frequency, a reinforcing occurs which gives rise to the resonance.

If the present results are compared to those of the previous section, we see that the power input for a rotating electric field, with a magnetic field normal to the plane of rotation, is always greater than for a nonrotating field with no magnetic field ($E_1 = E_0$). To show this more clearly, the ratio $\tilde{P} = P/P_{\omega_e=0}$ is plotted versus ω_e/ν_e for several values of ω/ν_e in Fig. 7.5. Thus, adding a static magnetic field is much more effective in increasing the power input to the plasma when the applied electric field frequency is high. It should also be recognized that even at resonance ($\omega = \omega_e$), the power input to the plasma is only $\frac{1}{2}\sigma_0 E_1{}^2$, or one-half that due to a d-c electric field of magnitude E_1.

7.3.3 Ion Cyclotron Resonance. In the preceding analysis, the ion motion was omitted entirely. As a result, the possibility of a resonance

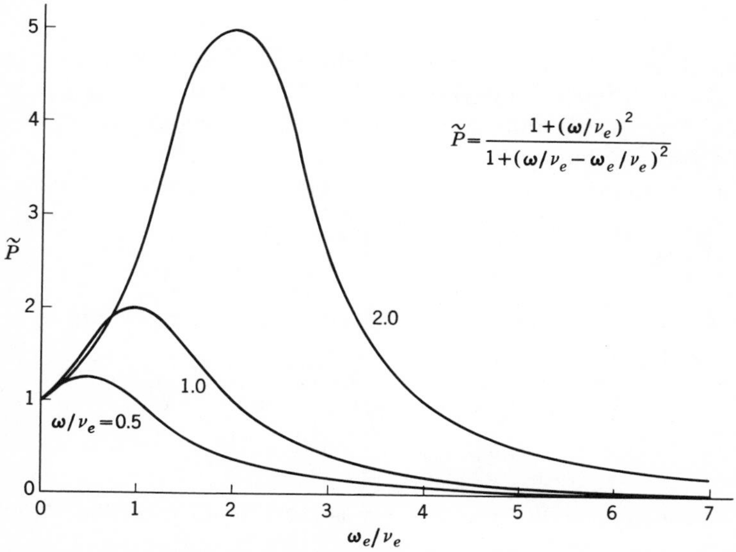

FIGURE 7.5 Influence of applied magnetic field in increasing power input to a plasma by an a-c electric field.

at the ion cyclotron frequency could not be investigated, and the limitations inherent in neglecting ion motion are not apparent. It is of interest, therefore, to consider forced oscillations in a plasma when the ion motion is included. To simplify the analysis, a fully ionized gas will be studied. The equations of motion analogous to Eq. (7.33), now with B in the $-z$ direction, are

$$\frac{d\mathbf{v}_e}{dt} = -\left(\frac{e\mathbf{E}}{m_e} + \mathbf{v}_e \times \boldsymbol{\omega}_e\right) - \nu m_e(\mathbf{v}_e - \mathbf{v}_I) \tag{7.46}$$

$$\frac{d\mathbf{v}_I}{dt} = \left(\frac{e\mathbf{E}}{m_e} + \mathbf{v}_I \times \boldsymbol{\omega}_I\right) - \nu m_e(\mathbf{v}_I - \mathbf{v}_e) \tag{7.47}$$

Following precisely the same procedure as before, we obtain two equations for V_e and V_I, where $v_e \equiv v_{e_x} + iv_{e_y} = V_e e^{i\omega t}$ and $v_I \equiv v_{I_x} + iv_{I_y} = V_I e^{i\omega t}$. They are

$$i\omega V_e = -\frac{eE_1}{m_e} - i\omega_e V_e - \nu(V_e - V_I) \tag{7.48}$$

$$i\omega V_I = \frac{eE_1}{m_I} + i\omega_I V_I - \nu(V_I - V_e)\gamma \tag{7.49}$$

where we have defined $\gamma = m_e/m_I$, and ν is the electron-ion collision frequency. Solving for V_e, we obtain the following relationship,

$$V_e = -\frac{eE_1}{m_e}\frac{1}{\nu\alpha + i(\omega + \omega_e)} \tag{7.50}$$

where $$\alpha = \frac{\omega}{\omega - \omega_I}$$

The justification for the analysis of the preceding section can now be seen since the principal interest was in $\omega \approx \omega_e \gg \omega_I$ so that $\alpha \approx 1$. In this case Eqs. (7.50) and (7.37) are identical if account is taken of the reversed B direction.

Substituting Eq. (7.50) into (7.49) gives an expression for V_I.

$$V_I = \frac{eE_1}{m_I}\frac{i(\omega + \omega_e)}{i[\nu(\omega - \omega_I) + \gamma\nu(\omega + \omega_e)] - (\omega - \omega_I)(\omega + \omega_e)} \tag{7.51}$$

As before the x component of ion velocity can be derived and is

$$v_{I_x} = \frac{eE_1}{m_I}\frac{(\omega + \omega_e)\cos(\omega t - \beta)}{\sqrt{(\omega - \omega_I)^2(\omega + \omega_e)^2 + \nu^2\omega^2}} \tag{7.52}$$

where $$\tan\beta = \frac{(\omega + \omega_e)(\omega - \omega_I)}{\nu\omega}$$

The x component of electron velocity is then found from Eq. (7.50),

$$v_{e_x} = -\frac{eE_1}{m_e}\cos(\omega t - \beta) \tag{7.53}$$

with β the same as above. As noted before, when $\omega \approx \omega_e \gg \omega_I$, the current flow due to ion motion is negligible compared to the electron current. Also, the phase angle for both reduces to $\tan^{-1}[(\omega - \omega_e)/\nu_e]$ approximately. It is of interest now to consider what happens when $\omega \approx \omega_I$ instead. First, the phase angle β becomes zero, so that both electron and ion motions are in phase with the applied electric field. Also, a resonance occurs when $\omega = \omega_I$ from Eq. (7.52). In this case the ratio of the amplitude of v_{I_x} compared to v_{e_x} is

$$\frac{|v_{I_x}|}{|v_{e_x}|} \cong \nu^{-1} \tag{7.54}$$

Hence, even at *resonance* the ion current is negligible compared to the electron current.

7.4 FREE LONGITUDINAL PLASMA OSCILLATIONS

Up to this point, only forced oscillations in a collision-dominated plasma have been considered. It had been assumed that the applied frequency was sufficiently low that charge inequality could be neglected, so that spatial variations were unimportant.

In order to study *free* longitudinal plasma oscillations, the restriction on frequency will be omitted, and the electric field resulting from charge separation will be accounted for. The argument will proceed from the macroscopic equations for the electron motion with an appropriately defined collision frequency, but in this case we will begin by neglecting collisions entirely. Of course, Maxwell's equations will be included in the formulation.

A free longitudinal plasma oscillation will, in general, be characterized by electric field and current density vectors, which are both parallel to the propagation direction. Since the longitudinal current flow will be equal and opposite to the displacement current, no magnetic field will be associated with the time-varying electric field.

The general solution for the free longitudinal oscillation is very involved, and the different effects are masked by the complexity of the resulting expressions. It will be simpler to consider each oscillation separately. For the frequency range in which the present macroscopic analysis fails, recourse must be had to analysis based on the Boltzmann equation for the electron distribution function. This topic will be deferred to Sec. 7.6.

7.4.1 Cold-Cold Approximation. Initially we will consider a plasma consisting of electrons and ions in which, in the absence of any disturbing force, the electrons and ions are stationary. Also, the oscillation frequency will be assumed very high so that ion motion can be neglected entirely. The electron motion will be governed by Maxwell's equations, the electron-momentum equation with $\nu_e = 0$ (Eq. 5.165), and the equation of electron-flux conservation. First, consider the electron-momentum equation.

$$\frac{\partial v_{e_x}}{\partial t} + v_{e_x} \frac{\partial v_{e_x}}{\partial x} = -\frac{e}{m_e} E_x \tag{7.55}$$

Since we are going to consider only small-amplitude oscillations, the second term on the left may be neglected, and Eq. (7.55) becomes

$$\frac{\partial v_{e_x}}{\partial t} = -\frac{e}{m_e} E_x \tag{7.56}$$

Next, the divergence of the electric field is related to the excess charge density by Poisson's equation. For the present case this is

$$\frac{\partial E_x}{\partial x} = \frac{e(n_I - n_e)}{K_0} \tag{7.57}$$

where the ion density n_I is constant in space and time. Again, for small perturbations we let $n_e = \bar{n}_e + n_e'$, where $\bar{n}_e$ is the average electron density in the absence of disturbances. It is of course equal to n_I for an initially neutral plasma. Thus,

$$\frac{\partial E_x}{\partial x} = -\frac{en_e'}{K_0} \tag{7.58}$$

Combining Eqs. (7.58) and (7.56) then gives

$$\frac{\partial^2 v_{e_x}}{\partial x\, \partial t} = \frac{e^2}{m_e K_0} n_e' \tag{7.59}$$

The remaining relation required is supplied by electron-flux conservation which also relates v_{e_x} and n_e'. This is

$$\frac{\partial n_e}{\partial t} = -\frac{\partial}{\partial x} n_e v_e \tag{7.60}$$

or introducing $n_e = \bar{n}_e + n_e'$, where $n_e' \ll \bar{n}_e$, this reduces to

$$\frac{\partial n_e'}{\partial t} = -\bar{n}_e \frac{\partial v_{e_x}}{\partial x} \tag{7.61}$$

and using Eq. (7.59), we obtain

$$\frac{\partial}{\partial x}\left(\frac{\partial^2 v_{e_x}}{\partial t^2} + \frac{e^2 \bar{n}_e}{m_e K_0} v_{e_x}\right) = 0 \tag{7.62}$$

so that finally

$$\frac{\partial^2 v_{e_x}}{\partial t^2} + \omega_p{}^2 v_{e_x} = 0 \qquad \omega_p{}^2 = \frac{e^2 n_e}{m_e k_0} \tag{7.63}$$

where the constant of integration is unessential.

This relation is an equation describing free oscillations of the electrons about their mean position with a frequency ω_p called the *plasma frequency*. Obviously, these waves do not propagate and thus are standing waves. When finite-temperature effects are included, we shall see that they can propagate.

The fact that no magnetic field is created in this type of oscillation can be verified readily. From Maxwell's equations, we have

$$(\nabla \times \mathbf{B})_x = K_0 \frac{\partial E_x}{\partial t} + j_x = K_0 \frac{\partial E_x}{\partial t} - \bar{n}_e e v_{e_x} \tag{7.64}$$

but from Eq. (7.56),

$$\begin{aligned}(\nabla \times \mathbf{B})_x &= -K_0 \frac{m_e}{e} \frac{\partial^2 v_{e_x}}{\partial t^2} - \bar{n}_e e v_{e_x} \\ &= -\frac{K_0 m_e}{e}\left(\frac{\partial^2 v_{e_x}}{\partial t^2} + \frac{\bar{n}_e e^2}{K_0 m_e} v_{e_x}\right) \equiv 0\end{aligned}$$

Since $\nabla \cdot \mathbf{B} = 0$, this shows that $\mathbf{B}$ is zero here.

7.4.2 Cold-Hot Approximation. In this approximation the ions are still assumed to be at zero temperature, but the electrons may now have thermal motion. As before, collisions will still be neglected. The two consequences of including a finite electron temperature are that (1) the electron pressure gradient must be considered in the momentum equation, and (2) the energy equation must also be considered. The appropriate system of equations are thus:

Momentum: $$n_e \frac{\partial v_{e_x}}{\partial t} + n_e v_{e_x} \frac{\partial v_{e_x}}{\partial x} + \frac{1}{m_e}\frac{\partial p_e}{\partial x} = -\frac{e n_e}{m_e} E_x \tag{7.65}$$

Energy: $$\frac{\partial}{\partial t}(n_e\langle\epsilon\rangle) + \frac{\partial}{\partial x}(n_e\langle\epsilon\rangle v_{e_x}) + p_e \frac{\partial v_{e_x}}{\partial x} = 0 \tag{7.66}$$

Continuity: $$\frac{\partial}{\partial t} n_e + \frac{\partial}{\partial x}(n_e v_{e_x}) = 0 \tag{7.67}$$

Poisson's equation: $$\frac{\partial E_x}{\partial x} = \frac{e}{K_0}(n_I - n_e) \tag{7.68}$$

The average energy per particle can be taken as $\langle\epsilon\rangle = (\mathfrak{N}/2)kT_e$. The degree of freedom for the electron gas is $\mathfrak{N}$. For the moment its numerical value will be unassigned. Thus,

$$n_e\langle\epsilon\rangle = \frac{n_e \mathfrak{N}}{2} kT_e = \frac{\mathfrak{N}}{2} p_e$$

so that the energy equation becomes

$$\frac{\mathfrak{N}}{2}\frac{\partial p_e}{\partial t} + \frac{\mathfrak{N}}{2}\frac{\partial}{\partial x}(p_e v_{e_x}) + p_e \frac{\partial v_{e_x}}{\partial x} = 0 \tag{7.69}$$

If we assume, as before, that $n_e = \bar{n}_e + n_e'$, $p_e = \bar{p}_e + p_e'$; neglect quadratic and higher-order terms in v_{e_x}, p'_e, and n'_e; and note that $\bar{n}_e = n_I$; then Eqs. (7.65), (7.67), (7.68), and (7.69) become

$$\bar{n}_e \frac{\partial v_{e_x}}{\partial t} + \frac{1}{m_e} \frac{\partial p_e}{\partial x} = -\frac{e\bar{n}_e E_x}{m_e} \tag{7.70}$$

$$\frac{\partial p_e}{\partial t} + \frac{\mathfrak{N} + 2}{\mathfrak{N}} \bar{p}_e \frac{\partial v_{e_x}}{\partial x} = 0 \tag{7.71}$$

$$\frac{\partial n'_e}{\partial t} + \bar{n}_e \frac{\partial v_{e_x}}{\partial x} = 0 \tag{7.72}$$

$$\frac{\partial E_x}{\partial x} = -\frac{en'_e}{K_0} \tag{7.73}$$

Next, in order to derive an equation for v_{e_x} alone, we take $\partial^2/\partial x\, \partial t$ of Eq. (7.70). Thus,

$$\bar{n}_e \frac{\partial^3 v_{e_x}}{\partial t^2\, \partial x} + \frac{1}{m_e} \frac{\partial^3 p_e}{\partial^2 x\, \partial t} = -\frac{\bar{n}_e e}{m_e} \frac{\partial^2 E_x}{\partial x\, \partial t} \tag{7.74}$$

Replacing $\partial p_e/\partial t$ from Eq. (7.71), and $\partial^2 E_x/\partial x\, \partial t$ from Eqs. (7.72) and (7.73), this becomes

$$n_e \frac{\partial^3 v_{e_x}}{\partial t^2\, \partial x} - \frac{1}{m_e} \bar{p}_e \frac{\mathfrak{N} + 2}{\mathfrak{N}} \frac{\partial^3 v_{e_x}}{\partial x^3} + \frac{e^2 \bar{n}_e^2}{K_0 m_e} \frac{\partial v_{e_x}}{\partial x} = 0$$

or

$$\frac{\partial^2 v_{e_x}}{\partial t^2} - \frac{\mathfrak{N} + 2}{\mathfrak{N}} \frac{kT_e}{m_e} \frac{\partial^2 v_{e_x}}{\partial x^2} + \omega_p^2 v_{e_x} = 0 \tag{7.75}$$

If we for the moment omit interest in plasma oscillations so as to consider low-frequency waves, then $\mathfrak{N} = 3$, corresponding to the three translational degrees of freedom in the electron gas. In this case, Eq. (7.75) describes sound waves with the phase velocity $(\frac{5}{3}kT_e/m_e)^{\frac{1}{2}}$. For high-frequency plasma oscillations, however, the electrons have effectively only one degree of freedom so that $\mathfrak{N} = 1$. Then Eq. (7.75) becomes

$$\frac{\partial^2 v_{e_x}}{\partial t^2} - \frac{3kT_e}{m_e} \frac{\partial^2 v_{e_x}}{\partial x^2} + \omega_p^2 v_{e_x} = 0 \tag{7.76}$$

The phase and group velocities for such free longitudinal plasma oscillations can be found, assuming that v_{e_x} varies as $e^{i(\omega t + \kappa x)}$. Then

$$\omega^2 = \omega_p^2 + \frac{3kT_e}{m_e} \kappa^2 \tag{7.77}$$

Since $v_{e_x} = f(x,t)$, now we see that these waves propagate unless $T_e = 0$, confirming our earlier result.

The phase velocity is given as ω/κ so that from Eq. (7.77) it is

$$V_p = \left(\frac{\omega_p^2}{\kappa^2} + \frac{3kT_e}{m_e}\right)^{\frac{1}{2}} \tag{7.78}$$

The group velocity is found as $\partial\omega/\partial\kappa$, so that from Eq. (7.77) it is found to be of the following form:

$$V_G = \frac{3kT_e}{m_e}\frac{\kappa}{\omega} = \frac{3kT_e/m_e}{V_p} \tag{7.79}$$

Thus, since $V_p \gg 3kT_e/m_e$ it can be seen that the group velocity will be quite small for this type of oscillation although its phase velocity will be high.

7.4.3 Collisional Damping. In the previous analysis for low-temperature plasmas, the pressure was included. This situation could be interpreted physically as one in which the electrons are fixed in space but are allowed to oscillate about their null positions with some random motion. The amplitude of the random motion is assumed to be smaller than the distance between particles. Such a description, however, neglects the fact that in a realistic plasma the electrons and ions are free to move and are not fixed in space. When such free-streaming motion is possible in a collision-free plasma, Landau damping arises, as will be discussed in Sec. 7.6 from the point of view of the Boltzmann equation. For the present, however, we can make some allowance for the fact that electrons are free to move through space within the framework of the macroscopic theory by including collisions in the analysis. In this case a damping term $-n_e v_e/\tau$ must be added to the right-hand side of the momentum equation (7.65). Also, in the energy equation, a term $n_e v_e^2 m_e/\tau$ should be added. However, since the equations are linearized, such second-order terms can be neglected. In this case Eq. (7.76) now becomes

$$\frac{\partial^2 v_{e_x}}{\partial t^2} - \frac{3kT_e}{m_e}\frac{\partial^2 v_{e_x}}{\partial x^2} + \omega_p{}^2 v_{e_x} + \frac{1}{\tau}\frac{\partial v_{e_x}}{\partial t} = 0 \tag{7.80}$$

Again, assuming v_{e_x} to be of the form $e^{i(\omega t + \kappa x)}$, we obtain

$$\omega^2 - \frac{i\omega}{\tau} - \left(\omega_p{}^2 + \frac{3kT_e}{m_e}\kappa^2\right) = 0 \tag{7.81}$$

Solving this for ω gives

$$\omega = \frac{i}{2\tau} \pm \frac{1}{2}\sqrt{4\omega_p{}^2 + \frac{12kT_e}{m_e} - \frac{1}{\tau^2}} \tag{7.82}$$

Since we are discussing now *nearly* collision-free longitudinal oscillations, the last term under the square root in Eq. (7.82) will be smaller than the other terms, and the only imaginary part of ω will be

$$\mathscr{I}(\omega) = \frac{1}{2\tau}$$

Thus, the solution for v_{e_x} will be

$$v_{e_x} \propto e^{-t/2\tau} e^{i[\mathscr{R}(\omega)t + \kappa x]} \tag{7.83}$$

so that the oscillations in question will be damped approximately in one mean free time by collisions. This is extremely rapid for high-density plasmas.

7.5 PROPAGATION OF TRANSVERSE WAVES

A *transverse wave* will be defined as one in which the current and electric field both lie in a plane normal to the direction of propagation, which will again be taken to be in the x direction. As in the preceding section, we restrict ourselves to high-frequency waves ($\omega \gg \omega_I$, where ω_I is the ion cyclotron frequency), so that the motion of the ions can be neglected and no mean mass motion occurs. The mean electron velocity will define the current flow. Allowance for an applied magnetic field along the direction of propagation will be made. It will be seen that this gives rise to the extraordinary wave.

If such an applied magnetic field were not along the propagation direction, the wave would not remain transverse. That is, in this case a component of the current flow would lie in the propagation direction, and since $\nabla \cdot \mathbf{j} \neq 0$, the excess charge could not be neglected. These would then be combined transverse and longitudinal waves.

If *in addition* to the above effect due to the orientation of the applied magnetic field, it were also desirable to include ion motion in the problem, the analysis in terms of a two-fluid model becomes intractable. Some progress can be made, however, if the frequency is low enough to make feasible a one-fluid macroscopic analysis. A brief discussion of the general hybrid-wave problem is given in Sec. 7.5.3, and the Alfv́en wave (one fluid) is treated in more detail in Chap. 9.

Initially, the transverse wave with no applied magnetic field present (the electromagnetic wave) will be studied. Then, adding a magnetic field to the problem, the extraordinary wave will be analyzed. Finally, damping of these waves by collisions will be accounted for.

7.5.1 Electromagnetic Waves—No Applied Magnetic Field. In this type of wave, no applied magnetic field exists, and the current and electric field will be parallel to each other, and normal to the direction of propagation. Plane, parallel waves are assumed so that

$$\partial/\partial y = \partial/\partial z = 0$$

and since $\mathbf{j}$ will have no x component, then

$$\nabla \cdot \mathbf{j} = \underbrace{\frac{\partial j_x}{\partial x}}_{\to 0} + \underbrace{\frac{\partial j_y}{\partial y}}_{\to 0} + \underbrace{\frac{\partial j_z}{\partial z}}_{\to 0} = 0$$

In this case the equation of charge conservation,

$$\frac{\partial p_e}{\partial t} + \nabla \cdot \mathbf{j} = 0 \tag{7.84}$$

shows that ρ_e = const. Thus, the transverse wave differs fundamentally from the longitudinal wave in that in the former, the charge density is zero while in the latter, it is the essential mechanism which gives rise to the oscillation.

The behavior of the electric field can be found from Maxwell's equation. Thus,

$$\nabla \times \mathbf{E} = -\frac{\partial \mathbf{B}}{\partial t} \tag{7.85}$$

$$\nabla \times \mathbf{B} = \mu_0 \mathbf{j} + \mu_0 K_0 \frac{\partial \mathbf{E}}{\partial t} \tag{7.86}$$

Taking the curl of Eq. (7.85) and substituting it into the time derivative of Eq. (7.86) gives

$$-\nabla \times (\nabla \times \mathbf{E}) = \mu_0 \frac{\partial \mathbf{j}}{\partial t} + \mu_0 K_0 \frac{\partial^2 \mathbf{E}}{\partial t^2} \tag{7.87}$$

or, expanding the left-hand side, this becomes

$$\nabla(\nabla \cdot \mathbf{E}) - \nabla^2 \mathbf{E} = -\mu_0 \frac{\partial \mathbf{j}}{\partial t} - \mu_0 K_0 \frac{\partial^2 \mathbf{E}}{\partial t^2} \tag{7.88}$$

We have already shown that $\rho_e = 0$ so that $\nabla \cdot \mathbf{E} = 0$ also. Then

$$\nabla^2 \mathbf{E} = \mu_0 \frac{\partial \mathbf{j}}{\partial t} + \mu_0 K_0 \frac{\partial^2 \mathbf{E}}{\partial t^2}$$

or for our case

$$\frac{\partial^2 E_y}{\partial x^2} = \mu_0 \frac{\partial j_y}{\partial t} + \mu_0 K_0 \frac{\partial^2 E_y}{\partial t^2} \tag{7.89}$$

The current $\mathbf{j}$ in this expression is expressible as $-n_e e v_{e_y}$, where we will assume $\mathbf{j}$ and $\mathbf{E}$ parallel and in the y direction. Then v_{e_y} can be found from the linearized electron-momentum equation with $\mathbf{B} = 0$ as

$$n_e m_e \frac{\partial v_{e_y}}{\partial t} = -n_e e E_y - \frac{n_e m_e v_{e_y}}{\tau} \tag{7.90}$$

where the electron pressure gradient $\partial p_e/\partial y$ has been set equal to zero. This can be seen from the electron equation similar to Eq. (7.71). Thus,

$$\frac{\partial p_e}{\partial t} + \bar{p}_e \frac{\mathfrak{N} + 2}{\mathfrak{N}} \nabla \cdot \mathbf{v}_e = 0 \tag{7.91}$$

and since $\nabla \cdot \mathbf{v}_e = 0$, p_e must be constant.

Next, assume that v_{e_y} and E_y are of the form $e^{i(\omega t - \kappa x)}$. Then Eqs. (7.89) and (7.90) become

$$\left(-\kappa^2 + \frac{\omega^2}{c_0{}^2}\right) E + i(\mu_0 n_e e \omega V) = 0 \tag{7.92}$$

$$\frac{e}{m_e} E + (\nu + i\omega) V = 0 \tag{7.93}$$

where $c_0 = (\mu_0 K_0)^{-\frac{1}{2}}$ is the speed of light in vacuum. Combination of these two then results in the dispersion relation,

$$-\kappa^2 + \frac{\omega^2}{c_0{}^2} - \frac{\mu_0 n_e e^2}{m_e} \frac{i\omega}{\nu + i\omega} = 0$$

or

$$-c_0{}^2\kappa^2 + \omega^2 - \frac{\omega_p{}^2}{\nu + i\omega} i\omega = 0 \tag{7.94}$$

which can be rewritten as

$$c_0\kappa = \omega \left[\left(1 - \frac{\omega_p{}^2}{\omega^2 + \nu^2}\right) - i\left(\frac{\omega_p{}^2}{\omega^2 + \nu^2} \cdot \frac{\nu}{\omega}\right)\right]^{\frac{1}{2}} \tag{7.95}$$

Since our interest in the present section is in nearly collision-free waves, $\nu \approx 0$ and Eq. (7.95) can be rewritten as follows:

$$c_0\kappa \cong \omega \left[\left(1 - \frac{\omega_p{}^2}{\omega^2 + \nu^2}\right)^{\frac{1}{2}} - \frac{i}{2} \frac{\dfrac{\omega_p{}^2}{\omega^2 + \nu^2} \cdot \dfrac{\nu}{\omega}}{\left(1 - \dfrac{\omega_p{}^2}{\omega^2 + \nu^2}\right)^{\frac{1}{2}}}\right] \tag{7.96}$$

Now, when $\omega^2 + \nu^2 > \omega_p{}^2$, the damping arises from the last term, so that we can write

$$E_y = E e^{-\{[\omega_p{}^2/(\omega^2+\nu^2)]\cdot\nu/2c_0\}/[1-\omega_p{}^2/(\omega^2+\nu^2)]^{\frac{1}{2}} x} e^{i[\omega t - \Re(\kappa) x]} \tag{7.97}$$

The e-folding length for damping is then simply

$$x_e = \frac{2c_0}{\nu} \frac{\omega^2 + \nu^2}{\omega_p{}^2} \left(1 - \frac{\omega_p{}^2}{\omega^2 + \nu^2}\right)^{\frac{1}{2}} \tag{7.98}$$

From Eq. (7.96) we can deduce that κ is real if $\nu = 0$ and $\omega > \omega_p$. In this case no damping can occur. From Eq. (7.98), however, we see that the inclusion of a small but finite ν does cause damping when $\omega > \omega_p$. This is then essentially the e-folding length due to collisions alone.

If, on the other hand, for $\omega^2 + \nu^2 < \omega_p{}^2$, then x_e found in the same way is

$$x_e = \frac{c_0}{\omega \left(\dfrac{\omega_p{}^2}{\omega^2 + \nu^2} - 1\right)^{\frac{1}{2}}} \tag{7.99}$$

In this case, when $\nu = 0$, the wave is damped, and as ν increases, so does x_e. The e-folding length is a very short distance. Finally, neglecting collisions, the phase velocity for transverse electromagnetic waves from Eq. (7.95) is found to be

$$V_p = \frac{c_0}{(1 - \omega_p{}^2/\omega^2)^{\frac{1}{2}}} \tag{7.100}$$

Clearly, since $\omega > \omega_p$, the phase velocity is greater than the speed of light. It is largest when $\omega \sim \omega_p$ and approaches c_0 when $\omega \rightarrow \infty$. At first glance this result would seem to contradict the theory of relativity, which requires that no signal can propagate faster than the speed of light. That there is no contradiction can be seen if one realizes that the phase velocity of an unterminated wave bears no relation to the velocity with which a disturbance will propagate. For a more extensive discussion of these questions the reader is referred to the book by Brillouin.[4]

7.5.2 Extraordinary Waves. If, in the preceding problem, a magnetic field were applied, the wave would no longer be transverse, in general. For the special case of a magnetic field applied in the direction of wave propagation, however, the transverse nature may be preserved. This situation exists since a transverse current will only cause another transverse current, owing to interaction with the magnetic field. With $\mathbf{j}$ remaining parallel to the wavefront, the excess charge is still zero.

As will be shown in this section, the applied magnetic field will cause the original plane-polarized electromagnetic wave to be split into two circularly polarized waves, one of which propagates through a plasma, even though the frequency may be less than the plasma frequency (extraordinary wave). As before, we will linearize the equations and can neglect the part of the magnetic field associated with the electromagnetic wave.

(*a*) *Collision-free Waves.* To simplify the equations, let us consider the electron collision frequency to be zero; we will modify this later. The electric field equation (7.88) becomes

$$-\mathbf{j}\,\frac{\partial^2 E_y}{\partial x^2} - \mathbf{k}\,\frac{\partial^2 E_z}{\partial x^2} = -\frac{1}{c_0{}^2}\frac{\partial^2}{\partial t^2}\,(\mathbf{j}E_y + \mathbf{k}E_z) + \mu_0 e n_e \frac{\partial}{\partial t}\,(\mathbf{j}v_{e_y} + \mathbf{k}v_{e_z}) \tag{7.101}$$

and the linearized equation of motion for electrons becomes

$$\frac{\partial \mathbf{v}_e}{\partial t} = -\frac{e}{m_e}\,(\mathbf{E} + \mathbf{v}_e \times \mathbf{B}) \tag{7.102}$$

In component form, Eqs. (7.101) and (7.102) become

$$\begin{aligned}
\frac{\partial^2 E_y}{\partial x^2} - \frac{1}{c_0{}^2}\frac{\partial^2 E_y}{\partial t^2} + \mu_0 e n_e \frac{\partial v_{e_y}}{\partial t} &= 0 \\
\frac{\partial^2 E_z}{\partial x^2} - \frac{1}{c_0{}^2}\frac{\partial^2 E_z}{\partial t^2} + \mu_0 e n_e \frac{\partial v_{e_z}}{\partial t} &= 0 \\
\frac{\partial v_{e_y}}{\partial t} + \frac{e}{m_e} E_y + \frac{e}{m_e} B_x v_{e_z} &= 0 \\
\frac{\partial v_{e_z}}{\partial t} + \frac{e}{m_e} E_z - \frac{e}{m_e} B_x v_{e_y} &= 0
\end{aligned} \tag{7.103}$$

The characteristic equations are obtained by allowing all quantities to vary like exp $i(\omega t + \kappa x)$, which yields

$$\begin{aligned}
\left(\kappa^2 - \frac{\omega^2}{c_0{}^2}\right) E_y - i\omega\mu_0 e n_e v_{e_y} &= 0 \\
\left(\kappa^2 - \frac{\omega^2}{c_0{}^2}\right) E_z - i\omega\mu_0 e n_e v_{e_z} &= 0 \\
i\omega v_{e_y} + \frac{e}{m_e} E_y + \omega_e v_{e_z} &= 0 \\
i\omega v_{e_z} + \frac{e}{m_e} E_z - \omega_e v_{e_y} &= 0
\end{aligned} \tag{7.104}$$

Next, let $E_i/\mu_0 n_e e = \mathcal{E}_i$, so that $(e/m_e)E_i = (\omega_p{}^2/c_0{}^2)\mathcal{E}_i$. Then in order for there to be a nontrivial solution for $\mathcal{E}_i$ and v_{e_i}, the determinant of the coefficients in Eqs. (7.104) must be zero. Thus,

$$\begin{array}{cccc} \mathcal{E}_y & \mathcal{E}_z & v_{e_y} & v_{e_z} \end{array}$$
$$\begin{vmatrix}
\kappa^2 - \dfrac{\omega^2}{c_0{}^2} & 0 & -i\omega & 0 \\
0 & \kappa^2 - \dfrac{\omega^2}{c_0{}^2} & 0 & -i\omega \\
\dfrac{\omega_p{}^2}{c_0{}^2} & 0 & i\omega & \omega_e \\
0 & \dfrac{\omega_p{}^2}{c_0{}^2} & -\omega_e & i\omega
\end{vmatrix} = 0 \tag{7.105}$$

Expanding this leads to the relation

$$\left(\kappa^2 - \frac{\omega^2}{c_0{}^2}\right)\left[-\omega^2\left(\kappa^2 - \frac{\omega^2}{c_0{}^2}\right) + \omega_e{}^2\left(\kappa^2 - \frac{\omega^2}{c_0{}^2}\right) - \frac{\omega^2\omega_p{}^2}{c_0{}^2}\right] + \frac{\omega_p{}^2}{c_0{}^2}\left[-\frac{\omega^2\omega_p{}^2}{c_0{}^2} - \omega^2\left(\kappa^2 - \frac{\omega^2}{c_0{}^2}\right)\right] = 0$$

which can be rearranged as follows:

$$\left(\kappa^2 - \frac{\omega^2}{c_0{}^2}\right)^2 - \frac{2\omega^2\omega_p{}^2}{c_0{}^2(\omega_e{}^2 - \omega^2)}\left(\kappa^2 - \frac{\omega^2}{c_0{}^2}\right) - \frac{\omega_p{}^4\omega^2}{c_0{}^4(\omega_e{}^2 - \omega^2)} = 0 \tag{7.106}$$

The solution of Eq. (7.106) is

$$\kappa^2 - \frac{\omega^2}{c_0^2} = \frac{2\omega^2\omega_p^2}{2c_0^2(\omega_e^2 - \omega^2)} \pm \frac{1}{2}\sqrt{\frac{4\omega^4\omega_p^4}{c_0^4(\omega_e^2 - \omega^2)^2} + \frac{4\omega_p^4\omega^2(\omega_e^2 - \omega^2)}{c_0^4(\omega_e^2 - \omega^2)^2}}$$

$$= \frac{\omega^2\omega_p^2}{c_0^2(\omega_e^2 - \omega^2)} \pm \frac{\omega_e\omega\omega_p^2}{c_0^2(\omega_e^2 - \omega^2)}$$

$$= -\frac{\omega_p^2\omega(\omega \pm \omega_e)}{c_0^2(-\omega_e + \omega)(\omega_e + \omega)}$$

or

$$\kappa^2 = \frac{\omega^2}{c_0^2} - \frac{\omega_p^2\omega}{c_0^2(\omega \mp \omega_e)} = \frac{\omega^2}{c_0^2}\left[1 - \frac{\omega_p^2}{\omega^2(1 \mp \omega_e/\omega)}\right] \tag{7.107}$$

If the magnetic field B, and hence ω_e, goes to zero, we obtain the previous results, where the critical frequency for propagation ω_{cr} is ω_p. With the magnetic field finite, the critical frequency is given by

$$\omega^2\left(1 \mp \frac{\omega_e}{\omega}\right) = \omega_p^2$$

The phase velocity is then calculated as ω/κ.

$$\left(\frac{V_p}{c_0}\right)^2 = \left[1 - \frac{\omega_p^2}{\omega^2(1 \mp \omega_e/\omega)}\right]^{-1} \tag{7.108}$$

where $(-)$ corresponds to the extraordinary wave and $(+)$ to the ordinary one. The $\mp$ sign also means that the wave is resolved into two circularly polarized waves, each with a different cutoff frequency. The polarization can be shown from Eqs. (7.104). Replace E_z from the second in the fourth equation.

$$i\omega v_{e_z}\left(1 + \frac{\omega_p^2}{c_0^2}\frac{1}{\kappa^2 - \omega^2/c^2}\right) = \omega_e v_{e_y}$$

If, then, $\kappa^2 - \omega^2/c_0^2$ found in Eq. (7.107) is substituted in this, the result is

$$v_{e_y} = \mp i v_{e_z} \tag{7.109}$$

Also, from the first two of Eqs. (7.104), we have

$$\frac{\mathcal{E}_y}{\mathcal{E}_z} = \frac{v_{e_y}}{v_{e_z}}$$

so that

$$\mathcal{E}_y = \mp i\mathcal{E}_z \tag{7.110}$$

and it should be noted that the minus sign in Eq. (7.110) corresponds to the minus sign in Eq. (7.108).

The result of Eq. (7.110) shows that the wave is circularly polarized, the minus sign corresponding to E_y lagging E_z by 90° (the extraordinary

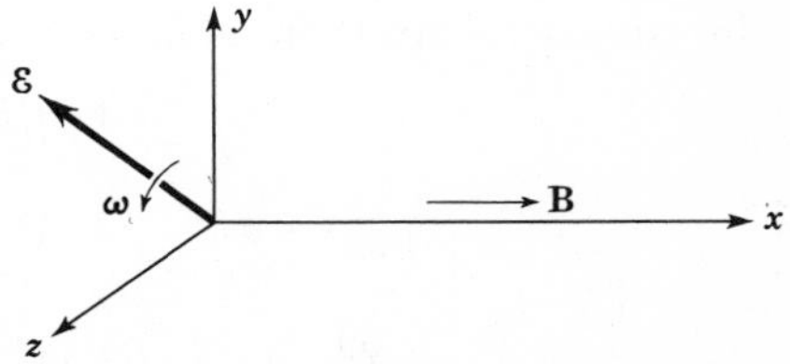

FIGURE 7.6 Polarized $\mathcal{E}$ field when $\mathcal{E}_y$ lags $\mathcal{E}_z$ by 90°.

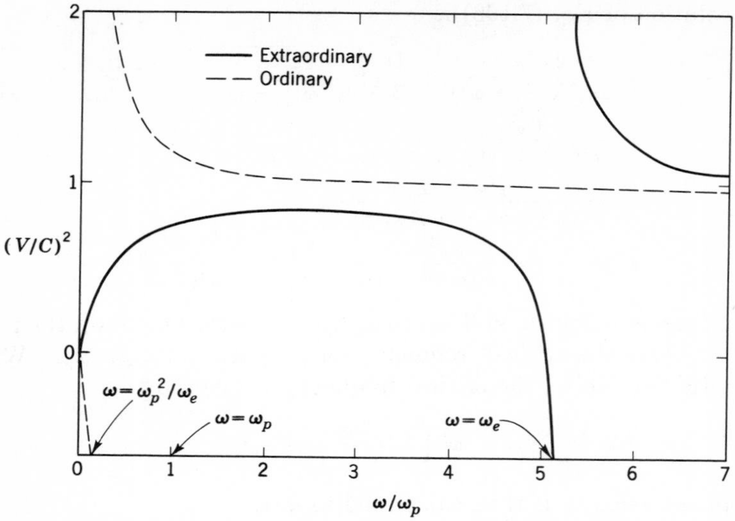

FIGURE 7.7 Phase velocity versus frequency showing anomalous behavior of extraordinary wave. (After L. Spitzer.)[5]

wave). This is shown in Fig. 7.6. However, this direction of rotation is exactly the direction of rotation of the electrons about the magnetic field. It can be anticipated then that for the wave corresponding to the minus sign, some unusual behavior will be found. That this is indeed so is shown in Fig. 7.7, where the phase velocity [Eq. (7.108)] is plotted versus wave frequency for $\omega_p/\omega_e = 0.2$.

In the electromagnetic wave, propagation below ω_p was not possible for $\nu \equiv 0$. In the present instance this conclusion must be modified. For the ordinary wave, propagation is now possible for frequencies somewhat less than the plasma frequency. However for the extraordinary wave, propagation for essentially any ω is seen to be possible. The singularity at $\omega = \omega_e$ corresponds to the resonance occurring when the wave rotates at the same angular speed and in the same direction as the electrons in the B field.

(*b*) *Damping via Collisions.* In most plasmas of interest, there will be sufficient electron collisions so that these should be taken into account. The equations are then as follows:

$$\begin{aligned}
\frac{\partial^2 E_y}{\partial x^2} - \frac{1}{c_0{}^2}\frac{\partial^2 E_y}{\partial t^2} + \mu_0 e n_e \frac{\partial v_{e_y}}{\partial t} &= 0 \\
\frac{\partial^2 E_z}{\partial x^2} - \frac{1}{c_0{}^2}\frac{\partial^2 E_z}{\partial t^2} + \mu_0 e n_e \frac{\partial v_{e_z}}{\partial t} &= 0 \\
\frac{\partial v_{e_y}}{\partial t} + \frac{e}{m_e}E_y + \frac{e}{m_e}B_x v_{e_z} + \nu_e v_{e_y} &= 0 \\
\frac{\partial v_{e_z}}{\partial t} + \frac{e}{m_e}E_z - \frac{e}{m_e}B_x v_{e_y} + \nu_e v_{e_z} &= 0
\end{aligned} \tag{7.111}$$

where ν is the electron collision frequency. The determinant then becomes

$$\begin{vmatrix} \kappa^2 - \dfrac{\omega^2}{c_0^2} & 0 & -i\omega & 0 \\ 0 & \kappa^2 - \dfrac{\omega^2}{c_0^2} & 0 & -i\omega \\ \dfrac{\omega_p^2}{c_0^2} & 0 & i\omega + \nu_e & \omega_e \\ 0 & \dfrac{\omega_p^2}{c_0^2} & -\omega_e & i\omega + \nu_e \end{vmatrix} = 0 \tag{7.112}$$

The solution of Eq. (7.112) is

$$\kappa^2 = \frac{\omega^2}{c_0^2} - \frac{\omega_p^2}{c_0^2}\,\frac{1}{1 \mp \omega_e/\omega - i\nu_e/\omega} \tag{7.113}$$

so it is seen that the effect of collisions is to modify the effective cyclotron frequency by $\pm i\nu_e$. Equation (7.113) can be rationalized as follows:

$$\kappa^2 = \frac{\omega^2}{c_0^2}\left[1 - \frac{\omega_p^2}{\omega^2}\,\frac{1 \mp \omega_e/\omega + i\nu_e/\omega}{(1 \mp \omega_e/\omega)^2 + \nu_e^2/\omega^2}\right] \tag{7.114}$$

We are interested in the effect of the collisions on the attenuation of waves; thus we can examine the imaginary part of κ when ν_e/ω is small. For this case the first term of the expansion of Eq. (7.114) leads to

$$\mathcal{I}(\kappa) \cong -\frac{\omega_p^2\nu_e}{2c_0\omega^2}\left[\left(1 \mp \frac{\omega_e}{\omega}\right)^2 + \frac{\nu_e^2}{\omega^2}\right]^{-1}\left[1 - \frac{\omega_p^2}{\omega^2}\,\frac{1 \mp \omega_e/\omega}{(1 \mp \omega_e/\omega)^2 + \nu_e^2/\omega^2}\right]^{-\frac{1}{2}}$$

or more simply

$$\mathcal{I}(\kappa) \cong -\frac{\omega_p^2\nu_e}{2c_0\omega^2}\left(1 \mp \frac{\omega_e}{\omega}\right)^{-2}\left(1 - \frac{\omega_p^2}{\omega^2}\,\frac{1}{1 \mp \omega_e/\omega}\right)^{-\frac{1}{2}} \tag{7.115}$$

If the problem of interest is propagation through a plasma, it is then obvious that $\mathcal{I}(\kappa)$ should be as small as possible. In order to see the dependence of $\mathcal{I}(\kappa)$ on ω, curves have been plotted in Fig. 7.8 for the ordinary and extraordinary waves for the same conditions as Fig. 7.7; that is, $\omega_p/\omega_e = 0.2$. It is interesting to see that the extraordinary wave is relatively little damped by collisions when $\omega < \omega_p$. When $\omega/\omega_p > 2$ to 3, however, such waves will be strongly damped. The ordinary wave, on the other hand, is little damped for any $\omega/\omega_p > 0.3$. The cross-hatched regions define values of ω/ω_p for which $\mathcal{I}(\kappa)$ becomes imaginary. In these regions the damping expressions must be calculated from the real part of Eq. (7.114). Also, at the points $\omega \cong \omega_e$ and $\omega = 5\omega_p$ the damping becomes infinite.

7.5.3 Hybrid Waves. In the preceding sections, orientations of the magnetic field other than along the direction of wave propagation,

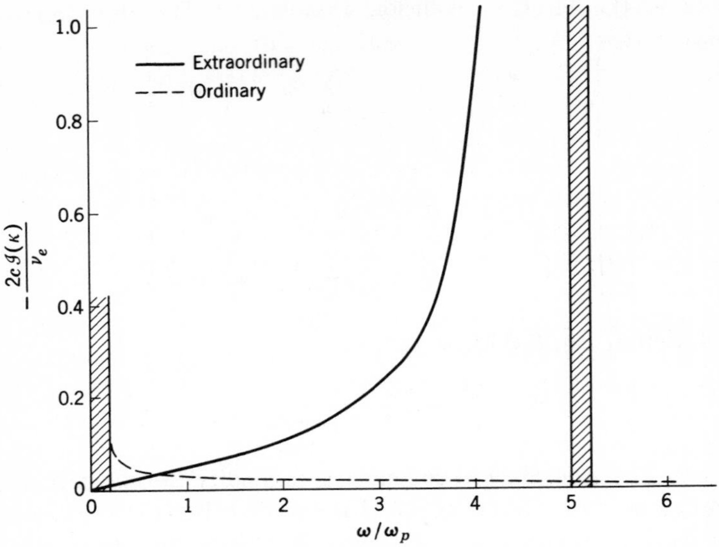

FIGURE 7.8 Collisional damping of ordinary and extraordinary transverse waves where $\omega_p = 0.2\omega_e$.

as well as ion motion, have been neglected. When these are included, the problem becomes very complex. In particular, the waves will in general exhibit characteristics of both the longitudinal (electrostatic) and electromagnetic oscillations.

For a cold-cold uniform plasma, the general behavior of waves propagating in the presence of a magnetic field is discussed in the monograph by Stix.[6] Aside from this multitude of complicated wave motions, one can proceed further in a simple fashion for very low frequency waves. In this case, provided $\omega < \omega_I$, excess charge can be neglected, regardless of the applied magnetic field orientation, and an approach using the macroscopic equations is feasible. Such a procedure is followed in Chap. 9, where the Alfvén wave is discussed in some detail. It is interesting to note the simplifications possible in the study of a very complex problem when a macroscopic one-fluid formulation of the governing equations is feasible.

7.6 DAMPING IN COLLISION–FREE PLASMAS

So far in our discussions of wave propagation in plasmas, the only damping mechanism considered has been due to collisions between particles. Another damping mechanism which has been neglected can occur even in a collision-free plasma. It is often referred to as *Landau* damping, after its discoverer.

This phenomenon is generally associated with the fact that some particles, because of their thermal velocity, can be approximately in phase with a wave. Then, since the plasma is collisionless, a particle can remain at a given speed for long periods of time, except for "smooth" changes due to the electric field of the wave. This allows some particles to ride the crests and troughs of the waves for long periods of time. Under these conditions, one should expect the distribution function to change, because some particles can absorb energy from the wave even in the absence of collision. In fact, the presence of collisions will generally prevent these changes in the distribution function.

The simplest problem that can be considered is longitudinal plasma oscillations of electrons and ions, which has previously been discussed in Sec. 7.4. In that section no damping of the wave occurred when collisions were neglected. Here, we will show that collisionless damping or amplification can exist, if the electrons have streaming motion with respect to the ions.† This result leads directly to Landau damping. Finally, collisionless ion cyclotron resonance in which the streaming motion of the ions leads to broadening of the response spectrum is considered.

7.6.1 Two-stream Instability. For the present let us consider the cold-cold approximation, but allow the electrons to be streaming in collision-free motion. In order to simplify the discussion, only motion in the x direction will be considered. First of all we have the one-dimensional momentum equation for a cold electron gas,

$$\frac{\partial v_{e_x}}{\partial t} + v_{e_x}\frac{\partial v_{e_x}}{\partial x} = -\frac{eE_x(x,t)}{m_e} \tag{7.116}$$

where the electron pressure gradient is assumed to be zero since we are postulating a cold electron gas. Next it is assumed that the electrons have a small propagating perturbation v'_{e_x} about a mean velocity U_e,

$$v_{e_x}(x,t) = U_e + v'_{e_x} = U_e + V'_{e_x}e^{i(\omega t-\kappa x)} \tag{7.117}$$

where ω is the circular frequency and κ is the wave number. Also, assume that the electric field is small. Substitution of (7.117) into (7.116) yields the following first-order equation for the electron perturbation velocity,

$$V'_{e_x} = \frac{-eE_x/m_e}{i(\omega - U_e\kappa)} \tag{7.118}$$

† Accordingly, the previous results, the conclusions of Sec. 7.4, are valid only if it is assumed that each electron is fixed in space, so that even if it has nonzero temperature, it must oscillate randomly about some null position. This is not a correct model of a plasma in which electrons move freely.

and a similar equation for the ions,

$$V'_{I_x} = \frac{eE_x/m_I}{i(\omega - U_I\kappa)} \tag{7.119}$$

where U_I is the mean ion velocity. In (7.119) it is also assumed that the ions are singly ionized.

Next, consider the continuity equation for electrons,

$$\frac{\partial n_e}{\partial t} + \frac{\partial}{\partial x}(n_e v_e) = 0 \tag{7.120}$$

and assume $n_e = \bar{n}_e + n'_e = \bar{n}_e + N'_e \exp i(\omega t - \kappa x)$ and $n_I = \bar{n}_I + n'_I = \bar{n}_I + N'_I \exp i(\omega t - \kappa x)$. Then the first-order equation for N'_e becomes

$$N'_e = \frac{\kappa \bar{n}_e V'_{ex}}{\omega - \kappa U_e} \tag{7.121}$$

Substitution of Eq. (7.118) into Eq. (7.121) yields

$$N'_e = \frac{-\kappa \bar{n}_e e E_x/m_e}{i(\omega - \kappa U_e)^2} \tag{7.122}$$

and a similar equation for ions,

$$N'_i = \frac{\kappa \bar{n}_I e E_x/m_I}{i(\omega - \kappa U_I)^2} \tag{7.123}$$

Substitution of these last two relations with $\bar{n}_e = \bar{n}_I$ into Poisson's equation, in which the electric field is also assumed to be propagating as $\exp i(\omega t - \kappa x)$, yields

$$1 = \frac{e^2 \bar{n}_e}{K_0}\left[\frac{1}{m_I(\omega - \kappa U_I)^2} + \frac{1}{m_e(\omega - \kappa U_e)^2}\right] \tag{7.124}$$

which may be rewritten in terms of the electron plasma oscillation frequency $\omega_{p_e}^2 = \bar{n}_e e^2/m_e K_0$ as follows:

$$\frac{1}{\omega_{p_e}^2} = \frac{m_e/m_I}{(\omega - \kappa U_I)^2} + \frac{1}{(\omega - \kappa U_e)^2} \tag{7.125}$$

One root of Eq. (7.125) corresponds to the electron oscillation in the limit $m_e/m_I \to 0$,

$$\omega = \pm\omega_{p_e} + \kappa U_e \tag{7.126}$$

where the term κU_e corresponds to the Doppler shift of the frequency due to the mass motion of the electrons. The other root corresponds to $\omega \approx \kappa U_I$. If $U_I \ll U_e$, corresponding to an electron beam in a stationary ion gas, then $\omega \ll \kappa U_e$ in the last term of Eq. (7.125), and ω may be neglected in that term. The dispersion relation may then be written as

$$(\omega - \kappa U_I)^2 = \frac{m_e/m_I}{1/\omega_{pe}^2 - 1/\kappa^2 U_e^2} \tag{7.127}$$

Now, as long as $\kappa^2 U_e^2 > \omega_{pe}^2$, ω is real and the wave is undamped. But when $\kappa^2 U_e^2 < \omega_p^2$, the right side of Eq. (7.127) is negative and ω is comples,

$$\omega = \kappa U_I \pm i \left(\frac{m_e/m_I}{1/\kappa^2 U_e^2 - 1/\omega_{pe}^2} \right)^{\frac{1}{2}} \tag{7.128}$$

which indicates that oscillations of one stream are amplified while those of the other are damped. This phenomenon is known as the *two-stream instability*. Next, consider two electron streams in a background of very heavy immobile ions. Then Eq. (7.125) becomes

$$\frac{1}{\omega_{pe}^2} = \frac{n_1/\bar{n}_e}{(\omega - \kappa U_1)^2} + \frac{n_2/\bar{n}_e}{(\omega - \kappa U_2)^2} \tag{7.129}$$

where n_1, n_2, and U_1, U_2 are the number density and velocity of the two electron streams, respectively. This can be extended to a large number N of electron beams passing through a neutralizing background of ions, as follows:

$$\frac{1}{\omega_{pe}^2} = \sum_{i=1}^{N} \frac{n_i/n_0}{(\omega - \kappa U_i)^2} \tag{7.130}$$

If $N \to \infty$, this relation can be replaced by an integral. To do this, consider a plasma with a random distribution of particle velocities described by a distribution function f_0. As usual, f_0 is defined as the number density of particles whose velocities lie within the range of $dc_x\, dc_y\, dc_z$. If we identify U_i with c_x, we can then write

$$n_i(c_x) = \int_{c_y=-\infty}^{+\infty} \int_{c_z=-\infty}^{+\infty} (f_0\, dc_x)\, dc_y\, dc_z \tag{7.131}$$

where n_i now is the number density of electrons traveling at velocity c_x.

Employing this concept, Eq. (7.130) can be rewritten as

$$\frac{1}{\omega_{pe}^2} = \frac{1}{\bar{n}_e} \iiint_{-\infty}^{\infty} \frac{f_0\, dc_x\, dc_y\, dc_z}{(\omega - \kappa c_x)^2} \tag{7.132}$$

Integration by parts with respect to c_x yields

$$\frac{1}{\omega_{pe}^2} = -\frac{1}{\kappa \bar{n}_e} \iiint_{-\infty}^{\infty} \frac{(\partial f_0/\partial c_x)\, d\mathbf{c}}{\omega - \kappa c_x} \tag{7.133}$$

As in the case of the two-stream instability, amplification or damping of infinitesimal disturbances can occur. In order to determine which occurs, the integral in Eq. (7.133) must be evaluated, and account taken of its singular nature. This is done in the next section after Eq. (7.133) is derived from the Boltzmann equation, including collisions.

7.6.2 Landau Damping. In the preceding section, it was shown that two moving streams of charged particles that do not collide with each other, nonetheless, may interact with each other via the electric field, and damping or amplification of a plasma oscillation may occur. This was then extended to a *longitudinal oscillation*† in an electron gas, where the ions form a motionless background. We must next determine whether the oscillation damps or amplifies. We could start with Eq. (7.133) of the previous section, but it is desirable to include collisions with the ions, since in this case only damping can occur. Thus, we will first rederive this relation to include collisions, but will use the alternate derivation, starting from the Boltzmann equation for electrons with $\mathbf{E} = \mathbf{i}E_x(x,t)$,

$$\frac{\partial f_e}{\partial t} + c_x \frac{\partial f_e}{\partial x} - \frac{eE_x}{m_e} \frac{\partial f_e}{\partial c_x} = \left(\frac{\partial f_e}{\partial t}\right)_c \tag{7.134}$$

where the plasma has zero variation in the y and z directions. The collision term $(\partial f_e/\partial t)_c$ will be retained for the present.

The method of solving Eq. (7.134) is identical to those used previously. Let f_e be perturbed slightly about a maxwellian distribution as follows:

$$f_e = f_0 + f_1 \qquad f_1 \ll f_0 \tag{7.135}$$

and also consider eE_x/m_e to be small. Now, it is desirable to simplify the expression for the collision integral $(\partial f_e/\partial t)_c$ by means of a relaxation model:[7]

$$\left(\frac{\partial f_e}{\partial t}\right)_c = -\frac{f_e - f_0}{\tau} \tag{7.136}$$

The implication is that the distribution function relaxes to the maxwellian f_0 in an e-folding time τ, which is called the *relaxation time*, and which may be a function of c_e. Obviously τ corresponds to a collision time, given by the usual expression,

$$\tau = \frac{1}{\langle c_e \rangle \sum_s n_s Q_{e_s}(c_e)}$$

† The restriction to longitudinal oscillation is not essential, as similar arguments should be valid for the transverse oscillation. Landau damping for the latter oscillation has not as yet been calculated.

Substitution of Eqs. (7.135), (7.136) into Eq. (7.134) and equating terms of the same order yield the following zero-order equation,

$$\frac{\partial f_0}{\partial t} + c_x \frac{\partial f_0}{\partial x} = 0$$

which is obviously satisfied by $f_0(\mathbf{x},\mathbf{c}_e,t) = f_0(\mathbf{c}_e)$. The first-order equation is

$$\frac{\partial f_1}{\partial t} + c_x \frac{\partial f_1}{\partial x} - \frac{eE_x}{m_e}\frac{\partial f_0}{\partial c_x} = -\frac{f_1}{\tau}$$

or

$$\frac{\partial f_1}{\partial t} + \frac{f_1}{\tau} + c_x \frac{\partial f_1}{\partial x} = \frac{eE_x}{m_e}\frac{\partial f_0}{\partial c_x} \tag{7.137}$$

In the absence of spatial variations and electric fields, the solution to this is $f_1(t) = f_1(0)e^{-t/\tau}$, so that the relaxation time is indeed τ.

Next we consider the electric field to be propagating as follows:

$$E_x = E_1 \exp i(\omega t - \kappa x) \tag{7.138}$$

and it is therefore natural to let f_1 vary in the same way:

$$f_1(c_e,x,t) = f_1(c_e) \exp i(\omega t - \kappa x) \tag{7.139}$$

Substitution of Eq. (7.137) into Eqs. (7.138) and (7.139) yields

$$f_1 = \frac{eE_1}{im_e}\frac{\partial f_0/\partial c_x}{\omega - i\nu - \kappa c_x} \tag{7.140}$$

where $\nu = \tau^{-1}$. From Eq. (7.135) the number density of electrons may be calculated:

$$n_e = \frac{eE_1}{im_e}\iiint_{-\infty}^{\infty} \frac{(\partial f_0/\partial c_x)\, d\mathbf{c}_e}{\omega - i\nu - \kappa c_x} + \iiint_{-\infty}^{\infty} f_0\, d\mathbf{c}_e$$

or

$$n_e - \bar{n}_e = \frac{eE_1}{im_e}\iiint_{-\infty}^{\infty} \frac{(\partial f_0/\partial c_x)\, d\mathbf{c}_e}{\omega - i\nu - \kappa c_x} \tag{7.141}$$

since $\bar{n}_e = \iiint_{-\infty}^{\infty} f_0\, d\mathbf{c}_e$. Next, consider Poisson's equation,

$$\nabla \cdot \mathbf{E} = e(n_I - n_e)/K_0$$

As before, we consider the ions to be heavy, so that their number density remains constant and equal to $\bar{n}_e$, the average electron density (singly ionized gas). Then Poisson's equation becomes, with the use of Eq. (7.141),

$$\frac{i\kappa E_1 K_0}{e} = \frac{eE_1}{im_e}\iiint_{-\infty}^{\infty} \frac{(\partial f_0/\partial c_x)\, d\mathbf{c}_e}{\omega - i\nu - \kappa c_x}$$

$$1 = -\frac{\omega_{pe}^2}{\kappa \bar{n}_e}\iiint_{-\infty}^{\infty} \frac{(\partial f_0/\partial c_x)\, d\mathbf{c}_e}{\omega - i\nu - \kappa c_x} \tag{7.142}$$

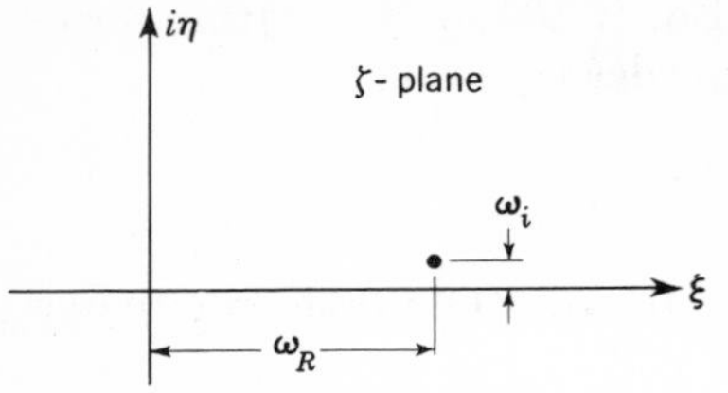

FIGURE 7.9 ζ Plane for complex integration.

where ω_{p_e} is the previously defined electron oscillation frequency $(e^2\bar{n}_e/K_0 m_e)^{\frac{1}{2}}$. This relation is the same as Eq. (7.133) of the previous section, but with the addition of a collision frequency. It is next necessary to evaluate the integral in Eq. (7.142). Since we are considering a longitudinal plasma oscillation, which we may recall was a standing wave in the absence of collisions, let us consider κ real and ω complex. The procedure, then, will be to choose a value of κ and solve for ω. Taking f_0 to be the maxwellian distribution,

$$f_0 = \bar{n}_e \left(\frac{m_e}{2\pi kT}\right)^{\frac{3}{2}} e^{-(m_e/2kT)(c_x^2 + c_y^2 + c_z^2)}$$

we can integrate Eq. (7.142) over c_y and c_z to get

$$1 = \frac{\omega_{p_e}^2}{(2\pi)^{\frac{1}{2}}\kappa^2 a^2} \int_{-\infty}^{\infty} \frac{\xi e^{-\xi^2/2}\, d\xi}{[(\omega - i\nu)/\kappa a] - \xi} \tag{7.143}$$

where $a = \sqrt{kT/m_e}$ and $\xi = c_x/a$. Now the integral in this relation will have a real and imaginary part because of the complex constant in its denominator. As a result, the most convenient procedure for evaluating it is by integration in the complex plane. The location of the singularity is shown in Fig. 7.9, where it has been assumed that $\nu = 0$. In the present analysis, attention will be restricted to the case wherein $\omega_i \cong 0$, so that the singularity essentially lies on the real axis. Then, since we cannot integrate through the singularity, we must indent the contour to pass over it. The total integral is then

$$\int_{-\infty}^{\infty} \frac{\xi e^{-\xi^2/2}\, d\xi}{(\omega_R/\kappa a) - \xi} = \lim_{\rho \to 0} \left(\int_{-\infty}^{\omega_R - \rho} \frac{\xi e^{-\xi^2/2}\, d\xi}{(\omega_R/\kappa a) - \xi} + \int_{C_\rho} \frac{\zeta e^{-\zeta^2/2}\, d\zeta}{(\omega_R/\kappa a) - \zeta} + \int_{\omega_R + \rho}^{+\infty} \frac{\xi e^{-\xi^2/2}\, d\xi}{(\omega_R/\kappa a) - \xi} \right) \tag{7.144}$$

where the path of integration is shown in Fig. 7.10.

Carrying out the limiting process shows that the total integral is given by

$$\int_{-\infty}^{\infty} \frac{\xi e^{-\xi^2/2}\, d\xi}{(\omega/\kappa a) - \xi} = P \int_{-\infty}^{\infty} \frac{\xi e^{-\xi^2/2}\, d\xi}{(\omega/\kappa a) - \xi} + i\pi \frac{\omega}{\kappa a} e^{-(\omega/\kappa a)^2/2} \tag{7.145}$$

where the first integral is the Cauchy principal value, and the second is the result of the pole. The first part can now be evaluated approximately

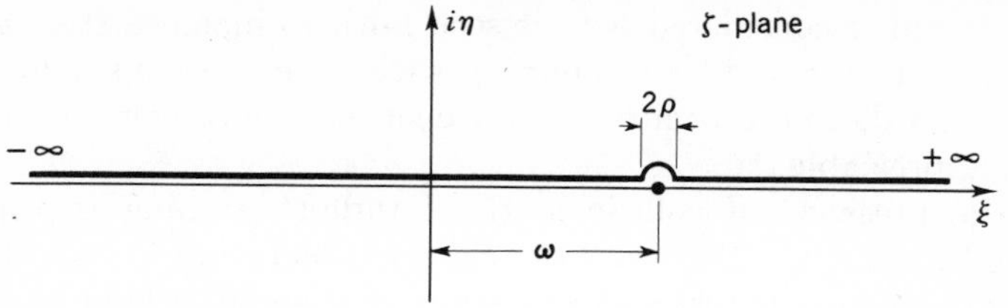

FIGURE 7.10 Path of integration in complex plane.

for κ very small. Thus,

$$\frac{\kappa a}{\omega}\int_{-\infty}^{\infty}\frac{\xi e^{-\xi^2/2}\,d\xi}{1-(\kappa a/\omega)\xi} = \frac{\kappa a}{\omega}\int_{-\infty}^{\infty}\xi e^{-\xi^2/2}\left[1+\frac{\kappa a\xi}{\omega}+\left(\frac{\kappa a\xi}{\omega}\right)^2 + \left(\frac{\kappa a\xi}{\omega}\right)^3+\cdots\right]d\xi \cong \left(\frac{\kappa a}{\omega}\right)^2\sqrt{2\pi}\left[1+3\left(\frac{\kappa a}{\omega}\right)^2\right] \quad (7.146)$$

where only the first two terms of the expansion have been retained. Substitution of this result into Eq. (7.145), and that into Eq. (7.146), yields

$$1 \cong \frac{\omega_{p_e}^2}{\omega^2}\left[1+3\left(\frac{\kappa a}{\omega}\right)^2 + i\sqrt{\frac{\pi}{2}}\left(\frac{\omega}{\kappa a}\right)^3 e^{-(\omega/\kappa a)^2/2}\right] \quad (7.147)$$

which is to be solved for ω. Obviously ω will be complex. However, we noted earlier that ω was assumed to have a very small imaginary part. It will be our task now to verify this assumption. When $\kappa \equiv 0$, then $\omega = \omega_{p_e}$ obviously. For $\kappa \ll \omega_{p_e}/a$, the expression in brackets in Eq. (7.147) will represent a small correction to ω_{p_e}; hence, we can set $\omega = \omega_{p_e}$ within the brackets as our first approximation. This gives

$$\omega^2 \cong \omega_{p_e}^2\left[1+3\left(\frac{\kappa a}{\omega_{p_e}}\right)^2 + i\sqrt{\frac{\pi}{2}}\left(\frac{\omega_{p_e}}{\kappa a}\right)^3 e^{-(\omega_{p_e}/\kappa a)^2/2}\right] \quad (7.148)$$

Finally, with κ small, the term within the brackets is 1 plus a small number. Its approximate square root is then simply

$$\omega \cong \omega_{p_e}\left[1+3\left(\frac{2\pi d}{\lambda}\right)^2 + i\sqrt{\frac{\pi}{8}}\left(\frac{\lambda}{2\pi d}\right)^3 e^{-(\lambda/d)^2/2}\right] \quad (7.149)$$

where we have defined $d = a/\omega_{p_e}$ as the Debye length, and $\lambda = 2\pi\kappa$ as the wavelength.

Using this result, it can be seen that now E_x is given by the following expression,

$$E_x \cong E_1 e^{i(\omega_R t - \kappa x)}[e^{(-\sqrt{\pi/8})(\lambda/2\pi d)^3 e^{-(\lambda/d)^2 t/2}}] \quad (7.150)$$

where $\omega_R \cong \omega_{p_e}[1 + 3(2\pi d/\lambda)^2]$. As can be seen, when the correction terms are omitted, we again have a wave which is undamped and which oscillates at the plasma frequency. The effect of the collisionless or

Landau damping considered here is seen both to increase the oscillation frequency and to introduce a damping with time. For very long wavelengths λ, no damping occurs. As λ decreases, however, the damping becomes appreciable.

In the presence of collisions, the Landau damping is apparently dominated by them. This may be seen by integrating Eq. (7.143) along the real axis when ν is real and κ is again very small. Then

$$1 = \frac{\omega_{p_e}^2}{\sqrt{2\pi}\,\kappa a}\frac{1}{\omega - i\nu}\int_{-\infty}^{\infty}\frac{\xi e^{-\xi^2/2}\,d\xi}{1 - \xi\kappa a(\omega - i\nu)^{-1}} \tag{7.151}$$

Expansion of the denominator and integration as before yields

$$1 \cong \frac{\omega_{p_e}^2}{(\omega - i\nu)^2}\left[1 + 3\left(\frac{\kappa a}{\omega - i\nu}\right)^2\right] \tag{7.152}$$

and, as before, only the first correction term in the expansion is retained. When $\kappa \equiv 0$, this shows that $\omega = i\nu \pm \omega_{p_e}$. Again, as a first approximation, we replace ω within the brackets by this expression and get

$$(\omega - i\nu)^2 \cong \omega_{p_e}^2\left[1 + 3\left(\frac{\kappa a}{\omega_{p_e}}\right)^2\right] \tag{7.153}$$

Finally, the square root in the brackets is approximated for κ small by expansion. Then

$$\omega \cong i\nu \pm \omega_{p_e}\left[1 + \frac{3}{2}\left(\frac{\kappa a}{\omega_{p_e}}\right)^2\right] \tag{7.154}$$

As before (Sec. 7.4.3), the damping is essentially due to collisions.

In summary, the Landau damping has been shown to be of little importance in collision-dominated plasmas, but essential in collision-free plasmas. For the latter case this damping mechanism can, in general, be neglected for long-wavelength disturbances. High-frequency waves with wavelengths as short as the Debye length can, however, be damped strongly by this means.

Also, it has been demonstrated that the inherent approximation in the earlier analysis, particles oscillating about fixed positions in space, automatically precludes any damping. That is, it is precisely the thermal motion of such collision-free plasmas that gives rise to the damping shown to exist here.

7.6.3 Ion Cyclotron Resonance and Damping. In this last section of the chapter the propagation of an extraordinary wave (Sec. 7.5.2) at frequencies on the order of the ion cyclotron resonance frequency will be discussed. In addition to the effects of collisions and finite temperature, the influence of the collision-free (Landau) damping will be included. To start the investigation, consider the Boltzmann equation for ions with the collision term replaced by a relaxation term:

$$\frac{\partial f}{\partial t} + \mathbf{c} \cdot \nabla f + \frac{eZ}{m_I} (\mathbf{E} + \mathbf{c} \times \mathbf{B}) \nabla_c f = \frac{f - f_0}{\tau} \tag{7.155}$$

In this problem spatial variations will be limited to the x axis, which will also be the direction of wave propagation and the applied magnetic field. The electric field vector will be perpendicular to x, and, as before, the magnetic field associated with the wave will be neglected. To solve Eq. (7.155) we proceed as in the previous section with $f = f_0 + f_1$ and $f_1 \ll f_0$. The first-order equation is then

$$\frac{\partial f_1}{\partial t} + \frac{f_1}{\tau} + (\mathbf{c} \cdot \nabla) f_1 + (\mathbf{c} \times \boldsymbol{\omega}_I) \cdot \nabla_c f_1 + \boldsymbol{\mathcal{E}} \cdot \nabla_c f_0 = 0 \tag{7.156}$$

where $\boldsymbol{\omega}_I = eZ\mathbf{B}/m_I$, and $\boldsymbol{\mathcal{E}} = eZ\mathbf{E}/m_I$. Next, assume the electric field to be plane-polarized with circular frequency ω and wave number κ.

$$\boldsymbol{\mathcal{E}} = \boldsymbol{\mathcal{E}}_1 e^{i(\omega t - \kappa x)} \tag{7.157}$$

As before, f_1 will be assumed to be of the same form,

$$f_1(\mathbf{c},x,t) = f_1(\mathbf{c}) e^{i(\omega t - \kappa x)} \tag{7.158}$$

so that $(\mathbf{c} \cdot \nabla) f_1 = -ic_x \kappa f_1$, and $\partial f_1/\partial t = i\omega f_1$. Then Eq. (7.156) becomes

$$[i\omega + \nu - ic_x\kappa + (\mathbf{c} \times \boldsymbol{\omega}_i) \cdot \nabla_c] f_1(\mathbf{c}) + \boldsymbol{\mathcal{E}}_1 \cdot \nabla_c f_0 = 0 \tag{7.159}$$

where we have set $\tau = \nu^{-1}$. Next, expand f_1 in the directions parallel and perpendicular to $\boldsymbol{\mathcal{E}}_1$ as in Chap. 5.

$$f_1(c) = \boldsymbol{\mathcal{E}}_1 \cdot \mathbf{c} h_1(c_x) + (\boldsymbol{\mathcal{E}}_1 \times \boldsymbol{\omega}_i) \cdot \mathbf{c} g_1(c_x) \tag{7.160}$$

Also, assuming f_0 to be maxwellian,

$$(\boldsymbol{\mathcal{E}}_1 \cdot \nabla_c) f_0 = -\frac{m_I}{kT} (\boldsymbol{\mathcal{E}}_1 \cdot \mathbf{c}) f_0 = -\left(\frac{\boldsymbol{\mathcal{E}}_1 \cdot \mathbf{c}}{a_I^2}\right) f_0 \tag{7.161}$$

where $a_I^2 = kT/m_I$. Now, substituting Eqs. (7.160) and (7.161) into Eq. (7.159), we obtain

$$\left[(i\omega + \nu - ic_x\kappa) h_1 + \omega_I^2 g_1 - \frac{f_0}{a_I^2}\right] (\mathbf{c} \cdot \boldsymbol{\mathcal{E}}_1) + [(i\omega + \nu - ic_x\kappa) g_1 + h_1] (\boldsymbol{\mathcal{E}}_1 \times \boldsymbol{\omega}_I) \cdot \mathbf{c} = 0$$

after some manipulation. Obviously, the quantities within brackets must be zero for this relation to be valid. Then we obtain two relations for g_1 and h_1.

$$[\nu + i(\omega - \kappa c_x)] h_1 + \omega_I^2 g_1 = \frac{f_0}{a_I^2} \tag{7.162}$$

$$[\nu + i(\omega - \kappa c_x)] g_1 - h_1 = 0 \tag{7.163}$$

Solving for g_1 and h_1, we obtain

$$g_1 = \frac{f_0/a_I^2}{[\nu + i(\omega - \kappa c_x)]^2 + \omega_I^2} \tag{7.164}$$

$$h_1 = \frac{(f_0/a_I^2)[\nu + i(\omega - \kappa c_x)]}{[\nu + i(\omega - \kappa c_x)]^2 + \omega_I^2} \tag{7.165}$$

Now the conduction current can be calculated as

$$\mathbf{j}_I = eZ \iiint_{-\infty}^{\infty} \mathbf{c} f \, d\mathbf{c} = eZ \iiint_{-\infty}^{\infty} \mathbf{c} f_1 \, d\mathbf{c} \tag{7.166}$$

since no current flows when the plasma is in equilibrium; that is, f_0 is symmetric. Using Eqs. (7.160), (7.164), and (7.165) in Eq. (7.166), we obtain the following expression for the current:

$$\mathbf{j}_I = \frac{eZ}{a_I^2} \iiint_{-\infty}^{\infty} \frac{\mathbf{c}(\boldsymbol{\mathcal{E}}_1 \cdot \mathbf{c})[\nu + i(\omega - \kappa c_x)] f_0}{[\nu + i(\omega - \kappa c_x)]^2 + \omega_I^2} \, d\mathbf{c} + \frac{eZ}{a_I^2} \iiint_{-\infty}^{\infty} \frac{\mathbf{c}[(\boldsymbol{\mathcal{E}} \times \boldsymbol{\omega}_I) \cdot \mathbf{c}] f_0}{[\nu + i(\omega - \kappa c_x)]^2 + \omega_I^2} \, d\mathbf{c} \tag{7.167}$$

The energy absorption is given by $\mathbf{j}_I \cdot \mathbf{E}$; thus we need only consider the current in the direction of $\mathbf{E}$. This is given by the first term. The second term represents a current perpendicular to both $\mathbf{E}$ and $\mathbf{B}$. The first term may be factored as follows:

$$(\mathbf{j}_I)_\parallel = \frac{eZ}{2a_I^2} \iiint_{-\infty}^{\infty} (\boldsymbol{\mathcal{E}}_1 \cdot \mathbf{c}) \mathbf{c} f_0 \left[\frac{1}{i(\omega - \omega_I - \kappa c_x) + \nu} + \frac{1}{i(\omega + \omega_I - \kappa c_x) + \nu} \right] d\mathbf{c} \tag{7.168}$$

Thus the plane wave splits into two oppositely polarized waves, with resonance possible only for the wave which rotates in the same direction as the motion of the ions in the magnetic field. We will therefore neglect the second term in Eq. (7.168), which is equivalent to studying a circularly polarized wave of twice the amplitude. The current will then be given by

$$(\mathbf{j}_I)_\parallel = \frac{eZ}{a_I^2} \iiint_{-\infty}^{\infty} \frac{(\boldsymbol{\mathcal{E}}_1 \cdot \mathbf{c}) \mathbf{c} f_0 \, d\mathbf{c}}{i(\omega - \omega_I - \kappa c_x) + \nu} \tag{7.169}$$

Since we have specified $(\mathbf{j}_I)_\parallel$ to $\boldsymbol{\mathcal{E}}_1$, we can for simplicity take $\mathbf{j} = (0, j_y, 0)$ and $\boldsymbol{\mathcal{E}}_1 = (0, \mathcal{E}_{1_y}, 0)$. Then, within the integral,

$$(\boldsymbol{\mathcal{E}}_1 \cdot \mathbf{c})\, \mathbf{c} = \mathcal{E}_{1_y} c_y^2$$

since any terms such as $\mathcal{E}_{1_y}c_yc_zf_0$ are identically zero because of the symmetry of f_0 and the fact that the integration is carried out from $+\infty$ to $-\infty$. Choosing f_0 maxwellian, integrating over c_y and c_z, and omitting the y subscript on j and $\mathcal{E}$, we obtain

$$(j_I)_\parallel = -\frac{in_I(eZ)^2E_1}{\sqrt{\pi}\, m_I\kappa U_I}\int_{-\infty}^{\infty}\frac{e^{-y^2}\,dy}{Z-y} \qquad (7.170)$$

where $U_I = \sqrt{2kT/m_I} = \sqrt{2}\,a_I$, $y = c_x/U_I$, and we have defined

$$Z = \frac{\omega - \omega_I - i\nu}{\kappa U_I}$$

The integral in Eq. (7.170) can be evaluated as follows:

$$I = \int_{-\infty}^{\infty}\frac{e^{-y^2}\,dy}{Z-y} = \int_{-\infty}^{0}\frac{e^{-y^2}\,dy}{Z-y} + \int_{0}^{\infty}\frac{e^{-y^2}\,dy}{Z-y}$$

If in the first of these we write $y = -x$, and in the second $y = x$, so that the variables of integration are changed, we can then write

$$I = \int_0^\infty \frac{e^{-x^2}\,dx}{Z+x} + \int_0^\infty \frac{e^{-x^2}\,dx}{Z-x}$$

or

$$I = -2Ze^{-Z^2}\int_0^\infty \frac{e^{-(x^2-Z^2)}}{x^2-Z^2}\,dx$$

which can be rewritten in the following manner,

$$I = -2Ze^{-Z^2}\int_1^\infty e^{Z^2\xi}\,d\xi\int_0^\infty e^{-\xi x^2}\,dx$$

as can readily be verified. Since we know the value of the second integral to be $\frac{1}{2}\sqrt{\pi/\xi}$, we have

$$I = -2Ze^{-Z^2}\int_1^\infty \frac{1}{2}\sqrt{\frac{\pi}{\xi}}\,e^{Z^2\xi}\,d\xi$$

which after some manipulation can be put in the form

$$I = \pi e^{-Z^2}\left(i + \frac{2}{\sqrt{\pi}}\int_0^Z e^{t^2}\,dt\right) \qquad (7.171)$$

Now, at cyclotron resonance, $\omega = \omega_I$, and Z is an imaginary number equal to $-i\nu/\kappa U_I$. Let us then define a new variable as $y_0 = it$, so that the upper limit in the integral of Eq. (7.171) is $y_0 = i(-i\nu/\kappa U_I)$. In this case we can write

$$I = i\pi e^{y_0^2}\,\mathrm{erfc}\,y_0 \qquad (7.172)$$

In combination with Eq. (7.170), this yields

$$(j_I)_\parallel = \frac{n_I(eZ)^2\sqrt{\pi}}{m_I\kappa}\sqrt{\frac{m_I}{2kT}}\,(e^{y_0^2}\,\mathrm{erfc}\,y_0)E_1 \qquad (7.173)$$

Now when the collisional damping goes to zero, $e^{y_0^2} \operatorname{erfc} y_0 \rightarrow 1$, and

$$(j_I)_\| = \frac{n_I(eZ)^2\lambda}{\pi\langle c_I\rangle} E_1 \tag{7.174}$$

since the average thermal speed of an ion is $\sqrt{8kT_I/\pi m_I}$, and the wavelength of the wave is $\lambda = 2\pi/\kappa$. Thus, in a collisionless plasma, the apparent mean free path of the ion is the wavelength of the wave divided by π. For a given wavelength, collisions always decrease the ion current. Consider a very slightly ionized gas so that the damping collision frequency is the collision frequency ν_{In} between ions and neutral particles. Then, for large values of the collision frequency y_0 becomes large, and

$$e^{y_0^2} \operatorname{erfc} y_0 \cong \frac{1}{y_0\pi^{\frac{1}{2}}}\left(1 - \frac{1}{2y_0^2} + \cdots\right) \tag{7.175}$$

so that Eq. (7.173) becomes

$$(j_I)_\| = \frac{n_I(eZ)^2E_1}{m_I\nu_{In}}\left(1 - \frac{\kappa^2U_I^2}{2\nu_{In}^2} + \cdots\right) \tag{7.176}$$

The coefficient in the above expression is obviously the d-c ion conductivity σ_{In}, while

$$y_0 = \frac{\nu_{In}}{\kappa U_I} = \frac{\lambda}{\pi^{\frac{3}{2}}\lambda_I} \tag{7.177}$$

where λ is the wavelength of the wave, and λ_I is the ion mean free path $\nu_{In}^{-1}\sqrt{8kT/\pi m_I}$. Thus Eq. (7.176) becomes

$$(j_I)_\| \cong \sigma_{In}E_1\left(1 - \frac{\pi^3\lambda_I^2}{\lambda^2}\right) \tag{7.178}$$

Thus, in the regime dominated by ion-neutral collisions, the ion current is proportional to the d-c ion conductivity; the second term in Eq. (7.178) is the correction for finite wavelengths. Obviously the analogous equation for electron cyclotron resonance is

$$(j_e)_\| = \sigma_e E_1\left(1 - \frac{\pi^3\lambda_e^2}{\lambda^2}\right) \tag{7.179}$$

The crossover point between collision-dominated and collision-free regimes is $y_0 \cong 1$; that is, if $\nu/\kappa U \ll 1$, then the phenomenon is essentially collision-free, and vice versa.[8]

In the event that it is desired to transmit an electromagnetic wave along the direction of the magnetic field in the vicinity of ion or electron cyclotron resonance, the question of its absorption must be considered.

We have, first, the wave equation for **E**.

$$\nabla^2\mathbf{E} - \frac{1}{c_0^2}\frac{\partial^2 \mathbf{E}}{\partial t^2} = \mu_0 \frac{\partial \mathbf{J}}{\partial t} \tag{7.180}$$

As before, taking $\mathbf{E} = E_1 \exp i(\omega t - \kappa x)$, $\mathbf{J} = (j_I)_\parallel \exp i(\omega t - \kappa x)$, letting $\omega = \omega_I$ (ion cyclotron resonance), and using Eq. (7.173) for $(j_I)_\parallel$, this becomes

$$\left(-\kappa^2 + \frac{\omega_I{}^2}{c_0{}^2}\right) E_1 = \frac{i\omega_I \mu_0 n_I (eZ)^2 \sqrt{\pi}}{m_I \kappa U_I} E_1 e^{y_0{}^2} \operatorname{erfc} y_0 \tag{7.181}$$

where the contribution to **J** due to electron current has been neglected. Since the ion plasma frequency is $\omega_{pI}^2 = n_I(eZ)^2/\kappa m_I$, this can be rewritten as

$$\kappa^3 - \left(\frac{\omega_I}{c_0}\right)^2 \kappa + \frac{i\omega_I \omega_{pI}^2 \sqrt{\pi}}{U_I c_0{}^2} e^{y_0{}^2} \operatorname{erfc} y_0 = 0 \tag{7.182}$$

When the wave is severely damped, the second term may be neglected; that is, the displacement current is neglected in comparison to the ion current. Then

$$\kappa \cong \left(\frac{\sqrt{3} - i}{2}\right) \pi^{\frac{1}{6}} \left(\frac{\omega_I \omega_{pI}^2}{c_0{}^2 U_I} e^{y_0{}^2} \operatorname{erfc} y_0\right)^{\frac{1}{3}} \tag{7.183}$$

Since the ratio of the imaginary part of κ to the real part, corresponding to damping, is $3^{-\frac{1}{2}}$, the wave is damped considerably over a wavelength.[9] Of course, this result applies only for $y_0 \ll 1$.

REFERENCES CITED

1. Rose, D. J., and M. Clark, Jr.: *Plasma and Controlled Fusion*, The M.I.T. Press, Cambridge, Mass., 1961.
2. Heitler, W.: *The Quantum Theory of Radiation*, Clarendon Press, Oxford, 1954.
3. Francis, G.: *Ionization Phenomena in Gases*, Butterworth Scientific Publications, London, 1960.
4. Brillouin, L.: *Wave Propagation and Group Velocity*, Academic Press Inc., New York, 1960.
5. Spitzer, L.: *The Physics of Fully Ionized Gases*, 2d ed., Interscience Publishers, Inc., New York, 1962.
6. Stix, T. H.: *The Theory of Plasma Waves*, McGraw-Hill Book Company, New York, 1962.
7. Bhatnagar, P. L., E. P. Gross, and M. Krook: "A Model for Collision Processes in Gases: part I, Small Amplitude Processes in Charged and Neutral One Component Systems," *Phys. Rev.*, **94**:511 (1954).
8. BenDaniel, D. J., H. Hurwitz, Jr., and G. W. Sutton: "Electron Conductivity at Cyclotron Resonance," *Phys. Fluids*, **6**:884 (1963).
9. Doyle, P. H., and J. Neufeld, "On Behaviour of Plasma at Ionic Resonance," *Phys. Fluids*, **2**:390 (1959).

GENERAL REFERENCES

Clauser, F. H. (gen. ed.): *Symposium on Plasma Dynamics,* Addison-Wesley Publishing Company, Inc., Reading, Mass., 1960.

Desirant, M., and J. L. Michels (eds.): *Electromagnetic Wave Propagation,* Academic Press Inc., New York, 1960.

Fried, B. D., and S. D. Conte: *Plasma Dispersion Function,* Academic Press Inc., New York, 1961.

Ginzburg, V. L.: *Propagation of Electromagnetic Waves in Plasmas,* Gordon and Breach, Science Publishers, Inc., New York, 1961.

International Summer Course in Plasma Physics (Riso), Danish Atomic Energy Commission, 1960.

Linhart, J. G.: *Plasma Physics,* North Holland Publishing Company, Amsterdam, 1960.

Ratcliffe, J. A.: *The Magneto-ionic Theory and Its Applications to the Ionosphere,* Cambridge University Press, London, 1959.

Spitzer, Lyman: *The Physics of Fully Ionized Gases,* 2d ed., Interscience Publishers, Inc., New York, 1962.

Stix, T. H.: *The Theory of Plasma Waves,* McGraw-Hill Book Company, New York, 1962.

Vlasov, A. A.: *Many-particle Theory and Its Application to Plasma,* Gordon and Breach, Science Publishers, Inc., New York, 1961.

part II

MAGNETOHYDRODYNAMIC FLOWS

8

MAGNETOHYDRODYNAMIC EQUATIONS

8.1 INTRODUCTION

Throughout Part I our attention was devoted exclusively to the basic principles underlying magnetohydrodynamics. No attempt was made to treat any flow problems. In Part II, on the other hand, our concern will be to understand such flow problems and to learn some of the techniques necessary to their solution.

In this chapter the various equations developed in Part I to describe the electromagnetic field (Chap. 2), the conservation of mass, momentum, and energy (Chap. 4), and the flow of electric current (Chap. 5) will be brought together and simplified. This complete system of equations will be referred to as the *magnetohydrodynamic equations*. In every flow situation to be considered in the remaining chapters of Part II these equations will provide the starting point.

Initially, the flow equations which had been developed in Chap. 4 from consideration of the microscopic phenomena will be derived by postulating a continuum plasma with appropriate characteristics. This approach is no more or less valid than the earlier treatment, but it does serve to illustrate more clearly the continuum nature of the plasmas whose flow characteristics we will be studying. Then the simplification of the complete system of equations will be discussed. The several useful approximations that are generally made will be referred to as the *magnetohydrodynamic approximations*. The basis for each of these approximations will be discussed in detail, and numerical examples will be offered to illustrate how one can estimate the validity of a specific assumption in a given flow problem.

The final portions of the chapter will be devoted to the question of similarity parameters. It will be shown that by reducing the magnetohydrodynamic equations to dimensionless form, one can derive all the similarity parameters associated with certain types of problems. In addition to the parameters found in this way, there are several others of some importance. These will be derived on physical grounds, for convenience.

8.2 CONTINUUM MODEL AND FLOW EQUATIONS

For present purposes, a continuum will be assumed to exist, in the presence of an electromagnetic field, with all of the normal characteristics of a fluid. In addition, it may be composed of several distinct species, some of which may be electrically charged, so that currents can flow within it. Magnetization and polarization of individual particles (see Chap. 2) will, however, be neglected. As a consequence of this ability to conduct electricity, the electromagnetic field will give rise to two principal effects: First, body forces which act on the fluid will be created; and second, energy will be exchanged with the fluid, which must be taken into account in the energy balance. With this continuum concept in mind, the equations of mass, momentum, and energy conservation will be derived.

8.2.1 Mass Conservation. Let $\rho = \rho(\mathbf{r},t)$ be the mass density at the point $\mathbf{r}$, at the time t; and let $\mathbf{v}(\mathbf{r},t)$ be its velocity. The rate of increase of mass within an arbitrary fixed volume $\mathcal{V}$ is

$$\frac{d}{dt}\int_V \rho \, d\mathcal{V} = \int_V \frac{\partial \rho}{\partial t} \, d\mathcal{V} \tag{8.1}$$

On the other hand, mass will be leaving the volume by passing through the boundary surface at the rate $\rho\mathbf{v} \cdot d\mathbf{S}$. Thus, if mass is to be conserved, we must have

$$\int_V \frac{\partial \rho}{\partial t} \, d\mathcal{V} = -\int_s \rho\mathbf{v} \cdot d\mathbf{S} \tag{8.2}$$

Applying Gauss' theorem to the right-hand side gives

$$\int_V \frac{\partial \rho}{\partial t} \, d\mathcal{V} = -\int_V \nabla \cdot (\rho\mathbf{v}) \, d\mathcal{V} \tag{8.3}$$

Since this must hold for any volume $\mathcal{V}$, and the functions ρ and $\mathbf{v}$ are continuous and have continuous derivatives, we conclude that

$$\frac{\partial \rho}{\partial t} + \nabla \cdot (\rho\mathbf{v}) = 0 \tag{8.4}$$

which is identical to Eq. (4.157).

8.2.2 Equation of Motion. Here it will be more convenient to consider a moving volume whose surface always encloses the same amount of fluid. If the forces which act on this fluid particle are divided into surface and body forces, then Newton's second law can be written as

$$\int_V \rho \frac{D\mathbf{v}}{Dt}\, d\mathcal{V} = \int_s \mathbf{f}\, dS + \int_V \mathbf{F}\, d\mathcal{V} \tag{8.5}$$

The surface force can be described in terms of a stress tensor [see Eq. (4.163)] with a scalar viscosity, as follows:

$$p_{ij} = [p + \tfrac{2}{3}\eta(\nabla \cdot \mathbf{v})]\, \delta_{ij} - \eta\left(\frac{\partial v_i}{\partial x_j} + \frac{\partial v_j}{\partial x_i}\right) \tag{8.6}$$

The stress tensor is to be interpreted as follows: Let S be a surface drawn within the fluid, and let 1 and 2 represent the material on the two sides of S. Let $d\mathbf{S}$ be an element of S, considered as an infinitesimal vector in the direction normal to dS, drawn from 1 into 2. Then the force $\mathbf{f}$ acting on $d\mathbf{S}$, regarded as the surface of 1, is given by its components†

$$f_i dS = -\sum_j p_{ij}\, dS_j \tag{8.7}$$

where dS_j are the components of $d\mathbf{S}$. Then the total force acting on the surface is

$$-\int_s \sum_j p_{ij}\, dS_j = -\sum_j \int_s p_{ij}\, dS_j \tag{8.8}$$

If Gauss' theorem is applied to this integral, we get

$$-\sum_j \int_V \frac{\partial p_{ij}}{\partial x_j}\, d\mathcal{V} = -\int_V \left(\sum_j \frac{\partial p_{ij}}{\partial x_j}\right) d\mathcal{V} \tag{8.9}$$

Therefore, Eq. (8.5) can be rewritten in components as

$$\int_V \rho \frac{Dv_i}{Dt}\, d\mathcal{V} = -\int_V \left(\sum_j \frac{\partial p_{ij}}{\partial x_j}\, d\mathcal{V}\right) + \int_V F_i\, d\mathcal{V} \tag{8.10}$$

Since this holds for any volume, and all functions as well as their derivatives are assumed continuous, we conclude

$$\rho \frac{Dv_i}{Dt} = -\sum_j \frac{\partial p_{ij}}{\partial x_j} + F_i \tag{8.11}$$

† The pressure tensor defined as in Eq. (8.6) is the negative of the usual definition. The usual one maintains a close correspondence to the stress tensor in elasticity theory from which it was deduced. If in Eq. (4.162) a pressure tensor defined as $\mathbf{p}_{(s)} = -\rho_s\langle \mathbf{cc}\rangle$ had been used, and p_{ij} had been defined as the negative of Eq. (8.6), one would have obtained the same equations, but the negative sign in Eq. (8.7) would not have been necessary.

The summation on the right-hand side can be rewritten as $-\nabla p + \psi$, where, making use of (8.6),

$$\psi = -\tfrac{2}{3}\nabla(\eta\nabla\cdot\mathbf{v}) + \eta[\nabla^2\mathbf{v} + \nabla(\nabla\cdot\mathbf{v})] + 2[(\nabla\eta)\cdot\nabla]\mathbf{v} + (\nabla\eta)\times(\nabla\times\mathbf{v}) \qquad (8.12)$$

and where η has implicitly been assumed to be a scalar (via the assumed form of p_{ij}), although it may be a function of the thermodynamic state.

Thus, Eq. (8.11) becomes

$$\rho\frac{D\mathbf{v}}{Dt} = -\nabla p + \psi + \mathbf{F} \qquad (8.13)$$

Neglecting body forces due to polarization and magnetization of the plasma, the expression for **F**, which is due to the motion of free charge alone, is

$$\mathbf{F} = \rho_e\mathbf{E} + \mathbf{J}\times\mathbf{B} \qquad (8.14)$$

In this case, the equation of motion becomes

$$\rho\frac{D\mathbf{v}}{Dt} = -\nabla p + \psi + \rho_e\mathbf{E} + \mathbf{J}\times\mathbf{B} \qquad (8.15)$$

This is identical to Eq. (4.163), where it should be recalled that **J** is the sum of the conduction current and the current flow due to convective transport of charge.

8.2.3 Conservation of Energy. Here again we consider a fixed amount of fluid moving with the flow. The rate of increase of its energy is given by

$$\int_V \frac{1}{2}\rho\frac{Dv^2}{Dt}\,d\mathcal{V} + \int_V \rho\frac{De}{Dt}\,d\mathcal{V} \qquad (8.16)$$

where it should be noted that $\frac{D}{Dt}(\rho\,d\mathcal{V}) = 0$ since the amount of mass is fixed. The first term is the rate of change of kinetic energy of the fluid particle, and the second is the rate of change of its internal energy.

In order for energy to be conserved, this must equal the energy inputs per unit of time from all other sources. These are:

1. $\int_V (\mathbf{E}\cdot\mathbf{J})\,d\mathcal{V}$, rate at which electromagnetic energy enters.

2. Energy entering per unit of time by heat conduction and diffusion of species. This is equal to

$$-\int_V \nabla\cdot(\mathcal{K}\,\nabla T)\,d\mathcal{V} + \sum_s \int_V \nabla\cdot(\mathbf{V}_s\rho_s h_s)\,d\mathcal{V}$$

where $\mathbf{V}_s$ is the species-diffusion velocity.

3. Rate at which surface forces are doing work. This can be obtained by integrating $\mathbf{v}\cdot\mathbf{f}$ over the surface of the fluid particle. From

Eq. (8.7) we have

$$\int_S \mathbf{v} \cdot \mathbf{f}\, dS = \int_S \sum_i v_i f_i\, dS = -\sum_{i,j} \int_S v_i p_{ij}\, dS_j$$

or, applying Gauss' theorem,

$$-\sum_{i,j} \int_S v_i p_{ij}\, dS_j = -\sum_{i,j} \int_V \frac{\partial}{\partial x_j} (v_i p_{ij})\, d\mathcal{V}$$
$$= -\int_V \sum_{i,j} \frac{\partial}{\partial x_j} (v_i p_{ij})\, d\mathcal{V}$$

which is the desired expression. Equating Eq. (8.16) to the sum of these terms gives

$$\int_V \frac{1}{2} \rho \frac{Dv^2}{Dt}\, d\mathcal{V} + \int_V \rho \frac{De}{Dt}\, d\mathcal{V} = \int_V \mathbf{E} \cdot \mathbf{J}\, d\mathcal{V} + \int_V \nabla \cdot (\mathcal{K}\, \nabla T)\, d\mathcal{V} - \sum_s \int_V \nabla \cdot (\mathbf{V}_s \rho_s h_s)\, d\mathcal{V} - \int_V \sum_{i,j} \frac{\partial}{\partial x_j} (v_i p_{ij})\, d\mathcal{V} \quad (8.17)$$

As before, since the volume is arbitrary and the functions and their derivatives are continuous, this becomes

$$\tfrac{1}{2}\rho \frac{Dv^2}{Dt} + \rho \frac{De}{Dt} = \mathbf{E} \cdot \mathbf{J} + \nabla \cdot (\mathcal{K}\, \nabla T) - \sum_s \nabla \cdot (\mathbf{V}_s \rho_s h_s) - \sum_{i,j} \frac{\partial}{\partial x_j} (v_i p_{ij}) \quad (8.18)$$

which is precisely Eq. (4.182) when **q** is given by Eq. (4.181).

Again, the last summation on the right can be rewritten as

$$-\sum_i \frac{\partial}{\partial x_i} (p\mathbf{v}_i) + \phi$$

where, from (8.6),

$$\phi = \eta \sum_i v_i \nabla^2 v_i + \tfrac{1}{3}\eta \sum_i v_i \frac{\partial}{\partial x_i} \left(\sum_j \frac{\partial v_j}{\partial x_j} \right) + \sum_{i,j} v_i \frac{\partial \eta}{\partial x_j} \left(\frac{\partial v_i}{\partial x_j} + \frac{\partial v_j}{\partial x_i} \right) - \tfrac{2}{3} \sum_i v_i \frac{\partial \eta}{\partial x_i} \left(\sum_j \frac{\partial v_j}{\partial x_j} \right) + \eta \sum_{i,j} \frac{\partial v_i}{\partial x_j} \left(\frac{\partial v_i}{\partial x_j} + \frac{\partial v_j}{\partial x_i} \right) - \tfrac{2}{3}\eta \left(\sum_j \frac{\partial v_j}{\partial x_j} \right)^2$$

In conclusion then we have shown that by properly defining a conducting-fluid continuum we can rederive the basic conservation equations developed in Chap. 4 for the microscopic picture. The microscopic description is essential to the correct formulation of the conservation equations; however, the concept of a continuum is indispensable for the study of flow phenomena. In order to complete the formulation of the magnetohydrodynamic flow problem, we must add Maxwell's equations to the conservation equations. This combined system will be referred to as the *magnetohydrodynamic equations.*

8.3 THE MAGNETOHYDRODYNAMIC APPROXIMATION

Since the *magnetohydrodynamic equations* combine the full complexity of Maxwell's equations with the fluid dynamic equations, it is clear that they will be extremely difficult to solve in their general form. Accordingly, some simplifications must be introduced if we are to proceed at all. The approach that will be followed will be similar to that of Elsasser.[1] Our interest will, however, be in engineering magnetohydrodynamics rather than in questions relating to astrophysics.

A number of approximations can be made which will be valid over a rather wide range of conditions. The first is to neglect the displacement current $K_0\,\partial\mathbf{E}/\partial t$ in Eq. (2.65) of Maxwell's equations, in the event that unsteady motions are of interest. To determine when $K_0\,\partial\mathbf{E}/\partial t$ can be neglected, we simply compare it to the conduction current $\mathbf{J} \cong \sigma\mathbf{E}$. If $\mathbf{E}$ is assumed to vary sinusoidally with time with a frequency of ω (radians per unit time), then the ratio of the amplitude of $K_0\,\partial\mathbf{E}/\partial t$ to the amplitude of $\mathbf{J}$ is approximately

$$\frac{K_0(\partial\mathbf{E}/\partial t)_{\max}}{(\sigma\mathbf{E})_{\max}} = \frac{K_0\omega}{\sigma}$$

The magnitude of this ratio can be calculated for a typical case of interest. The value for σ for a large number of engineering applications can be taken to be approximately 100 mhos/m. The value of K_0 will be close to its value in a vacuum, which is approximately 9×10^{-12} farads/m. This gives

$$\frac{K_0(\partial\mathbf{E}/\partial t)_{\max}}{(\sigma\mathbf{E})_{\max}} \cong 10^{-13}\omega$$

which shows that even at microwave frequencies, the displacement current may be neglected.

Another useful simplication is to neglect the current flow due to the transport of excess charge $\rho_e\mathbf{v}$ as compared to the conduction current. Whether and under what conditions this can be done will now be seen. First, the order of magnitude of ρ_e can be obtained from the equation

$K_0\nabla \cdot \mathbf{E} = \rho_e$ [Eq. (2.15)]. If **E** varies linearly over some small region, then

$$\rho_e \cong \frac{K_0 E}{L}$$

where E and L are a reference or characteristic electric field and length. Then a comparison of the $\rho_e\mathbf{v}$ and $\sigma\mathbf{E}$ representing the conduction current shows

$$\frac{\rho_e \mathbf{v}}{\sigma \mathbf{E}} \cong \frac{(K_0E/L)V}{\sigma E} = \frac{K_0 V}{L\sigma}$$

Here V is some characteristic velocity. Again some representative values will be chosen:

$$\begin{aligned} K_0 &= 10^{-11} \text{ farads/m} \\ V &= 10^5 \text{ m/sec} \\ L &= 1 \text{ m} \\ \sigma &= 100 \text{ mhos/m} \end{aligned}$$

In this case we find that

$$\frac{K_0 V}{L\sigma} \cong 10^{-8}$$

so that the contribution to current flow due to the transport of excess charge can be safely neglected.

In order to determine whether the electrostatic body force in the equation of motion (8.13) can be neglected, a comparison can be made between $\rho_e\mathbf{E}$ and $\mathbf{J} \times \mathbf{B}$. The order of magnitude of ρ_e was found from the earlier discussion, so that the order of magnitude of $\rho_e\mathbf{E}$ is

$$\rho_e \mathbf{E} \cong \frac{K_0 E^2}{L}$$

The order of magnitude of the **J** term can be obtained from Ohm's law when $\rho_e\mathbf{v}$ is neglected. In this case the $\mathbf{J} \times \mathbf{B}$ term is found to be

$$\mathbf{J} \times \mathbf{B} \cong \sigma(E + VB)B$$

If, however, it is assumed that E is the same order of magnitude as VB, then

$$\mathbf{J} \times \mathbf{B} \cong \sigma V B^2$$

The ratio of the electrostatic force to the Lorentz force is then simply

$$\frac{\rho_e \mathbf{E}}{\mathbf{J} \times \mathbf{B}} \cong \frac{K_0 E^2}{\sigma L V B^2} \cong \frac{K_0 V^2 B^2}{\sigma L V B^2} = \frac{K_0 V}{\sigma L}$$

As before, this is a negligible quantity.

By virtue of the preceding arguments, three approximations have been shown to be valid; that is, $K_0\, \partial\mathbf{E}/\partial t$ can be neglected in Maxwell's equation, current flow due to charge transport is quite small, and $\rho_e\mathbf{E}$ can be neglected in the equation of motion. All three taken together can be considered to be the *magnetohydrodynamic approximations*.

In substantiating these approximations, the numerical values assigned to L, σ, B, K_0, and V were chosen for problems of interest in engineering magnetohydrodynamics. However, it should be recognized that our interest has only been to illustrate the use of such relations in estimating the importance of these factors. In each new situation these approximations should always be reevaluated.

8.4 SIMPLIFIED EQUATIONS

With the use of the above simplifications, the more general equations are simplified. These are collected and are reproduced below:

Maxwell's equations:
$$\nabla \times \mathbf{E} = -\frac{\partial \mathbf{B}}{\partial t} \tag{8.19}$$

$$\nabla \times \mathbf{B} = \mu_0 \mathbf{j} \tag{8.20}$$
$$\nabla \cdot \mathbf{B} = 0 \tag{8.21}$$
$$K_0 \nabla \cdot \mathbf{E} = \rho_e \tag{8.22}$$

Conservation of mass:
$$\frac{\partial \rho}{\partial t} + \nabla \cdot (\rho\mathbf{v}) = 0 \tag{8.23}$$

Equation of motion:
$$\rho\frac{D\mathbf{v}}{Dt} = -\nabla p + \psi + \mathbf{j} \times \mathbf{B} \tag{8.24}$$

Conservation of energy:

$$\rho\left(\frac{De}{Dt} + \frac{1}{2}\frac{Dv^2}{Dt}\right) = \mathbf{E}\cdot\mathbf{j} + \nabla\cdot(\mathfrak{K}\,\nabla T)$$
$$-\sum_s \nabla\cdot(\mathbf{V}_s\rho_s h_s) - \nabla\cdot(p\mathbf{v}) + \phi \tag{8.25}$$

Ohm's law with ion slip neglected:

see poxvii

$$\mathbf{j} = \sigma[\mathbf{E} + \mathbf{v} \times \mathbf{B} - \beta(\mathbf{j} \times \mathbf{B})] \tag{8.26}$$

β not Hall Param!. $\leftarrow \dfrac{1}{e n_e}$

In addition to the above there is the equation of state:

$$p = p(\rho,T)$$

the caloric equation of state:

$$e = e(\rho,T)$$

and the relations for the transport properties:

$$\mathfrak{K} = \mathfrak{K}(\rho,T) \qquad \eta = \eta(\rho,T) \qquad \sigma = \sigma(\rho,T)$$

$$\frac{\sigma}{n_e e} = \frac{n_e e^2 \tau}{m_e\, n_e e} \qquad \omega = \frac{eB}{m} \qquad \frac{\sigma}{n_e e} = \frac{\omega\tau}{B} \quad \text{check Rosa} \quad pg\,^{29}$$

where it is, of course, understood that the first two may be tensors under certain conditions. It is of interest to note that if the variable ρ_e is not considered, there is no need to consider Eq. (8.22). That is, when this equation is omitted, the remaining equations are sufficient to solve for all variables including **E** but excluding ρ_e. If then a solution were obtained for **E** we would be able to find ρ_e from Eq. (8.22).

After all the above simplifications, there are still left 25 equations for 25 unknowns [considering Eq. (8.21) an initial condition for the time-unsteady situation]. The situation may be further simplified by eliminating the variables **E** and **j** from the system of equations. This is done by solving Eq. (8.26) for **E**:

$$\mathbf{E} = \frac{\mathbf{j}}{\sigma} - \mathbf{v} \times \mathbf{B} + \beta(\mathbf{j} \times \mathbf{B}) \tag{8.27}$$

Substitution of **j** from Eq. (8.20) then gives

$$\mathbf{E} = \frac{\nabla \times \mathbf{B}}{\mu_0 \sigma} - \mathbf{v} \times \mathbf{B} + \beta\left(\frac{\nabla \times \mathbf{B}}{\mu_0} \times \mathbf{B}\right) \tag{8.28}$$

which when combined with Eq. (8.19) gives

$$\frac{\partial \mathbf{B}}{\partial t} + \nabla \times \frac{\nabla \times \mathbf{B}}{\mu_0 \sigma} - \nabla \times (\mathbf{v} \times \mathbf{B}) + \nabla \times \left[\frac{\beta}{\mu_0}(\nabla \times \mathbf{B}) \times \mathbf{B}\right] = 0 \tag{8.29}$$

which is the general induction equation. If σ is assumed to be constant, it takes more familiar forms. Expanding the triple products on the left-hand side of Eq. (8.29) leads to

$$\begin{aligned}\frac{\partial \mathbf{B}}{\partial t} = (\mathbf{B} \cdot \nabla)\mathbf{v} - (\mathbf{v} \cdot \nabla)\mathbf{B} + (\nabla \cdot \mathbf{B})\mathbf{v} - (\nabla \cdot \mathbf{v})\mathbf{B} - \frac{\nabla(\nabla \cdot \mathbf{B})}{\mu_0 \sigma} \\ + \frac{\nabla^2 \mathbf{B}}{\mu_0 \sigma} - \frac{\beta}{\mu_0}\{(\nabla \times \mathbf{B})(\nabla \cdot \mathbf{B}) - (\mathbf{B} \cdot \nabla)(\nabla \times \mathbf{B}) \\ + [(\nabla \times \mathbf{B}) \cdot \nabla]\mathbf{B}\}\end{aligned} \tag{8.30}$$

Making use of the relation $\nabla \cdot \mathbf{B} = 0$ and assuming $\beta = 0$, the more familiar form of the induction equation is obtained,

$$\frac{\partial \mathbf{B}}{\partial t} = (\mathbf{B} \cdot \nabla)\mathbf{v} - (\mathbf{v} \cdot \nabla)\mathbf{B} - (\nabla \cdot \mathbf{v})\mathbf{B} + \alpha \nabla^2 \mathbf{B}$$

where

$$\alpha = \frac{1}{\mu_0 \sigma} \tag{8.31}$$

Returning to the problem of simplifying the system of equations, it is seen that if **j** in Eqs. (8.24) and (8.25) is replaced by $(1/\mu_0)\nabla \times \mathbf{B}$ from

Eq. (8.20), then the following system of equations is found:

$$\text{Conservation of mass:} \quad \frac{\partial \rho}{\partial t} + \nabla \cdot (\rho \mathbf{v}) = 0 \tag{8.32}$$

$$\text{Equation of motion:} \quad \rho \frac{D\mathbf{v}}{Dt} = -\nabla p + \boldsymbol{\psi} + \frac{(\nabla \times \mathbf{B}) \times \mathbf{B}}{\mu_0} \tag{8.33}$$

Conservation of energy [see Eq. (4.182)]:

$$\rho \frac{De}{Dt} = -p\nabla \cdot \mathbf{v} - \Phi + \nabla \cdot (\mathcal{K} \nabla T) + \frac{(\nabla \times \mathbf{B})^2}{\mu_0{}^2 \sigma}$$

where $$\Phi = \tfrac{2}{3}\eta(\nabla \cdot \mathbf{v})^2 - \eta[\nabla^2(v^2) - (\nabla \times \mathbf{v})^2 - 2\mathbf{v} \cdot \nabla^2 \mathbf{v}] \tag{8.34}$$

Induction equation:

$$\frac{\partial \mathbf{B}}{\partial t} = \nabla \times (\mathbf{v} \times \mathbf{B}) - \frac{1}{\mu_0} \nabla \times \frac{\nabla \times \mathbf{B}}{\sigma} - \nabla \times \left[\frac{\beta}{\mu_0} (\nabla \times \mathbf{B}) \times \mathbf{B}\right] \tag{8.35}$$

As before it is assumed that p, e, and the transport properties η, $\mathcal{K}$, and σ are all known as functions of ρ and T.

Finally, it should be noted that in neglecting $K_0\ \partial \mathbf{E}/\partial t$, Maxwell's equations are no longer relativistically invariant. Since the fluid dynamic equations, with electromagnetic effects absent, are only galilean-invariant, this does not seem inconsistent.

8.5 SIMILARITY PARAMETERS

In general, it can be said that the complexity of a physical problem is directly related to the number of dimensionless parameters that appear in it. A number of flow problems have been solved exactly for an incompressible viscous fluid in which the Reynolds number appears as a parameter. Similarly, many inviscid compressible-flow problems have been solved exactly when *two* dimensionless parameters appear.

In view of this, the value of investigating the dimensionless ratios that arise in problems of magnetohydrodynamics is apparent. They can be derived in two ways. The first method, which is purely formal, consists in reducing the *magnetohydrodynamic equations* to dimensionless form. In doing this, all the parameters that will appear are found. The second procedure is simply to resort to physical arguments to form the particular ratio in question. Both methods will be illustrated in this section in the course of developing and explaining the significant dimensionless ratios.

Following the first procedure, the system of equations from which **j** and **E** were eliminated will be used. In order to simplify the presentation, a perfect gas will be assumed, and energy transport by diffusion of species will be neglected. This is not to imply that ionized gases should be considered perfect (since in general they are not), but only that by such a procedure one finds parameters (Prandtl number, Mach number) which are already familiar. The forms of the new magnetohydrodynamic parameters are independent of this assumption. The equations of interest are Eqs. (8.33) to (8.35).

For a perfect gas we note the following:

$$\frac{De}{Dt} = C_V \frac{DT}{Dt} \qquad p_0 = \rho_0 R_0 T_0 \qquad R_0 = C_{p_0} - C_{V_0} \qquad \gamma = \frac{C_{p_0}}{C_{V_0}}$$

Here R_0 is the specific gas constant defined as $R_0 \equiv \mathcal{R}/\text{molecular weight}$; $\mathcal{R}$, the universal gas constant, is defined as $\mathcal{R} \equiv kN$, where k is Boltzmann's constant; and N is Loschmidt's number $= 6.023 \times 10^{23}$ molecules per mole of gas. Then, the following dimensionless variables are defined:

$$\tilde{x} = \frac{x}{L_0} \qquad \tilde{t} = \frac{t}{L_0/V_0} \qquad \tilde{\rho} = \frac{\rho}{\rho_0} \qquad \tilde{B} = \frac{B}{B_0}$$

$$\tilde{p} = \frac{p}{p_0} \qquad \tilde{T} = \frac{T}{T_0} \qquad \tilde{C}_V = \frac{C_V}{C_{V_0}} \qquad \tilde{\eta} = \frac{\eta}{\eta_0}$$

$$\tilde{\mathcal{K}} = \frac{\mathcal{K}}{\mathcal{K}_0} \qquad \tilde{v} = \frac{v}{V_0} \qquad \tilde{\sigma} = \frac{\sigma}{\sigma_0} \qquad \tilde{\beta} = \frac{\beta}{\beta_0}$$

where the values of each of the variables at some arbitrary point are taken as reference values and denoted by $(\ \ )_0$. For the flow over an airfoil the values in the free stream would be the reference values, and for the flow through a duct the reference values could be evaluated at the entrance section.

It should be noted that the time over which an unsteady phenomenon occurs is assumed to be infinitely long compared to the transit time of a fluid particle. This time of transit is approximately L_0/V_0.

If the above relations are substituted into Eqs. (8.33) to (8.35), there is found

$$\tilde{\rho}\frac{\tilde{D}\tilde{v}}{D\tilde{t}} = -\frac{1}{\gamma_0 \mathfrak{M}_0^2}\tilde{\nabla}\tilde{p} + \frac{1}{R_e}\tilde{\Psi} + S(\tilde{\nabla} \times \tilde{\mathbf{B}}) \times \tilde{\mathbf{B}} \tag{8.36}$$

$$\tilde{\rho}\tilde{C}_V\frac{\tilde{D}\tilde{T}}{D\tilde{t}} = -(\gamma_0 - 1)\tilde{p}(\tilde{\nabla}\cdot\tilde{\mathbf{v}}) - \frac{\gamma_0(\gamma_0 - 1)}{R_e}\mathfrak{M}_0^2\tilde{\Phi} + \frac{\gamma_0}{R_e P_R}\tilde{\nabla}\cdot(\tilde{\mathcal{K}}\,\tilde{\nabla}\tilde{T}) + \frac{\gamma_0(\gamma_0 - 1)}{R_m}S\mathfrak{M}_0^2\frac{(\tilde{\nabla}\times\tilde{\mathbf{B}})^2}{\mu_0^2\tilde{\sigma}} \tag{8.37}$$

$$\frac{\partial\tilde{\mathbf{B}}}{\partial\tilde{t}} = \tilde{\nabla}\times(\tilde{\mathbf{v}}\times\tilde{\mathbf{B}}) - \frac{1}{R_m}\left\{\tilde{\nabla}\times\frac{\tilde{\nabla}\times\tilde{\mathbf{B}}}{\tilde{\sigma}} - \omega\tau\tilde{\beta}\,\tilde{\nabla}\times[(\tilde{\nabla}\times\tilde{\mathbf{B}})\times\tilde{\mathbf{B}}]\right\} \tag{8.38}$$

where the dimensionless ratios are defined as follows:

Reynolds number:	$R_e \equiv \rho_0 V_0 L_0/\eta_0$
Magnetic Reynolds number:	$R_m \equiv \mu_0\sigma_0 V_0 L_0$
Mach number:	$\mathfrak{M}_0 \equiv V_0/\sqrt{\gamma_0 R_0 T_0}$
Hall parameter:	$\omega\tau \equiv \sigma_0\beta_0 B_0$
Magnetic force number:	$S \equiv B_0^2/\mu_0\rho_0 V_0^2$
Prandtl number:	$P_R \equiv C_{p_0}\eta_0/\mathcal{K}_0$

First, observe that if two magnetohydrodynamic flows are to be dynamically similar: γ_0, $\omega\tau$, R_e, $\mathfrak{M}_0$ (Mach number in absence of magnetic effects), P_R, R_m, and S must be the same. It is also seen that three new dimensionless ratios occur because of the coupling of the electromagnetic and fluid-flow fields. The additional complexity introduced by these three new parameters should be greater than the considerable difficulties experienced when compressibility and viscosity effects must be added to incompressible, inviscid flows.

Before proceeding to a discussion of other possible dimensionless parameters, it will be of value to first consider the physical significance of the three new magnetohydrodynamic parameters. The first one found was the magnetic Reynolds number R_m. It can be considered a measure of how easily the fluid slips through the magnetic field. This can be illustrated readily. In Eq. (8.20), suppose that B is composed of the sum of an applied field $\mathbf{B}_0$ and an induced field $\mathbf{b}$. Then

$$\mathbf{j} = \frac{1}{\mu_0} \nabla \times (\mathbf{B}_0 \times \mathbf{b}) = \frac{1}{\mu_0} \nabla \times \mathbf{b} \tag{8.39}$$

Reducing this to dimensionless form with $\mathbf{j}_0 = \sigma_0 V_0 B_0$, we obtain

$$(\mu_0 \sigma_0 V_0 B_0)\tilde{\mathbf{j}} = \tilde{\nabla} \times \tilde{\mathbf{b}} \frac{B_0}{L_0}$$

or

$$R_m \tilde{\mathbf{j}} = \tilde{\nabla} \times \tilde{\mathbf{b}} \tag{8.40}$$

Clearly then, when R_m is very large, a small current will create a large induced magnetic field. When it is very small, on the other hand, moderate-sized currents will only produce induced fields which are essentially only small perturbations on the applied field. The second dimensionless parameter uncovered was the magnetic force number S. It can be thought of as the ratio of the magnetic body force to the inertia force. When it is small, the magnetic field is ineffectual in perturbing the flow field. On the other hand, if it is of the order of 1 or larger, large magnetic effects can be expected. Another interesting interpretation can be placed on S if we observe that the Alfvén speed of propagation of a magnetohydrodynamic wave, which will be discussed later, is given by

$$A = \frac{B_0}{\sqrt{\mu_0 \rho_0}} \tag{8.41}$$

Then it is possible to write

$$S = \frac{B_0{}^2}{\mu_0 \rho_0 V_0{}^2} = \frac{A^2}{V_0{}^2} \tag{8.42}$$

so that S can be interpreted as the square of the ratio of the Alfvén speed to the flow velocity. In other words it is related to a magnetohydrodynamic Mach number:

$$\mathfrak{M}_m = \frac{V_0}{A} = \frac{1}{\sqrt{S}}$$

In flow problems where wave motion plays an important role, the above number is of considerable significance.

The last of the three new dimensionless groups found was the Hall parameter $\omega\tau$. From a macroscopic point of view, it can be interpreted as the ratio of the Hall current to the current parallel to the electric field:

$$\frac{\sigma_0\beta_0 j_0 B_0}{j_0} = \sigma_0\beta_0 B_0 \equiv \omega\tau$$

Alternately, from the microscopic point of view, it can be viewed as the ratio of the number of gyrations of an electron in the presence of a magnetic field during one mean collision time.

Depending upon the flow situation, other dimensionless ratios may arise. If necessary they can be derived by some suitable rearrangement of the basic equations. However, it will be simpler here to present them from physical arguments. We first consider the magnetic-interaction number I, which is defined as the ratio of magnetic body force to fluid inertia force. It is similar to S except that in this case the current $\mathbf{j}$ is taken from Ohm's law [$\mathbf{j} = \sigma(\mathbf{E} + \mathbf{v} \times \mathbf{B})$], neglecting the Hall effect and ion slip, with $\mathbf{E}$ assumed to be of the same order as $\mathbf{v} \times \mathbf{B}$. In this case I is given as

$$I = \frac{\text{magnetic body force}}{\text{inertia force}} = \frac{\sigma_0 V_0 B_0^2}{\rho_0 V_0^2/L_0} = \frac{\sigma_0 B_0^2 L_0}{\rho_0 V_0}$$

This parameter generally appears when the problem cannot be conveniently formulated with $\mathbf{j}$ and $\mathbf{E}$ eliminated [Eqs. (8.33) to (8.35)].

Another interesting parameter arises in the consideration of magnetohydrodynamic boundary layers. As is well known, the viscous boundary-layer thickness is inversely proportional to $\sqrt{R_e}$. That is, when $R_e \rightarrow \infty$, this boundary layer becomes infinitely thin and can be neglected in first approximation. This is seen clearly in Eq. (8.36). A similar phenomenon arises in magnetohydrodynamics, when the problem of flow over a body is considered, where the magnetic field and flow are both aligned at infinity and $R_m \rightarrow \infty$. In this case it is found that a thin layer of current can flow along the body surface (normal to the flow direction). This layer is infinitely thin (surface current) when $R_m = \infty$. If R_m is large but finite, it is found that the current layer's thickness is inversely proportional to $\sqrt{R_m}$. Thus one can define a magnetic Prandtl number to be

$$P_m \equiv \frac{R_m}{R_e} = \frac{\mu_0\sigma_0\eta_0}{\rho_0}$$

It is clearly analogous to the gas dynamic Prandtl number, which is often interpreted as the ratio of viscous to thermal boundary-layer thicknesses.

In addition to the above, another dimensionless ratio is frequently of importance. It is the ratio of magnetic to viscous forces. Again the magnetic force is derived by taking **j** from Ohm's law, and so one finds

$$H_a^2 = \frac{\text{magnetic body force}}{\text{viscous force}} = \frac{\sigma_0 V_0 B_0^2}{\eta_0 V_0 / L_0^2} = \frac{\sigma_0 B_0^2 L_0^2}{\eta_0}$$

The Hartmann number H_a is traditionally defined as the square root of the above quantity. Accordingly, the above quantity has been defined as H_a^2. Its relation to the parameters previously considered is readily shown.

$$H_a^2 = SR_eR_m = IR_e$$

REFERENCE CITED

1. Elsasser, W. M.: "Dimensional Relations in Magnetohydrodynamics," *Phys. Rev.*, **95**:1 (1954).

GENERAL REFERENCES

Cole, G. H. A.: "Some Aspects of Magnetohydrodynamics," *Advan. Phys.*, **5**:452–497 (1956); *Quart. Suppl. Phys. Mag.*

Cowling, T. G.: *Magnetohydrodynamics*, Interscience Publishers, Inc., New York, 1957.

Elsasser, W. M.: "Dimensional Relations in Magnetohydrodynamics," *Phys. Rev.*, **95**:1 (1954).

Ferraro, V. C. A., and C. Plumpton: *Magneto-fluid Mechanics*, Oxford University Press, Fair Lawn, N.J., 1961.

Landshof, R. K. M.: "Magnetohydrodynamics," *The McGraw-Hill Encyclopedia of Science and Technology*, vol. 8, p. 55, McGraw-Hill Book Company, New York, 1960.

Lundquist, S.: "Studies in Magneto-hydrodynamics," *Arkiv Fysik*, **5**(15):297 (February, 1952).

Pai, S. I.: *Magnetogasdynamics*, Prentice-Hall, Inc., Englewood Cliffs, N.J., 1962.

Resler, E. L., and W. R. Sears: "Prospects for Magneto-aerodynamics," *J. Aeron. Sci.*, **25**:235 (April, 1958).

9

ALFVÉN AND SHOCK WAVES

9.1 INTRODUCTION

In this chapter the study of specific magnetohydrodynamic flow problems is initiated. In Part I the basic concepts necessary to a clear understanding of magnetohydrodynamics were covered. In Chap. 8 these concepts were assembled, and a suitable set of equations necessary for the study of macroscopic flows was identified. Within this framework then the first flow problems to be considered will involve wave motion. To begin with, infinitesimal waves which can propagate in the type of continuum which was previously defined in Chap. 8 will be studied. These will consist of the Alfvén and magnetoacoustic waves. In addition to the questions of phase and group velocity, some discussion of the dissipative effects of finite conductivity and viscosity is included. It should be noted that these waves differ from those in Chap. 7 in that no consideration at all is given to the microscopic phenomena other than what has been included in the continuum model selected.

Following this discussion of infinitesimal waves, the question of finite discontinuities is considered. Generally speaking, shock waves and related gas dynamic discontinuities are well understood in nonconducting gases. Accordingly, the present treatment will be restricted to those new concepts and phenomena which arise when the gas is an electrical conductor, and flows through electric and magnetic fields. In the succeeding sections of this chapter, the equations governing the general magnetohydrodynamic discontinuity will be developed. Working from these, the Rankine-Hugoniot equation and the entropy increase across a shock wave will be derived and discussed. The Friedrichs[1] approach will then be explored, in order to deduce some of the qualitative features of the magnetohydrodynamic shock wave. The concluding section will describe shocks in perfect gases.

Before proceeding further, it would be of interest to mention some of the problems in which magnetohydrodynamic waves and shocks play a part. Originally, interest in all types of magnetohydrodynamic waves and discontinuities was stimulated by the study of astrophysical phenomena. The first puzzling problem considered, for which these waves offered a solution, was the heating of the solar corona. By various measurements it had been determined that the solar corona is at a temperature on the order of 10^6°K, whereas the solar photosphere is at a temperature of only 5700°K. The question then is: How does the corona assume a temperature so much higher than that of the photosphere? One explanation suggested that since the photosphere is highly turbulent, magnetohydrodynamic shock waves would be generated and propagated into the corona. There the shock would cause a jump in temperature as it passed through the plasma. If a sufficiently large number of such shocks propagated into the corona, its high temperature could be explained on this basis. Another explanation can be given on the basis of the dissipation of energy when a magnetohydrodynamic wave passes through a medium of finite conductivity such as the corona.

In addition to the problem of the heating of the solar corona, another area of interest for magnetohydrodynamic waves and shocks arose when attempts were made to explain the origin of cosmic rays. It was assumed that a galactic magnetic field exists, which is a property of interstellar space or matter, so that a magnetohydrodynamic wave or shock propagating through such a magnetic field could accelerate charged particles to energies corresponding to that of cosmic rays.

After this original stimulation of the subject, the question of controlled fusion further promoted the study of such waves. Here attempts are being made to heat a plasma, via the passage of a shock wave, to the extremely high temperatures needed to initiate and sustain a fusion reaction.

And lastly, recent investigations of the pulsed-plasma accelerator as a space propulsion rocket have made use of the concept of an MHD shock wave. Further details of this will be given in Chap. 13.

9.2 MAGNETOHYDRODYNAMIC WAVES

Preliminary to the investigation of finite MHD discontinuities (shock waves), the study of infinitesimal disturbances will be taken up. We start from Eqs. (8.21), (8.23), (8.33), and (8.35). Initially the discussion will be limited to nondissipative waves, and so the energy equation will be replaced by the isentropic relationship for adiabatic nondissipative flows—entropy is constant—while the viscosity η, thermal conductivity $\mathcal{K}$, and electrical resistivity σ^{-1} will be taken as zero. To further simplify the discussion, the Hall effect and ion-slip phenomena will be neglected. Within these assumptions our equations are

$$\nabla \cdot \mathbf{B} = 0 \tag{9.1}$$

$$\frac{\partial \mathbf{B}}{\partial t} = \nabla \times (\mathbf{v} \times \mathbf{B}) \tag{9.2}$$

$$\frac{\partial \rho}{\partial t} = -\nabla \cdot (\rho \mathbf{v}) \tag{9.3}$$

$$\frac{\partial \mathbf{v}}{\partial t} + (\mathbf{v} \cdot \nabla)\mathbf{v} = -\frac{1}{\rho}\nabla p + \frac{1}{\rho\mu_0}(\nabla \times \mathbf{B}) \times \mathbf{B} \tag{9.4}$$

First, it will be assumed that each variable is only slightly perturbed from its equilibrium value.

$$\begin{aligned} \mathbf{B} &= \mathbf{B}_0 + \mathbf{b} \qquad & \rho &= \rho_0 + \rho' \\ p &= p_0 + p' \qquad & \mathbf{v} &= \mathbf{v}' \end{aligned} \tag{9.5}$$

Here the applied magnetic field will be taken to have only x and y components, so that $\mathbf{B}_0 = (B_{0_x}, B_{0_y}, 0)$. Also, a differential change in pressure $p = p(\rho, S)$ can be expressed as

$$dp = \left(\frac{\partial p}{\partial \rho}\right)_s d\rho + \left(\frac{\partial p}{\partial S}\right)_\rho dS$$

and since $dS = 0$ in the present case, we can write

$$p' = \left(\frac{\partial p}{\partial \rho}\right)_s \rho'$$

Then since $(\partial p/\partial \rho)_s$ is the local speed of sound in the plasma, this can be rewritten as

$$p' = a^2 \rho' \tag{9.6}$$

Substituting Eqs. (9.5) and (9.6) into Eqs. (9.1) to (9.4) yields the desired perturbation equations:

$$\nabla \cdot \mathbf{b} = 0 \tag{9.7}$$

$$\frac{\partial \mathbf{b}}{\partial t} = \nabla \times (\mathbf{v}' \times \mathbf{B}_0) \tag{9.8}$$

$$\frac{\partial \rho'}{\partial t} = -\rho_0 \nabla \cdot \mathbf{v}' \tag{9.9}$$

$$\frac{\partial \mathbf{v}'}{\partial t} = -\frac{a^2}{\rho_0}\nabla \rho' + \frac{1}{\rho_0 \mu_0}(\nabla \times \mathbf{b}) \times \mathbf{B}_0 \tag{9.10}$$

If we consider only plane waves propagating in the x direction then $\partial/\partial y = \partial/\partial z = 0$, so that the following system of equations is obtained from Eqs. (9.7) to (9.10):

$$\frac{\partial b_x}{\partial x} = 0 \tag{9.11a}$$

$$\frac{\partial b_x}{\partial t} = 0 \tag{9.11b}$$

$$\frac{\partial b_y}{\partial t} = B_{0_x}\frac{\partial v_y'}{\partial x} - B_{0_y}\frac{\partial v_x'}{\partial x} \tag{9.12}$$

$$\frac{\partial b_z}{\partial t} = B_{0_x}\frac{\partial v_z'}{\partial x} \tag{9.13}$$

$$\frac{\partial \rho'}{\partial t} = -\rho_0\frac{\partial v_x'}{\partial x} \tag{9.14}$$

$$\frac{\partial v_x'}{\partial t} = -\frac{a^2}{\rho_0}\frac{\partial \rho'}{\partial x} - \frac{1}{\rho_0\mu_0}B_{0_y}\frac{\partial b_y}{\partial x} \tag{9.15}$$

$$\frac{\partial v_y'}{\partial t} = \frac{1}{\rho_0\mu_0}B_{0_x}\frac{\partial b_y}{\partial x} \tag{9.16}$$

$$\frac{\partial v_z'}{\partial t} = \frac{1}{\rho_0\mu_0}B_{0_x}\frac{\partial b_z}{\partial x} \tag{9.17}$$

9.2.1 Transverse Waves.

The first observation to be made is that $b_x = 0$ from Eq. (9.11). Then if Eqs. (9.13) and (9.17) are combined to eliminate v_z', we find that b_z is described by a wave equation.

$$\frac{\partial^2 b_z}{\partial t^2} = A_x{}^2\frac{\partial^2 b_z}{\partial x^2} \tag{9.18}$$

where $A_x \equiv B_{0_x}/\sqrt{\rho_0\mu_0}$ is the Alfvén velocity, and an identical relation applies to v_z'. Clearly then only b_z and v_z' vary in the wave motion described by Eq. (9.18), and these are transverse waves whose phase velocity corresponds to the Alfvén velocity. It is interesting to note that pressure and density do not vary in such transverse waves. Thus, the transverse wave motion is apparently possible even in an incompressible fluid.

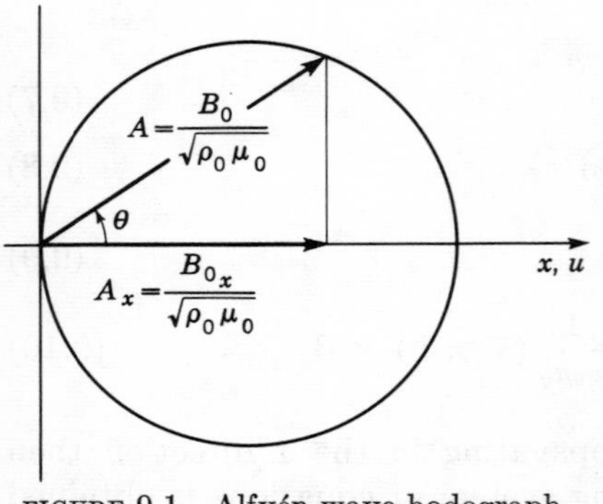

FIGURE 9.1 Alfvén wave hodograph.

Before proceeding further, it is important to note that the phase velocity of these waves is the Alfvén speed, based on the component of the applied magnetic field in the direction of propagation only. This can perhaps be seen more clearly in Fig. 9.1. Here the abscissa is aligned in the x direction, and the component along this direction of the vector **A** is precisely the Alfvén speed of a wave propagating at an angle θ to the direction of applied field. As can be seen, when $\theta = 90°$, the phase velocity has dropped to zero.

9.2.2 Magnetoacoustic Waves. The transverse waves described above are not the only waves that may exist in a compressible conducting medium. To continue the investigation, let us differentiate Eq. (9.12) once with respect to time and replace v_y' from Eq. (9.16) and v_x' from (9.15) to obtain

$$\frac{\partial^2 b_y}{\partial t^2} = \frac{B_0{}^2}{\rho_0\mu_0}\frac{\partial^2 b_y}{\partial x^2} + \frac{a^2}{\rho_0} B_{0_y} \frac{\partial^2 \rho'}{\partial x^2} \tag{9.19}$$

Also, if Eq. (9.14) is differentiated once with respect to time and v_x' is replaced from Eq. (9.15), there is obtained

$$\frac{\partial^2 \rho'}{\partial t^2} = a^2 \frac{\partial^2 \rho'}{\partial x^2} + \frac{B_{0_y}}{\mu_0}\frac{\partial^2 b_y}{\partial x^2} \tag{9.20}$$

Again, similar equations can be derived for v_x' and v_y'. In contrast to the previous case [Eq. (9.18)], these are two *coupled* wave equations for b_y and ρ'.

Let us look for solutions of the form

$$b_y = \tilde{b}_y e^{i(kx-\omega t)}$$
$$\rho' = \tilde{\rho} e^{i(kx-\omega t)}$$

where k is the wave number, ω is the local frequency, and $\tilde{b}_y$ and $\tilde{\rho}$ are the wave amplitudes. Substituting these into Eqs. (9.19) and (9.20) yields

$$\left(u^2 - \frac{B_0{}^2}{\rho_0\mu_0}\right)\tilde{b}_y - \frac{a^2 B_{0_y}}{\rho_0}\tilde{\rho} = 0 \tag{9.21}$$

$$(u^2 - a^2)\tilde{\rho} - \frac{B_{0_y}}{\mu_0}\tilde{b}_y = 0 \tag{9.22}$$

where use has been made of the relationship that $\mathbf{u} = \omega\mathbf{k}/k^2$, or in our case $u = \omega/k$. Now, in order for there to be a nontrivial solution for $\tilde{\rho}$ and $\tilde{b}_y$, the determinant of their coefficients must be zero. Thus,

$$\begin{vmatrix} u^2 - A^2 & -\dfrac{a^2 B_{0_y}}{\rho_0} \\ -\dfrac{B_{0_y}}{\mu_0} & u^2 - a^2 \end{vmatrix} = 0$$

or

$$(u^2 - A^2)(u^2 - a^2) - a^2 A_y{}^2 = 0 \tag{9.23}$$

the roots of which can be written as

$$u_{f,s} = \tfrac{1}{2}\left(\sqrt{a^2 + 2aA_x + A^2} \pm \sqrt{a^2 - 2aA_x + A^2}\right) \tag{9.24}$$

where $A \equiv |\mathbf{B}_0|/\sqrt{\rho_0\mu_0}$ and $A_i \equiv B_{0_i}/\sqrt{\rho_0\mu_0}$. Thus, there are two phase velocities u_f and u_s, corresponding respectively to the fast and slow waves possible for the second system, in which b_y, v'_x, and v'_y can vary.

Now when $B_{0_y} = 0$, Eq. (9.24) shows that $u_f = a$ and $u_s = A_x$. Also, when $B_{0_x} = 0$, we find that $u_f = (A^2 + a^2)^{\frac{1}{2}}$ and $u_s = 0$. For other angles θ between the applied magnetic field and direction of wave propagation, the different wave phase velocities are most conveniently displayed by means of a graphical presentation suggested by Friedrichs.[1] In Fig. 9.2 it has been assumed that the applied field is in the x direction but that the direction of wave propagation k lies at an angle θ. In this case the phase velocity will have both an x and a y component (u_x and u_y), whose values will depend on whether the wave is fast, slow, or transverse and on the value of θ. Essentially these diagrams are hodographs of the phase velocity. It is interesting to observe that u_f if always greater than the Alfvén wave speed, and that u_s is always less than it.

Finally, some limiting cases of interest will be investigated. If the fluid is incompressible then $a \to \infty$, and we find that $u_f \to a \to \infty$, and therefore $u_s \to A_x$. Thus, we have two waves in this case. Both are Alfvén waves with phase velocities of $B_{0_x}/\sqrt{\rho_0\mu_0}$. In one, b_z and v'_z vary, while in the other b_y and v'_y vary. For this case the ellipse for the slow wave merges with the circle of the transverse wave in the first part of Fig. 9.2, and the ellipse of the fast wave becomes a circle of infinite radius. Also, if the fluid is compressible, then a remains finite and there are three

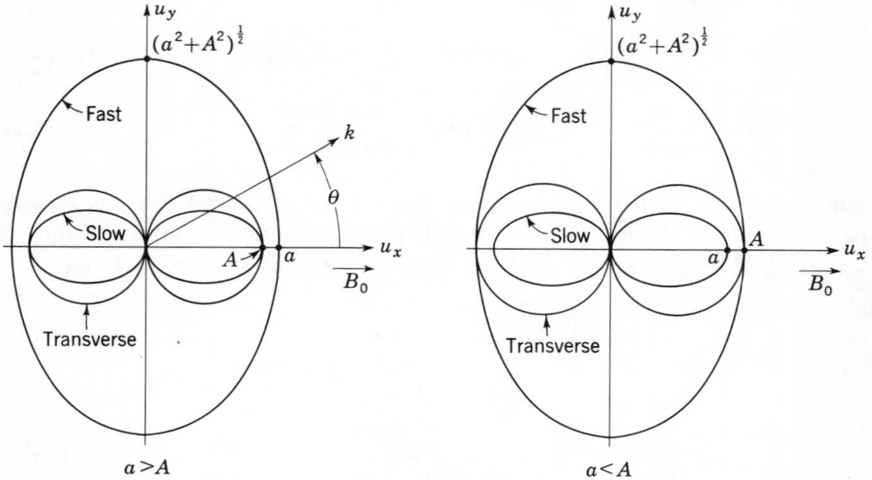

FIGURE 9.2 Graphical presentation of three wave phase velocities. Applied field in x direction. Wave propagation at angle θ to x axis. (After H. Grad, in *The Magnetohydrodynamics of Conducting Fluids*, edited by D. Bershader, Stanford University Press, Stanford, Calif., 1959.)

waves: a fast wave where $u_f = a$; a slow wave where $u_s = A_x$, which becomes an Alfvén wave; and a transverse Alfvén wave.

As a last example, consider the case when B_0^2 is large enough so that $A^2 \gg a^2$. In this case $u_f \to B_0/\sqrt{\rho_0\mu_0}$ and $u_s \to aB_{0_x}/|B_0| = a \cos \theta$. Now the ellipse of the fast wave in the second part of Fig. 9.2 becomes a circle of radius A, and the slow-wave ellipse becomes a circle of diameter a. The Alfvén wave is of course unaffected.

Another feature of the magnetohydrodynamic waves considered in this section is their group velocity. For the Alfvén (transverse) wave we can show that the phase and group velocities are equal in magnitude but differ in direction. We start with the Alfvén wave phase velocity.

$$u = \frac{B_{0_x}}{\sqrt{\rho_0\mu_0}} = \frac{\mathbf{B}_0 \cdot \mathbf{k}}{k\sqrt{\rho_0\mu_0}} = \frac{\omega}{k}$$

Thus

$$\omega = \frac{\mathbf{B}_0 \cdot \mathbf{k}}{\sqrt{\rho_0\mu_0}} \tag{9.25}$$

so that the frequency depends on the orientation between the wave vector $\mathbf{k}$ and the applied field $\mathbf{B}_0$. Now the group velocity is given as $\partial\omega/\partial\mathbf{k} \equiv \mathbf{i}\,\partial\omega/\partial k_x + \mathbf{j}\,\partial\omega/\partial k_y + \mathbf{k}\,\partial\omega/\partial k_z$, so that

$$\mathbf{G} = \frac{\mathbf{B}_0}{\sqrt{\rho_0\mu_0}} \tag{9.26}$$

and it can be seen that the group velocity is in the direction of the applied magnetic field at an angle θ to the direction of the phase velocity. Generally, the expression of Eq. (9.25) is referred to as the *dispersion relation.*

An obvious consequence of a group velocity which is in the direction of the applied field is that the wavefront of an arbitrary pulse disturbance will propagate one-dimensionally, for example, as shown in Fig. 9.3. In other words, an arbitrary pulse disturbance in an incompressible fluid will propagate at the Alfvén speed along a line of constant B, and will in fact remain within the flux tube which originally contained it. On the other hand, an infinitesimal oscillator located at some point in the fluid will generate wave trains moving at a velocity (the phase velocity) in any arbitrary direction. Of course, the magnitude of its velocity will vary with θ and will be zero when normal to $\mathbf{B}$.

The more general question of actually obtaining the shape of the wavefront surfaces just discussed for the magnetoacoustic waves requires the application of the method of geometrical optics.[2] It is quite complex, and will not be considered further here.

So far, dissipative effects due to finite viscosity and conductivity have been omitted. To include them, we again start from Eqs. (8.33) and (8.35), but restrict our attention to an incompressible fluid with conduc-

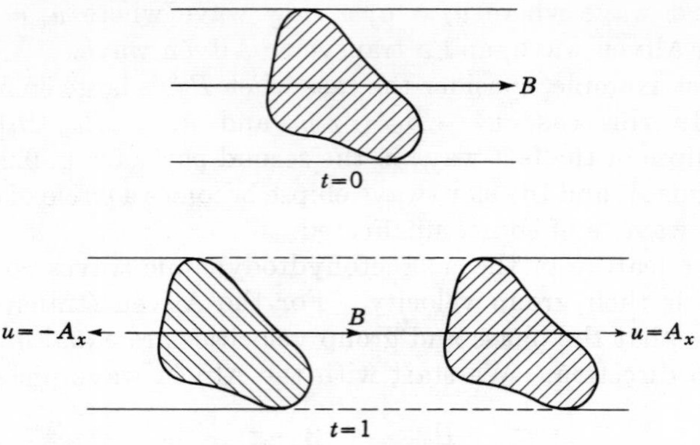

FIGURE 9.3 Propagation of arbitrary disturbances in incompressible fluid. (After H. Grad, in *The Magnetodynamics of Conducting Fluids*, edited by D. Bershader, Stanford University Press, Stanford, Calif., 1959.)

tivity σ and viscosity η constant, and no Hall effect. In this case we have

$$\frac{D\mathbf{v}}{Dt} = -\frac{1}{\rho_0}\nabla p + \nu\,\nabla^2\mathbf{v} + \frac{(\nabla\times\mathbf{B})\times\mathbf{B}}{\rho_0\mu_0} \tag{9.27}$$

and

$$\frac{\partial\mathbf{B}}{\partial t} = (\mathbf{B}\cdot\nabla)\mathbf{v} - (\mathbf{v}\cdot\nabla)\mathbf{B} + \alpha\,\nabla^2\mathbf{B} \tag{9.28}$$

where $\nu = \eta/\rho_0$ and $\alpha = 1/\mu_0\sigma$. As before, it is assumed that $\mathbf{B} = \mathbf{B}_0 + \mathbf{b}$, $\mathbf{v} = \mathbf{v}'$, and $p = p_0 + p'$, where $\mathbf{b}$, $\mathbf{v}'$, and p' are all very small quantities. With the use of these assumptions, Eqs. (9.27) and (9.28) reduce to the following:

$$\frac{\partial\mathbf{v}'}{\partial t} = -\frac{1}{\rho_0}\nabla p' + \nu\,\nabla^2\mathbf{v}' + \frac{1}{\rho_0\mu_0}(\nabla\times\mathbf{b})\times\mathbf{B}_0 \tag{9.29}$$

and

$$\frac{\partial\mathbf{b}}{\partial t} = (\mathbf{B}_0\cdot\nabla)\mathbf{v}' + \alpha\,\nabla^2\mathbf{b} \tag{9.30}$$

since $\mathbf{B}_0$ is a constant.

Now the first of these equations can be further simplified. Rewrite the last term as follows:

$$\begin{aligned}(\nabla\times\mathbf{b})\times\mathbf{B}_0 &= -\mathbf{B}_0\times(\nabla\times\mathbf{b})\\ &= -\nabla(\mathbf{b}\cdot\mathbf{B}_0) + (\mathbf{B}_0\cdot\nabla)\mathbf{b} + (\mathbf{b}\cdot\nabla)\mathbf{B}_0 + \mathbf{b}\times(\nabla\times\mathbf{B}_0)\\ &= -\nabla(\mathbf{b}\cdot\mathbf{B}_0) + (\mathbf{B}_0\cdot\nabla)\mathbf{b}\end{aligned}$$

Then Eq. (9.29) becomes

$$\frac{\partial\mathbf{v}'}{\partial t} = -\frac{1}{\rho_0}\nabla\left(p' + \frac{\mathbf{b}\cdot\mathbf{B}_0}{\mu_0}\right) + \frac{1}{\rho_0\mu_0}(\mathbf{B}_0\cdot\nabla)\mathbf{b} + \nu\,\nabla^2\mathbf{v}' \tag{9.31}$$

If then the divergence of Eq. (9.31) is taken, we see immediately that

$$\nabla^2\left(p' + \frac{\mathbf{b}\cdot\mathbf{B}_0}{\mu_0}\right) = 0$$

Now the quantity within parentheses is a harmonic function which must go to zero at infinity. Accordingly, by Gauss' mean-value theorem it must be zero everywhere, and Eq. (9.31) is now

$$\frac{\partial \mathbf{v}'}{\partial t} = \frac{1}{\rho_0\mu_0}(\mathbf{B}_0\cdot\nabla)\mathbf{b} + \nu\,\nabla^2\mathbf{v}' \tag{9.32}$$

If, as before, attention is restricted to waves propagating only in the x direction, Eqs. (9.30) and (9.32) become

$$\frac{\partial \mathbf{v}'}{\partial t} = \frac{B_{0_x}}{\rho_0\mu_0}\frac{\partial \mathbf{b}}{\partial x} + \nu\frac{\partial^2\mathbf{v}'}{\partial x^2} \tag{9.33}$$

and

$$\frac{\partial \mathbf{b}}{\partial t} = B_{0_x}\frac{\partial \mathbf{v}'}{\partial x} + \alpha\frac{\partial^2\mathbf{b}}{\partial x^2} \tag{9.34}$$

where $\mathbf{b}$ and $\mathbf{v}'$ are transverse vectors, as in the earlier discussion of the Alfvén wave.

Differentiating Eq. (9.34) once with respect to time yields

$$\frac{\partial^2 \mathbf{b}}{\partial t^2} = B_0\frac{\partial^2\mathbf{v}'}{\partial x\,\partial t} + \alpha\frac{\partial}{\partial t}\left(\frac{\partial^2\mathbf{b}}{\partial x^2}\right) \tag{9.35}$$

Then, differentiating Eq. (9.33) with respect to x yields

$$\frac{\partial^2 \mathbf{v}'}{\partial x\,\partial t} = \frac{B_0}{\rho_0\mu_0}\frac{\partial^2\mathbf{b}}{\partial x^2} + \nu\frac{\partial^2}{\partial x^2}\left(\frac{\partial\mathbf{v}'}{\partial x}\right) \tag{9.36}$$

and substituting $\partial\mathbf{v}'/\partial x$ from Eq. (9.34) gives

$$\frac{\partial^2 \mathbf{v}'}{\partial x\,\partial t} = \frac{B_0}{\rho_0\mu_0}\frac{\partial^2\mathbf{b}}{\partial x^2} + \frac{\nu}{B_0}\frac{\partial^2}{\partial x^2}\left(\frac{\partial\mathbf{b}}{\partial t} - \alpha\frac{\partial^2\mathbf{b}}{\partial x^2}\right) \tag{9.37}$$

Combining this with Eq. (9.35) finally yields the desired relation for $\mathbf{b}$:

$$\frac{\partial^2 \mathbf{b}}{\partial t^2} = A^2\frac{\partial^2\mathbf{b}}{\partial x^2} + (\nu+\alpha)\frac{\partial^2}{\partial x^2}\left(\frac{\partial\mathbf{b}}{\partial t}\right) - \nu\alpha\frac{\partial^4\mathbf{b}}{\partial x^4} \tag{9.38}$$

In a similar way an equation for $\mathbf{v}'$ can be derived:

$$\frac{\partial^2 \mathbf{v}'}{\partial t^2} = A^2\frac{\partial^2\mathbf{v}'}{\partial x^2} + (\nu+\alpha)\frac{\partial^2}{\partial x^2}\left(\frac{\partial\mathbf{v}'}{\partial t}\right) - \nu\alpha\frac{\partial^4\mathbf{v}'}{\partial x^4} \tag{9.39}$$

As expected, when ν and α are zero, these relations reduce to the wave equations for the transverse waves already deduced.

Again, when either ν or α is zero and the nonzero quantity is small, a convenient estimate can be made of the distance within which an

Alfvén wave will dissipate. Assume a solution of the form

$$b = b_0 e^{i(kx-\omega t)} \tag{9.40}$$

where $k = k_R + ik_I$, ω is a real quantity, and b is either component (b_y or b_z) of $\mathbf{b}$. Substituting this into Eq. (9.38) with $\nu = 0$, we get

$$\omega^2 = A^2k^2 - i\omega\alpha k^2$$

or

$$k = \frac{\omega}{(A^2 - i\omega\alpha)^{\frac{1}{2}}}$$

When α is small, this can be conveniently separated into real and imaginary parts as follows:

$$k = k_R + ik_I \cong \frac{\omega}{A}\left(1 + \frac{i\omega\alpha}{2A^2}\right) = \frac{\omega}{A} + i\frac{\omega^2\alpha}{2A^3}$$

Thus, the solution, Eq. (9.40), is of the form

$$b = b_0 e^{-\omega^2\alpha x/2A^3} e^{i(k_R x-\omega t)} \tag{9.41}$$

and the first exponential represents a decay with distance from the source of the disturbance, while the second represents the simple sinusoidal traveling wave with phase velocity $A = \omega/k_R$. The distance within which b reduces to $1/e$ of its initial amplitude b_0 (the e-folding length) is then

$$x_e = \frac{2A^3}{\omega^2\alpha} \tag{9.42}$$

By a similar argument the e-folding length when $\alpha = 0$ and ν is small is

$$x_e = \frac{2A^3}{\omega^2\nu} \tag{9.43}$$

Since in laboratory plasmas $\nu \ll \alpha$ ($P_m \ll 1$), the wave will be damped primarily by the fluid's finite electrical resistivity. In general, then, when it is of interest to observe a particular frequency oscillation, a minimum applied magnetic field will be necessary. For lower field strengths the disturbance will damp out in too short a distance to be observed.

9.3 THE MAGNETOHYDRODYNAMIC DISCONTINUITY

In considering a surface of discontinuity in a plasma, the assumption is made that the several dependent variables of the flow change suddenly across such a surface. Clearly, this is an idealization, since physically there is a smooth but rapid transition through a region small compared to the overall dimensions of interest. For example, a shock wave in normal pressure and temperature air is considered a discontinuity, since it has a thickness less than 10^{-3} mm when the Mach number is greater than 1.1.[3] Such thicknesses are obviously small compared to any apparatus of practical dimensions. On the other hand, a shock wave in a stellar atmosphere can also be considered a discontinuity, even though it may be miles thick, since the physical dimensions of the problem may range in the millions of miles.

In considering magnetohydrodynamic discontinuities in detail, it will prove convenient to consider only plane shocks and steady motion. Then, if the point of view of an observer positioned on a discontinuity which is propagating to the left into a stationary plasma is taken, the plasma is seen flowing into the wave from the left and out of it to the right, as shown in Fig. 9.4. The velocity V_1 is the shock velocity, one of several measures of the shock strength. For simplicity, it is assumed that $\mathbf{B}_1$ lies in the xy plane. In general, $\mathbf{B}_2$ and $\mathbf{v}_2$ will not.

Before deriving the general jump conditions, it should be pointed out, following DeHoffman and Teller,[4] that if a transformation from the coordinate system of Fig. 9.4 to a coordinate system moving with the velocity $-V_1(B_1)_t/B_n$ in the y direction is made, $\mathbf{v}$ and $\mathbf{B}$ will be parallel on *each* side of the discontinuity. Here $(\ )_t$ denotes the tangential component, and $(\ )_n$ denotes normal component. The fact that $\mathbf{v}$ and $\mathbf{B}$ are parallel on side 1 follows clearly from the fact that B is invariant on such a transformation, provided $V_1(B_1)_t/B_n$ is nonrelativistic. The fact that they remain parallel on side 2 can be easily shown. In the steady flow of a fluid of infinite conductivity and zero excess charge, it is known that

$$\nabla \times \mathbf{E} = 0 \qquad \nabla \cdot \mathbf{E} = 0$$

and

$$\mathbf{E} = -\mathbf{v} \times \mathbf{B}$$

Therefore, substituting $\mathbf{E}$ in the first two relations,

$$\nabla \cdot (\mathbf{v} \times \mathbf{B}) = \nabla \times (\mathbf{v} \times \mathbf{B}) = 0 \tag{9.44}$$

so that the vector $(\mathbf{v} \times \mathbf{B})$ does not change in crossing the discontinuity. Since it is zero on side 1, it must remain zero on side 2. Accordingly,

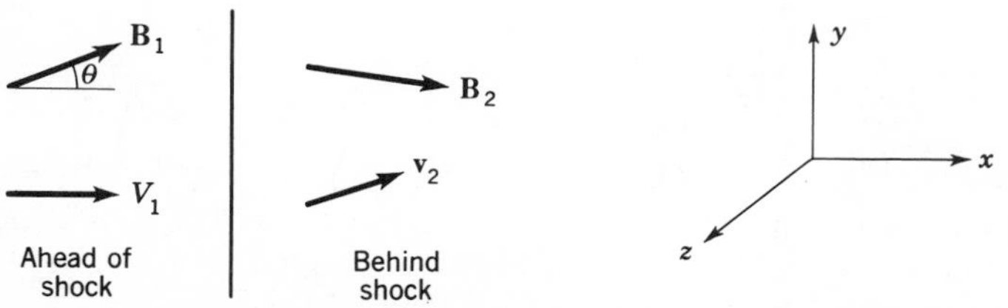

FIGURE 9.4 Variables and shock orientation for shock wave.

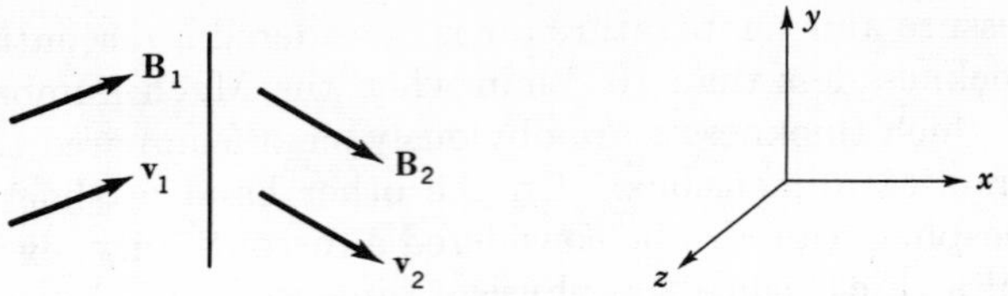

FIGURE 9.5 Alternate configuration for shock analysis.

$\mathbf{v}_2$ and $\mathbf{B}_2$ must be parallel. If it were desirable then, Figure 9.4 could be presented as in Fig. 9.5. Either presentation is a valid one.

9.4 GENERAL SHOCK RELATIONS

As we will be dealing with a plasma of infinite electrical conductivity, it will be most convenient to begin with (8.32) and (8.35). If viscosity, thermal conductivity, the Hall effect, and electrical resistivity are neglected, the steady-state forms of these equations are

$$\nabla \cdot (\rho \mathbf{v}) = 0 \tag{9.45}$$

$$\nabla \cdot \mathbf{B} = 0 \tag{9.46}$$

$$\rho(\mathbf{v} \cdot \nabla)\mathbf{v} = -\nabla p + \frac{1}{\mu_0} (\nabla \times \mathbf{B}) \times \mathbf{B} \tag{9.47}$$

$$\rho(\mathbf{v} \cdot \nabla)H = \frac{1}{\mu_0} (\nabla \times \mathbf{B}) \times \mathbf{B} \cdot \mathbf{v} \tag{9.48}$$

$$\nabla \times (\mathbf{v} \times \mathbf{B}) = 0 \tag{9.49}$$

where the energy equation has been written in terms of H instead of e, and where $H \equiv h + \frac{1}{2}v^2$ is the total enthalpy. Then, if it is assumed that $\partial/\partial y = \partial/\partial z = 0$, all dependent variables will vary only with the distance normal to the shock front x, and the above equations reduce to

$$\frac{d}{dx} (\rho u) = 0 \tag{9.50}$$

$$\rho u \frac{du}{dx} = -\frac{dp}{dx} - \frac{B_z}{\mu_0}\frac{dB_z}{dx} - \frac{B_y}{\mu_0}\frac{dB_y}{dx} \tag{9.51}$$

$$\rho u \frac{dv}{dx} = \frac{B_x}{\mu_0}\frac{dB_y}{dx} \tag{9.52}$$

$$\rho u \frac{dw}{dx} = \frac{B_x}{\mu_0}\frac{dB_z}{dx} \tag{9.53}$$

$$\rho u \frac{dH}{dx} = \left(-u\frac{B_z}{\mu_0} + w\frac{B_x}{\mu_0}\right)\frac{dB_z}{dx} - \left(\frac{uB_y}{\mu_0} - \frac{vB_x}{\mu_0}\right)\frac{dB_y}{dx} \tag{9.54}$$

$$\frac{d}{dx} (uB_y - vB_x) = 0 \tag{9.55}$$

$$\frac{d}{dx} (wB_x - uB_z) = 0 \tag{9.56}$$

where Eq. (9.46) shows that B_x is a constant. After some rearrangement, each of these equations can be expressed in "conservation" form, $\frac{d}{dx}\{\quad\} = 0$.† A single integration then yields

$$[\rho u] = 0 \tag{9.57}$$

$$\left[\rho u^2 + p + \frac{1}{2\mu_0}(B_y^2 + B_z^2)\right] = 0 \tag{9.58}$$

$$\left[\rho uv - \frac{B_x B_y}{\mu_0}\right] = 0 \tag{9.59}$$

$$\left[\rho uw - \frac{B_x B_z}{\mu_0}\right] = 0 \tag{9.60}$$

$$[uB_y - vB_x] = 0 \tag{9.61}$$

$$[wB_x - uB_z] = 0 \tag{9.62}$$

$$\left[\rho uH + \frac{u}{\mu_0}(B_y^2 + B_z^2) - \frac{B_x}{\mu_0}(vB_y + wB_z)\right] = 0 \tag{9.63}$$

where [ ] means the change, and, therefore, [ ] = 0 means that the enclosed quantity is the same on each side of the discontinuity.

If the magnetic field and plasma state ahead of the shock, as well as the shock velocity V_1, are considered known, then the above are seven equations for eight unknowns ρ_2, h_2, p_2, u_2, v_2, w_2, B_{y_2}, and B_{z_2}. Supplementing the above with a caloric equation of state, $h = h(\rho,T)$, and a thermal equation of state, $p = p(\rho,T)$, this system of equations is completed.

9.5 RANKINE–HUGONIOT EQUATION

Our investigation is begun by rearranging (9.57) and (9.63) in such a way that one equation which does not involve any of the flow-velocity components u, v, and w is obtained. This will then be the magnetohydrodynamic analog of the well-known Rankine-Hugoniot equation. First, (9.63) is rewritten as follows:

$$m\left\{[h] + \tfrac{1}{2}m^2[\tau^2] + \tfrac{1}{2}[v^2 + w^2]\right\} + \left[\frac{u}{\mu_0}(B_y^2 + B_z^2)\right] - \frac{B_x}{\mu_0}[vB_y + wB_z] = 0 \tag{9.64}$$

where $\tau = 1/\rho$ and $m = \rho u$. Then, using (9.59) and (9.60), the two components u and v of the tangential velocity can be eliminated. The result-

† It should be noted that the energy equation in terms of h rather than H would have resulted in the simple relation $m\, dh/dx - u\, dp/dx = 0$ rather than (9.54). However, the above equation cannot be put into conservation form; so the energy equation in terms of H must be used.

ing relation is simply

$$[h] + \tfrac{1}{2}m^2[\tau^2] + \frac{1}{\mu_0}[\tau B_t^2] - \frac{1}{2m^2}\frac{B_x^2}{\mu_0^2}[B_t^2] = 0 \tag{9.65}$$

where now $B_t^2 = B_z^2 + B_y^2$.

Our final step is to replace m^2 in terms of other variables, excluding u, v, and w. From (9.58),

$$m^2 = \frac{p_2 - p_1 + \dfrac{1}{2\mu_0}(B_{t_2}^2 - B_{t_1}^2)}{\tau_1 - \tau_2} \tag{9.66}$$

Also, by replacing v in (9.61) from (9.59),

$$m^2 = \frac{B_x^2}{\mu_0}\frac{[B_y]}{[\tau B_y]} \tag{9.67}$$

A similar equation is obtained by replacing w in (9.62) from (9.60):

$$m^2 = \frac{B_x^2}{\mu_0}\frac{[B_z]}{[\tau B_z]} \tag{9.68}$$

Now, the m^2 in the second term of (9.65) is replaced by (9.66). In the last term of this equation, $[B_t^2]/m^2 = [B_z^2]/m^2 + [B_y^2]/m^2$ is written. Then (9.67) is used to replace m^2 in the second, and (9.68) in the first. Making these substitutions and observing that $h = e + p/\rho$, (9.65) becomes

$$e_2 - e_1 + \tfrac{1}{2}(p_2 + p_1)(\tau_2 - \tau_1) + \frac{1}{4\mu_0}\{(B_{z_2} - B_{z_1})^2 + (B_{y_2} - B_{y_1})^2\}(\tau_2 - \tau_1) = 0 \tag{9.69}$$

This is the magnetohydrodynamic equivalent of the Rankine-Hugoniot equation. If B, the magnetic field, is zero, the familiar gas dynamic form is recovered. Considering the last term, it is noted that if $\mathbf{B}_t$ on each side of the shock were parallel, it would be possible to simply write $\{(B_{t_2} - B_{t_1})^2\}$. However, these two fields are not parallel in general, and so the above form has been retained. The question of which types of shocks have B_{t_1} parallel to B_{t_2} will be considered later.

Before proceeding further, some interesting facts can be learned about magnetohydrodynamic shock waves from (9.69). First it is observed that if $[\rho] = 0$, that is, the fluid is incompressible, then the internal energy of the shock is unchanged, $[e] = 0$. If two state variables are unchanged, the thermodynamic state of the fluid is also unchanged. This then leads to the interesting conclusion that $[S] = 0$ in such shock waves. Of course, one can ask: What does change in such a wave if the thermodynamic state does not? The answer is simply that the tangential components of velocity and magnetic field may. Shock waves of this type will be referred to as *Alfvén shocks*, and will be considered in detail later.

If the possibility of constant density is excluded, it can be seen from (9.69) that when $[\rho] > 0$ (the shock is compressive), then $[e] > 0$. Also, since it is known from thermodynamics that for all gases an increase in pressure corresponds to an increase in density, therefore $[p] > 0$. If, on the other hand, the shock is expansive, then $[\rho] < 0$, $[p] < 0$, and $[e] < 0$.

Which of the two possibilities above actually takes place cannot be decided until we consider the entropy. That is, from the second law of thermodynamics it is known that entropy must increase across a magnetohydrodynamic shock wave if the state of the plasma is altered. Our problem then is to derive an expression relating $[S]$ to $[\rho]$ or $[p]$, so that it may be determined whether $[\rho] > 0$ or $[\rho] < 0$ across magnetohydrodynamic shock waves.

9.6 ENTROPY JUMPS

Let us proceed in the following manner. Assume e and τ to be functions of both S and p. That is,

$$e = e(S,p) \qquad \tau = \tau(S,p)$$

Then expand each in a double Taylor series expansion about the state 1.

$$\begin{aligned} e_2(S_2,p_2) = e_1(S_1,p_1) &+ (S_2 - S_1)\left(\frac{\partial e}{\partial S}\right)_p + \cdots \\ &+ (p_2 - p_1)\left(\frac{\partial e}{\partial p}\right)_s + \tfrac{1}{2}(p_2 - p_1)^2\left(\frac{\partial^2 e}{\partial p^2}\right)_s \\ &+ \tfrac{1}{6}(p_2 - p_1)^3\left(\frac{\partial^3 e}{\partial p^3}\right)_s + \cdots \end{aligned} \tag{9.70}$$

Note that the partial derivatives are evaluated at point 1. Similarly, for ρ^{-1},

$$\tau_2 = \tau_1 + (S_2 - S_1)\left(\frac{\partial \tau}{\partial S}\right)_p + \cdots + (p_2 - p_1)\left(\frac{\partial \tau}{\partial p}\right)_s + \cdots \tag{9.71}$$

The following thermodynamic relation is also available:

$$de = T\,dS - p\,d\tau = \left(\frac{\partial e}{\partial S}\right)_p dS + \left(\frac{\partial e}{\partial p}\right)_s dp$$

Thus

$$\left(\frac{\partial e}{\partial S}\right)_p = T \qquad \left(\frac{\partial e}{\partial p}\right)_s = -p\left(\frac{\partial \tau}{\partial p}\right)_s$$

Substituting the above into (9.69) and retaining only the lowest-order terms in ΔS and $\Delta\tau$, we find after considerable manipulation

$$\begin{aligned} T_1(S_2 - S_1) &= \tfrac{1}{12}(p_2 - p_1)^3\left(\frac{\partial^2 \tau}{\partial p^2}\right)_s \\ &- \frac{1}{4\mu_0}\left(\frac{\partial \tau}{\partial p}\right)_s \{(B_{z_2} - B_{z_1})^2 + (B_{y_2} - B_{y_1})^2\}(p_2 - p_1) + \cdots \end{aligned} \tag{9.72}$$

As pointed out earlier, $(\partial\tau/\partial p)_s < 0$ for all fluids. Also, for all real fluids so far investigated it has been found that $(\partial^2\tau/\partial p^2)_s > 0$. Thus, since one must have $\Delta S > 0$, the pressure and density must rise across a weak magnetohydrodynamic shock wave.

From the above relation it is also possible to learn that the entropy rise across a weak shock is of the third order in $[p]$ and $[B_z]$ or $[B_y]$. Thus, for small changes in p and B, the flow across the shock can be assumed to be essentially isentropic. An obvious result, then, is that the behavior of a weak shock is essentially that of a magnetohydrodynamic wave.

For the more general case of a shock of arbitrary strength, Ericson and Bazer[5] have given a proof yielding the same conclusions that have been reached above. However, in their proof they have assumed $(\partial p/\partial e)_\tau > 0$ and $(\partial p/\partial\tau)_e < 0$, in addition to the two assumptions already made, $(\partial\tau/\partial p)_s < 0$ and $(\partial^2\tau/\partial p^2)_s > 0$. Insofar as a real gas obeys these two additional conditions, their proof is quite general. One should be cautioned, however, that there may be some gases for which they do not hold. For a perfect gas the above assumptions can be shown to be satisfied exactly.

9.7 FRIEDRICHS' SHOCK EQUATIONS

In the preceding discussion, the Rankine-Hugoniot equation for the general magnetohydrodynamic shock was presented. From this relation, since it contained only thermodynamic variables, it was possible to show that *if the entropy increases across a shock, the pressure and density also increase.* It was also shown that in the limit of very weak shock waves the motion is essentially that of a magnetohydrodynamic wave.

Next, shocks of arbitrary strength are considered in the hopes that some classification of such shocks similar to that obtained for magnetohydrodynamic waves can be achieved. Following Friedrichs,[1] the mean value of any quantity is defined as

$$\widetilde{(\quad)} \equiv \tfrac{1}{2}[(\quad)_1 + (\quad)_2]$$

Then, defining suitable average values, (9.57) to (9.62) can be written as follows:

$$m[\tau] - [u] = 0 \tag{9.73}$$

$$m[u] + [p] + \frac{1}{\mu_0}\{\tilde{B}_y[B_y] + \tilde{B}_z[B_z]\} = 0 \tag{9.74}$$

$$m[v] - \frac{B_x}{\mu_0}[B_y] = 0 \tag{9.75}$$

$$m[w] - \frac{B_x}{\mu_0}[B_z] = 0 \tag{9.76}$$

$$m\tilde{\tau}[B_y] + \tilde{B}_y[u] - B_x[v] = 0 \tag{9.77}$$

$$m\tilde{\tau}[B_z] + \tilde{B}_z[u] - B_x[w] = 0 \tag{9.78}$$

In order for there to be a nontrivial solution for $[u]$, $[v]$, $[w]$, $[B_y]$, $[B_z]$, and $[\tau]$, one must require that the following determinant be zero. Thus,

$$\begin{array}{cccccc} [u] & [v] & [w] & [B_y] & [B_z] & [\tau] \end{array}$$
$$\begin{vmatrix} -1 & 0 & 0 & 0 & 0 & m \\ m & 0 & 0 & \dfrac{1}{\mu_0}\tilde{B}_y & \dfrac{1}{\mu_0}\tilde{B}_z & \dfrac{[p]}{[\tau]} \\ 0 & m & 0 & -\dfrac{1}{\mu_0}B_x & 0 & 0 \\ 0 & 0 & m & 0 & -\dfrac{1}{\mu_0}B_x & 0 \\ \tilde{B}_y & -B_x & 0 & m\tilde{\tau} & 0 & 0 \\ \tilde{B}_z & 0 & -B_x & 0 & m\tilde{\tau} & 0 \end{vmatrix} = 0$$

or expanding,

$$\left\{m^2\tilde{\tau} - \frac{B_x{}^2}{\mu_0}\right\}\left\{m^4\tilde{\tau} + m^2\left(\frac{\tilde{\tau}[p]}{[\tau]} - \frac{\tilde{B}^2}{\mu_0}\right) - \frac{[p]}{[\tau]}\frac{B_x{}^2}{\mu_0}\right\} = 0 \tag{9.79}$$

where we have defined $\tilde{B}^2 \equiv B_x{}^2 + (\tilde{B}_y)^2 + (\tilde{B}_z)^2$. This is in reality an equation for the permissible values of m, the mass flux. When the expression in the second pair of braces is set equal to zero, the following equation results for m,

$$m^4\tilde{\tau} + m^2\left\{\frac{\tilde{\tau}[p]}{[\tau]} - \frac{\tilde{B}^2}{\mu_0}\right\} - \frac{[p]}{[\tau]}\frac{B_x{}^2}{\mu_0} = 0 \tag{9.80}$$

which leads to two values of m as follows:

$$m_{f,s} = \frac{1}{\sqrt{2}}\left\{\frac{\tilde{B}^2}{\mu_0\tilde{\tau}} - \frac{[p]}{[\tau]} \pm \sqrt{\frac{[p]^2}{[\tau]^2} + \frac{\tilde{B}^2}{\mu_0{}^2\tilde{\tau}^2} - \frac{2[p]}{[\tau]\tilde{\tau}}\frac{(\tilde{B}_y{}^2 + \tilde{B}_z{}^2 - B_x{}^2)}{\mu_0}}\right\}^{\frac{1}{2}}$$

Thus, there are at least two solutions for m.

Similarly, if the first pair of braces had been set equal to zero, there would have been obtained

$$m_A = B_x\sqrt{\frac{1}{\mu_0\tilde{\tau}}} \tag{9.81}$$

So it can be seen that there are three permissible values of m. Since $m = \rho_1 V_1$, this implies that there are three types of magnetohydrodynamic shock waves, each with its own speed of propagation. They will be referred to as *fast*, *slow*, and *Alfvén* shocks, and will be described in the following sections.

Before completing this section, however, it should be noted that the solution of the six simultaneous, linear, homogeneous equations for the six unknowns $[\tau]$, $[u]$, $[v]$, $[w]$, $[B_y]$, and $[B_z]$ can be determined to within an arbitrary constant. The resulting solutions are

$$[\tau] = -Cm\left(m^2\tilde{\tau} - \frac{B_x^2}{\mu_0}\right)\left(m^2\tilde{\tau} - \frac{\tilde{B}^2}{\mu_0}\right) \tag{9.82}$$

$$[u] = -Cm^2\left(m^2\tilde{\tau} - \frac{B_x^2}{\mu_0}\right)\left(m^2\tilde{\tau} - \frac{\tilde{B}^2}{\mu_0}\right) \tag{9.83}$$

$$[v] = Cm^2\left(\frac{1}{\mu_0} B_x\tilde{B}_y\right)\left(m^2\tilde{\tau} - \frac{\tilde{B}^2}{\mu_0}\right) \tag{9.84}$$

$$[w] = Cm^2\left(\frac{1}{\mu_0} B_x\tilde{B}_z\right)\left(m^2\tilde{\tau} - \frac{\tilde{B}^2}{\mu_0}\right) \tag{9.85}$$

$$[B_y] = Cm^3\tilde{B}_y\left(m^2\tilde{\tau} - \frac{\tilde{B}^2}{\mu_0}\right) \tag{9.86}$$

$$[B_z] = Cm^3\tilde{B}_z\left(m^2\tilde{\tau} - \frac{\tilde{B}^2}{\mu_0}\right) \tag{9.87}$$

where C is an arbitrary constant.

From the above relations some knowledge of shock waves of arbitrary strength can be obtained. It should be remembered, however, that all such results will be qualitative since mean quantities are being used throughout.

9.8 FAST AND SLOW SHOCKS

At this point only shocks described in the second pair of braces of (9.79), the fast and slow shocks, will be considered. Rearranging this expression gives

$$m^2 = \frac{(-[p]/[\tau])(m^2 - B_x^2/\mu_0\tilde{\tau})}{m^2 - \tilde{B}^2/\mu_0\tilde{\tau}} \tag{9.88}$$

Now m^2 must be positive. Therefore, either

$$m_s^2 < \frac{B_x^2}{\mu_0\tilde{\tau}}$$

or

$$m_f^2 > \frac{\tilde{B}^2}{\mu_0\tilde{\tau}} > \frac{B_x^2}{\mu_0\tilde{\tau}}$$

The first situation corresponds to the slow shock, while the second represents a fast shock.

It is interesting to observe that whereas m^2 can be less than $B_x^2/\mu_0\tilde{\tau}$ corresponding to a slow shock, and can be greater than $\tilde{B}^2/\mu_0\tilde{\tau}$ corresponding to a fast shock, it cannot lie in between these two values. If it did, (9.88) shows that m^2 would be negative, which is not possible. Also, it can be seen that if $m^2 = B_x^2/\mu_0\tilde{\tau}$, (9.88) cannot be satisfied. This corresponds to the Alfvén shock to be discussed in the next section. Finally,

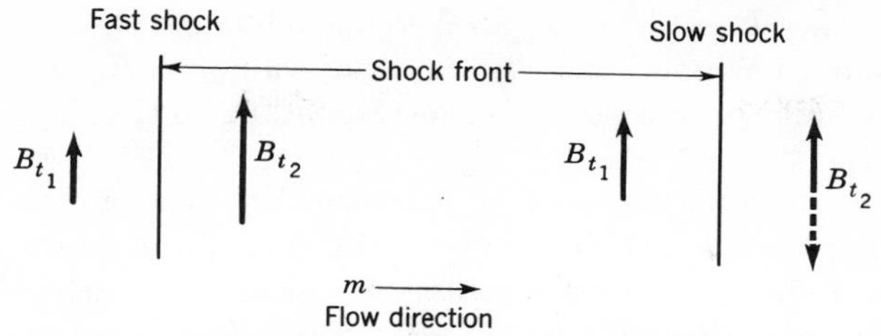

FIGURE 9.6 Field orientation before and after shocks.

when $m^2 = \tilde{B}^2/\mu_0\bar{\tau}$, (9.88) becomes infinite. Thus, it can be concluded that when $B_x^2/\mu_0\bar{\tau} < m^2 < \tilde{B}^2/\mu_0\bar{\tau}$, no shock exists.

The interesting conclusion that one can draw from the above observations is that although the shock velocity of a weak slow shock should correspond to $B_x^2/\mu_0\bar{\tau}$, the shock velocity of a weak fast shock should tend toward $\tilde{B}^2/\mu_0\bar{\tau}$. In other words, the latter shock velocity depends on the orientation of the magnetic field in the region into which it propagates, rather than on its normal component alone.

So far only the range of shock strengths corresponding to each type of shock has been shown. Next, an attempt will be made to deduce the change in magnetic field across the fast and slow shocks.

First, note that $2\tilde{B}_y[B_y] = [B_y^2]$. Then, using (9.86) and (9.87),

$$[B_t^2] = [B_y^2 + B_z^2] = 2Cm^3(\tilde{B}_y^2 + \tilde{B}_z^2)\left(m^2\bar{\tau} - \frac{\tilde{B}^2}{\mu_0}\right) \tag{9.89}$$

Replacing C from (9.82) gives

$$[B_t^2] = -\frac{2m^2[\tau]\tilde{B}_t^2}{m^2\bar{\tau} - B_x^2/\mu_0} \tag{9.90}$$

Since it was learned earlier that $[\tau] < 0$, it is now found that $|B_t|$ rises across a fast shock and drops across a slow shock. It is also of interest to consider the direction in which B_t changes (see Fig. 9.6). For a slow shock $|B_{t_2}| < |B_{t_1}|$. Thus, B_{t_2} may lie in the same direction as B_{t_1} or could reverse direction (dotted arrow). For the fast shock, $|B_{t_2}| > |B_{t_1}|$. Then B_{t_2} must be larger than B_{t_1}. Also, it must lie in the same direction since $|B_{t_2}|$ must increase monotonically from $|B_{t_1}|$ to some larger value. In the limit of a very strong fast shock it can be shown that $[B_t]$ has a limiting value. From (9.82) and (9.86) write

$$[B_t] = \frac{-m^2[\tau]}{m^2\bar{\tau} - B_x^2/\mu_0}\tilde{B}_t$$

or

$$B_{t_2} = \frac{1+k}{1-k}B_{t_1} \tag{9.91}$$

where

$$k = -\frac{m^2[\tau]}{2(m^2\bar{\tau} - B_x^2/\mu_0)}$$

As $m^2 \to \infty$, then $k \to (\tau_1 - \tau_2)/(\tau_1 + \tau_2) > 0$ but less than unity. Thus $0 < k < 1$ in this limit, and the limiting value of B_{t_2} is obtained in terms of the finite jump in density, corresponding to the shock of infinite strength.

Another interesting aspect of such shock waves can be seen from Fig. 9.6. For one particular value of m^2 a slow shock can reduce B_{t_2} to zero. Such a shock is called a *switch-off* shock. Similarly, if B_{t_1} is zero in a fast shock, it is possible to have $B_{t_2} > 0$. This is called a *switch-on* shock. From (9.67) and (9.68) it is seen that m^2 takes on the following values: $m^2_{s.\text{off}} = (B_x{}^2/\mu_0)\rho_1$, $m^2_{s.\text{on}} = (B_x{}^2/\mu_0)\rho_2$.

So far in our discussion, the discontinuity being considered could be three-dimensional in the sense that B and v on both sides of the front may not lie in the same plane. It is possible, however, to show that the *fast* and *slow* shock waves (characterized by $m \neq 0$, $[\rho] \neq 0$) are indeed two-dimensional.† Let us assume that $B_x = 0$. Since by definition $u_1 = V_1$, $v_1 = w_1 = 0$ (see Fig. 9.4), then Eqs. (9.59) and (9.60) show that

$$v_2 = w_2 = 0$$

Then from (9.61) and (9.62) we obtain the following relations:

$$u_1 B_{y_1} = u_2 B_{y_2} \tag{9.92}$$

$$u_1 B_{z_1} = u_2 B_{z_2} \tag{9.93}$$

Thus, $B_{y_1}/B_{z_1} = B_{y_2}/B_{z_2}$ and $B_{t_1} \| B_{t_2}$. In this case, there is no loss in generality in assuming $B_{z_1} = B_{z_2} = 0$. This same result can be shown to be true when $B_x \neq 0$. Thus, a simplified set of equations is obtained for the two-dimensional fast or slow magnetohydrodynamic shock wave.

With $B_z = w = 0$, these equations are

$$[\rho u] = 0 \tag{9.94}$$

$$\left[\rho u^2 + p + \frac{1}{2\mu_0} B_y{}^2\right] = 0 \tag{9.95}$$

$$\left[\rho u v - \frac{B_x B_y}{\mu_0}\right] = 0 \tag{9.96}$$

$$[u B_y - v B_x] = 0 \tag{9.97}$$

$$\left[\rho u H + \frac{u}{\mu_0} B_y{}^2 - \frac{v}{\mu_0} B_x B_y\right] = 0 \tag{9.98}$$

or, if preferable,

$$\rho_1 V_1 = \rho_2 u_2 = m \tag{9.99}$$

$$m V_1 + p_1 + \frac{B_{y1}^2}{2\mu_0} = m u_2 + p_2 + \frac{B_{y2}^2}{2\mu_0} \tag{9.100}$$

† However, the Alfvén shock is in general three-dimensional (see Sec. 9.11).

$$mv_2 = \frac{B_x}{\mu_0}(B_{y_2} - B_{y_1}) \tag{9.101}$$

$$V_1 B_{y_1} = u_2 B_{y_2} - v_2 B_x \tag{9.102}$$

$$mH_1 + V_1 \frac{B_{y_1}^2}{\mu_0} = mH_2 + \frac{V_1 B_{y_1}}{\mu_0} B_{y_2} \tag{9.103}$$

where
$$H = h + \frac{u^2 + v^2}{2}$$

The above set of equations will be useful when we wish to solve for the flow behind the shock wave, knowing the flow in front of it and the shock strength. In a later section, such a procedure will be illustrated for a perfect gas.

Before concluding this section, a feature of the magnetohydrodynamic shock which has not been touched upon should be discussed. Since $B_{t_1} \neq B_{t_2}$ in a magnetohydrodynamic shock, a current sheet coincident with the shock discontinuity must exist in order that $\nabla \times \mathbf{B} = \mu_0 \mathbf{J}$ be fulfilled. In fact, the current will flow out of the page for the slow shock shown in Fig. 9.6, and into the page for the fast shock.

9.9 SHOCKS WITH $B_x = 0$

In order to proceed further without specifying an equation of state, we consider the case for which $B_x = 0$. Here (9.101) shows that $v_2 = 0$, so that the flow is normal to the shock front on each side. Then (9.100), (9.102), and (9.103) become

$$mV_1 + p_1 + \frac{B_{y_1}^2}{2\mu_0} = mu_2 + p_2 + \frac{B_{y_2}^2}{2\mu_0} \tag{9.104}$$

$$u_1 B_{y_1} = u_2 B_{y_2} \tag{9.105}$$

$$m(h_1 + \tfrac{1}{2}V_1^2) + V_1 \frac{B_{y_1}^2}{\mu_0} = m(h_2 + \tfrac{1}{2}u_2^2) + u_2 \frac{B_{y_2}^2}{\mu_0} \tag{9.106}$$

where
$$m = \rho_1 V_1 = \rho_2 u_2$$

If the following quantities are defined,

$$p^* = p + \frac{B_y{}^2}{2\mu_0}$$

$$e^* = e + \frac{B_y{}^2}{2\mu_0 \rho}$$

then the equation of the nonmagnetic Rankine-Hugoniot form can again be derived.

$$e_2^* - e_1^* + \tfrac{1}{2}(p_2^* + p_1^*)(\tau_2 - \tau_1) = 0 \tag{9.107}$$

The surprising result is thus found that magnetohydrodynamic shock waves with $B_x = 0$ are directly analogous to conventional shock waves if a modified pressure p^* and a new internal energy e^* are defined. All the results of conventional theory then carry over directly. In particular, we can make use of those general results available for conventional shocks which do not depend on the explicit form of the equation of state.

In the preceding qualitative discussion it had been pointed out that, in the limit, weak magnetohydrodynamic shock waves seem to propagate with the speed of a magnetohydrodynamic wave. For the present case ($B_x = 0$), only a fast shock will exist, so that one may suppose that its speed of propagation will be

$$V_1 = \sqrt{a_1^2 + \frac{B_{y1}^2}{\mu_0 \rho_1}} \tag{9.108}$$

where a perfect gas has been assumed, a is the speed of sound, and $B_{y_1}/\sqrt{\mu_0 \rho_1}$ is the Alfvén speed in the medium ahead of the wave. The validity of this assumption can be verified by considering the shock equations for a perfect gas but with $B_x = 0$ [see Eqs. (9.112) to (9.115)]. If they are written in terms of ratios[6] p_2/p_1, ρ_2/ρ_1, then we have

$$\frac{\rho_1 V_1^2}{p_1}\left(1 - \frac{\rho_1}{\rho_2}\right) = \frac{p_2}{p_1} - 1 + \frac{B_1^2}{2\mu_0 p_1}\left(\frac{\rho_2^2}{\rho_1^2} - 1\right) \tag{9.109}$$

and

$$\frac{\rho_1 V_1^2}{p_1}\left(1 - \frac{\rho_1^2}{\rho_2^2}\right) = \frac{2\gamma}{\gamma - 1}\left(\frac{p_2}{p_1}\frac{\rho_1}{\rho_2} - 1\right) + \frac{2B_1^2}{\mu_0 \rho_1}\left(\frac{\rho_2}{\rho_1} - 1\right) \tag{9.110}$$

Then if p_2/p_1 is eliminated between these, the following relation is obtained:

$$\frac{B_1^2}{2\mu_0 p_1}(2 - \gamma)\frac{\rho_2^2}{\rho_1^2} + \left[\gamma\left(\frac{B_1^2}{2\mu_0 p_1} + 1\right) + \frac{\gamma - 1}{2}\frac{\rho_1^2 V_1^4}{p_1^2}\right]\frac{\rho_2}{\rho_1} - \frac{\gamma + 1}{2}\frac{\rho_1^2 V_1^4}{p_1^2} = 0 \tag{9.111}$$

Then if the shock strength is weak, $\rho_2/\rho_1 \cong 1$, and we find the result of Eq. (9.108) for V_1 as anticipated. The more general treatment of shocks in a perfect gas when $B_x \neq 0$ will be deferred to Sec. 9.13.

If in addition to assuming a weak shock, it is assumed that $B_{y_1} \to 0$, then $V_1 \to a$. Alternately, if it is assumed that $B_{y_1} \to \infty$, then $V_1 \to B_{y_1}/\sqrt{\mu_0 \rho_1}$. This, however, is not an Alfvén wave since it propagates normal to the magnetic field, whereas the Alfvén wave phase velocity is zero normal to the field lines.

Another interesting feature of such shock waves as are being considered here ($B_x = 0$) can be seen from (9.105). Since it was concluded earlier that there must be $\rho_2 > \rho_1$, then since $\rho_1 V_1 = \rho_2 u_2$ it is clear that $u_2 < V_1$. In this case, $B_{y_2} > B_{y1}$, and so the magnetic field in front of the shock is amplified upon its passage (see Fig. 9.6).

9.10 ALFVÉN SHOCKS

An Alfvén shock will be defined here to be a magnetohydrodynamic shock across which the density does not change (i.e., a shock in an incompressible fluid). As shown earlier in Sec. 9.4, in this case the gas state does not change and $[S] = 0$. It can also be shown with the aid of (9.73) that $[u] = 0$. Thus, (9.74) reduced to

$$\tilde{B}_y[B_y] + \tilde{B}_z[B_z] = \tfrac{1}{2}(B_{t2}^2 - B_{t1}^2) = 0$$
$$\therefore \qquad [B_t^2] = 0$$

Thus, it has been proved that the magnitude of the magnetic field does not change in an Alfvén shock.

From (9.75) and (9.76) it can be concluded that $[B_t] \neq 0$, $[v] \neq 0$, $[w] \neq 0$. Thus, in an Alfvén shock the principal effect is the *rotation* of the tangential component of magnetic field in the plane of the shock without any change in magnitude. It is now clear why the distinction was made between two- and three-dimensional shocks earlier. The Alfvén shock is in general a three-dimensional one. In the special case when B_{t_2} is rotated 180°, this Alfvén shock corresponds to one case of the slow shock described earlier. Thus, the Alfvén shock is continuously connected with the slow shock. This connection will be seen more clearly in the next section.

9.11 FRIEDRICHS' DIAGRAM

A quite useful device for summarizing many of the characteristics of the slow, fast, and Alfvén shocks has been proposed by Friedrichs.[1] It consists of a diagram on which are plotted the transverse components of magnetic field, and is shown in Fig. 9.7. In this figure the plane of the page corresponds to the plane of the shock front. The tangential component of magnetic field ahead of the shock is denoted by B_0. All other arrows correspond to the tangential component of magnetic field after the shock. For the fast and slow shocks the magnetic field remains in the same plane (two-dimensionality), whereas for the Alfvén shock it rotates out of the plane but does not change magnitude. In a slow shock the magnetic field is reduced, and can reverse direction. The fast shock in-

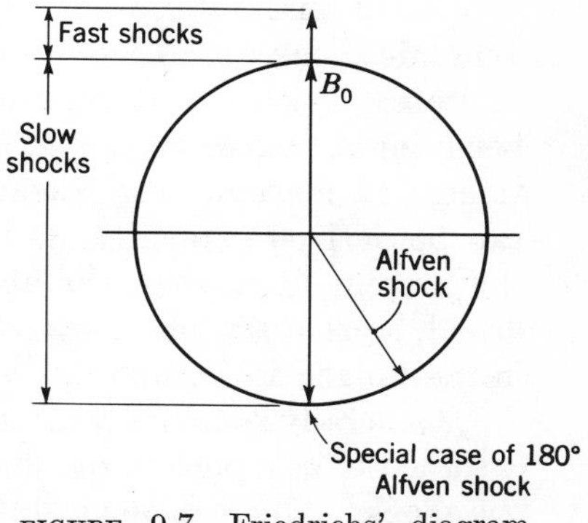

FIGURE 9.7 Friedrichs' diagram illustrating fast, slow, and Alfvén shocks.

creases the magnetic field up to a limiting value for the shock of infinite strength. Finally, the special case for which the Alfvén shock is rotated 180° is seen to correspond to one case of a slow shock.

9.12 OTHER DISCONTINUITIES

Earlier in this chapter a shock discontinuity was defined as one through which mass flows. If this restriction is now relaxed, several additional discontinuities can be discussed.

First, if $u = 0$ and $B_x \neq 0$, (9.58) to (9.62) show that

$$[v] = [w] = [B_t] = [p] = 0$$

However, $[\rho]$ does not necessarily have to be zero, and so a change in temperature and in density can occur across such a discontinuity. In gas dynamics these are referred to simply as *contact* surfaces. In magnetohydrodynamics they can also be referred to as a special *contact* discontinuity.

Another type of discontinuity can occur if $u = 0$ and $B_x = 0$. In this case, (9.58) to (9.62) show that $[B_t]$ and $[u_t]$ are arbitrary, and we can only conclude that $[p + (1/2\mu_0)B_t^2] = 0$. This type will be referred to as *shear-flow* discontinuities. They have been studied at length by Friedrichs,[1] who concluded that such a discontinuity could not be maintained if B_x were nonzero at the shock.

Since it is the intent of this chapter to consider principally magnetohydrodynamic shock waves, the study of the contact and shear-flow discontinuities will not be pursued any further. Additional details can be found in Landau's book.[7]

9.13 SHOCKS IN PERFECT GASES

Additional information concerning the nature of magnetohydrodynamic shock waves can be obtained by specifying the required equation of state. With this done, one can in principle obtain solutions for the behavior of such shock waves by numerically solving the associated equations. If, however, the plasma is assumed to be a perfect gas, solutions can be derived explicitly, as has been shown by several authors.[6,8] In the present discussion, the approach of Bazar and Ericson[8] will be followed, so that the shock-strength parameter will be chosen as the jump in the tangential component of magnetic field.

Generally speaking a plasma through which a shock passes cannot be assumed to be a perfect gas, since its degree of ionization will change after the shock. There is one instance, however, in which such an assumption should be reasonably valid. Consider a low-temperature plasma which is singly ionized, that is, consists of only two species, electrons and singly ionized atoms. Because of its low temperature, the contribution of excited states to its thermodynamic properties can be neglected. Then, if the temperature after the shock remains sufficiently low so that excited states and second or higher degrees of ionization are negligible, the plasma can be accurately described as a perfect gas. It is of interest to note that the type of plasma just described corresponds to that believed to exist in most astrophysical situations. To illustrate the procedure, consider a perfect gas with constant specific heats C_p and C_V. In this case

$$p = \rho RT \qquad h = C_p T$$
$$R = C_p - C_V \qquad \gamma = \frac{C_p}{C_V}$$

With the above, the system of equations (9.99) to (9.103), which refer to the shock geometry of Fig. 9.4, can be rewritten for a two-dimensional shock as

$$\rho_1 V_1{}^2 + p_1 + \frac{B_{y_1}^2}{2\mu_0} = \rho_1 V_1 u_2 + p_2 + \frac{B_{y_2}^2}{2\mu_0} \tag{9.112}$$

$$\frac{B_x}{\mu_0} B_{y_1} = \frac{B_x}{\mu_0} B_{y_2} - \rho_1 V_1 v_2 \tag{9.113}$$

$$V_1 B_{y_1} = u_2 B_{y_2} - B_x v_2 \tag{9.114}$$

$$V_1\left(\frac{\gamma p_1}{\gamma - 1} + \frac{\rho_1 V_1{}^2}{2} + \frac{B_{y_1}^2}{\mu_0}\right) = \frac{\gamma}{\gamma - 1} p_2 u_2 + \frac{\rho_1 V_1}{2}(u_2{}^2 + v_2{}^2) + \frac{V_1 B_{y_1}}{\mu_0} B_{y_2} \tag{9.115}$$

The solution of these four equations can be determined, once the state of the gas ahead of the shock is specified, and the jump in tangential magnetic field $f \equiv [B_y]/|\mathbf{B}_1|$ is chosen as parameter. The solution can be derived by straightforward algebraic manipulation, as described by Bazar and Ericson.[8] The resulting relations for $[\rho]$, $[p]$, and the shock velocity are given below,

$$\frac{[\rho]}{\rho_1} = f\left\{\frac{-\frac{1}{2}\gamma f \sin\theta - 1 + q \pm \sqrt{r}}{2q\sin\theta - (\gamma - 1)f}\right\} \tag{9.116}$$

$$\frac{[p]}{p_1} = \frac{\gamma f}{q}\left\{-\frac{1}{2}h + \frac{[\rho]/(f - \sin\theta)\rho_1}{1 - ([\rho]/\rho_1 f)\sin\theta}\right\} \tag{9.117}$$

$$V_1 = \frac{A_{1_x}}{\left\{\left(1 + \frac{[\rho]}{\rho_1}\right)\left(1 - \frac{[\rho]}{\rho_1 f}\sin\theta\right)\right\}^{\frac{1}{2}}} \tag{9.118}$$

where θ is the angle between the magnetic field ahead of the shock and the normal to the shock. In addition, the following quantities have been defined:

$$q \equiv \frac{\gamma p_1 \mu_0}{B_1^2}$$

$$A_{1_x} \equiv \sqrt{\frac{B_x^2}{\mu_0 \rho_1}}$$

$$r \equiv f^2(\tfrac{1}{2}\gamma^2 \sin^2\theta - \gamma + 1) + f \sin\theta(2 - \gamma)(1 + q) + 4q \sin^2\theta + (1 - q)^2$$

The quantity q may be recognized as proportional to the ratio of the gas pressure to magnetic field intensity ahead of the shock. It can also be thought of as the square of the ratio of the speed of sound to the Alfvén speed ahead of the shock. Thus,

$$\frac{a_1^2}{A_{1_x}^2} = \frac{\gamma p_1/\rho_1}{B_1^2/\mu_0\rho_1} = \frac{\gamma p_1 \mu_0}{B_1^2} \equiv q$$

The quantity A_{1_x} is of course the Alfvén speed ahead of the shock based on the normal component of magnetic field. r is a function of f and the conditions ahead of the shock, which has been defined for convenience.

The above solution applies to the fast shocks as it stands, and to the slow shocks if f is replaced by $-f$. It should also be observed that these equations yield more solutions than are admissible. Those which are nonadmissible can be eliminated by requiring that the entropy increase across the shock for all admissible ones. On the basis of this solution, Bazar and Ericson have proposed the following classification of magnetohydrodynamic shock waves.

Alfvén shocks: $[B_y^2] = 0$

Fast shocks: $[B_y^2] > 0$

Type 1: $q \geq 1 - \dfrac{\gamma}{\gamma - 1} \sin^2\theta$

Type 2: $q < 1 - \dfrac{\gamma}{\gamma - 1} \sin^2\theta$

Slow shocks: $[B_y^2] < 0$

Type 1: $q \geq 1 - \gamma \sin^2\theta$

Type 2: $q < 1 - \gamma \sin^2\theta$

The information of consequence here is that there are two types of fast and slow shocks. Shocks of type 1 yield single-valued solutions for each value of $[B_y]$, while those of type 2 yield double-valued solutions. In other words, for a fixed value of q, a small value of θ ahead of the shock will give shocks of type 1 (single-valued). As θ is increased, eventually a type 2 shock will occur, and the multivalued phenomenon arises. Of course, if q is sufficiently large, the solution will always be single-valued.

In order to understand the above phenomena more clearly, some calculations of shock velocity for one particular choice of parameters are shown in Figs. 9.8 and 9.9.

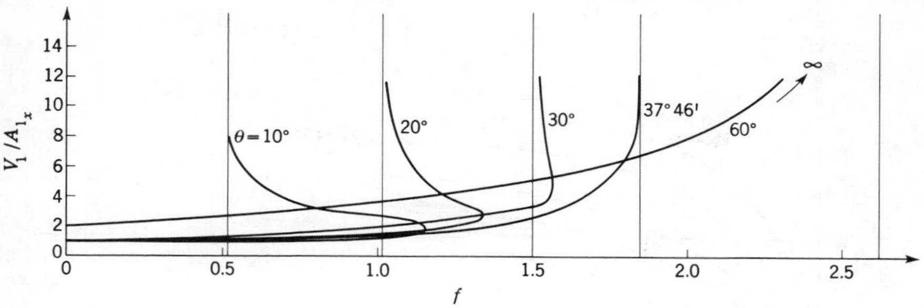

q = 1/16 γ = 5/3 Type 1: θ ≥ 37°46′ Type 2: θ < 37°46′

FIGURE 9.8 Fast magnetic shocks.

Here it can be seen that when $\theta < 37°46'$ for the fast shock, the solutions are double-valued, and when θ is larger than this, the normal single-valued solutions arise. The vertical lines drawn on Fig. 9.8 denote the maximum value that f can reach for a shock with an infinite velocity. Obviously, this value of $f_{\max}$ depends on θ. It may be recalled that in Sec. 9.9 it was shown that

$$\frac{B_{y_2}}{B_{y_1}} = \frac{1+k}{1-k} \tag{9.119}$$

and that when $V_1 \to \infty$,

$$k \to \frac{\tau_1 - \tau_2}{\tau_1 + \tau_2}$$

Now, as has been verified by Bazar and Ericson,[8] the limiting value of the density jump $[\rho]/\rho_1$ across a magnetohydrodynamic shock of infinite velocity is the same as in a gas dynamic shock and is $2/(\gamma - 1)$. For a $\gamma = \frac{5}{3}$ then k becomes

$$k = \frac{\rho_2/\rho_1 - 1}{\rho_2/\rho_1 + 1} = \frac{3}{5}$$

Thus,

$$\frac{B_{y_2}}{B_{y_1}} = \frac{1+k}{1-k} = 4$$

However, the parameter f used by Bazar and Ericson is

$$f_{\max} = \frac{B_{y_2} - B_{y_1}}{|\mathbf{B}_1|} = \left(\frac{B_{y_2}}{B_{y_1}} - 1\right)\sin\theta = 3\sin\theta$$

Thus, the value of $f_{\max}$ corresponding to a fast shock with $V_1 \to \infty$ has been obtained from the consideration of mean quantities, and agrees with the exact solution being considered here.

In Fig. 9.9 the slow-shock solutions are shown. The type 1 solution corresponds to $\theta = 60°$, while the other curves correspond to type 2, or multivalued, solutions. Proceeding along any one of the curves of

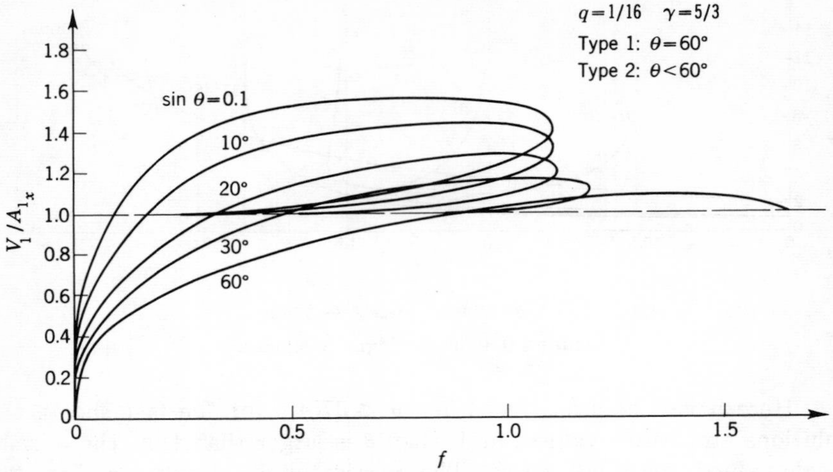

FIGURE 9.9 Slow magnetic shocks.

type 2, the value of V_1/A_{1_x} increases, reaches a maximum, and finally reduces to unity as f varies. In the course of the rise of f, the value of B_{y_2} is reduced, falls to zero, and reverses direction, just as had been shown in Fig. 9.8.

In addition to the above calculated results, Bazar and Ericson were also able to show that for the fast shock

$$V_1 > c_{f,1}$$
$$u_2 < c_{f,2}$$

where c_f is the fast magnetohydrodynamic disturbance speed. Accordingly, the flow velocity in front of the shock exceeds the disturbance speed while the velocity behind it is less than the disturbance speed. This is in direct analogy to the reduction of a supersonic flow, normal to a gas dynamic shock front, to a subsonic flow behind it.

Finally, if a perfect gas is assumed, the Rankine-Hugoniot equation (9.69) can be written as follows. Write $e = (p/\rho)/(\gamma - 1)$, and let $B_z = 0$, so that

$$\frac{1}{\gamma - 1}\left[\frac{p_2}{\rho_2} - \frac{p_1}{\rho_1}\right] + \tfrac{1}{2}(p_2 + p_1)\frac{\rho_1 - \rho_2}{\rho_1\rho_2} + \frac{1}{4\mu_0}(B_{y_2} - B_{y_1})^2 \frac{\rho_1 - \rho_2}{\rho_1\rho_2} = 0 \quad (9.120)$$

Introducing the notation previously used and solving for the pressure jump, the result is

$$\frac{[p]}{p_1} = \frac{\gamma[\rho]/\rho_1}{2 - (\gamma - 1)[\rho]/\rho_1}\left\{2 + \frac{(\gamma - 1)f^2}{2q}\right\} \quad (9.121)$$

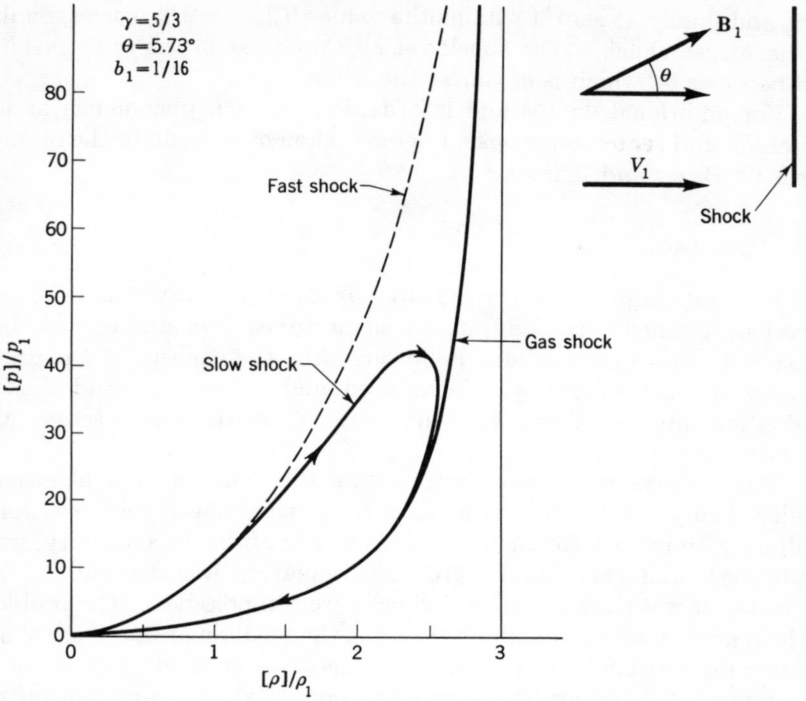

FIGURE 9.10 Rankine-Hugoniot curve for a magnetohydrodynamic shock in a perfect gas with $\gamma = \frac{5}{3}$. (After Ericson and Bazar.[5])

For one case Ericson and Bazar have plotted the familiar Rankine-Hugoniot curve shown in Fig. 9.10.

In this figure the curves for the fast and slow shocks are shown, along with the curve for the purely gas dynamic shock. As can be seen, for a given jump in density the pressure jump will always be greater, because of the magnetic field, than it would have been in its absence. Also, the limiting value of $[\rho]/\rho_1 = 3$ is shown for a shock of infinite strength, and it is seen that the slow shock is not only less than this value but cannot ever approach it.

The curves for the fast and slow shock shown are for shocks of type 2. Thus they correspond to the previously discussed multivalued situation. For example, on the fast-shock curve as $[p]$ increases, $[B_y]$ first increases, reaches a maximum, and then drops to a finite value when $[p] \to \infty$. Then, on the other hand, as $[p]$ rises from zero to infinity, the shock velocity does also. For the slow shock consider a point traveling along the upper portion of the curve, starting from zero. At zero, $[B_y] = 0$. As the point moves along the upper curve, $[B_y]$ increases. As it moves onto the lower portion of the curve $[B_y]$ eventually reduces to zero, and finally at zero it attains the value $[B_y] = -2B_{y_1}$ corresponding to the Alfvén shock. The shock velocity proceeds in the same fashion, and becomes b_1, which is of course the Alfvén speed.

For additional details and information on such phenomena as the switch-on and switch-off shocks, reference should be made to the original paper by Bazar and Ericson.[8]

9.14 SUMMARY

In this chapter both magnetohydrodynamic waves and shocks have been studied. Initially, infinitesimal waves were studied and their phase velocities determined. Following this, the concept of the group velocity of such waves was introduced and discussed. And finally, dissipation due to finite viscosity and electrical conductivity was investigated.

Shock waves have been treated from the point of view of discontinuity theory. With this as a basis, the general shock relations, for a medium with infinite conductivity on each side of the discontinuity, were established, and the Rankine-Hugoniot equation was derived. Using the latter, it was shown that such shocks are compressive. The problem of the magnetohydrodynamic shock when the medium ahead of the shock has zero rather than infinite conductivity has been studied by Lyubimov.[9] His treatment, however, is restricted to normal shock waves within the assumption of a perfect gas. Unless the gas behind the shock has been fully ionized, this assumption will not be valid.

Further qualitative information on shocks proceeding into a gas of infinite conductivity was obtained by defining mean quantities, following Friedrichs,[1] and showing that the same classification scheme that is applied to magnetohydrodynamic waves can be applied to shocks. Next, a method of solution of the general shock relations for a perfect gas was described. Some of the results of such a solution were presented, and it was seen that the preceding qualitative conclusions could be taken to apply exactly in this case. Knowing the solution for a perfect gas, it was also shown how the Rankine-Hugoniot curve could be obtained, and a sample curve for one special case was presented. Application of this solution for a perfect gas could also have been made to the flow of an infinitely conducting plasma over a wedge when the flow and magnetic field upstream of the wedge are parallel. However, such problems were not considered since they are of limited interest in engineering magnetohydrodynamics.

It was also found from the perfect-gas solution that, under some conditions, more than one shock can exist for a single value of shock strength. The important question of which, if either, of these shocks could exist was not considered. Very recently several studies along this line have been carried out. They have each used somewhat different approaches and are apparently not in complete agreement. Ludford[10] considered the structure of a magnetohydrodynamic shock wave and concluded that, within the assumptions of his analysis, there is no transition that will connect the state ahead of an Alfvén shock with that behind. Accordingly, an Alfvén shock is presumed not to exist. R. V. Polovin[11] considered the interesting question of whether or not a shock is stable with respect to decomposition into more than one shock. He concluded that fast shocks are stable in the above sense, as are slow shocks which do not reverse the sign of the magnetic field. Alfvén shocks are also stable. Thus, his study excludes only those slow shocks which would have reversed B_y. All in all, the question of which of the multitude of magnetohydrodynamic shocks can exist seems largely unsettled.

REFERENCES CITED

1. Friedrichs, K. O., and H. Kranzer: "Nonlinear Wave Motion, Notes on Magnetohydrodynamics, VIII," *N.Y. Univ. Rept.* NYO 6486, July 31, 1958.
2. Bazar, J., and O. Fleischman: "Propagation of Weak Hydromagnetic Discontinuities," *Phys. Fluids,* **2**:366 (1959).
3. Shapiro, A. H.: *The Dynamics and Thermodynamics of Compressible Fluid Flow,* vol. 1, The Ronald Press Company, New York, 1953.
4. DeHoffman, F., and E. Teller: "Magnetohydrodynamic Shocks," *Phys. Rev.,* **80**:692 (1951).
5. Ericson, W. B., and J. Bazar: "On Certain Properties of Hydromagnetic Shocks," *Phys. Fluids,* **3**:631 (1960).
6. Helfer, H. L.: "Magnetohydrodynamic Shock Waves," *Astrophys. J.,* **117**:177 (1953).
7. Landau, L. D., and E. M. Lifshitz: *Electrodynamics of Continuous Media,* Pergamon Press, New York, 1960.
8. Bazar, J., and W. B. Ericson: "Hydromagnetic Shocks," *Astrophys. J.,* **129**:758 (1958).
9. Lyubimov, G. A.: "Investigation of a Stationary Discontinuity Surface in an Electromagnetic Field with a Gas Conductivity Jump," *ARS J.,* **30**:416 (1960).
10. Ludford, G. S. S.: "The Structure of a Hydromagnetic Shock in Steady Plane Motion," *J. Fluid Mech.,* **5**:67 (1959).
11. Polovin, R. V.: "Shock Waves in Magnetohydrodynamics," *Soviet Phys. Usp. English Transl.,* **3**:677 (1961).

GENERAL REFERENCE

Anderson, J. E.: *Magnetohydrodynamic Shock Waves,* The M.I.T. Press, Cambridge, Mass., 1963.

Banos, A.: "Magnetohydrodynamic Waves," in L. N. Ridenour and W. A. Nierenberg (eds.), *Modern Physics for the Engineer,* Second Series, McGraw-Hill Book Company, New York, 1961.

10

EXACT SOLUTIONS FOR MAGNETOHYDRODYNAMIC CHANNEL FLOWS

10.1 INTRODUCTION

This chapter contains a discussion of magnetohydrodynamic channel-flow problems for which exact solutions can be obtained. The value of such exact solutions to appropriately simplified physical problems is that they provide a guide for the construction of approximate solutions to more complex problems. In addition to this well-known application of such exact solutions in fluid mechanics, there is another reason for studying them in the new science of magnetohydrodynamics. In magnetohydrodynamic flow problems, the introduction of electromagnetic phenomena to the fluid dynamic phenomena creates not only new difficulties for the solution of problems, but also new physical phenomena. Exact solutions of appropriately simplified problems, then, are a convenient vehicle for obtaining insight into this new physical behavior. Only parallel-walled channels will be considered, in order to minimize the complexity due to geometrical considerations and to permit the desired exact solutions.

Basically, two flow problems are treated: the Hartmann and the Couette flows. The classical Hartmann flow is generalized to include arbitrary electric energy extraction from or addition to the flow. A brief discussion is also given of the heat transfer for this flow. In addition to the classical Couette flow, nonperfect-gas effects are considered and some numerical results presented. The general nature of the transient problem is discussed, and the exact solution to the Couette flow when the magnetic Prandtl number is unity is presented.

As an example of new physical phenomena which can be studied by means of the exact solutions of simple problems, a discussion of the Hall effect is included. In particular, the influence of electrode geometry for channel flows in the presence of the Hall effect is described.

With this preparation, the Hartmann flow, modified to take into account the Hall effect, is again treated. Despite the complexity thereby introduced, an exact solution is again possible. Calculations showing the flow pattern, the induced magnetic field distribution, and the current distributions are presented. The next section deviates from the chapter heading in that it does not concern itself completely with exact solutions. The nature of secondary flows which arise because of the finite width of channels is considered, and one exact solution is demonstrated for the Hartmann flow through a finite-width channel of nonconducting walls. For more general and more difficult secondary-flow problems, a variational technique leads to convenient approximate solutions. The procedure to be followed in this technique is discussed, and several examples are presented. The final section considers a somewhat different channel-flow problem. Here a nonuniform two-dimensional applied magnetic field is established in a parallel-wall channel. Because of the complexity of the resulting equations, it is necessary to apply a perturbation expansion and thereby simplify the problem. By this procedure, a linearized system of equations is obtained for which some exact solutions exist. The results of calculations based on these solutions are presented.

Finally, it should be noted that a number of topics that could probably belong to this chapter have not been treated. One of these is the end-effect problem, which relates to the disturbance due to entry of the fluid into the magnetic field region and its exit from it. Some discussion of these problems has been included, however, in Chap. 14. Other problems which have not been considered are MHD vortex flow, stability of laminar channel flow, and turbulent channel flows. The first of these adds little new physical information to the MHD channel-flow problem. The second topic is treated in other books[1] in some detail, and very little is known about the third topic.[2]

10.2 HARTMANN FLOW

The first investigation of magnetohydrodynamic channel flow was carried out by Hartmann in the 1930s.[3] It is with this classical example of MHD flow that we will begin this chapter. The configuration that will be discussed in the present and in latter sections is shown in the Fig. 10.1. The problem to be considered will be the steady flow of an incompressible

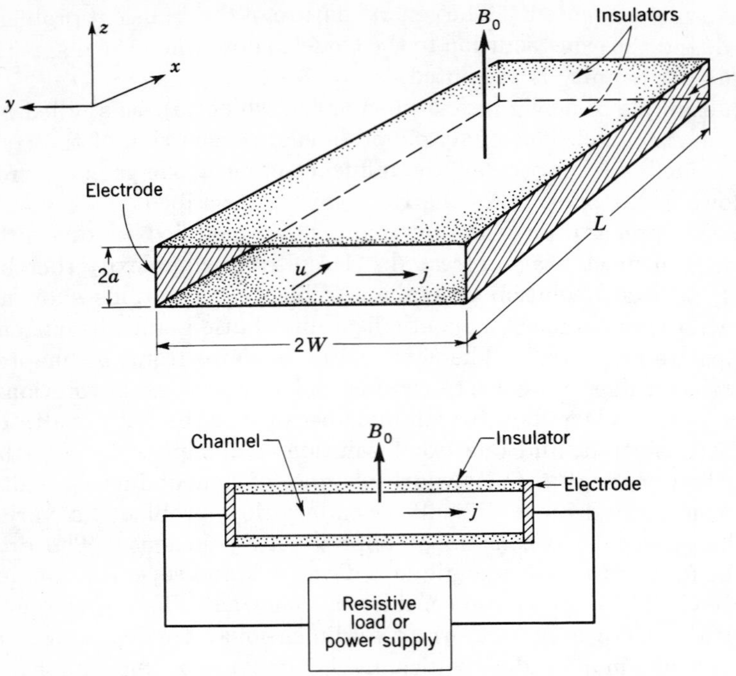

FIGURE 10.1 Channel geometry for Hartmann flow.

electrically conducting fluid in the positive x direction, with a magnetic field applied in the positive z direction. This applied magnetic field will be assumed to be uniform and constant; that is, it is assumed to be generated by either an air-core solenoid or an electromagnet with a saturated iron core. In the present section the Hall effect will be neglected. In the classical Hartmann flow, to be discussed here, end effects are neglected (L much greater than a), and secondary flows are not considered (W much greater than a). The electrodes are assumed to be made of materials of infinite electrical conductivity. Insulators may have finite conductivity, but if they do, their electrical resistances are to be considered as parallel to the channel or load resistance.

In order to proceed with the analysis, it is assumed that all variables are functions of z alone except for p and T which may be functions of x. In addition, the following assumptions regarding the variables are made:

$$\mathbf{v} = (u,0,0) \qquad \mathbf{j} = (0,j_y,0)$$
$$\mathbf{B} = \mathbf{B}_0 + \mathbf{b} = (b_x,0,B_0) \qquad \mathbf{E} = (0,E_y,0)$$

where E_y and B_0 are constants.

The general equations for the problem under consideration will be repeated for convenience.

Ohm's law: $$\mathbf{j} = \sigma(\mathbf{E} + \mathbf{v} \times \mathbf{B}) \tag{10.1}$$

Mass conservation: $$\nabla \cdot (\rho \mathbf{v}) = 0 \tag{10.2}$$

Equation of motion: $$\rho \frac{D\mathbf{v}}{Dt} + \nabla p = \mathbf{j} \times \mathbf{B} + \boldsymbol{\psi} \tag{10.3}$$

Energy equation:

$$\rho \frac{De}{Dt} = -p\nabla \cdot \mathbf{v} - \Phi + \nabla \cdot (\mathcal{K} \nabla T) + \frac{j^2}{\sigma} \tag{10.4}$$

Maxwell's equations: $$\mathbf{j} = \frac{1}{\mu_0} \nabla \times \mathbf{B} \tag{10.5a}$$

$$\nabla \cdot \mathbf{B} = 0 \tag{10.5b}$$

$$\nabla \times \mathbf{E} = -\frac{\partial \mathbf{B}}{\partial t} \tag{10.6a}$$

$$\nabla \cdot \mathbf{E} = \frac{\rho_e}{K_0} \tag{10.6b}$$

The boundary conditions needed for the solution to this problem will be considered next. The condition on velocity is simply $u(\pm a) = 0$. The boundary conditions on temperature are also reasonably simple. They are either that $T(\pm a)$ or $\partial T/\partial z(\pm a)$ is constant. The latter represents the boundary condition of constant heat flux all along the wall, and the former represents constant wall temperature. The final boundary condition is on the induced magnetic field. It will be assumed that at the center of the channel $b_x = 0$. The boundary condition on b_x is often quoted as being that $b_x(\pm a) = 0$. However, this will only be the correct boundary condition in the event that the net current flow through the channel is zero. This will occur only for the open-circuit condition, regardless of the amount of current flowing in the channel. However, the boundary condition $b_x = 0$ at the center of the channel will always be satisfied because of symmetry. It should be noted that when we wish to consider the more general case of Hartmann flow when net electric currents can flow to an external load, it is necessary to pay some attention to the configuration outside the channel. In other words, when a net current flows, some induced field will be created outside the channel. If unsaturated iron exists in this region external to the channel, the calculation of the total induced field will be very complex. In many practical cases, the applied field will be created by either an air-core solenoid or a saturated electromagnet. There is, however, one situation in which the induced magnetic field calculated in this section will indeed be that found within the channel, whether or not any net current flows: that is, when return straps are used and all the net current that flows out through one electrode is returned along the outside of the insulated walls. Then, considering the conducting fluid, the insulating walls, and return straps, the net current flow is zero.

Proceeding to the solution, it should be recognized that assuming the dependent variables to be of the form already stated automatically satisfies Eqs. (10.5*b*), (10.2), (10.5*a*), and (10.6*a*). The assumption that E_y is constant corresponds to the fact that there is a constant potential over each electrode, and the electrodes are infinitely far apart so that there are no variations in the y direction. Also, by the same assumption, $\nabla \cdot \mathbf{E} = 0$, so that Eq. (10.6*b*) is satisfied, and there is no excess charge in the fluid.

From the Ohm's law equation (10.1), within the simplifications made, there is obtained

$$j_y = \sigma(E_y - uB_0) \tag{10.7}$$

Then from the equation of motion (10.3), we get

$$\frac{\partial p}{\partial x} = j_y B_0 + \eta \frac{d^2 u}{dz^2} \tag{10.8}$$

$$\frac{\partial p}{\partial z} = -j_y b_x \tag{10.9}$$

From the first we observe that since the two terms on the right-hand side are functions only of z, then p can at most be a linear function of x. Accordingly we write

$$p = p_0 + p_x x + p'(z) \tag{10.10}$$

Combining Eqs. (10.7) and (10.8), and noting the above definition, we find

$$\eta \frac{d^2 u}{dz^2} - \sigma B_0^2 u - p_x + \sigma B_0 E_y = 0 \tag{10.11}$$

If it is desired to calculate the pressure gradient in the z direction, Eqs. (10.7) and (10.9) can be combined to give

$$\frac{dp'}{dz} = -\sigma(E_y - uB_0)b_x \tag{10.12}$$

Thus, this pressure gradient is dependent on the induced magnetic field and, in fact, will be small when the field is small. Its numerical value can be calculated, once the solution for u and b_x have been obtained.

Finally, the induced magnetic field can be calculated as follows:

$$\frac{1}{\mu_0} \frac{db_x}{dz} = j_y \tag{10.13}$$

Fortunately, the three unknown quantities here, u, b_x, and p', are uncoupled and can be solved for separately. This, in addition to the fact that the governing equations are linear, makes an exact solution of the problem possible.

Introduce the following dimensionless variables:

$$U = \frac{u}{\bar{u}} \qquad Z = \frac{z}{a} \qquad X = \frac{x}{a}$$

$$K = \frac{E_y}{\bar{u}B_0} \qquad P = \frac{p}{\rho\bar{u}^2} \qquad \bar{u} = \frac{1}{2a}\int_{-a}^{a} u\,dz \qquad \tilde{b}_x = \frac{b_x}{B_0R_m} \tag{10.14}$$

$$H_a{}^2 = \frac{\sigma B_0{}^2a^2}{\eta} \qquad R_e = \frac{\rho\bar{u}a}{\eta} \qquad R_m = \mu_0\bar{u}\sigma a$$

The equation for U is then

$$\frac{d^2U}{dZ^2} - H_a{}^2U - R_eP_x + KH_a{}^2 = 0 \tag{10.15}$$

with boundary conditions of

$$U(\pm 1) = 0$$

The solution for U is found to be

$$U = \left(K - \frac{R_eP_x}{H_a{}^2}\right)\frac{\cosh H_a - \cosh H_aZ}{\cosh H_a} \tag{10.16}$$

and if we make use of the fact that $\int_{-1}^{1} U\,dZ = 2$, then

$$K - \frac{R_eP_x}{H_a{}^2} = \frac{H_a}{H_a - \tanh H_a} \tag{10.17}$$

so that
$$U = \frac{H_a(\cosh H_a - \cosh H_aZ)}{H_a\cosh H_a - \sinh H_a} \tag{10.18}$$

It is of interest to observe that R_e is proportional to mean velocity, so that the above yields a relationship between essentially mass flow and pressure gradient. If the pressure gradient is fixed and the Hartmann number increased, then the mass flow will drop. By the same token, if the mass flow is fixed as the Hartmann number is increased, then the pressure gradient necessary to achieve the fixed mass flow also rises.

Although Eq. (10.18) appears independent of pressure gradient and mass flow, it must be remembered that $U = u/\bar{u}$, and $\bar{u}$ is a measure of the mass flow. Accordingly, if a plot of $U = f(H_a,Z)$ is made, it is correct only when the mass flow is constant ($\bar{u}$ = const, P_x varies as H_a). If P_x is assumed constant, $\bar{u}$ varies, and the curves should be interpreted accordingly.

The solution for $J_y = j_y/\sigma B_0\bar{u}$ is simply

$$J_y(Z) = K - U(Z) \tag{10.19}$$

If $K = 1$, it corresponds to an open-circuit condition, and if $K = 0$, this corresponds to a short-circuit condition. The total current flowing through the external circuit per unit channel length is given by

$$J = \int_{-1}^{1} J_y \, dZ = 2(K - 1) \tag{10.20}$$

If $K < 1$, this is a pump or accelerator; if $K = 1$, this corresponds to a flowmeter. As can be seen, for a fixed flow rate and Hartmann number, a $K < 1$ will increase the pressure gradient while a $K > 1$ will decrease it.

The solution for the induced magnetic field b_x can be derived from Eq. (10.13):

$$\tilde{b}_x = R_m \left[(K - 1)Z + \frac{\sinh H_a Z - Z \sinh H_a}{H_a \cosh H_a - \sinh H_a} \right] \tag{10.21}$$

It can be seen here that when $K = 1$, the familiar result for induced field is obtained. However, when $K \neq 1$, the induced field is quite different from the previous result. The introduction of the parameter K modifies the usual Hartmann flow in that the current distribution changes as does the induced magnetic field. In addition, for a given Hartmann number, the relationship between the pressure gradient and mean flow or flow rate is altered by K.

In order to illustrate more clearly the influence of these various parameters on the Hartmann flow, calculations have been carried out for the flow velocity in the channel, the current distribution across the channel, and the induced magnetic field. In Fig. 10.2 are shown the velocity profiles over the channel height for several values of the Hartmann number. It can clearly be seen that as the Hartmann number is increased, the velocity profile becomes flatter, and the velocity gradient near the channel wall becomes steeper. The current distributions which are plotted in Fig. 10.3 have been calculated for three typical values of

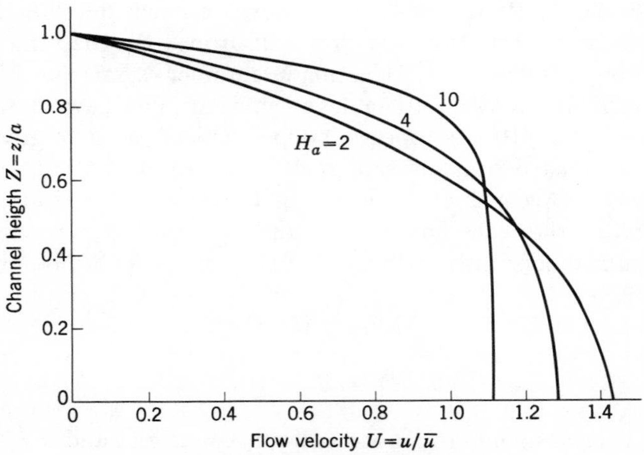

FIGURE 10.2 Hartmann velocity profiles.

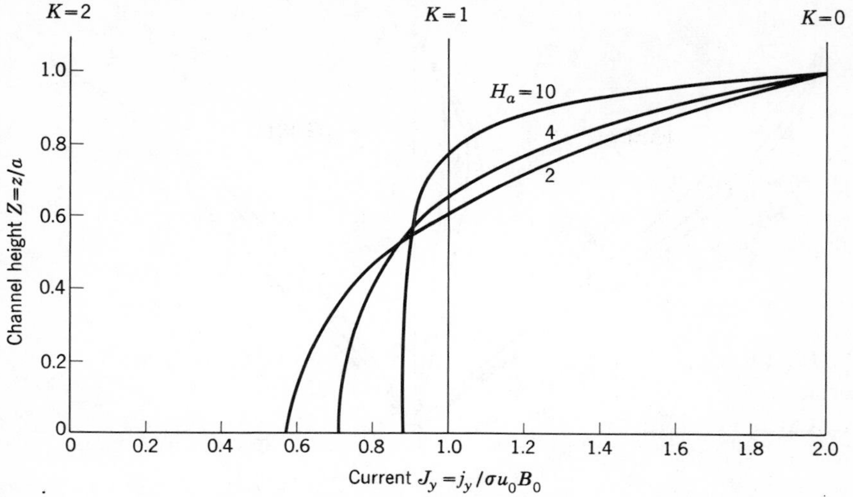

FIGURE 10.3 Current distributions for the Hartmann flow problem.

the parameter K. The current scale shown corresponds to the $K = 2$ case. For $K = 1$, the zero of this scale should be shifted to the position shown, and similarly for $K = 0$. When $K = 1$, the channel is open-circuited, and the net current flow is zero. This is the case that is usually discussed. When $K = 0$, on the other hand, the channel is short-circuited, and all the current flows in one direction. Clearly the net is nonzero. When $K = 2$, all the current flows to the right in the channel, and it must be presumed that this net current flow has been supplied by an external power supply. This is the case of an MHD accelerator or pump. The induced magnetic field which corresponds to these current distributions is shown in Fig. 10.4. The curves for $K = 1$ correspond to the usual form of induced magnetic field discussed. The curves for $K = 0$ demonstrate the fact that the induced magnetic field is considerably larger when a net current can flow in the channel. Similar curves apply for $K = 2$, except that the magnetic induction lies in the other direction, as a result of the current flowing in the opposite direction. As noted before, these calculated magnetic fields are valid within the MHD channel, provided that any ferromagnetic material near the channel is saturated or that there are backstraps along the insulators to carry the current to and from the external load or power supply.

Before leaving the subject of Hartmann flow, it should be noted that a number of experimental investigations have been carried out.[1] In all instances, aside from the turbulent flow regime, they have provided excellent agreement with the theory just described. Unfortunately, measurements have been made only of the flow pressure drop versus Hartmann number. No experimental confirmation of the distributions

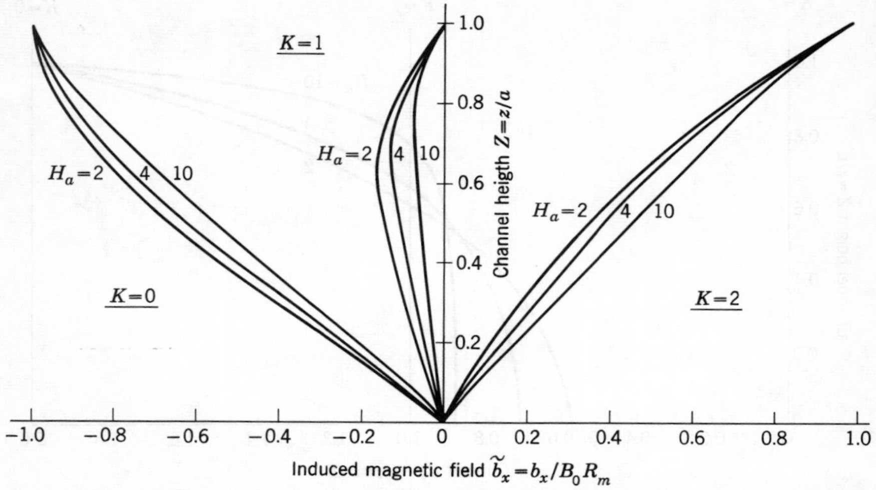

FIGURE 10.4 Induced magnetic field distributions for the Hartmann flow problem.

with Z have been obtained. Also, all experiments to date have been carried out in liquid metals. None have been attempted in partially ionized gases.

10.2.1 Temperature and Heat Transfer. Based on the preceding assumptions and taking $e = C_vT$ for an incompressible liquid, the energy equation (10.4) reduces to

$$\rho u C_v \frac{\partial T}{\partial x} = \eta \left(\frac{du}{dz}\right)^2 + \mathcal{K}\frac{\partial^2 T}{\partial z^2} + \frac{j_y^{\,2}}{\sigma} \tag{10.22}$$

Then, introducing the new dimensionless variable

$$\theta = \frac{T - T_w}{\bar{u}^2/C_v}$$

we obtain

$$\frac{\partial^2 \theta}{\partial Z^2} = (R_e P_R)U\frac{\partial \theta}{\partial X} - P_R\left[\left(\frac{dU}{dZ}\right)^2 + H_a{}^2 J_y{}^2\right] \tag{10.23}$$

where $$P_R = \frac{C_v \eta}{\mathcal{K}}$$

It is observed that in the present context, $H_a{}^2$ is essentially the ratio of the heat generated by Joule heating to that generated by viscous dissipation. Since we assume constant properties here, the energy and momentum equations are uncoupled, and the above can be solved, using the previously obtained solution for $U(z)$.[4]

For the case in which $T(\pm a) = \text{const} = T_w$, the above reduces to

$$\frac{d^2\theta}{dZ^2} = -P_R\left[\left(\frac{dU}{dZ}\right)^2 + H_a{}^2 J_y{}^2\right] \tag{10.24}$$

with the boundary conditions that

$$\theta(\pm 1) = 0$$
$$\frac{d\theta}{dZ}(0) = 0$$

From the earlier solution,

$$\frac{dU}{dZ} = -\frac{H_a{}^2 \sinh H_a Z}{H_a \cosh H_a - \sinh H_a}$$

and $J_y = K - U = \dfrac{H_a(K-1)\cosh H_a - K \sinh H_a + H_a \cosh H_a Z}{H_a \cosh H_a - \sinh H_a}$

Accordingly, Eq. (10.24) can be rewritten as follows:

$$\frac{d^2\theta}{dZ^2} = -C_1 P_R(C_2{}^2 + H_a{}^2 \cosh 2H_a Z + 2H_a C_2 \cosh H_a Z) \qquad (10.25)$$

where
$$C_1 = \left(\frac{H_a}{H_a \cosh H_a - \sinh H_a}\right)^2$$
$$C_2 = H_a(K-1)\cosh H_a - K \sinh H_a$$

Integrating this equation twice, using the boundary conditions, one obtains the solution for θ in the following form:

$$\theta = C_1 P_R \left[\frac{C_2{}^2}{2}(1 - Z^2) + \tfrac{1}{4}(\cosh 2H_a - \cosh 2H_a Z) + \frac{2C_2}{H_a}(\cosh H_a - \cosh H_a Z)\right] \qquad (10.26)$$

In Fig. 10.5 the temperature distribution as a function of Z, for various values of K and Hartmann number, is shown. Several interesting observations can readily be made. First, it should be recalled that, in the solution, both viscous heating and Joule heating were included in the analysis. We then see that when the channel operates in the open-circuit condition, $K = 1$, the current flow is so small that viscous dissipation dominates the temperature distribution. In this case, the temperature along the central line of the channel exceeds the temperature on the wall by only a very small amount, and the Hartmann number has a relatively small effect on the temperature distribution. The difference in θ between the curves of $H_a = 2$ and 10 is only 0.1 on the center line and does not appear on the scale drawn. Now when $K = 0$, the short-circuit condition, the current flow is quite large, and since the Joule heating depends on the square of the current, the increase in Hartmann number amounts to a very large increase in temperature in the center of the channel. In fact, the temperature in the center of the channel for a Hartmann number of 10 is essentially 60 times larger than in the open-circuit case. Clearly the heat flux to the channel walls is also increased

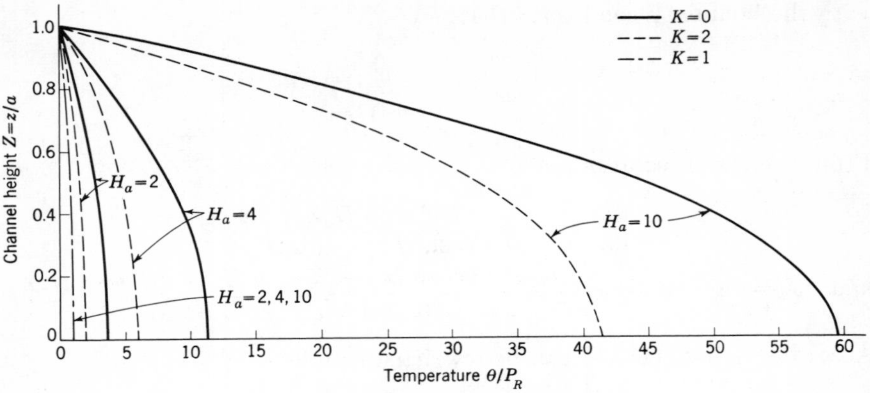

FIGURE 10.5 Hartmann flow temperature distributions.

as the Hartmann number is increased for the short-circuit case. Similar considerations apply when $K = 2$.

The heat-transfer problem solved (T_w = const) is the simplest one-dimensional problem that could have been considered. It is a special case of the more general one-dimensional problem in which the heat flux at the wall is assumed to be constant. This more general problem can be formulated as follows: If the heat flux at the wall is independent of x, and the problem is assumed to be one-dimensional in nature, then the temperature must be of the form

$$T = Ax + g(z) \tag{10.27}$$

where the boundary condition (q_w = const) is the same as

$$\frac{dg}{dz}(\pm a) = \text{const}$$

Substitution of Eq. (10.27) into Eq. (10.22) leads to the following relationship,

$$\rho u C_v A = \mathcal{K}\frac{d^2g}{dz^2} + \eta\left(\frac{du}{dz}\right)^2 + \frac{j_y{}^2}{\sigma} \tag{10.28}$$

where $g(z)$ can be evaluated as before by two integrations. The constant A can be evaluated by integrating the above equation once over z. Therefore,

$$A = \frac{q_w + \int_{-a}^{a} [\eta\,(du/dz)^2 + j_y{}^2/\sigma]\,dz}{\rho \bar{u} C_v a} \tag{10.29}$$

Now, if q_w were chosen such that it were equal to

$$\int_{-a}^{a}\left[\eta\left(\frac{du}{dz}\right)^2 + \frac{j_y{}^2}{\sigma}\right]dz$$

then clearly $A = 0$, and we recover the simpler problem already considered. Physically, this corresponds to the specification that all the heat generated by friction and Joule heating is transferred out of the channel, and is identical to the constant-temperature wall case. In the event that q_w is not constant (or that T is other than linear along the channel walls), then we have a two-dimensional problem. Such two-dimensional problems offer many more difficulties for solution than the simple case considered here.[5]

10.3 COUETTE FLOW

In this section another simple magnetohydrodynamic flow will be considered, for which some exact solutions will be possible. If, in a parallel-wall channel, one wall is stationary and the other is moving, we have what is generally referred to as Couette flow. In this section the Couette flow of a conducting fluid in the presence of a magnetic field applied normal to the two parallel walls will be analyzed. Such a situation is depicted in Fig. 10.6. Actually one of the motives for studying Couette flow is to learn more about the influence of MHD forces on boundary-layer flows. Although it is not exactly analogous to a true boundary layer, it is a useful area of study, since it is sufficiently similar and considerably easier to solve.

As far as flow is concerned, it is not essential that the flow of Fig. 10.6 be considered the limit of a more realistic geometry. However, when electromagnetic phenomena are present, such questions are quite important. As far as a more realistic geometry is concerned, two possibilities exist and are shown in Fig. 10.7. In the first, the fluid flows in an annular space, because of the rotation of the outer cylinder relative to the inner stationary one. The radial magnetic field is assumed to exist, and the currents induced are supposed to flow through some external load via end electrodes. The annular gap is then assumed small compared to the cylinder radius and length. The second geometry is essentially the same as the first except that now the outer cylinder moves

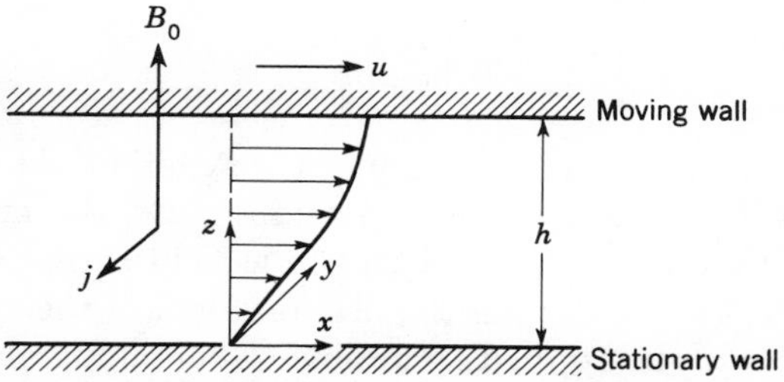

FIGURE 10.6 Magnetohydrodynamic Couette flow.

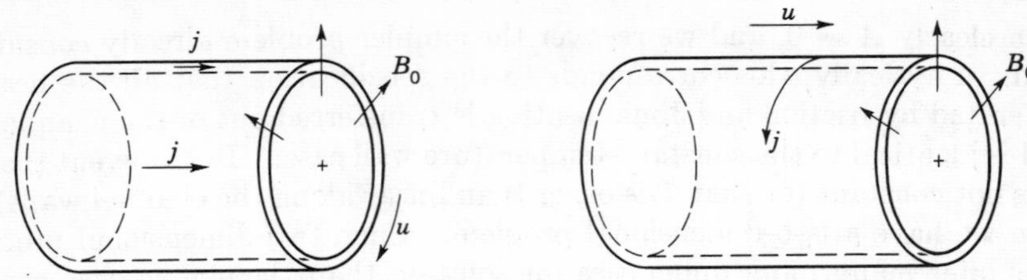

FIGURE 10.7 Realistic Couette flow geometries. (*a*) left; (*b*) right.

axially relative to the inner one, and a circumferential current flows because of the radial magnetic field. As far as the fluid dynamic behavior is concerned, one can consider the problem of Fig. 10.6. There is some difference, however, when one considers the induced magnetic field, since the boundary conditions will differ, depending on the particular geometry chosen.

Finally, it should be noted that in reality a radial magnetic field extending from $y = +\infty$ to $y = -\infty$ cannot be created in practice. Thus, a more proper physical picture is one in which a magnetic field normal to the cylinder walls is applied over a portion of the circumference. Then one must suppose that the length of the circumference is much larger than the gap between the cylinders.

The present problem is mathematically quite similar to the previous one, and similar assumptions will be made. As before, end effects and secondary flows will be neglected, and a uniform applied magnetic field will be assumed to exist. Also, the Hall effect and ion-slip phenomena will be neglected again. As before it will be assumed that all variables are functions of z alone and that the unknown variables have the form

$$\mathbf{v} = (u,0,0) \qquad \mathbf{j} = (0,j_y,0)$$
$$\mathbf{B} = \mathbf{B}_0 + \mathbf{b} = (b_x,0,B_0) \qquad \mathbf{E} = (0,E_y,0)$$

where B_0 and E_y are constants.

The boundary conditions on velocity are

$$u(h) = u_\infty$$
$$u(0) = 0$$

The boundary condition for the induced magnetic field corresponding to Fig. 10.7*a* will be that $b_x(h)$ is a constant. On the other hand, the boundary condition of the induced magnetic field corresponding to Fig. 10.7*b* will be that $b_x(h) = 0$. In the first problem, if the radial magnetic field were assumed to be applied all around the circumference, the correct condition would be $b_x(0) = 0$. However, the more realistic geometry shown in Fig. 10.8 is to be preferred. If there is no net current flowing,

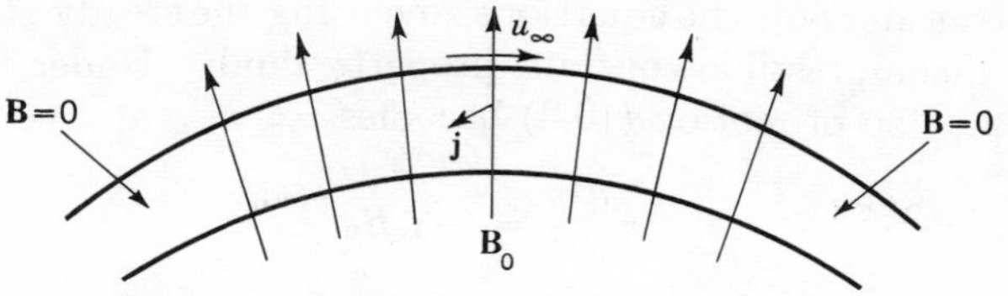

FIGURE 10.8 Realistic applied field geometry for Couette flow.

the constant should be zero. When there is some net current, the constant should be simply the product of μ_0 and the mean value of the current density. In order to visualize this more clearly, consider the arbitrarily assumed current distribution shown in Fig. 10.9. In *a*, a current distribution is shown for which there is a net current flowing in the y direction, as well as a current reversal along the lower wall. In the second figure, a qualitative picture of the induced magnetic field is shown. Outside the channel wall the induced magnetic field extends uniformly to infinity, since a doubly infinite channel is being assumed. In the event that the current flow had been uniform or symmetric about $z = h/2$ (such as had been the case in the Hartmann flow), the zero of b_x would have occurred at $z = 0$. Since most of the current flow is along the upper wall, the zero of b_x shifts into that region. Finally b_x returns to the negative of its value at the upper edge through a minimum. This minimum occurs at the zero point of current in the y direction since $db_x/dz = \mu_0 j_y$.

In the second problem, limiting the extent of the applied magnetic field to a portion of the circumference does not alter the boundary condition since the conducting fluid in the remainder of the annulus merely serves as a current return path. Thus it is essentially an infinite solenoid, and $b_x = 0$ at its outer surface. The resistance of the fluid in the remainder of the annulus can be interpreted as the external load.

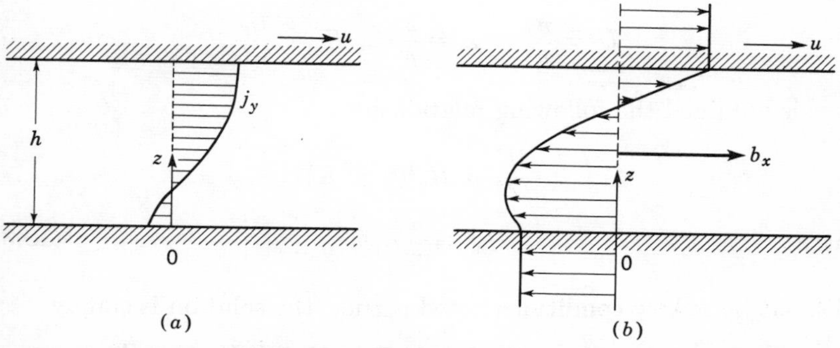

FIGURE 10.9 Current distribution and induced magnetic field for geometry of Fig. 10.8.

Let us consider now the equations governing the steady-state Couette flow for an incompressible constant-property fluid. Under these conditions the equation of motion (10.3) becomes

$$\eta \frac{d^2u}{dz^2} = -j_y B_0 \tag{10.30}$$

$$\frac{dp}{dz} = -j_y b_x \tag{10.31}$$

and Ohm's law becomes

$$j_y = \sigma(E_y - uB_0) \tag{10.32}$$

Finally, for Maxwell's equations, the equation for the induced magnetic field is obtained. It is found to be precisely Eq. (10.13):

$$j_y = \frac{1}{\mu_0}\frac{db_x}{dz} \tag{10.33}$$

A number of important observations can be made. First, in the steady-state problem it can be seen that E_y can be taken as constant, since $\nabla \times \mathbf{E} = 0$. Then it is seen that the heat-transfer and fluid-flow problems are uncoupled, so that they can be solved separately, as was done in the previous section. Most important, however, is the fact that the fluid flow and the induced magnetic field are uncoupled and can be determined separately. In the present analysis, the flow velocity u can be evaluated first, and the induced magnetic field b_x or the fluid temperature T can be determined. Only the fluid flow and the induced magnetic field will be considered in this section.

Substituting Eq. (10.32) into (10.30), there is found

$$\frac{d^2u}{dz^2} = -\frac{\sigma}{\eta}(E_y - uB_0)B_0 \tag{10.34}$$

Then if the following new variables are introduced,

$$U = \frac{u}{\bar{u}} \qquad Z = \frac{z}{h} \qquad K = \frac{E_y}{\bar{u}B_0}$$

there is obtained the following relationship:

$$\frac{d^2U}{dZ^2} = H_a^2(u - K)$$

where

$$H_a^2 = \frac{\sigma}{\eta} B_0^2 h^2 \tag{10.35}$$

With the boundary conditions noted earlier, the solution is simply

$$U = K + \frac{(1 - K)\sinh H_a Z - K \sinh H_a(1 - Z)}{\sinh H_a} \tag{10.36}$$

Assuming the Hartmann number to be zero, the classical solution for no applied magnetic field is indeed recovered. It is, of course, $U = Z$.

As in the previous section, the current is found to be

$$J_y = K - U = \frac{K \sinh H_a(1 - Z) - (1 - K) \sinh H_a Z}{\sinh H_a} \tag{10.37}$$

The induced magnetic field can be then calculated from the relationship

$$b_x = \mu_0 \int j_y \, dz + c \tag{10.38}$$

in which the constant c can be chosen to maintain $b_x = 0$ at the top or bottom surface of the channel, or can be taken equal to

$$c = \frac{\mu_0}{h} \int_0^h j_y \, dz$$

The first choice corresponds to the solenoid model, the second to the rotating-cylinder concept with a full radial field, and the last to the rotating cylinder with a partial radial field.

In any event, carrying out the integration yields the following result:

$$\tilde{b}_x = -\frac{K \cosh H_a(1 - Z) + (1 - K) \cosh H_a Z}{H_a \sinh H_a} \tag{10.39}$$

If the solenoid model is chosen, the constant is found to be

$$c = \frac{\coth H_a}{H_a}$$

and then the expression for the induced magnetic field becomes

$$\tilde{b}_x = \frac{\cosh H_a - \cosh H_a Z}{H_a \sinh H_a} \tag{10.40}$$

To complete the solution, it should be noted that the pressure gradient in the z direction can be calculated from Eq. (10.31), now that the induced magnetic field and current distribution have been obtained.

Before leaving the subject of incompressible Couette flow, it would be of value to present some velocity and induced magnetic field profiles based on the solution just obtained. In Fig. 10.10 they are shown for the case of $K = 0$ (short-circuited) and Hartmann number equal to 4. As far as the velocity profile is concerned, it can be seen that when the Hartmann number increases, the velocity gradient at the moving wall increases. In other words, the force necessary to move this wall is greater, the larger H_a. Again, for the case of $K = 0$, the current flow distribution is exactly $-U$. For this case, then, all current flows in the same direction, having a maximum value at the moving wall and being zero at the lower wall. The calculation for b_x is shown in b for the bound-

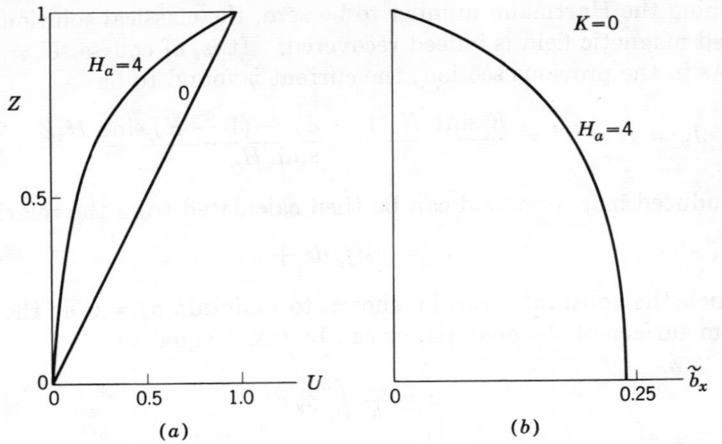

FIGURE 10.10 Velocity and induced magnetic field profiles for incompressible Couette flow.

ary condition $b_x(h) = 0$. As expected for this case, the maximum of b_x occurs at the stationary wall.

10.3.1 Variable Properties. In order to investigate flows with variable properties, Bleviss[6] has considered Couette flow for the hypersonic motion of high-temperature ionized air.

The geometry selected corresponds to Fig. 10.7*b*, with a radial magnetic field distributed uniformly about the annulus. Under these conditions, the assumption of $E_y = 0$ for the short-circuit condition is appropriate. As before, Eqs. (10.1) and (10.3) give

$$\frac{d}{dz}\left(\eta \frac{du}{dz}\right) = \sigma B_0{}^2 u \tag{10.41}$$

$$\frac{dp}{dz} = \sigma u B_0 b_x \tag{10.42}$$

where now provision is made for the viscosity to vary over the channel height, and Eq. (10.42) is of greater significance than before. From Eq. (10.41) it can be seen that since η and σ can be functions of temperature, the flow field and the thermodynamic state of the plasma are coupled. In addition, it can be seen from Eq. (10.42) that the induced magnetic field is also coupled to the flow and the plasma state. Such a coupling of the three unknowns, u, b_x, and h, yields an extremely difficult problem, and one for which an exact solution cannot be anticipated. Accordingly, it is assumed that the right-hand side of Eq. (10.42) is small, so that $dp/dz \cong 0$ and b_x is uncoupled from the remainder of the problem. Simple solutions are then possible under the *assumption of constant pressure.*

Within the assumption stated, the energy equation (10.4) reduces to the following form when use is made of the momentum equation,

$$\frac{d}{dz}(u\tau - q) = 0 \tag{10.43}$$

where

$$\tau = \eta \frac{du}{dz} \tag{10.44}$$

$$q = -\mathcal{K} \frac{dT}{dz} \tag{10.45}$$

If an effective Prandtl number is defined, then (10.45) can be rewritten as

$$q = -\frac{\eta}{P_R}\left[\frac{dh}{dz} - \left(\frac{\partial h}{\partial p}\right)_T \frac{dp}{dz}\right]$$

but with the assumption of constant pressure,

$$q = -\frac{\eta}{P_R}\frac{dh}{dz} \tag{10.46}$$

where

$$P_R = \frac{\eta C_P}{\mathcal{K}}$$

It is of some interest to observe that when $E_y = 0$, there is no net energy transfer between the electromagnetic field and the fluid flow. The only effect of the applied magnetic field is to convert a portion of the flow kinetic energy to thermal energy by means of Joule heating.

In the present problem, the equations which must be solved are (10.41) and (10.43), along with (10.44) and (10.46). In addition, $h = h(p,T)$, as well as $\eta = \eta(p,T)$ and $\sigma = \sigma(p,T)$, must all be specified. For the case considered by Bleviss, these have all been chosen to correspond to high-temperature air. Other choices could equally well have been made. Since thermal equilibrium has been assumed to exist, heat transfer by diffusion of disassociated or ionized species could be accounted for by using an effective thermal conductivity $\mathcal{K}$. At the worst, this would cause P_R to be a variable, but this could be readily included in the numerical analysis.

Following the procedure described above, numerical solutions were obtained.[6] Of most interest are the solutions for the heat-transfer problem. In this case, the following conditions were chosen, where $(\ )_\infty$ refers to the moving wall, and $(\ )_w$ refers to the stationary wall:

$$T_\infty = 300°\text{K} \qquad p = 10^{-2}\ \text{atm}$$
$$T_w = 1200°\text{K} \qquad \gamma = 1.4$$
$$\mathfrak{M}_\infty = 20, 30 \qquad P_R = 0.70$$

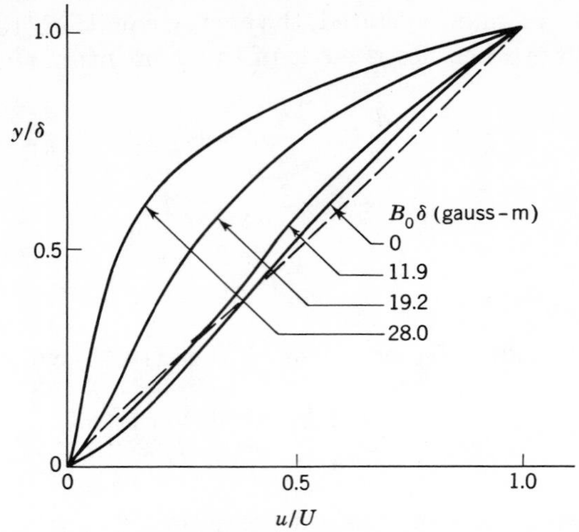

FIGURE 10.11 Velocity profiles for hypersonic Couette flow. (After Bleviss.[6])

The behavior of the temperature and velocity profiles for the $\mathfrak{M} = 30$ case is shown in Figs. 10.11 and 10.12.

As expected, the stronger the applied magnetic field, the more the flow is retarded. However, in this case there is also considerable heating of the fluid due to Joule heating. It can also be seen that the heat transfer at the stationary wall has increased. The behavior of these parameters can be more clearly seen in Fig. 10.13.

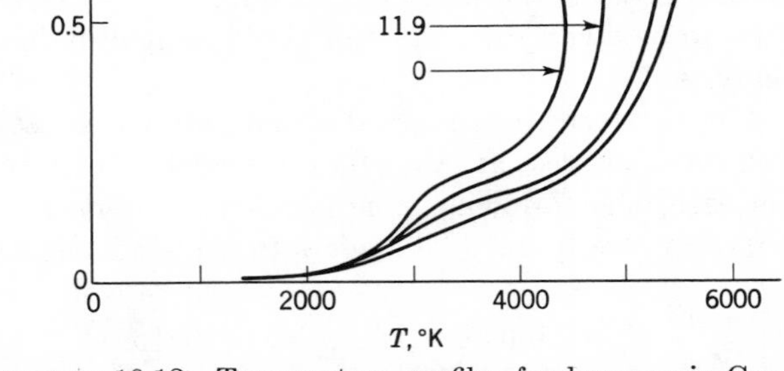

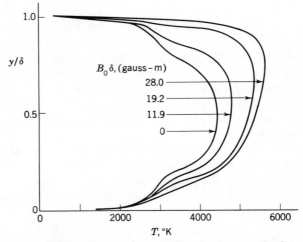

FIGURE 10.12 Temperature profiles for hypersonic Couette flow. (After Bleviss.[6])

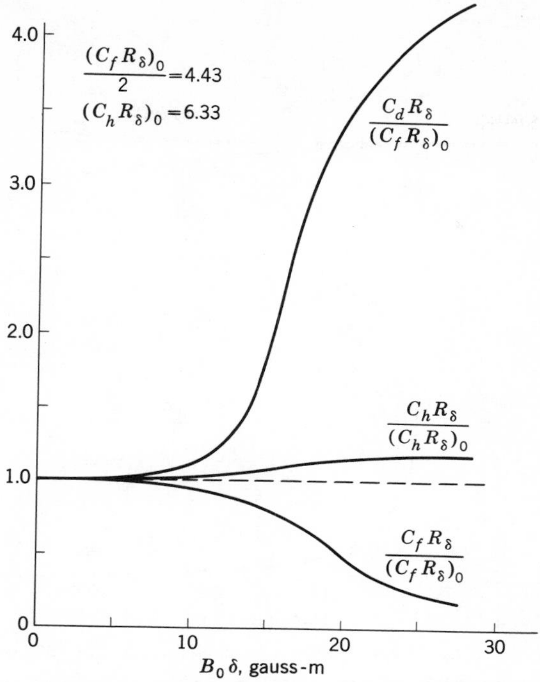

FIGURE 10.13 Skin friction and heat flux in hypersonic Couette flow. (After Bleviss.[6])

In this figure the variable quantities have been defined as follows:

$$c_d \equiv \frac{\tau_\infty}{\rho_\infty u^2/2}$$

$$c_f \equiv \frac{\tau_w}{\rho_\infty u^2/2}$$

$$c_h \equiv \frac{q_w}{(h_w - h_r)\rho_\infty u}$$

$$R_\delta \equiv \frac{\rho_\infty u \delta}{\eta_\infty}$$

where τ_∞ is essentially the total shear (skin friction + magnetic body force) being experienced by the stationary wall and h_r is the recovery enthalpy or enthalpy at the wall when $q_w = 0$.

It is interesting to see that while the skin friction is decreased by the magnetic field, the total drag is considerably increased. Clearly the total drag is mostly due to the magnetic body forces in this case. On the other hand, the increase in heat transfer is relatively small. Accordingly the Reynolds analogy does not hold.

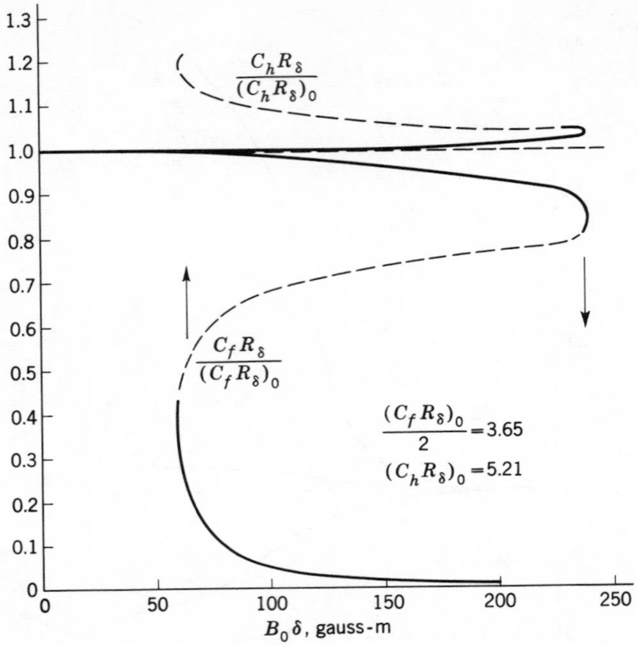

FIGURE 10.14 Skin friction and heat flux for $\mathfrak{M}_\infty = 20$. (After Bleviss.[6])

In addition to the above results, calculations have been carried out for $\mathfrak{M}_\infty = 20$. For this condition an unusual hysterisis behavior was found, and is shown in Fig. 10.14. It is seen that as $B_0\delta$ is increased, the skin friction drops slowly at first, and then suddenly decreases to a very low value. Similarly, when $B_0\delta$ is decreased, $c_f R_\delta$ rises slowly, until it suddenly approaches its value without an applied field. The dashed portion should represent an unattainable and unstable solution.

A similar behavior is found to exist for the heat-transfer coefficient. The calculations for the lower portion of this curve were carried out only to $B_0\delta = 85.2$. Had it been continued, it is expected that the curve would have dropped below unity. Again the dashed curve should be an unattainable solution.

The reason that the above hysterisis phenomenon does not occur when $\mathfrak{M} = 30$, but does when $\mathfrak{M} = 20$, is the temperature dependence of σ, shown qualitatively in Fig. 10.15. Along the A portion the plasma conductivity is due to electron-ion collisions, whereas along the B portion it is only very slightly ionized. For the $\mathfrak{M}_\infty = 30$ case, the temperatures throughout are sufficiently high so that σ lies mostly along the A portion and does not vary rapidly with temperature. When $\mathfrak{M} = 20$, however, at sufficiently low B_0 values, σ lies on the B portion. As B_0 is increased, temperatures also rise, and σ goes over to the A portion. This transition apparently leads to the jump phenomenon found. Of course, an additional factor is that when σ varies very steeply with T, then a reinforcing phenomenon occurs. That is, as B increases, the Joule heating increases, which raises the temperature, which in turn causes σ to rise steeply, and this leads to an even stronger interaction (σuB), so that the Joule heating is again raised. This cycle continues until a stable condition is reached, presumably when σ lies along A.

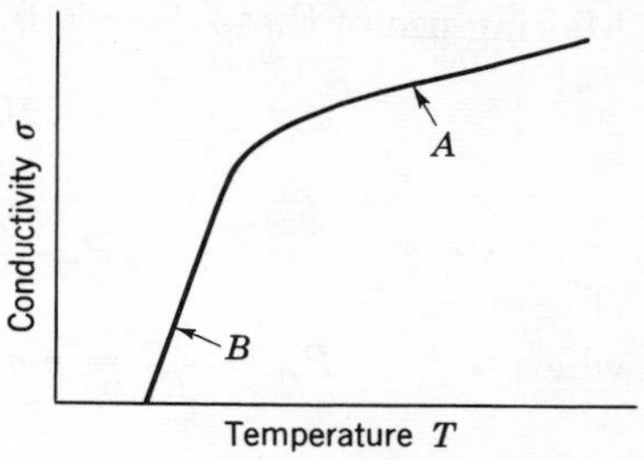

FIGURE 10.15 Plasma conductivity.

10.4 TRANSIENT COUETTE FLOW

In this section transient Couette flow will be considered, in order to illustrate some of the time-dependent phenomena that can be expected in channel flows. In the normal Couette flow, the equations for u and b_x are uncoupled, and an exact solution can be obtained conveniently. For the transient problem, however, the previous assumption that E_y was either zero or a constant is no longer valid. Accordingly, the current density appearing in the momentum equation must be derived from Eq. (10.5*a*). When this is done, the equations become coupled, and an exact solution will be very difficult to find unless the equations can be uncoupled again. It is shown in this section that the equations can indeed be uncoupled when the magnetic Prandtl number is unity. An exact solution is then obtained from the resulting equations.

The equations governing the transient Couette flow are derived from Eqs. (10.1) through (10.6*b*), and are as follows:

$$\rho \frac{\partial u}{\partial t} = \frac{B_0}{\mu} \frac{\partial b_x}{\partial z} + \eta \frac{\partial^2 u}{\partial z^2} \tag{10.47}$$

$$\frac{\partial b_x}{\partial t} = B_0 \frac{\partial u}{\partial z} + \frac{1}{\sigma \mu_0} \frac{\partial^2 b_x}{\partial z^2} \tag{10.48}$$

Define the following dimensionless variables:

$$U = \frac{u}{u_\infty} \qquad \tilde{b}_x = \frac{b_x}{B_0 R_m} \qquad Z = \frac{z}{h}$$

$$\tau = \frac{t\eta}{\rho h^2} \qquad R_m = \mu_0 \sigma u_\infty h \qquad {H_a}^2 = \frac{\sigma {B_0}^2 h^2}{\eta}$$

Making use of these, Eqs. (10.47) and (10.48) reduce to the following set,

$$\frac{\partial U}{\partial \tau} = H_a{}^2 \frac{\partial \bar{b}_x}{\partial Z} + \frac{\partial^2 U}{\partial Z^2} \tag{10.49}$$

$$P_m \frac{\partial \bar{b}_x}{\partial \tau} = \frac{\partial U}{\partial Z} + \frac{\partial^2 b_x}{\partial Z^2} \tag{10.50}$$

where $$P_m = \frac{R_m}{R_e} = \mu_0 \sigma \nu = \text{magnetic Prandtl number}$$

If the magnetic Prandtl number is assumed to be 1, and the following two new variables are defined,

$$v = U + H_a \bar{b}_x$$
$$w = U - H_a \bar{b}_x$$

then Eqs. (10.49) and (10.50) reduce to the following:

$$\frac{\partial v}{\partial \tau} = H_a \frac{\partial v}{\partial Z} + \frac{\partial^2 v}{\partial Z^2} \tag{10.51}$$

$$\frac{\partial w}{\partial \tau} = -H_a \frac{\partial w}{\partial Z} + \frac{\partial^2 w}{\partial Z^2} \tag{10.52}$$

Clearly then the solution for w is the same as for v except for a change in the sign of H_a, the Hartmann number. Accordingly, the solution for v yields the solution of the problem in exact form. Boundary and initial conditions for the transient Couette flow are

$$\begin{aligned} b_x(0,Z) &= 0 \qquad & u(0,Z) &= 0 \\ b_x(\tau,0) &= 0 & u(\tau,0) &= 0 \\ b_x(\tau,1) &= 0 & u(\tau,1) &= 1 \end{aligned}$$

so that the boundary conditions on the variable v are

$$\begin{aligned} v(0,Z) &= 0 \\ v(\tau,0) &= 0 \\ v(\tau,1) &= 1 \end{aligned}$$

The procedure then is to solve Eq. (10.51) for v, obtain from this the solution for w, and from these two derive the solutions for u and b_x. The solutions can be obtained in exact although not closed form by the classical method of separation of variables. The result is

$$v(Z,\tau) = \frac{\sinh H_a Z}{\sinh H_a} e^{-H_a(Z-1)/2} + 2\pi e^{-H_a(Z-1)/2} \sum_{n=1}^{\infty} \frac{(-1)^n n \sin n\pi Z}{H_a{}^2/4 + (n\pi)^2} e^{-[H_a{}^2/4 + (n\pi)^2]\tau} \tag{10.53}$$

With the aid of this solution one obtains u and b_x as follows:

$$u(Z,\tau) = \cosh\left[\frac{H_a(Z-1)}{2}\right]\left\{\frac{\sinh H_a Z}{\sinh H_a} + 2\pi \sum_{n=1}^{\infty}\left[\frac{(-1)^n n \sin n\pi Z}{H_a^2/4 + (n\pi)^2}\right] e^{-[H_a^2/4+(n\pi)^2]\tau}\right\} \tag{10.54}$$

$$\tilde{b}_x(Z,\tau) = \sinh\left[\frac{H_a(Z-1)}{2}\right]\left\{\quad '' \quad\right\}$$

or

$$\tilde{b}_x(Z,\tau) = u(Z,\tau) \tanh \frac{H_a(Z-1)}{2} \tag{10.55}$$

The solution which has been obtained here is valid only for the special case of magnetic Prandtl number equal to unity. In almost all conducting liquids and plasmas of practical interest, however, $P_m \cong 0$. Accordingly, several authors[7,8] have analyzed the present problem by neglecting the induced magnetic field completely and then proceeding to a calculation of the flow. Following this procedure, however, offers no insight into the form of the induced magnetic field or the electric field which will be created by $\partial b_x/\partial t$.

10.5 THE HALL EFFECT–TENSOR CONDUCTIVITY

Up to this point in the discussion, the assumption has been made that the plasma electrical conductivity can be assumed to be approximately constant throughout the channel. Although this is a reasonable approximation for conducting liquids, it must be recognized that it is not a very good one for compressible gaseous plasmas. Nonetheless, it has so far proved to be a useful approximation in that it has made it possible to identify many of the physical features of the flow and induced magnetic field.

Following the same line of reasoning, an attempt will now be made to learn something about the influence of the Hall effect on the flow in an MHD channel. First, recall the "generalized" Ohm law from Chap. 8 in which ion-slip and pressure-diffusion effects are neglected.

$$j = \sigma[\mathbf{E} + \mathbf{v} \times \mathbf{B} - \beta(\mathbf{j} \times \mathbf{B})] \tag{10.56}$$

where $\beta = 1/n_e e$

$\sigma = n_e e^2 \tau / m_e$

Next, consider a *uniform* flow through a two-dimensional channel (Fig. 10.16). In this case Eq. (10.56) can be rearranged as follows:

$$j_x = \frac{\sigma}{1 + (\omega\tau)^2}[E_x - \omega\tau(E_y - UB)] \tag{10.57}$$

$$j_y = \frac{\sigma}{1 + (\omega\tau)^2}(E_y - UB + \omega\tau E_x) \tag{10.58}$$

where $\sigma\beta B = \omega\tau$. From the above we observe that as a consequence of the Hall effect, axial current can flow (j_x) where none was possible before.

In principle, this axial current can be suppressed if the expression in brackets on the right-hand side of Eq. (10.57) can be made zero. Alternatively, the axial electric field E_x will be zero if the channel electrodes are continuous conductors. The consequences of either of these assumptions can be readily found as follows:

$$E_x = 0: \qquad j_x = -\frac{\sigma\omega\tau(E_y - uB)}{1 + (\omega\tau)^2} = -\omega\tau j_y$$

$$j_y = \frac{\sigma}{1 + (\omega\tau)^2}(E_y - uB)$$

$$j_x = 0: \qquad E_x = \omega\tau(E_y - uB)$$

$$j_y = \frac{\sigma}{1 + (\omega\tau)^2}[E_y - uB + (\omega\tau)^2(E_y - uB)]$$

or

$$j_y = \sigma(E_y - uB)$$

The immediate conclusion is that if continuous electrodes are used and $E_x = 0$, then an axial current will flow which could be as large as or larger than the crosswise current (if $\omega\tau > 1$). Also, the crosswise current is reduced as though the conductivity had been reduced. Again, this reduction can be considerable if $\omega\tau > 1$.

When $j_x = 0$, on the other hand, it can be seen that j_y is not reduced at all. Now in order to keep $j_x = 0$, it can be seen from the above that one must have

$$E_x = \omega\tau(E_y - uB)$$

Since such an axial field cannot exist in the presence of electrodes which are continuous conductors, it is clear that the electrodes must be segmented. One possible arrangement, which is the simplest, is shown in Fig. 10.17. Here each pair of electrodes is connected separately to an external load or power supply, so that no net current can flow axially. In the event that u is uniform and the segment widths are very small compared to the channel height, j_x should be zero identically. When u is not uniform, or finite-width segments must be considered, then

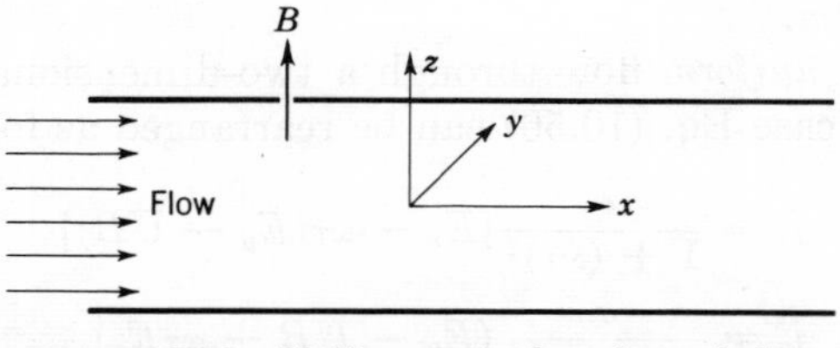

FIGURE 10.16 Uniform-velocity channel flow.

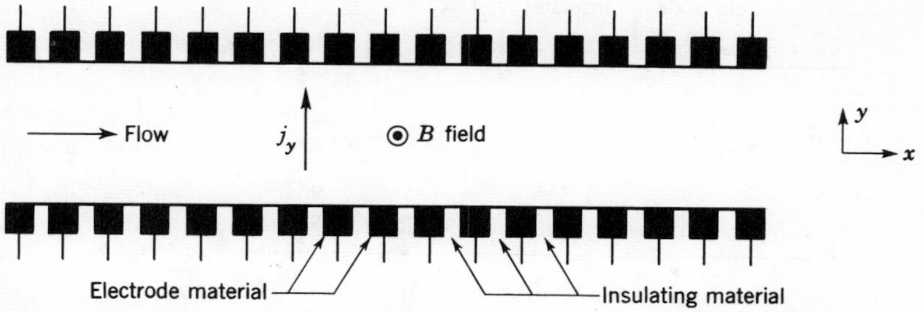

FIGURE 10.17 Segmented-electrode geometry for reducing Hall current flow.

j_x should not be identically zero despite the fact that its mean value will be.

The purpose of this section is to discuss some of the phenomena arising when the electrodes are of finite width but the flow is uniform. In the following section nonuniform flows (due to viscosity) will be considered, but under the assumption of infinitely finely segmented electrodes.

Let us consider the following problem. For the steady-state situation we know that $\nabla \times \mathbf{E} = 0$, or in the two-dimensional case,

$$\frac{\partial E_x}{\partial y} = \frac{\partial E_y}{\partial x} \tag{10.59}$$

Also, adding $\partial j_x/\partial x$ and $\partial j_y/\partial y$ from Eqs. (10.57) and (10.58) and assuming u and B constant give

$$\frac{\partial j_x}{\partial x} + \frac{\partial j_y}{\partial y} = \frac{\sigma}{1 + (\omega\tau)^2}\left[\left(\frac{\partial E_x}{\partial x} + \frac{\partial E_y}{\partial y}\right) - \omega\tau\left(\frac{\partial E_y}{\partial x} - \frac{\partial E_x}{\partial y}\right)\right] \tag{10.60}$$

so that, since $\nabla \cdot \mathbf{j} = 0$ in the steady state,

$$\frac{\partial E_x}{\partial x} + \frac{\partial E_y}{\partial y} = 0 \tag{10.61}$$

Then defining $E = -\nabla V$, it can be seen that V satisfies Laplace's equation,

$$\nabla^2 V = \frac{\partial^2 V}{\partial x^2} + \frac{\partial^2 V}{\partial y^2} = 0 \tag{10.62}$$

and that the electric field within the channel can be found by solving for V. Before proceeding further, however, the appropriate boundary conditions must be determined. Along an electrode, V must be constant.

$$V = \mp \frac{V}{2} \qquad \text{(electrode)} \tag{10.63}$$

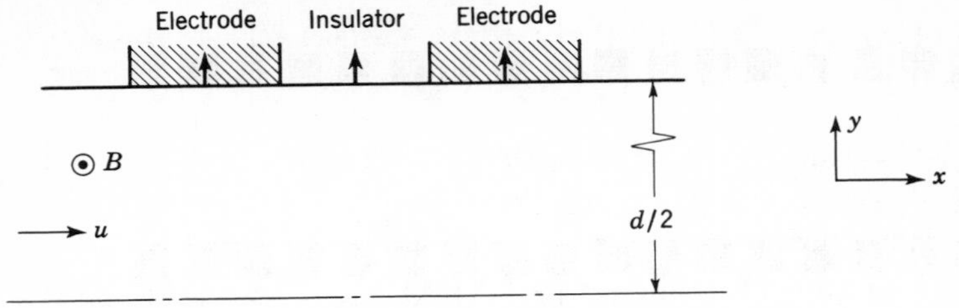

FIGURE 10.18 Finite segmented-electrode channel.

Along the insulator there must be no normal component of current. Thus $j_y = 0$, and

$$\omega\tau \frac{\partial V}{\partial x} + \frac{\partial V}{\partial y} = -uB$$

Defining $V = \phi - uBy$, this reduces to

$$\omega\tau \frac{\partial \phi}{\partial x} + \frac{\partial \phi}{\partial y} = 0 \qquad \text{(insulator)} \tag{10.64}$$

Accordingly, the boundary condition on the potential is that lines of constant potential must cross the insulator surfaces at the angle $\tan^{-1} \omega\tau$ while the electrodes are at a constant potential.

Having this information, one can proceed to determine the solution for **E** within the region of Fig. 10.18. Using the technique of graphical flux plotting, with the aid of some conformal mapping concepts, solutions were obtained.[9] Assuming the channel width large compared to the electrode width made it possible to assume the current flow to be uniform in the center of the channel. Also, for convenience in the mapping, the electrode and insulator widths were assumed equal. Within these restrictions, calculations were made for $\omega\tau = 1$, and are reproduced in Fig. 10.19.

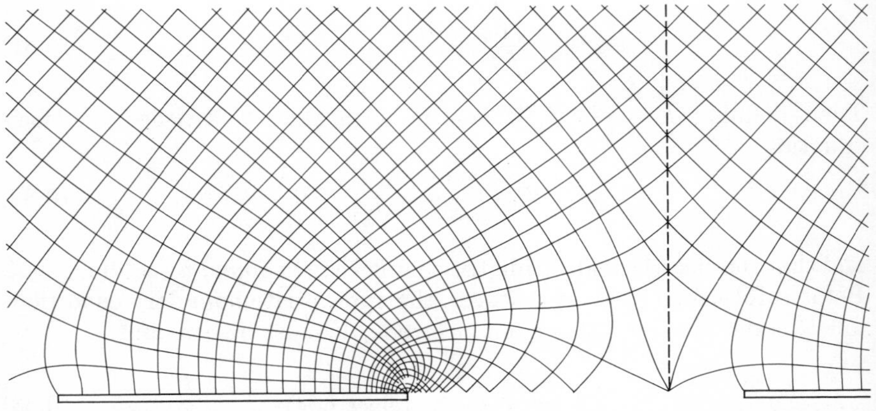

FIGURE 10.19 Flux plot for current streamlines and potential lines for segmented electrodes with $\omega\tau = 1$.

In line with the earlier discussion the lines of constant potential, which slope to the right in the above figure, enter the insulator at a 45° angle ($\omega\tau = 1$). Also, the streamlines enter the electrodes normally since each electrode is a surface of constant potential. Actually, the above figure can also be interpreted as a map of current flow streamlines. To see how this may be done we recognize that $\nabla \cdot \mathbf{j} = 0$ so that

$$j_x = \sigma_{\text{eff}} \frac{\partial Z}{\partial y} \tag{10.65}$$

$$j_y = -\sigma_{\text{eff}} \frac{\partial Z}{\partial x} \tag{10.66}$$

Also, associated with the potential function already defined there is a streamline function ψ given by

$$\frac{\partial \psi}{\partial y} = \frac{\partial \phi}{\partial x}$$

$$\frac{\partial \psi}{\partial x} = -\frac{\partial \phi}{\partial y}$$

Now refer to Eqs. (10.57) and (10.58), where $\mathbf{E}$ is written in terms of the streamline function ψ and the modified potential function ϕ.

$$j_x = \sigma_{\text{eff}} \left(-\frac{\partial \psi}{\partial y} + \omega\tau \frac{\partial \phi}{\partial y} \right) \tag{10.67}$$

$$j_y = \sigma_{\text{eff}} \left(\frac{\partial \psi}{\partial x} - \omega\tau \frac{\partial \phi}{\partial x} \right) \tag{10.68}$$

By comparison, $Z = -\psi + \omega\tau\phi$. Since lines of constant Z are current streamlines, it is a simple matter to derive a picture of the current flow pattern from a flux plot giving ψ and ϕ. In fact, for $\omega\tau = 1$, current streamlines cross the orthogonal squares of Fig. 10.19 along a diagonal, as shown in Fig. 10.20.

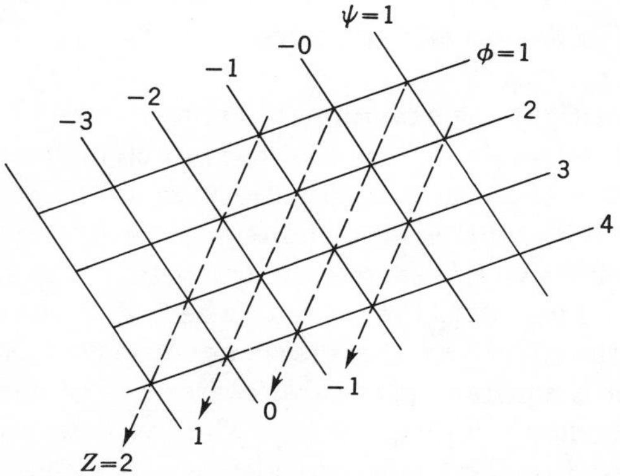

FIGURE 10.20 Derivation of current streamlines from electric field flux plot.

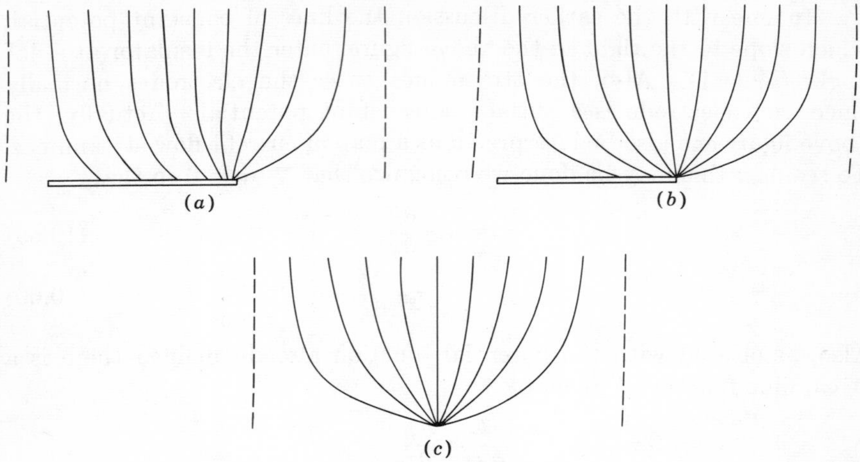

FIGURE 10.21 Current flow lines.

Among the interesting conclusions which can be drawn from the flux plot of Fig. 10.19 is the observation that a large percentage of the current tends to flow into one corner of each electrode. In fact, for the case shown it is estimated that 50 per cent of the current flows into the first 8 per cent of the electrode width.

Finally, to complete the investigation, calculations have been carried out for $\omega\tau = 3$ as well as for an infinitely thin (wire) electrode. The results are shown in Fig. 10.21. Since with $\omega\tau = 3$ almost all the current flows into the right-hand edge, the results are essentially the same as for the infinitely thin electrode.

For the wire electrode, the interesting fact emerges from the analysis that the current distribution is independent of $\omega\tau$. Why this should be so is apparent if one recognizes that the current streamline function is harmonic and it or its normal derivative is specified on all four boundaries of the region in question.

Further investigations extending the above results have been carried out by Yeh and Sutton.[10] If the electrode pitch distance were infinitely small, the effective transverse conductivity would be equal to the scalar electron conductivity; the effect of finite-size electrodes and insulators is to decrease the effective transverse conductivity. The theoretical reduction is shown in Fig. 10.22 for $\omega\tau = 1$, where it is seen that increasing pitch decreases the effective transverse conductivity. On the other hand, increasing $\omega\tau$ for a constant pitch also decreases the effective transverse conductivity, as shown in Fig. 10.23. Finally, increasing the electrode width as compared to the insulator width is deleterious.[11]

Within this section, the changes in flow and current patterns that

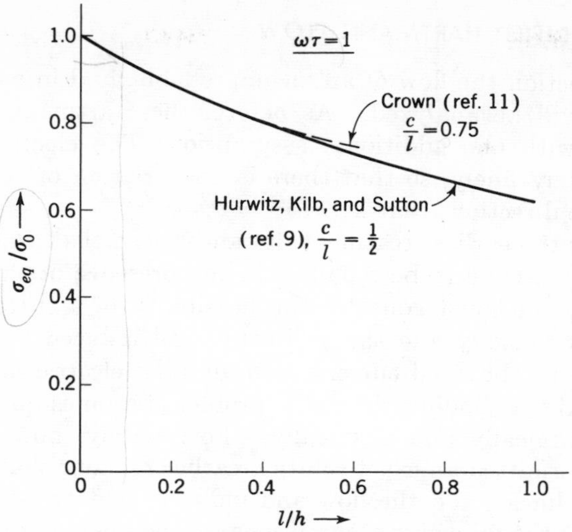

FIGURE 10.22 Effect of electrode pitch on effective transverse electrical conductivity for $\omega\tau = 1$.

one can expect in a channel flow due to the Hall effect have been illustrated. The sort of electrode geometry that this leads to was also discussed, along with an idealization convenient (infinitely finely segmented) for further analysis. In the next section, channel flows will be studied with the Hall effect present but with the ideal electrode geometry.

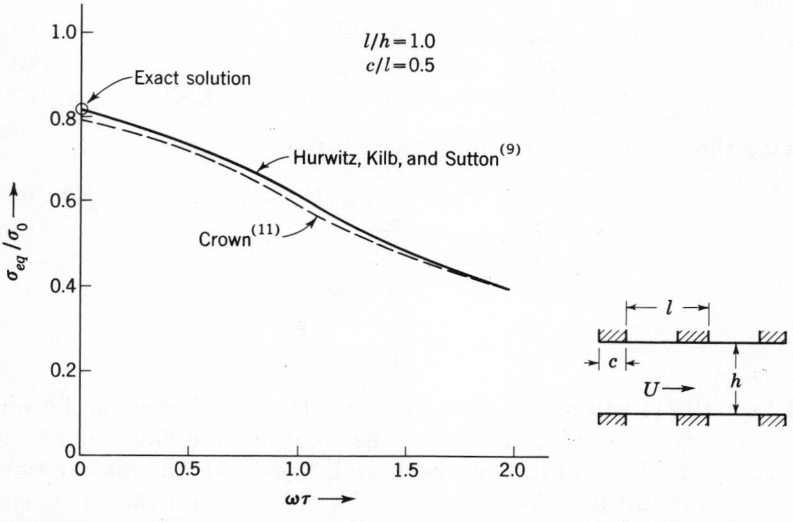

FIGURE 10.23 Effect of $\omega\tau$ on effective transverse electrical conductivity for segmented electrodes.

10.6 THE MODIFIED HARTMANN FLOW

In this section the flow of an incompressible fluid in which the Hall effect exists will be analyzed. As before, the Hartmann flow will be treated, but with one additional assumption: The electrodes are segmented infinitely finely, so that there is no variation of current flow in the transverse direction; that is, $\partial/\partial y = 0$.

Recalling the earlier treatment, it can be seen that a number of the assumptions will have to be modified in the presence of the Hall effect. In particular, one must consider the possibility of a current j_x flowing axially, a flow velocity v in the y direction, an induced field b_y in the y direction due to the axial current, and an axial electric field E_x. As a result of the above modifications, the problem becomes quite a bit more complex algebraically and physically. Fortunately, however, the features which permitted an exact solution earlier remain; that is, the equations are still linear, and the flow and induced field are still uncoupled.

As before, the following assumptions can be made in order that Eqs. (10.5b), (10.2), (10.5a), and (10.6a) be satisfied:

$$\begin{aligned} \mathbf{b} &= (b_x, b_y, 0) \\ \mathbf{v} &= (u, v, 0) \\ \mathbf{j} &= (j_x, j_y, 0) \\ \mathbf{E} &= [E_x = C_1,\ E_y = C_2,\ E_z(z)] \end{aligned}$$

Expanding the generalized Ohm Law [Eq. (10.56)] into its three components and making use of the above assumptions lead to the following equations:

$$j_x = \sigma(E_x + vB_0 - \beta j_y B_0) \tag{10.69}$$
$$j_y = \sigma(E_y - uB_0 + \beta j_x B_0) \tag{10.70}$$
$$0 = \sigma[E_z + uB_y - vB_x - \beta(j_x b_y - j_y b_x)] \tag{10.71}$$

Solving the first two for j_x and j_y, there is found

$$j_x = \tilde{\sigma}[E_x + vB_0 - \omega_0\tau(E_y - uB_0)] \tag{10.72}$$
$$j_y = \tilde{\sigma}[E_y - uB_0 + \omega_0\tau(E_x + vB_0)] \tag{10.73}$$

where
$$\tilde{\sigma} = \frac{\sigma}{1 + \omega_0^2\tau^2}$$
$$\omega_0 = \frac{eB_0}{m_e}$$

and Eq. (10.71) will not be used further. It should be noted, however, that $E_z(z)$ can be calculated after the solutions for flow velocity and induced magnetic field are obtained, and, if desired, the distribution of excess charge can be calculated from Eq. (10.71). Further, it must be noted that when E_z is a function of z, this implies that lines of constant potential in the plane of the electrodes are curved. Accordingly, the finely segmented electrodes mentioned earlier must be considered curved, the curvature being calculable once the solution has been derived.

Now expanding the momentum equation into its three components, one obtains

$$\frac{\partial p}{\partial x} = j_y B_0 + \eta \frac{\partial^2 u}{\partial z^2} \tag{10.74}$$

$$\frac{\partial p}{\partial y} = -j_x B_0 + \eta \frac{\partial^2 v}{\partial z^2} \tag{10.75}$$

$$\frac{\partial p}{\partial z} = j_x b_y - j_y b_x \tag{10.76}†$$

and substituting for j_x and j_y, the first two become

$$\frac{\partial p}{\partial x} = \tilde{\sigma} B_0[E_y - uB_0 + \omega_0\tau(E_x + vB_0)] + \eta \frac{\partial^2 u}{\partial z^2} \tag{10.77}$$

$$\frac{\partial p}{\partial y} = -\tilde{\sigma} B_0[E_x + vB_0 - \omega_0\tau(E_y - uB_0)] + \eta \frac{\partial^2 v}{\partial z^2} \tag{10.78}$$

The above two equations must then be solved subject to the following boundary conditions:

$$u(\pm a) = v(\pm a) = 0$$

The induced magnetic field is calculated as before:

$$b_y = \mu_0 \int_{-a}^{z} j_x \, dz \tag{10.79}$$

$$b_x = \mu_0 \int_{0}^{z} j_y \, dz \tag{10.80}$$

Before proceeding to the solution, note that $\partial p/\partial y$ and E_x are constants to be determined. If it is assumed that there is no net crossflow in the y direction, then $\partial p/\partial y$ can be evaluated. Also if it is required that there be no net current flow in the axial direction, then this can be used to evaluate E_x. It is of interest also to note that the present problem can be thought of as the limit of the annular flow with a radial magnetic field. In this case there will indeed be a net crossflow, and $\partial p/\partial y$ can properly be taken to be zero. This latter problem was considered by Sato,[12] while the problem being discussed in the present section was treated by Sherman and Sutton.[13]

Solving the two simultaneous second-order linear differential equations (10.77) and (10.78) for U and V yields the solution in the following form:

$$U = -c_1 \sin bz \sinh az + c_2 \cos bz \cosh az + c_3 \tag{10.81}$$

$$V = c_1 \cos bz \cosh az + c_2 \sin bz \sinh az + c_4 \tag{10.82}$$

† Equation (10.76) shows that the $\partial p/\partial z$ is a function of z alone, and Eqs. (10.74) and (10.75) show that $\partial p/\partial x$ and $\partial p/\partial y$ are constants. Thus the proper form for p is simply $p = p_0 + p_x x + p_y y + \tilde{p}(z)$.

where the constants a, b, c_1, c_2, and c_3 are functions of the parameters H_a, $\omega_0\tau$ (based on B_0 not B), and $K = E_y/\bar{u}B_0$, and where U and V have been made dimensionless by the mean velocity $\bar{u}$ and $Z = z/a$. The results of a typical calculation are presented in Fig. 10.24. It can be seen from these calculations that as the Hall parameter $\omega_0\tau$ increases, the velocity profile changes from the characteristic Hartmann profile (square shape) to the typical Poissuelle profile. This is quite a surprising result, but can be explained on the basis of the current flow which will be discussed later.

It can also be seen that the crossflow is nonexistent when $\omega_0\tau = 0$, increases to a maximum value, and then again returns to 0 as $\omega_0\tau$ increases in value. Again, the reversal to zero at large $\omega_0\tau$ can be explained on the basis of the current flow patterns.

The peculiar shape of the V curves is simply due to the fact that both $V\ (\pm a) = 0$ and the net integrated V must be zero.

After some manipulation, the solutions for U and V can be used to derive b_x and b_y. Again, some sample calculations were made, and are shown in Fig. 10.25, where R_m is the magnetic Reynolds number, and $\bar{b}_x = b_x/B_0R_m$. Unless R_m is the order of unity or larger, it can be seen that b_x will be small compared to the applied field. Since the net current flowing across the channel in the y direction is nonzero, $b_x\ (\pm a) \neq 0$. On the other hand, specifying the net axial current to be zero does make $b_y = 0$ at $z = \pm a$. Both go through zero by reasons of symmetry.

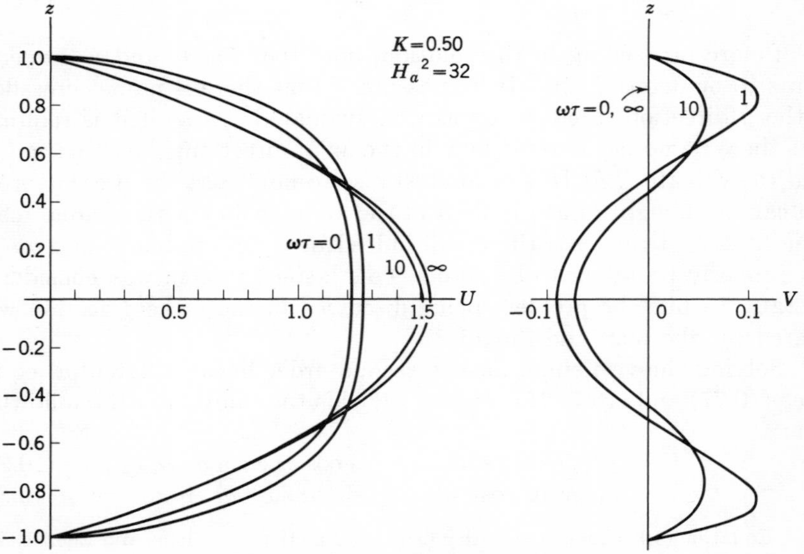

FIGURE 10.24 The flow pattern in the modified Hartmann flow.

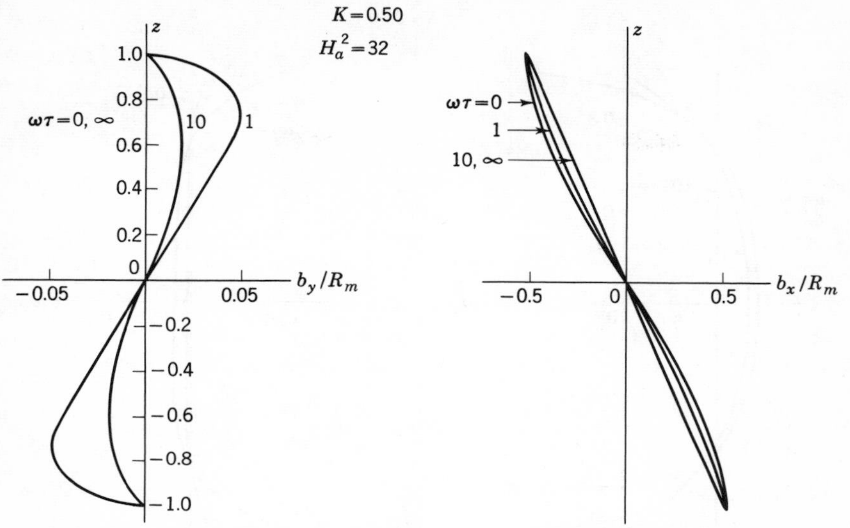

FIGURE 10.25 Induced magnetic field in modified Hartmann flow.

Also, since the axial currents are small compared to the crosswise ones, $b_y \ll b_x$.

To determine the currents, use is made of Eqs. (10.69) and (10.70), along with the solutions for U and V. For the cases already calculated, the current distributions are shown in Fig. 10.26. A number of important observations can be made. When $\omega_0\tau = 0$ (conventional Hartmann flow), there is a current reversal near the walls caused by the lower flow velocity there, and consequent reduction in the UB_0 there. It is this reverse current flow which creates the characteristic Hartmann velocity profile by accelerating the fluid near the wall relative to the central flow. As $\omega_0\tau$ is increased, this current reversal is reduced, then eliminated, and ultimately ($\omega_0\tau = \infty$) the current becomes constant over the channel, since it is proportional to E_x, which is independent of z. When the current is uniform, then $\mathbf{j} \times \mathbf{B}$ is constant over the channel, and an originally parabolic velocity profile should again be parabolic. From the distribution of J_x we observe that the crosswise Lorentz force over the central portion of the channel is in the opposite sense to the force near the walls. Then since $V = 0$ at $Z = \pm 1$, the crossflow velocity profile which is predicted by the current flow is indeed observed. Of course, when $J_x = 0$, so is $V = 0$.

In addition to the work by Sato cited earlier, it should be noted that a similar analysis was carried out by Gubanov[14] for the case of a fully ionized plasma. The governing equations differ somewhat in that the pressure-diffusion term in the generalized Ohm law cannot be neglected

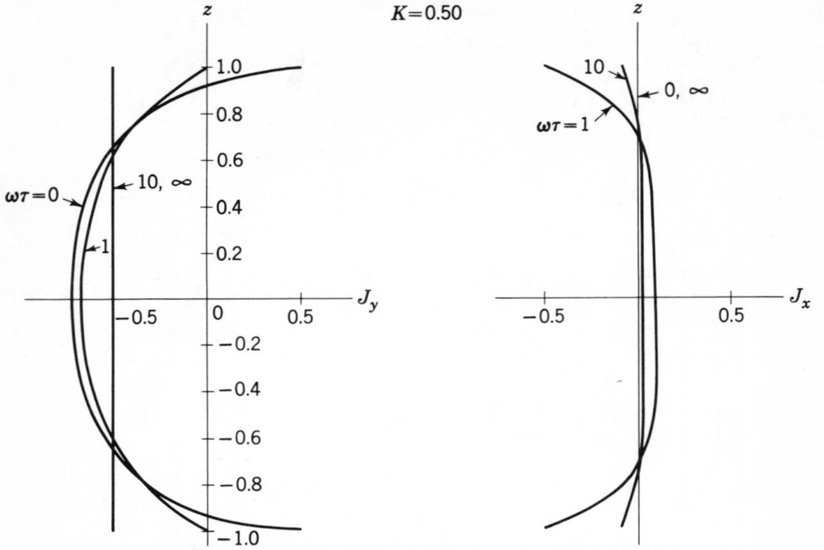

FIGURE 10.26 Current distributions in modified Hartmann flow.

as was done here. When pressure diffusion is neglected, the assumption of a slightly ionized gas is implicit.

In addition to the study of tensor conductivity with the Hartmann flow problem as a vehicle, the other logical problem, the Couette flow, has also been studied.[15] Since the results do not differ from the present in any essential way, it will not be considered further.

10.7 SECONDARY FLOWS

Throughout the preceding sections it was assumed that the channel walls parallel to the magnetic field (electrodes) were infinitely far apart, so that current or fluid flowing along these walls could be neglected. In this section, the nature of these secondary flows will be investigated for channels of finite dimensions.

A particularly valuable solution has been obtained by Shercliff.[16] He considers the Hartmann flow (Fig. 10.1) through a *finite*-width duct with nonconducting walls. An exact solution for both the secondary-flow pattern and the induced magnetic field is obtained. Consider the coordinate system shown in Fig. 10.27. The mathematical formulation and approximations in the present problem will be identical to those for the Hartmann flow treated earlier, with the following exceptions. The variables b_x, u, j_y, and p can now be functions of y as well as of z, and a new variable j_z which can be a function of y and z must also be considered.

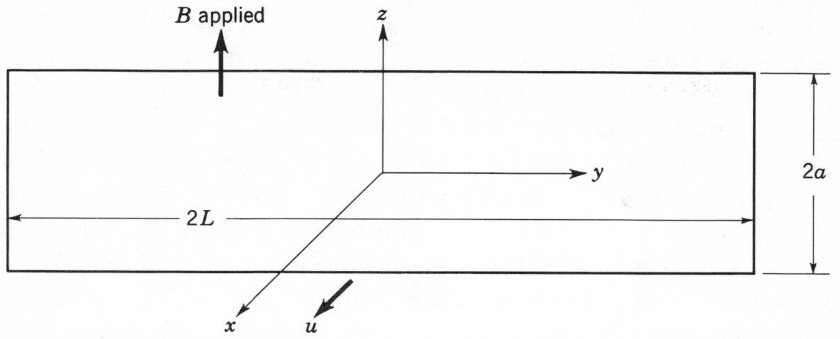

FIGURE 10.27 Coordinates and geometry appropriate for the secondary-flow problem.

Considering Eqs. (10.1) through (10.6) presented earlier and making use of the assumptions mentioned above, the following relations are obtained:

$$\frac{\partial p}{\partial x} = B_0 j_y + \eta \left(\frac{\partial^2 u}{\partial y^2} + \frac{\partial^2 u}{\partial z^2} \right) \tag{10.83}$$

$$\frac{\partial p}{\partial y} = b_x j_z \tag{10.84}$$

$$\frac{\partial p}{\partial z} = b_x j_y \tag{10.85}$$

$$j_y = \sigma (E_y - uB_0) = \frac{1}{\mu_0} \frac{\partial b_x}{\partial z} \tag{10.86}$$

$$j_z = \sigma E_z = -\frac{1}{\mu_0} \frac{\partial b_x}{\partial y} \tag{10.87}$$

$$\frac{\partial E_z}{\partial y} = \frac{\partial E_y}{\partial z} \tag{10.88}$$

In the original Hartmann flow, $\partial/\partial y = 0$ so that from Eq. (10.88), $E_y = \text{const}$. In this case, it was feasible to replace E_y with $K\bar{u}B_0$, so that j_y in Eq. (10.83) could be replaced by $\sigma B_0(K\bar{u} - u)$. It was in this way that the velocity and magnetic fields could be uncoupled and the problem solved simply. In the present instance such a procedure is not possible, since E_y is not constant, and the second expression for j_y in Eq. (10.86) must be used. This couples u and b_x.

Combining Eqs. (10.83) and (10.86) gives

$$\frac{B_0}{\mu_0} \frac{\partial b_x}{\partial z} + \eta \left(\frac{\partial^2 u}{\partial y^2} + \frac{\partial^2 u}{\partial z^2} \right) + K\eta = 0 \tag{10.89}$$

Also, combining Eqs. (10.86), (10.87), and (10.88) gives

$$B_0 \mu_0 \sigma \frac{\partial u}{\partial z} + \left(\frac{\partial^2 b_x}{\partial y^2} + \frac{\partial^2 b_x}{\partial z^2} \right) = 0 \tag{10.90}$$

These are the two coupled equations for u and b_x.

The axial pressure gradient $(-\,\partial p/\partial x)$ has been taken to be $K\eta$. The transverse pressure gradients $\partial p/\partial y$ and $\partial p/\partial z$ can be determined from Eqs. (10.84) and (10.85), once the solution has been obtained.

Since no current can flow outside the channel in the nonconducting-wall case, the induced magnetic field at the boundary of the fluid must be zero. This is in exact analogy to the fact that the field outside of a doubly infinite solenoid is zero. A number of authors have considered problems in which currents can flow in the channel walls.[2,5] For this case the boundary conditions on b_x are much more complex, and the solution of the problem is considerably more difficult. Such conducting-wall problems will not be treated here. The boundary condition on u is simply that it be zero on all solid-wall boundaries. The boundary conditions required for Eqs. (10.89) and (10.90) are then

$$b_x = 0 \qquad \text{at } y = \pm L,\ z = \pm a$$
$$u = 0 \qquad \text{at } y = \pm L,\ z = \pm a$$

The procedure for the solution of these equations is to define two new dependent variables, in a fashion similar to that done in Sec. 10.4.

$$u_1 = u + \frac{b_x}{\mu_0\sqrt{\sigma\eta}}$$
$$u_2 = u - \frac{b_x}{\mu_0\sqrt{\sigma\eta}}$$

Then Eqs. (10.89) and (10.90) reduce to

$$\left(\frac{\partial^2 u_1}{\partial y^2} + \frac{\partial^2 u_1}{\partial z^2}\right) + \frac{H_a}{a}\frac{\partial u_1}{\partial z} + K = 0 \tag{10.91}$$
$$\left(\frac{\partial^2 u_2}{\partial y^2} + \frac{\partial^2 u_2}{\partial z^2}\right) - \frac{H_a}{a}\frac{\partial u_2}{\partial z} + K = 0 \tag{10.92}$$

The boundary conditions are again

$$u_1 = u_2 = 0 \qquad \text{at } y = \pm L,\ z = \pm a$$

If the channel walls were conductors, then, as noted earlier, b_x could no longer be considered zero at the boundary, and the boundary conditions on u_1 and u_2 would no longer be separable. In such cases the equations for u and b_x must remain coupled.

Clearly if only the sign of H_a is changed in Eq. (10.92), u_2 satisfies the same equation and boundary conditions as u_1, so that a solution for u_1 alone will suffice. The solution for u_1 is obtained by expressing K over the range $-L < y < L$ as a cosine Fourier series. Thus,

$$K = \frac{4K}{\pi}\sum_{n=0}^{\infty}\frac{(-1)^n}{2n+1}\cos\frac{(2n+1)\pi y}{2L}$$

The solution for u_1 is then found to be

$$u_1 = \frac{16KL^2}{\pi^3} \sum_{n=0}^{\infty} \frac{(-1)^n}{(2n+1)^3} \left[1 + \frac{e^{m_1 z} \sinh m_2 a - e^{m_2 z} \sinh m_1 a}{\sinh (m_1 - m_2) a} \right] \times \cos \frac{(2n+1)\pi y}{2L} \tag{10.93}$$

where m_1 and m_2 are the roots of

$$m^2 + \frac{H_a}{a} m - \frac{(2n+1)^2 \pi^2}{4L^2} = 0 \tag{10.94}$$

The solution for u_2 is again Eq. (10.93), but with Eq. (10.94) changed to

$$m^2 - \frac{H_a}{a} m - \frac{(2n+1)^2 \pi^2}{4L^2} = 0 \tag{10.95}$$

Obtaining from this solution the solution for u and integrating over the channel area give the value of the mean velocity,

$$\bar{u} = \frac{32KL^2}{\pi^4} \sum_{n=0}^{\infty} \frac{1}{(2n+1)^4} \left[1 - \frac{2NL^2 (\cosh N - \cosh H_a)}{(2n+1)^2 \pi^2 a^2 \sinh N} \right]$$

where
$$N^2 = H_a^2 + (2n+1)^2 \pi^2 \frac{a^2}{L^2}$$

Although no numerical calculations have been made of the flow or current distribution, it is instructive to show them qualitatively. In Fig. 10.28 are shown contours of constant u, while in Fig. 10.29 are shown current streamlines.

It is seen that flow boundary layers now form on all four walls. Also, current passes through a current boundary layer on the sidewall before returning along the horizontal walls.

An important question to be asked, now that a solution is available for a channel of arbitrary aspect ratio, is the following. At what aspect ratio L/a does it become important to consider the influence of the side-

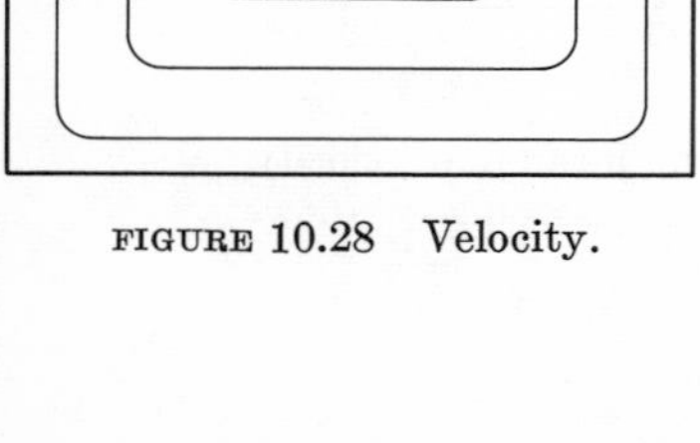

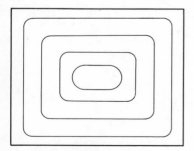

FIGURE 10.28 Velocity.

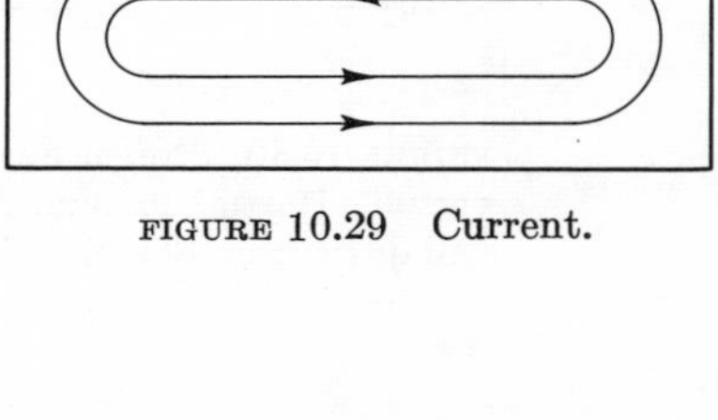

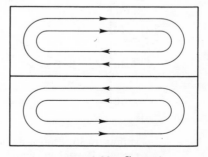

FIGURE 10.29 Current.

walls? This can be answered by comparing the pressure gradients required to achieve some specific mean velocity for different aspect ratios. Making use of the previously derived result for Hartmann flow, and the present solution for $L/a = 1$, the results shown in Fig. 10.30 are obtained. From these results several interesting conclusions can be drawn. First, it is seen that in the purely fluid dynamic case, twice the pressure gradient would be needed to achieve the same mean velocity in a square channel of height a as compared to the very wide channel. Then as Hartmann number increases, the penalty paid for using a square channel becomes smaller (for example, a 15 per cent higher pressure gradient would be needed at $H_a = 30$). Since in most practical problems the Hartmann number is of the order of 100 or more, it can be seen that secondary flows are not critical, at least for aspect ratios of the order of unity or larger. It should be noted that the smaller importance of aspect ratio with higher Hartmann number follows directly from the fact that as H_a is increased, the velocity boundary layers become thinner.

Continuing along the same line of thought, Shercliff has shown that the boundary-layer concept can be used to investigate other channel shapes for which no exact solutions have been found. Via this technique the flow through a circular channel has been analyzed, and results similar to the present have been found. It is also pointed out that below some critical value of H_a, the boundary-layer approximation breaks down since the channel tends to become filled with the boundary layer.

In addition to the boundary-layer technique of obtaining solutions to secondary-flow problems, another approximate technique has been developed by Tani.[17] It is somewhat more general than the boundary-layer approach, since the latter is limited to problems of secondary flow in nonconducting channels, for which the equations can be decoupled.

For many years variational techniques have been very effectively applied to problems in the theory of elasticity; they have rarely been used

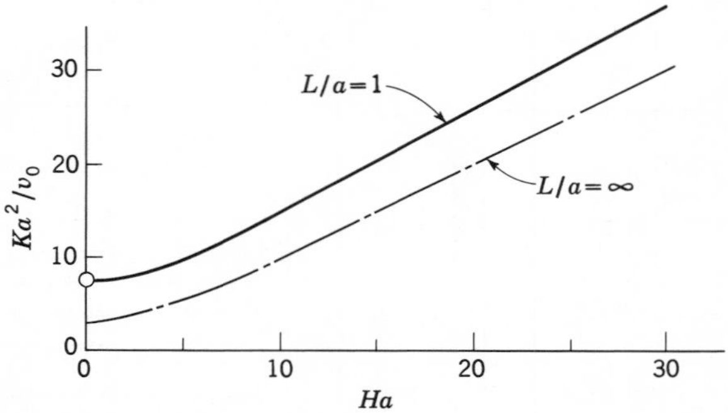

FIGURE 10.30 Pressure gradient and mean flow velocity versus Hartmann number for a secondary flow. (Adapted from Shercliff.[16])

in fluid dynamic problems. Their great utility in elasticity problems is due to the fact that they can be conveniently applied to linear problems. This, of course, explains why they are little used in fluid dynamics since most such problems are nonlinear. For secondary-flow problems of the type being considered here, it may be recalled that the governing equations for u and b_x, although coupled, are linear. Accordingly, a variational technique may be tried.

First, consider the following integral,

$$I(u,b_x) = \iint_S F[y,z;u,u_y,u_z;b_x,(b_x)_y,(b_x)_z]\,dy\,dz \tag{10.96}$$

where F is some given function of y, z, u, u_y, u_z, b_x, $(b_x)_y$, $(b_x)_z$. Clearly, the value of the integral depends on the choice of the functions $u(y,z)$ and $b_x(y,z)$. Now, let us pose the following problem: What functions $u(y,z)$ and $b_x(y,z)$ minimize the value of I? As is well known from variational calculus, the necessary conditions that u and b_x minimize I are the Euler equations:

$$\frac{\partial F}{\partial u} - \frac{\partial}{\partial y}\left(\frac{\partial F}{\partial u_y}\right) - \frac{\partial}{\partial z}\left(\frac{\partial F}{\partial u_z}\right) = 0 \tag{10.97}$$

$$\frac{\partial F}{\partial b_x} - \frac{\partial}{\partial y}\left[\frac{\partial F}{\partial (b_x)_y}\right] - \frac{\partial}{\partial z}\left[\frac{\partial F}{\partial (b_x)_z}\right] = 0 \tag{10.98}$$

In other words, when F satisfies these two relations, u and b_x will minimize I. It should be noted that, as shown by Tani, the Euler equations are the desired necessary condition only when u and b_x take on specified values on the boundary (insulated walls) or $\partial b_x/\partial n = 0$ on the boundary (perfectly conducting walls).

Next, F is assumed to have the following form:

$$F = ku - \frac{1}{2}\left[\left(\frac{\partial u}{\partial y}\right)^2 + \left(\frac{\partial u}{\partial z}\right)^2\right] + \frac{1}{2}\frac{B_0}{\mu_0\eta}\left(u\frac{\partial b_x}{\partial y} - b_x\frac{\partial u}{\partial y}\right) + \frac{1}{2}\frac{1}{\mu_0{}^2\eta\sigma}\left[\left(\frac{\partial b_x}{\partial y}\right)^2 + \left(\frac{\partial b_x}{\partial z}\right)^2\right] \tag{10.99}$$

If this relation is substituted into Euler's equations (10.97) and (10.98), the original coupled differential equations of the problem are returned [Eqs. (10.89) and (10.90)]. The procedure to be followed then is to assume u and b_x to be represented by a series of simple terms, where each term is multiplied by some arbitrary constant. An example of one such assumption that can be made is that u and b_x are polynomials of some convenient order. In any event, these approximate representations of u and b_x are substituted in Eq. (10.99) to obtain F, which is then substituted into Eq. (10.96). The integrations are carried out, and the constants are determined in order to make I minimum. In this way an approximate solution for u and b_x is derived.

In order to test the feasibility of such an approach, Tani made the following assumptions for u and b_x:

$$\frac{u}{\bar{u}} = \frac{\cosh H_a - \cosh (H_a z/a)}{\cosh H_a - 1}\left(a_1 \cos\frac{\pi y}{2L} + a_2 \cos\frac{3\pi}{2}\frac{y}{L}\right) \tag{10.100}$$

$$\frac{b_x}{B_0 R_m} = \frac{\sinh (H_a z/a) - (z/a) \sinh H_a}{H_a(\cosh H_a - 1)}\left(b_1 \cos\frac{\pi}{2} + b_2 \cos\frac{3\pi}{2}\frac{y}{L}\right) \tag{10.101}$$

The form of these assumptions obviously corresponds to the fact that, in general, the solution should tend to the solution of the Hartmann flow problem. Making the above assumptions, substituting into the previous equations, and deriving values for the constants a_1, a_2, b_1, and b_2, Tani found that the resulting solution was in excellent agreement with the previously described exact solution, the error being no more than a few per cent.

In addition to the above calculation, Tani also considered the secondary flow when the Hall effect was present. In order to omit the nonlinear convection terms in the momentum equation, he assumed a very small Reynolds number. To simplify this very complex problem further, he assumed a very small magnetic Reynolds number. Within these assumptions, a solution was obtained for the crossflow induced by the Hall effect in a square channel with nonconducting walls. A sample calculation was made for a Hartmann number 5, as shown in Fig. 10.31.

In this figure the crossflow, whose existence was deduced earlier in Sec. 10.6, can be seen, in addition to the details of how this crossflow behaves in the vicinity of the channel sidewalls.

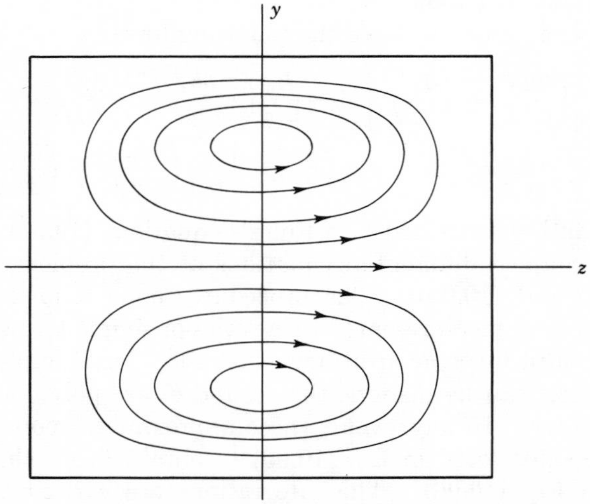

FIGURE 10.31 The streamlines of crossflow induced by the Hall effect. (After Tani.[17])

In conclusion, then, it can be said that the use of the variational technique for obtaining approximate solutions to the linear secondary-flow problem is extremely convenient and accurate, since, in almost all instances, channel cross sections are not simple geometric shapes, and existence of such an approximate technique can be very useful.

10.8 INVISCID TWO-DIMENSIONAL CHANNEL FLOWS

In most of the preceding discussion, the exact solutions of *viscous* channel flows were considered. In this section, by way of contrast, some *inviscid* magnetohydrodynamic channel flows will be studied. The solutions will not be as exact as in the preceding investigations, since it will be necessary to linearize the governing equations. Nonetheless, the linear equations will be solved exactly and some numerical solutions presented.

In general, when the problem being considered is too complicated to be solved directly (i.e., nonlinear partial differential equations), it is usual to use the perturbation approach. In the present case, two parameters appear in the equations governing the problem, I and R_m, both of which have been discussed earlier. For cases of practical interest, both these parameters will be small, so that it is reasonable to expand each dependent variable in a double power series in I and R_m, and subsequently neglect higher-order terms.

In order to illustrate this concept, consider the following equations for a steady, inviscid incompressible flow:

$$\begin{aligned} &\nabla \cdot \mathbf{B} = 0 \qquad \nabla \times \mathbf{B} = \mu_0 \mathbf{j} \\ &\mathbf{j} = \sigma(\mathbf{E} + \mathbf{v} \times \mathbf{B}) \\ &\nabla \cdot \mathbf{v} = 0 \\ &\rho(\mathbf{v} \cdot \nabla)\mathbf{v} + \nabla p = \mathbf{j} \times \mathbf{B} \end{aligned} \tag{10.102}$$

If $\mathbf{E} = 0$, no essential features will be lost, and the discussion will be simplified. In this case one obtains

$$\begin{aligned} &\nabla \cdot \mathbf{B} = 0 \qquad \nabla \times \mathbf{B} = \mu_0 \sigma \mathbf{v} \times \mathbf{B} \\ &\nabla \cdot \mathbf{v} = 0 \\ &\rho(\mathbf{v} \cdot \nabla)\mathbf{v} + \nabla p = \sigma(\mathbf{v} \times \mathbf{B}) \times \mathbf{B} \end{aligned} \tag{10.103}$$

Next, the following nondimensional quantities are defined:

$$\mathbf{B}' = \frac{\mathbf{B}}{B_{\text{ref}}} \qquad \mathbf{v}' = \frac{\mathbf{v}}{u_{\text{ref}}} \qquad p' = \frac{p}{\rho u_{\text{ref}}^2} \qquad \mathbf{r}' = \frac{\mathbf{r}}{y_0}$$

Substituting these into the system of equations (10.103) yields the follow ing, where the ( )′ notation has been omitted, and all variables are understood to be dimensionless.

$$\begin{aligned} &\nabla \cdot \mathbf{B} = 0 \qquad \nabla \times \mathbf{B} = R_m \mathbf{v} \times \mathbf{B} \\ &\nabla \cdot \mathbf{v} = 0 \\ &(\mathbf{v} \cdot \nabla)\mathbf{v} + \nabla p = I(\mathbf{v} \times \mathbf{B}) \times \mathbf{B} \end{aligned} \tag{10.104}$$

where
$$I = \frac{\sigma B_{\text{ref}}^2 y_0}{\rho u_{\text{ref}}} \qquad R_m = \mu\sigma u_{\text{ref}} y_0$$

Next, define the following double-power-series expansions in the two parameters R_m and I.

$$\begin{aligned} \mathbf{B} &= \mathbf{B}_0 + R_m\mathbf{B}_1 + I\mathbf{B}_2 + R_m I \mathbf{B}_3 + \cdots \\ \mathbf{v} &= \mathbf{v}_0 + R_m\mathbf{v}_1 + I\mathbf{v}_2 + R_m I \mathbf{v}_3 + \cdots \\ p &= p_0 + R_m p_1 + I p_2 + R_m I p_3 + \cdots \end{aligned}$$

If these are substituted into the system of equations (10.104), and coefficients of like powers of R_m and I are equated to zero, the following recursive system of equations is derived:

Zeroth order:
$$\begin{aligned} &\nabla \cdot \mathbf{B}_0 = 0 \qquad \nabla \times \mathbf{B}_0 = 0 \\ &\nabla \cdot \mathbf{v}_0 = 0 \\ &(\mathbf{v}_0 \cdot \nabla)\mathbf{v}_0 + \nabla p_0 = 0 \end{aligned} \tag{10.105}$$

First order in I:

$$\begin{aligned} &\nabla \cdot \mathbf{B}_2 = 0 \qquad \nabla \times \mathbf{B}_2 = 0 \\ &\nabla \cdot \mathbf{v}_2 = 0 \\ &(\mathbf{v}_0 \cdot \nabla)\mathbf{v}_2 + (\mathbf{v}_2 \cdot \nabla)\mathbf{v}_0 + \nabla p_2 = (\mathbf{v}_0 \times \mathbf{B}_0) \times \mathbf{B}_0 \end{aligned} \tag{10.106}$$

First order in R_m:

$$\begin{aligned} &\nabla \cdot \mathbf{B}_1 = 0 \qquad \nabla \times \mathbf{B}_1 = \mathbf{v}_0 \times \mathbf{B}_0 \\ &\nabla \cdot \mathbf{v}_1 = 0 \\ &(\mathbf{v}_0 \cdot \nabla)\mathbf{v}_1 + (\mathbf{v}_1 \cdot \nabla)\mathbf{v}_0 + \nabla p_1 = 0 \end{aligned} \tag{10.107}$$

First order in $R_m I$:

$$\begin{aligned} &\nabla \cdot \mathbf{B}_3 = 0 \qquad \nabla \times \mathbf{B}_3 = \mathbf{v}_0 \times \mathbf{B}_2 + \mathbf{v}_2 \times \mathbf{B}_0 \\ &\nabla \cdot \mathbf{v}_3 = 0 \\ &(\mathbf{v}_1 \cdot \nabla)\mathbf{v}_2 + (\mathbf{v}_2 \cdot \nabla)\mathbf{v}_1 + (\mathbf{v}_3 \cdot \nabla)\mathbf{v}_0 + (\mathbf{v}_0 \cdot \nabla)\mathbf{v}_3 + \nabla p_3 \\ &\quad = (\mathbf{v}_0 \times \mathbf{B}_1) \times \mathbf{B}_0 + (\mathbf{v}_0 \times \mathbf{B}_0) \times \mathbf{B}_1 + (\mathbf{v}_1 \times \mathbf{B}_0) \times \mathbf{B}_0 \end{aligned} \tag{10.108}$$

The procedure for solving this system of equations is as follows. For the zeroth-order case, $\mathbf{B}_0$ is taken to be the applied field in the flow region, and $\mathbf{v}_0$ and p_0 are the velocity and pressure in the flow when no magnetic field is applied. The first-order solution in I then leads to $\mathbf{B}_2 = 0$, and $\mathbf{v}_2$ and p_2 must be solved for, based on the zeroth-order solution. In the first order in R_m equations, it is seen that $\mathbf{v}_1$, $p_1 = 0$ can be assumed, and

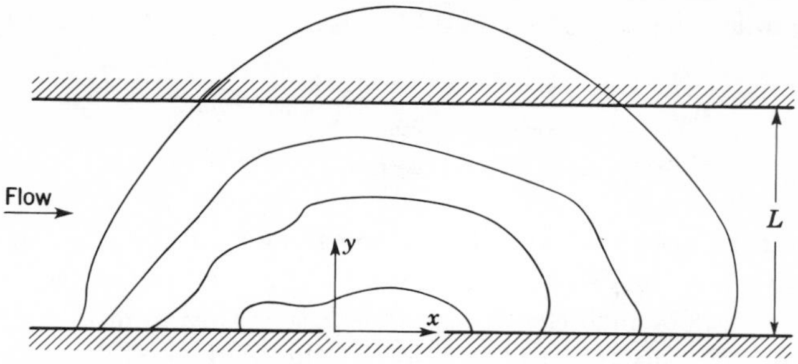

FIGURE 10.32 Inviscid two-dimensional channel flow with applied magnetic field.

$\mathbf{B}_1$ can be solved, based on the zeroth-order solutions. Finally, from the first order in R_mI equations, one can determine $\mathbf{B}_3$, knowing $\mathbf{v}_2$ and $\mathbf{B}_0$, and solve for $\mathbf{v}_3$ and p_3, knowing $\mathbf{v}_0$, $\mathbf{v}_1$, $\mathbf{v}_2$, $\mathbf{B}_0$, and $\mathbf{B}_1$. Summarizing them, we have

$\mathbf{B}_0$ = applied field	$\mathbf{v}_0, p_0$ = unperturbed flow solution
$\mathbf{B}_1$ = to be solved for	$\mathbf{v}_1, p_1 = 0$
$\mathbf{B}_2 = 0$	$\mathbf{v}_2, p_2$ = to be solved for
$\mathbf{B}_3$ = to be solved for	$\mathbf{v}_3, p_3$ = to be solved for

Next a particular problem is considered. The two-dimensional flow of an incompressible fluid through a parallel-wall channel in which the magnetic field vector lies in the plane of the flow (Fig. 10.32) is to be solved for.

If this flow is considered to be the limit of an annular flow when the height of the annulus is small compared to the radius of the inner cylinder, then the electric field in the problem is identical to zero. Also, the zeroth-order solution for the flow will be simply a uniform flow and uniform pressure. Thus,

$$\mathbf{v}_0 = (1,0,0) \qquad \text{and} \qquad p_0 = \text{const}$$

For the problem described above, the first order in I system of equations (10.106) reduces to the following set where x' and y' are written x and y for convenience:

$$-\frac{\partial v_2}{\partial y} + \frac{\partial p_2}{\partial x} = -B_{0_y}^2 \tag{10.109}$$

$$\frac{\partial v_2}{\partial x} + \frac{\partial p_2}{\partial y} = B_{0_x}B_{0_y} \tag{10.110}$$

$$\frac{\partial B_{0_x}}{\partial x} + \frac{\partial B_{0_y}}{\partial y} = 0 \tag{10.111}$$

$$\frac{\partial B_{0_y}}{\partial x} - \frac{\partial B_{0_x}}{\partial y} = 0 \tag{10.112}$$

where the following boundary conditions must be met:

$$
\begin{aligned}
u_2(-\infty,y) &= 0 \\
v_2(-\infty,y) &= v_2(x,0) = v_2(x,Y) = v_2(+\infty,y) = 0 \\
p_2(-\infty,y) &= p_2(\infty,y) = 0
\end{aligned}
$$

Nothing can be specified for u_2 far downstream of the applied magnetic field region ($x = \infty$) since the Lorentz force is nonconservative and introduces vorticity into the flow. It is interesting to note that the total Lorentz force on the fluid (or reaction at the field source) is calculable to the first order without solving for the flow. The distribution of pressure on the surface, however, cannot be obtained without the complete solution.

To proceed further, a specific form of the applied field must be selected. A number of authors have assumed B_0 to be due to a current-carrying wire imbedded in the lower wall of Fig. 10.32 and aligned normal to the flow direction. A number of other choices are also possible, but only the imbedded wire case will be considered here in detail. The magnetic field due to a wire imbedded in a wall a distance y_0 below it has the components

$$B_{0_x} = \frac{x}{x^2 + (y+1)^2} \tag{10.113}$$

$$B_{0_y} = -\frac{1+y}{x^2 + (y+1)^2} \tag{10.114}$$

where B_0 has been made dimensionless, with the absolute value of the field at $x = 0$, $y = 0$. By way of illustration, the channel and applied field are shown in Fig. 10.33 in which is also illustrated the qualitative nature of the flow pattern to be expected.

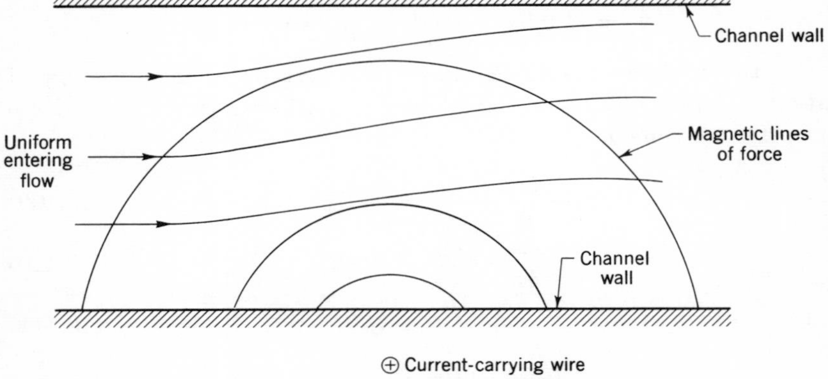

FIGURE 10.33 Flow perturbation due to magnetic field of imbedded wire.

As has been shown by Levy,[18] the above problem can be solved in closed form when $L = \infty$. First, consider the solution to be the sum of a particular and complementary solution. In general, the particular solution can be taken to be

$$(v_2)_p = \tfrac{1}{2}B_{0_y} \int_{-\infty}^{x} B_{0_x}\, dx \tag{10.115}$$

$$(p_2)_p = -\tfrac{1}{2}B_{0_x} \int_{-\infty}^{x} B_{0_x}\, dx + \frac{1}{2}\int_{-\infty}^{x} (B_{0_x}^2 - B_{0_y}^2)\, dx \tag{10.116}$$

For the present problem the integration can be carried out in closed form. Thus

$$(v_2)_p = \frac{\tfrac{1}{2}(y+1)[x^2 - (y+1)^2]}{[x^2 + (y+1)^2]^3} \tag{10.117}$$

$$(p_2)_p = \frac{\tfrac{1}{2}x[(y+1)^2 + \tfrac{1}{3}x^2]}{[x^2 + (y+1)^2]^3} \tag{10.118}$$

The complementary solution must be harmonic so that the following definition can be made:

$$w(z) = p_c + iv_c \qquad z = x + iy$$

where $w(z)$ is analytic function. The appropriate boundary condition on $y = 0$ is given by $v = v_p + v_c = 0$. Thus,

$$v_p + \mathcal{I}(w) = 0 \qquad \text{on } y = 0, \text{ for all } x$$

or

$$\mathcal{I}w(z) = \frac{\tfrac{1}{2}x(\pi/2 + \tan^{-1}x)}{x^2+1} \qquad \text{on } y = 0$$

Finally, the appropriate $w(z)$, analytic in the upper half plane, is

$$w(z) = \frac{i\pi/4}{z+i} - \frac{\tfrac{1}{2}z \ln \dfrac{1-iz}{2}}{z^2+1} \tag{10.119}$$

Clearly, the real and imaginary parts of Eq. (10.119) added to Eqs. (10.118) and (10.117), respectively, yield the solution for pressure and velocity.

In addition to the problem considered above, the case when $L \neq \infty$ has also been considered.[18,19] For this case some of the results are plotted in Figs. 10.34 to 10.36.

In the first of these, observe that the component of velocity normal to the flow direction v is zero at both walls and achieves a maximum in between. Since v must return to zero at $+\infty$, it is seen to be reduced in magnitude downstream of the central portion of the channel. In Fig. 10.35 the fact that the flow becomes rotational by action of the magnetic field can be seen more clearly. Initially $u = 1$; however, at $x = 0$ and as $x \to \infty$, it is seen that u obtains a velocity defect near the lower wall

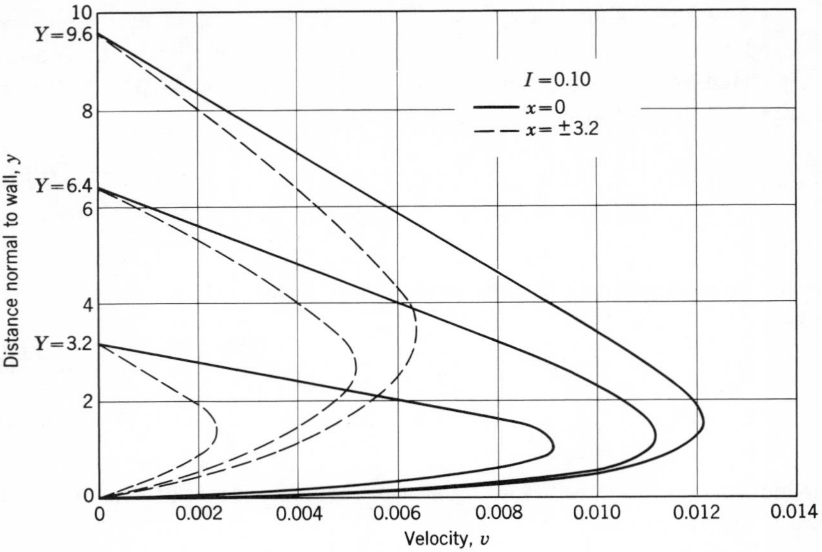

FIGURE 10.34 Vertical velocity component in inviscid two-dimensional MHD channel flow.

and is slightly greater than unity over the remainder of the channel. Finally, the pressure distribution existing along the lower wall is shown in Fig. 10.36. Here it is found that the pressure gradient in the region of the wire is large, adverse, and essentially the same for $Y > 3.2$. It is this adverse pressure gradient which may possibly cause separation of the

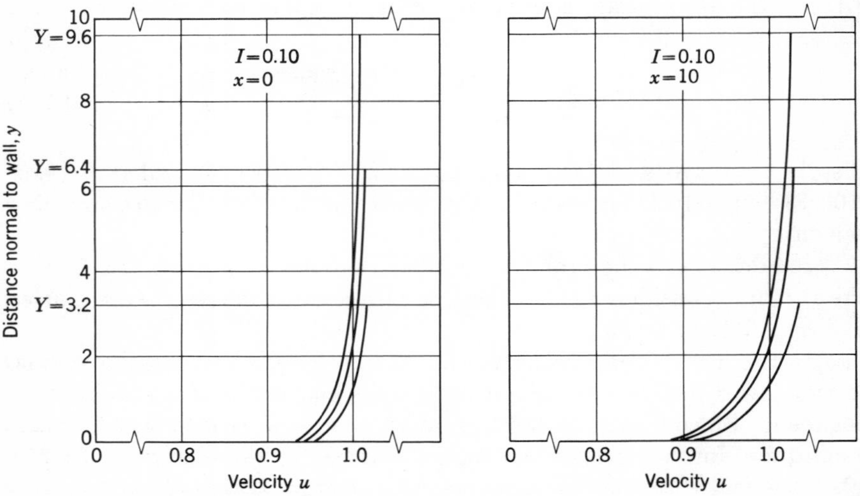

FIGURE 10.35 Axial velocity component in inviscid two-dimensional MHD channel flow.

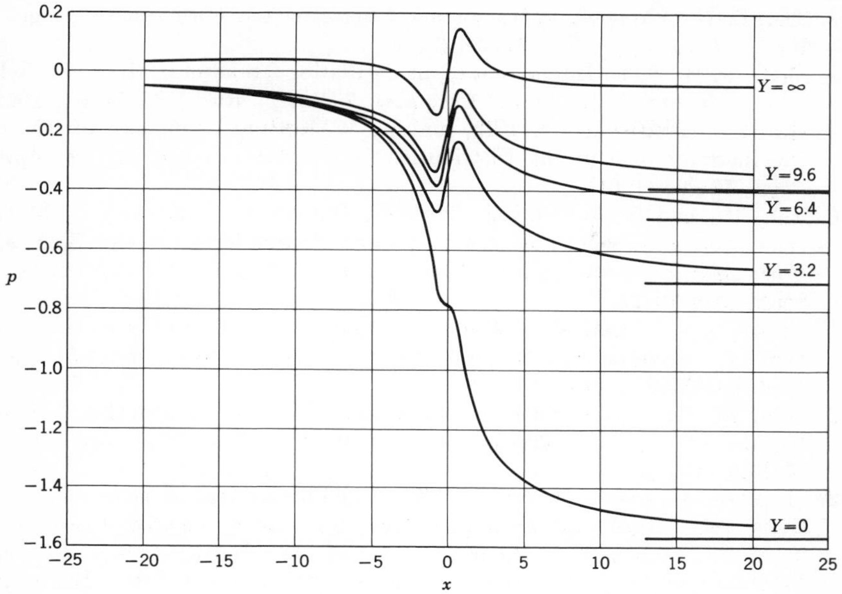

FIGURE 10.36 Pressure distribution in inviscid two-dimensional MHD channel flow. (After Levy.[18])

boundary layer along the lower wall. Also one can see that the overall pressure drop is higher, the smaller the Y, being identically zero when $Y \to \infty$.

In addition to the incompressible flow considered here, solutions have been obtained for the compressible subsonic and supersonic cases.[18] The related problem in an axially symmetric pipe has also been considered.[20]

REFERENCES CITED

1. Cowling, T. G.: *Magnetohydrodynamics,* Interscience Publishers, Inc., New York, 1957.
2. Harris, L. P.: *Hydromagnetic Channel Flow,* John Wiley & Sons, Inc., New York, 1960.
3. Hartmann, J., and F. Lazarus: *Kgl. Danske Videnskab. Selskab, Mat.-Fys. Medd.,* **15**(6, 7), (1937).
4. Alpher, R. A.: "Heat Transfer in Magnetohydrodynamic Flow between Parallel Plates," *Intern. J. Heat Mass Transfer,* **3**:108 (1961).
5. Nigam, S. D., and S. N. Singh: "Heat Transfer by Laminar Flow between Parallel Plates under the Action of Transverse Magnetic Field," *Quart. J. Mech. Appl. Math.,* **13**:85 (1960).
6. Bleviss, Z. O.: "Magnetogasdynamics of Hypersonic Couette Flow," *J. Aerospace Sci.,* **25**:601 (1958).

7. Tao, L. N.: "Magnetohydrodynamic Effects on the Formation of Couette Flow," *J. Aerospace Sci.*, **27**:334 (1960).
8. Shair, F. H.: "The Interaction of an Oscillating Transverse Magnetic Field with Fluid in Couette Flow," *Gen. Elec. TIS Rept.* R62SD33, March, 1962.
9. Hurwitz, H., Jr., R. W. Kilb, and G. W. Sutton: "Influence of Tensor Conductivity on Current Distribution in an MHD Generator," *J. Appl. Phys.*, **32**:205 (1961).
10. Yeh, H., and G. W. Sutton: "Current Output and Efficiency of MHD Generators with Segmented Electrodes and Non-uniform Velocity Profiles," *Proc. Magnetoplasmadynamic Elec. Power Conf.*, New Castle, England, September, 1962.
11. Crown, J. C.: "Analysis of Magnetohydrodynamic Generators Having Segmented Electrodes and Anisotropic Conductivity," *United Aircraft Res. Lab. Rept.* R-1852-2, February, 1961.
12. Sato, H.: "The Hall Effect in the Viscous Flow of Ionized Gas between Parallel Plates under Transverse Magnetic Field," *J. Phys. Soc. Japan*, **16**:1427 (1961).
13. Sherman, A., and G. W. Sutton: "The Combined Effect of Tensor Conductivity and Viscosity on an MHD Generator with Segmented Electrodes," in A. B. Cambel, T. P. Anderson, and M. M. Slawsky (eds.), *Proc. 4th Biennial Gas Dynamics Symp.*, Northwestern University Press, Evanston, Ill., 1962.
14. Gubanov, A. I., and O. E. Pushkavev: "The Hartmann Problem in Magneto Plasma Dynamics," *Soviet Phys. Tech. Phys. English Transl.*, **6**:445 (1961).
15. Peletier, L. A., and L. Van Wijngaarden: "Couette Flow of a Fully Ionized Gas, Considered as a Two Component Fluid," *Appl. Sci. Res. Sect. B*, **9**:141 (1961).
16. Shercliff, J. A.: "Steady Motion of Conducting Fluids in Pipes under Transverse Magnetic Fields," *Proc. Cambridge Phil. Soc.*, **49**:136 (1953).
17. Tani, I.: "Steady Flow of Conducting Fluids in Channels under Transverse Magnetic Fields with Consideration of Hall Effect," *J. Aerospace Sci.*, **29**:287 (1962).
18. Levy, R. H.: "Exact Solutions to a Class of Linearized Magnetohydrodynamic Flow Problems," *Phys. Fluids*, **5**:1416 (1962).
19. Sherman, A.: "The Effect of Non-uniform Magnetic Fields on Internal Flows of Conducting Fluids," *Advan. Astronaut. Sci.*, vol. 6, The Macmillan Company, New York, 1961.
20. Ehlers, F. E.: "Linearized Magnetogasdynamic Channel Flow with Axial Symmetry," *ARS J.*, **31**:334 (1961).

GENERAL REFERENCES

Harris, L. P.: *Hydromagnetic Channel Flows*, John Wiley & Sons, Inc., New York, 1960.

Shercliff, J. A.: *Theory of Electromagnetic Flow Measurement*, Cambridge University Press, New York, 1962.

11

CHANNEL FLOWS—QUASI-ONE-DIMENSIONAL APPROXIMATION

11.1 INTRODUCTION

The quasi-one-dimensional approximation has for a number of years been a useful device for the study of compressible fluid flow through many types of ducts. For example, in the study of jet and rocket engines, it has been used to design inlets, combustion chambers, exhaust nozzles, and turbomachinery blade passages. Many other problems of pipe flow with the combined effects of friction, heat addition, area change, mass addition, etc., can also be successfully treated by such methods. For a complete description of the quasi-one-dimensional approach to conventional fluid dynamic problems, such as those just described, reference can be made to the book by Shapiro[2] and the article by Crocco.[1]

In this chapter, our goal will be to present the foundations and limitations of the quasi-one dimensional approximation, as applied to compressible channel flows in magnetohydrodynamics. An attempt will be made to identify and clarify the new phenomena introduced by the existence of the Lorentz body force and Joule heating, as well as to describe some methods of solution of the complex equations governing the phenomena. In order to keep the treatment within reasonable bounds, we will consider only steady, inviscid flows, with no heat transfer.

After the approximations inherent in the quasi-one-dimensional approach are presented and discussed, the appropriate flow equations are derived from the *magnetohydrodynamic equations*. Some attention is given to flows in which the Hall effect must be considered, and to the electrode geometries that can be employed in this case.

Following these preliminary discussions, methods of obtaining exact closed-form solutions to these equations are discussed and some examples are presented. Finally, some general observations on the nature of perfect-gas flows are presented, followed by a discussion of the methods of treating real-gas flows.

11.2 THE QUASI-ONE-DIMENSIONAL APPROXIMATION

In principle, the subject of magnetohydrodynamic channel flows can encompass channel cross sections of any shape. Similarly, the channel wall could be an electrical insulator, a conductor, or a combination of both. Since the greatest engineering interest lies in channels in which energy is either added to or extracted from the flow, our attention will be restricted to nearly rectangular channel cross sections and to channels with two opposing walls of electrically insulating material and two of electrically conducting material (electrodes). Such a duct is shown in Fig. 11.1.

The approximations which will permit a reduction of the full magnetohydrodynamic equations to a much simpler system of first-order ordinary differential equations can be discussed with reference to the assumed channel shape shown in Fig. 11.1. The following four groups of assumptions are presented first, and then their physical basis will be discussed.

1. All nonuniformities in the end regions (entrance and exit) can be neglected.

2. The only significant components of the velocity and applied magnetic field are u and B_z, as shown in Fig. 11.1. In the absence of the Hall effect, the only important component of the electric field will be E_y.

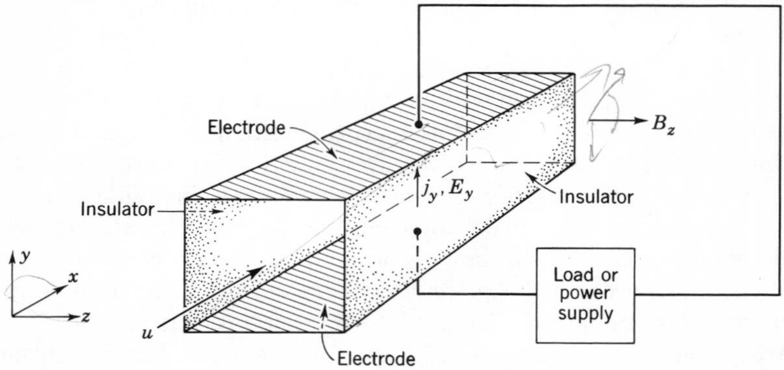

FIGURE 11.1 Quasi-one-dimensional magnetohydrodynamic flow channel.

When the Hall effect must be considered, the additional component E_x may exist. All of these are taken to be approximately uniform over the cross section.

3. The pressure and temperature are also assumed to be approximately uniform over the cross section.

4. The induced magnetic field is small enough to be neglected.

The end effects mentioned in the first statement are considered in some detail in Chap. 14. It will suffice here to point out that such effects will, in general, be negligible when the length of the channel is large compared to its height and width. With reference to the second assumption, if the channel cross section varies rapidly in the axial direction, crosswise velocity components v and w would exist, and u would not be uniform over a cross section in the yz plane. Similarly, lines of constant electric and magnetic potential (neglecting induced magnetic fields) would be curved, and x components of **B** and **E** would exist. Thus, the validity of statement 2 depends on whether or not the channel cross section varies slowly enough. If the Hall effect exists, an axial electric field E_x can appear, in addition to the one due to a too rapid area variation. In either case an axial current j_x can be caused to flow, which will then interact with the applied magnetic field B_z to give a sidewise thrust. Such a force would be partially balanced by a pressure gradient across the duct, and so assumption 3 would be violated. This then shows that not only does the duct area have to vary slowly, but also any transverse pressure variation due to axial currents should be small.

Before the physical basis of assumption 4 can be appreciated, there should be some discussion of the form of the induced magnetic fields. Generally speaking, the current which creates the induced magnetic field flows normal to and through the electrodes. A cross section in the xz plane then has the current flowing normal to it and is shown in Fig. 11.2.

If it is assumed that the magnetic permeability of the region surrounding the channel is that of free space (applied field provided by air-core solenoid or saturated iron-core magnet), a case of some practical

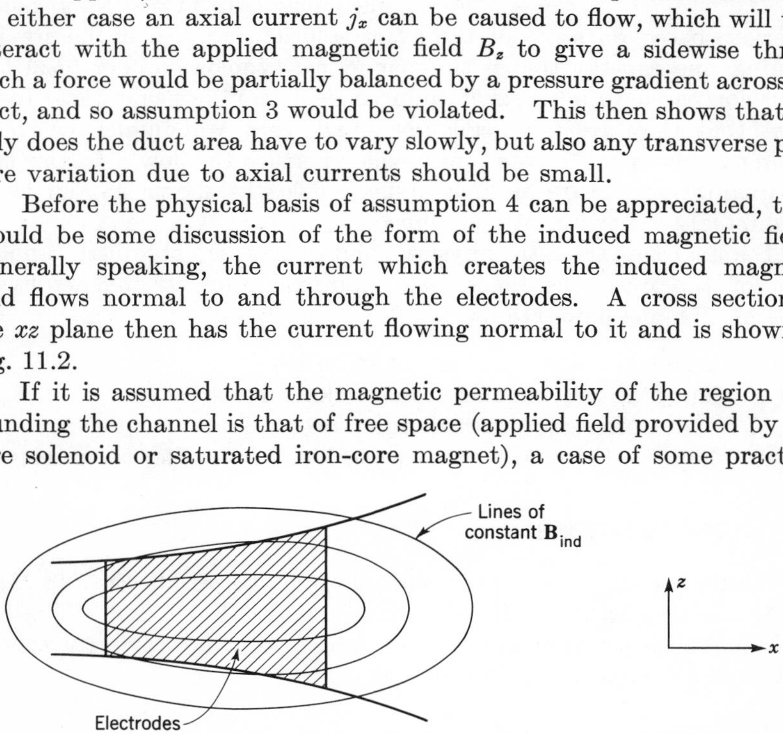

FIGURE 11.2 Magnetohydrodynamic channel showing the induced magnetic field.

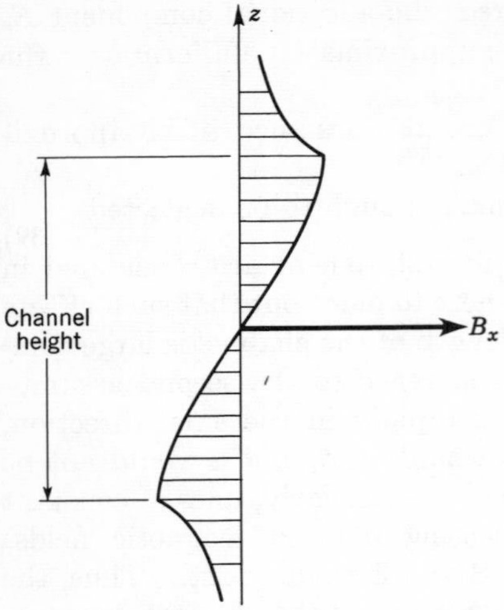

FIGURE 11.3 Variation of axial component of induced magnetic field with z for very long channels.

interest, then it can be seen that the induced magnetic field is similar to what one would expect to find about and in a current-carrying conductor.† The peak value of this field occurs in the regions along the outer periphery of the electrode. If the electrodes are very long compared to their height, it is necessary to consider only the x component of induced field and how it varies with z. This variation is shown qualitatively in Fig. 11.3. If the induced magnetic field is to be neglected, even in channels with large length-to-height ratios, it is clear that the value of B_x at the upper or lower channel edges must be small compared to the applied magnetic field. As a general criterion, based on some of the exact solutions studied in the previous chapter, one can say that if the magnetic Reynolds number ($\mu_0 \sigma VL$) is small compared to unity, such induced fields can be neglected. In the event that they are not negligibly small, they will interact with the flowing currents and create forces which perturb the flow. In this case, the qualitative picture of such induced fields as shown in Fig. 11.3 is undoubtedly somewhat oversimplified.

Summarizing then, the physical conditions which permit the application of the quasi-one-dimensional approximation to magnetohydrodynamic channel flows are four:

1. Large ratio of channel length to height
2. Slowly varying channel cross-sectional area
3. Small transverse pressure difference
4. Magnetic Reynold's number considerably smaller than unity

11.3 FLOW EQUATIONS

Assuming the preceding assumptions to be valid, Eqs. (8.23) to (8.26) can be greatly simplified. First consider Eq. (8.23). The form of the mass conservation law suitable here is the one which corresponds to a stream tube of variable area, and is

$$\frac{d}{dx}(\rho u A) = 0 \tag{11.1}$$

† The induced magnetic field in the presence of an unsaturated iron core is discussed in Sec. 11.6.

It can be readily derived by integrating Eq. (8.23) over the volume enclosed between two x positions along a channel, applying the divergence theorem, and letting $\Delta x \to 0$. We assume $\partial/\partial t$ is assumed zero, and ρ and u ($v \cong w \cong 0$) are taken to be uniform over the cross section.

With reference to the equation of motion (8.24) and the conservation of energy, where we take the form in terms of H [see Eq. (4.189) rather than Eq. (8.25)], similar assumptions are made; that is,

$$\partial/\partial t = \partial/\partial y = \partial/\partial z = 0$$

and $v = w = j_z = 0$. We assume $\mathcal{K} = \eta = 0$ as noted earlier. In this case Eq. (8.24) becomes

$$\rho u \frac{du}{dx} = -\frac{dp}{dx} + j_y B_z \tag{11.2}$$

and Eq. (4.189) reduces to

$$\rho u \frac{dH}{dx} = j_y E_y + j_x E_x \tag{11.3}$$

Applying similar assumptions to Ohm's law [Eq. (8.26)], one finds two equations. They are as follows:†

$$j_y = \frac{\sigma}{1 + (\omega\tau)^2} (E_y - uB_z + \omega\tau E_x) \tag{11.4}$$

$$j_x = \frac{\sigma}{1 + (\omega\tau)^2} [E_x - \omega\tau(E_y - uB_z)] \tag{11.5}$$

where we have set $\sigma B_z/en_e = \omega\tau$. The above system of equations is then complete when h and σ are both given as functions of the gas state [i.e., $h = h(p,\rho)$, $\sigma = \sigma(p,\rho)$].

Reviewing these relations, our first observation is that there are six equations [counting $h = h(p,\rho)$] for the ten unknowns: ρ, p, u, A, j_x, j_y, E_x, E_y, B_z, h.

It is clear, then, that the variation along the channel of four of these must be specified, or their relationship to the remaining six variables given, before the number of equations equals the number of variables and the problem can be solved. When this is the case, two types of problems can be distinguished. The first is the direct problem, wherein E_x, E_y, B_z, and A are given, and the resulting equations are solved to yield the flow velocity and state of the gas along the channel. The second is the inverse problem, which can best be described by an example. Suppose that any four variables, excluding A, are specified. A would appear as part of the solution, and the channel would have to be built accordingly, in order to make the solution valid.

† Note that Eqs. (11.4) and (11.5) include ion slip if the following identifications are made: $\omega\tau = \omega_e\tau_e/(1 + \omega_e\tau_e\omega_I\tau_I)$; $\sigma = \sigma_0/(1 + \omega_e\tau_e\omega_I\tau_I)$, where σ_0 is the scalar electrical conductivity.

It can also be seen that this system of equations is of first order, so that the value of each variable must be known at some initial station. When this requirement is satisfied, the equations can, in general, be solved either analytically or numerically.

Before proceeding to the discussion of these equations, their solution, and the physical phenomena involved, some attention should be devoted to the Hall current j_x, Hall field E_x, and electrode geometry. If the electrodes are solid, continuous electrical conductors, they will, in essence, short-circuit out any Hall field that might be generated. For problems of this type, one must set $E_x = 0$. Once this is done, j_x can be omitted from the problem since it is given by Eq. (11.5) as

$$j_x = \frac{-\sigma\omega\tau}{1 + (\omega\tau)^2}(E_y - uB_z) = -\omega\tau j_y \tag{11.6}$$

where Eq. (11.4) has been used. Since the only place that j_x had appeared previously was in the energy equation (11.3), and it had been multiplied by E_x which is now zero, it can be concluded that the only way that the Hall effect appears is to reduce j_y. That is,

$$j_y = \frac{\sigma}{1 + (\omega\tau)^2}(E_y - uB_z) \tag{11.7}$$

Alternately, one can consider the conductivity to have been reduced by the factor $1 + \omega^2\tau^2$.

Such a reduction in electrical conductivity can be avoided if the Hall current is prevented from flowing. This can be accomplished by segmenting the electrodes and maintaining multiple external loads or power supplies. The possibility of using such electrodes was pointed out in Chap. 10. Obviously, since the electrodes are separated by insulators, no net axial current can flow. If the segments are made infinitely thin and are spaced infinitely closely, then j_x should be zero everywhere. When this is true, it is found that our system of equations is the same as if $\omega\tau$ had been zero, with one exception. The exception is that now E_x is no longer zero but is given by

$$E_x = \omega\tau(E_y - uB_z) \tag{11.8}$$

At this point it can be seen that a system of first-order ordinary differential equations has been obtained for the study of compressible magnetohydrodynamic channel flows. The consequences of the Hall effect can even be included, provided the discussion is limited to the two cases, $j_x = 0$ or $E_x = 0$. A discussion of these equations and corresponding channel flows will be given next.

11.4 GENERAL NATURE OF PERFECT-GAS FLOWS

In the study of compressible magnetohydrodynamic channel flows, some general conclusions about their behavior would be extremely useful. Unfortunately, it is not possible to draw any such general conclusions from the system of equations as they now stand. They are entirely too complex. If, however, our attention is restricted to perfect gases, some progress can be made. For such gases, the perfect-gas and caloric equations of state are

$$p = \rho R T \tag{11.9}$$

and

$$h = C_p T \tag{11.10}$$

where R is the specific gas constant, and C_p is the specific heat at constant pressure. Both are assumed to be constant. Making use of Eq. (11.10) and assuming either $j_x = 0$ or $E_x = 0$, the energy equation (11.3) becomes

$$\rho u C_p \frac{dT}{dx} + \rho u^2 \frac{du}{dx} = E_y j_y \tag{11.11}$$

and this along with Eqs. (11.1), (11.2), and (11.9) form the complete set if j_y is given by

$$j_y = \sigma'(E_y - uB_z) \tag{11.12}$$

where $\sigma' = \sigma$ when $\omega\tau > 0$ but $j_x = 0$, or $\omega\tau = 0$

$\sigma' = \dfrac{\sigma}{1 + (\omega\tau)^2}$ when $\omega\tau > 0$ and $E_x = 0$

Generally, when a perfect gas is assumed, it is also usual to assume a constant electrical conductivity σ'. There are situations, however, in which it may be of some interest to consider a variable conductivity. In particular, the electrical conductivity of a slightly ionized gas varies rapidly with temperature. If a moderate temperature range were considered for such a gas, the thermodynamic properties should vary slowly enough to make the perfect-gas assumption reasonable, while the conductivity will vary a great deal. In this case, it is possible to consider a perfect gas of varying conductivity, as is done in Sec. 11.5.

Some of the qualitative aspects of channel flows of compressible perfect gases will now be considered. Defining the Mach number and ratio of specific heats as

$$\mathfrak{M} = \frac{u}{\sqrt{\gamma p/\rho}} = \frac{u}{a} \qquad \gamma = \frac{C_p}{C_v}$$

where a is the conventional speed of sound, and C_v is the specific heat at constant volume, Eqs. (11.1), (11.2), (11.9), (11.11), and (11.12) can be solved for du/dx, $d\mathfrak{M}/dx$, dT/dx, dp/dx. The results are

$$\frac{du}{dx} = \frac{1}{\mathfrak{M}^2 - 1}\left[\frac{u}{A}\frac{dA}{dx} - \frac{\sigma' B_z^2}{p}(u - u_3)(u - u_1)\right] \tag{11.13}$$

$$\frac{d\mathfrak{M}}{dx} = \frac{1 + \dfrac{\gamma - 1}{2}\mathfrak{M}^2}{\mathfrak{M}^2 - 1}\left[\frac{\mathfrak{M}}{A}\frac{dA}{dx} - \frac{\sigma' B_z^2}{ap}(u - u_3)(u - u_2)\right] \tag{11.14}$$

$$\frac{dT}{dx} = -\frac{1}{\mathfrak{M}^2 - 1}\left\{\frac{u^2}{AC_p}\frac{dA}{dx} - (u - u_3)\left[\frac{\sigma' B_z^2 u}{pC_p}(u - u_1) - \frac{\sigma' B_z^2 u_3(\mathfrak{M}^2 - 1)}{\rho u C_p}\right]\right\} \tag{11.15}$$

$$\frac{dp}{dx} = -\frac{1}{\mathfrak{M}^2 - 1}\left\{\frac{\rho u^2}{A}\frac{dA}{dx} - (u - u_3)\left[\frac{\gamma\sigma' B_z^2\mathfrak{M}}{a}(u - u_1) - \sigma' B_z^2(\mathfrak{M}^2 - 1)\right]\right\} \tag{11.16}$$

where

$$u_1 = \frac{\gamma - 1}{\gamma}\frac{E_y}{B_z}$$

$$u_2 = \frac{1 + \gamma\mathfrak{M}^2}{2 + (\gamma - 1)\mathfrak{M}^2}u_1$$

$$u_3 = \frac{E_y}{B_z}$$

and where σ' may be a function of the gas state in general, and thereby a function of x. In general, a flow described by the above equations can choke at some position along the channel, depending on flow conditions. That is, as $\mathfrak{M} \to 1$, then du/dx, dT/dx, etc., $\to \infty$. It is of interest, therefore, to consider the situations for which no choking occurs.

First, consider a channel flow in which the velocity remains constant. In this case $du/dx = 0$ and Eqs. (11.13) to (11.16) reduce to the following set:

$$\frac{dA}{dx} = \frac{\sigma' B_z^2 A}{pu}(u - u_3)(u - u_1) \tag{11.17}$$

$$\frac{d\mathfrak{M}}{dx} = \frac{\gamma - 1}{2\gamma}\frac{\sigma' B_z^2}{pa}u_3(u - u_3) \tag{11.18}$$

$$\frac{dT}{dx} = -\frac{\sigma' B_z^2}{\rho u C_p}u_3(u - u_3) \tag{11.19}$$

$$\frac{dp}{dx} = -\sigma' B_z^2(u - u_3) \tag{11.20}$$

and it is found that the factor $1/(\mathfrak{M}^2 - 1)$ has been eliminated. Accordingly, a constant-velocity channel flow will not choke. In a similar way it can be shown that flows with constant p, T, or ρ also do not choke.

The question of choking is not quite as clear for constant-area flows, $dA/dx = 0$. Here Eqs. (11.13) to (11.16) reduce to

$$\frac{du}{dx} = \frac{1}{1 - \mathfrak{M}^2}\left[\frac{\sigma' B_z{}^2}{p}(u - u_3)(u - u_1)\right] \tag{11.21}$$

$$\frac{d\mathfrak{M}}{dx} = \frac{1 + \left(\frac{\gamma - 1}{2}\right)\mathfrak{M}^2}{1 - \mathfrak{M}^2}\left[\frac{\sigma' B_z{}^2}{ap}(u - u_3)(u - u_2)\right] \tag{11.22}$$

$$\frac{dT}{dx} = \frac{1}{\mathfrak{M}^2 - 1}\left[\frac{\sigma' B_z{}^2 u}{pC_p}(u - u_3)(u - u_1)\right] + \frac{\sigma' B_z{}^2 u_3}{\rho u C_p}(u - u_3) \tag{11.23}$$

$$\frac{dp}{dx} = \frac{1}{\mathfrak{M}^2 - 1}\left[\frac{\sigma' B_z{}^2 \gamma \mathfrak{M}}{a}(u - u_3)(u - u_1)\right] + \sigma' B_z{}^2(u - u_3) \tag{11.24}$$

When $\mathfrak{M} \to 1$, it is seen that $u_2 \to u_1$. Therefore, if as $\mathfrak{M} \to 1$, then $u \to u_1$ or u_3, the above derivatives remain finite, and choking does not occur. An appropriate choice of initial conditions should lead to a "tunnel" at $u = u_1$ or u_3.

In one case, choking will always occur. Nothing has been said so far about E_y or B_z; so it is permissible to assume that $E_y = KuB_z$, where K is a constant. In this case, $u_3 = Ku$ and $u_1 = [(\gamma - 1)/\gamma]Ku$, so that it is no longer possible to have $u - u_3$ or $u - u_1 \to 0$ anywhere in the channel, and choking must be a possibility.

If, on the other hand, it is assumed that E_y/B_z is a constant, the tunnels mentioned above should exist. This case has been studied in detail by Resler and Sears.[3] It will be instructive to reproduce some of their discussion here. First divide Eq. (11.21) by Eq. (11.22):

$$\frac{du}{d\mathfrak{M}} = \frac{u}{\mathfrak{M}\left(1 + \frac{\gamma - 1}{2}\mathfrak{M}^2\right)} \frac{u - u_1}{u - u_2} \tag{11.25}$$

This is a differential equation for u as a function of $\mathfrak{M}$. The independent variable x for the moment has been eliminated. It should, therefore, be possible to integrate this equation, obtain $u = f(\mathfrak{M})$, and present the results graphically on a u versus $\mathfrak{M}$ plot.† As no closed analytic solution for this equation has been found, a graph showing the qualitative behavior of such flows has been prepared by Resler and Sears, and is shown in Fig. 11.4. The various distinct regions noted there are defined as follows:

(I)	$\mathfrak{M} > 1$	(II)	$\mathfrak{M} < 1$
(*A*)	$u_3 < u$	(*A*)	$u_3 < u$
(*B*)	$u_2 < u < u_3$	(*B*)	$u_1 < u < u_3$
(*C*)	$u_1 < u < u_2$	(*C*)	$u_2 < u < u_1$
(*D*)	$u < u_1$	(*D*)	$u < u_2$

† It is interesting to note that such a procedure is analogous to that of preparing a "phase plane" plot of velocity versus position in the theory of nonlinear vibrations, in which case the independent variable which does not appear explicitly is time.

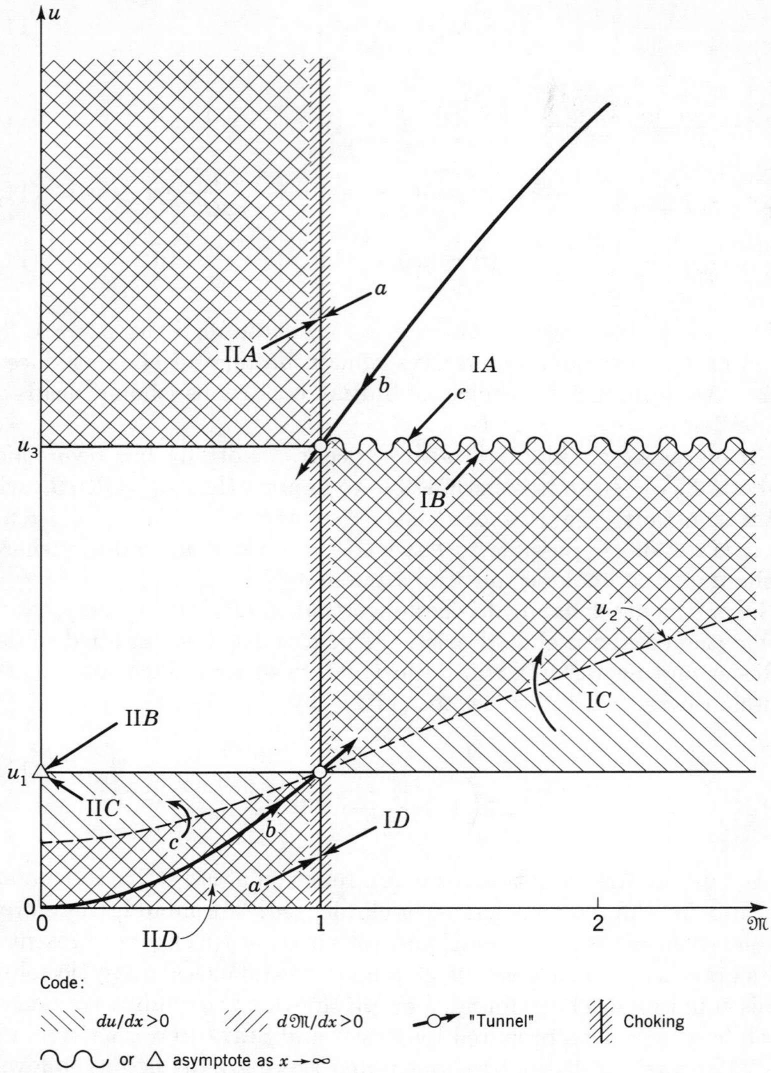

FIGURE 11.4 u versus $\mathfrak{M}$ map for constant-area channel flow when E_y/B_z is constant. (After Resler and Sears.[3])

The arrows shown in this figure denote the qualitative behavior of u and $\mathfrak{M}$ with increasing x. They can be interpreted in this way if it is assumed that E_y/B_z is a constant, so that u_1 and u_2 are independent of x. We also observe the two arrows which denote tunnels through $\mathfrak{M} = 1$. That is, if the initial condition in a duct fell on either curve, the flow would accelerate or decelerate through $\mathfrak{M} = 1$ without choking. The equations for these lines are solutions of the differential equation for

u versus $\mathfrak{M}$ mentioned earlier, and can be obtained by numerical integration once values for γ and E_y/B_z are specified. The fact that choked flow will occur when $\mathfrak{M} = 1$ (except at the two tunnels) is seen from Eqs. (11.21) and (11.22), which show du/dx and $d\mathfrak{M}/dx$ becoming infinite as $\mathfrak{M}$ approaches unity. It is interesting to observe on this "map" that for some initial conditions, an initially supersonic flow will decelerate but will asymptotically approach a Mach number larger than 1 (arrow c in region IA). For other initial conditions, the deceleration will proceed to choking (arrow a in region IA). In the subsonic regime by contrast (region IIA), all flows will proceed to a choked condition. It should be noted that the triangle at $u = u_1$ corresponds to an $\mathfrak{M} = 0$ flow. This implies an infinitely high temperature which is somewhat unrealistic; so it should be understood that this condition is only approached in the limit.

The phenomenon of choking and the tunnels described above can be illustrated *quantitatively* if, instead of assuming constant E_y/B_z, one requires both E_y and B to be constant. For this case, a closed analytic solution has been carried out by Neuringer[4] and Borman and Podolsky.[5]

The basic equations are given by Eqs. (11.1), (11.2), (11.11), and (11.12). They are as follows:

Mass conservation:
$$\rho u = \rho_0 u_0 \tag{11.26}$$

Momentum conservation:
$$\rho u \frac{du}{dx} + \frac{dp}{dx} = \sigma' B_z(E_y - uB_z) \tag{11.27}$$

Energy conservation:
$$\rho u \frac{d}{dx}(C_p T + \tfrac{1}{2}u^2) = \sigma' E_y(E_y - uB_z) \tag{11.28}$$

where it should be noted that σ' is the reduced conductivity, defined in Eq. (11.12). It is convenient to define a constant K' as

$$K' \equiv \frac{E_y}{u_0 B_z}$$

where u_0 is the entrance velocity. Then, if we write $C_p T = \left(\frac{\gamma - 1}{\gamma}\right)^{-1} \frac{p}{\rho}$, and if we define the following nondimensional quantities,

$$U = \frac{u}{u_0} \qquad P = \frac{p}{\rho_0 u_0^2} \qquad X = \frac{x}{L} \qquad I_L = \frac{\sigma' B_z^2 L}{\rho_0 u_0}$$

Eqs. (11.27) and (11.28) can be written as follows:

$$\frac{dU}{dX} + \frac{dP}{dX} = I_L(K' - U) \tag{11.29}$$

$$\frac{d}{dX}\left(\frac{\gamma}{\gamma - 1} PU + \tfrac{1}{2}U^2\right) = K' I_L(K' - U) \tag{11.30}$$

A first integral is obtained by eliminating $I_L(K' - U)$ between these two equations. Then we get

$$\frac{d}{dX}\left(\frac{\gamma}{\gamma - 1} PU + \tfrac{1}{2}U^2\right) = K'\left(\frac{dU}{dX} + \frac{dP}{dX}\right) \tag{11.31}$$

which integrates immediately to

$$\frac{\gamma}{\gamma - 1} PU + \tfrac{1}{2}U^2 = K'(U + P) + \text{const} \tag{11.32}$$

At the inlet, $U = 1$ and $P = p_0/\rho_0 u_0^2 = 1/(\gamma \mathfrak{M}_0^2)$, which allows the constant to be evaluated. Rearrangement of Eq. (11.32) then yields

?? Zauderer says

$$P = \frac{\tfrac{1}{2}U^2 - K'U + (1 + 1/\gamma\mathfrak{M}_0^2)K' - \tfrac{1}{2} + 1/[(\gamma - 1)\mathfrak{M}_0^2]}{K' - \dfrac{\gamma}{\gamma - 1} U} \tag{11.33}$$

To obtain the change in velocity with distance along the channel, Eq. (11.33) is differentiated with respect to x and substituted into Eq. (11.29). After some manipulation and rearrangement, we obtain

$$\left[\left(K' - \frac{\gamma}{\gamma - 1} U\right)^2 + (U - K')\left(K' - \frac{\gamma}{\gamma - 1} U\right) + \frac{\gamma}{\gamma - 1}\left(\frac{U^2}{2} - K'U + \delta K'\right)\right]\frac{dU}{dx} = I_L(K' - U)\left(K' - \frac{\gamma}{\gamma - 1} U\right)^2 \tag{11.34}$$

where $\delta = 1 + \dfrac{1}{\gamma\mathfrak{M}_0^2} - \left[\dfrac{1}{2} + \dfrac{1}{(\gamma - 1)\mathfrak{M}_0^2}\right]\dfrac{1}{K'}$

Integrating once, then, yields the desired result:

$$I_x = \left[\frac{\gamma(\gamma - 1)}{2} - 1 - \gamma(\gamma - 1)u_0^*\delta\right] \ln\left|\frac{1 - u^*}{1 - u_0^*}\right| + \left(\frac{\gamma^2}{\gamma - 1} u_0^*\delta - \frac{\gamma + 1}{2}\right)\left\{\frac{u^* - u_0^*}{\left(1 - \dfrac{\gamma}{\gamma - 1} u^*\right)\left(1 - \dfrac{\gamma}{\gamma - 1} u_0^*\right)} + \frac{(\gamma - 1)^2}{\gamma} \ln\left|\frac{\dfrac{\gamma - 1}{\gamma} - u^*}{\dfrac{\gamma - 1}{\gamma} - u_0^*}\right|\right\} \tag{11.35}$$

where we have put $u^* = (1/K')u/u_0$, so that $u_0^* = 1/K'$. In order to allow for a σ' which changes with x, the quantity I_x has been defined as

$$I_x = \frac{B_z^2}{\rho_0 u_0} \int_0^x \sigma'(x)\, dx \tag{11.36}$$

Two tunnels are shown in Fig. 11.4; the lower one allows acceleration, and the upper one deceleration, through the speed of sound. In each instance, there is only one value of u_0^* for chosen $\mathfrak{M}_0$ and γ which will take u^* through the tunnel. When the lower tunnel is approached, $u^* \to (\gamma - 1)/\gamma$. Accordingly, the second logarithmic term $\to -\infty$, and there is no solution beyond this point. If the coefficient of the last term of Eq. (11.36) is set equal to zero, however, u_0^* for the lower tunnel is found to be

$$u_0^* = \frac{\gamma^2 - 1}{\gamma} \frac{\mathfrak{M}_0{}^2}{(\gamma - 1)\mathfrak{M}_0{}^2 + 2} \tag{11.37}$$

For the upper tunnel, the coefficient of the first term of Eq. (11.36) is set equal to zero, which yields

$$u_0^* = \frac{(\gamma - 1)(\gamma\mathfrak{M}_0{}^2 + 1) + \sqrt{(\gamma - 1)(\gamma - 1 + 2\gamma\mathfrak{M}_0{}^4) + 2\gamma\mathfrak{M}_0{}^2(3 - \gamma)}}{\gamma[(\gamma - 1)\mathfrak{M}_0{}^2 + 2]} \tag{11.38}$$

The quantitative nature of these results can be illustrated by considering an example for which $\gamma = \frac{5}{3}$ and $\mathfrak{M}_0 = 0.5$. For this case, Eq. (11.37) yields (u_0^*) tunnel $= 0.123$. For this choice of u_0^*, as well as two other choices, curves have been calculated, and are shown in Fig. 11.5. It is

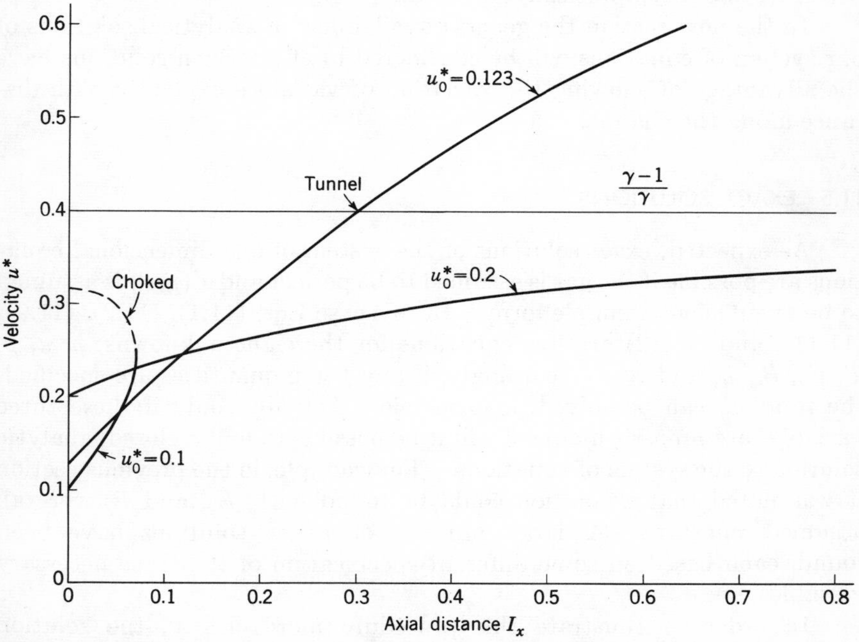

FIGURE 11.5 Velocity variation with distance in constant-area channel for several initial conditions with $\gamma = \frac{5}{3}$, $\mathfrak{M}_0 = 0.5$.

first observed that when u_0^* is too small, I_x reaches a maximum, and the flow chokes. On the other hand, when u_0^* is too large, u^* approaches $(\gamma - 1)/\gamma$ asymptotically. For the special case of $u_0^* = 0.123$, u^* passes smoothly through $(\gamma - 1)/\gamma$ (and $\mathfrak{M} = 1$), and approaches unity asymptotically. A similar result would have been found for the initially supersonic case ($\mathfrak{M}_0 > 1$).

In the event that σ' is a constant, the parameter I_x can be properly interpreted as the axial distance x. A σ' which decreases with distance will have the effect of stretching the x coordinate for the problem, whereas if σ' increases, it corresponds to a shrinking of x. Generally, the former situation will exist.

In this section some of the general features of magnetohydrodynamic channel flows of a perfect gas with arbitrary conductivity have been discussed. It has been found that, in general, the Lorentz force and Joule heating can cause choking. For the special flows wherein u, T, p, or ρ is constant, it was shown that no choking is possible. Finally, the constant-area flow was considered in more detail. For the case in which $E_y/B_z = \text{const}$, we found that for a special choice of the initial condition no choking would occur. The condition of passing through Mach number 1 with no choking was called the *tunnel*. For any other initial conditions it was seen that the flow either choked or approached some constant Mach number asymptotically.

In the next section the general availability of analytical solutions of our system of equations will be considered briefly. Such solutions have the advantage of showing the variation of variables explicitly with distance along the channel.

11.5 EXACT SOLUTIONS

As expected, exact solutions of the system of one-dimensional equations are possible if the gas is assumed to be perfect and $\sigma'(p,T)$ is assumed to be of sufficiently simple form. In this case Eqs. (11.1), (11.2), (11.9), (11.11), and (11.12) are five equations for the eight unknowns: ρ, u, p, T, E_y, B_z, j_y, and A. Accordingly, if any three quantities are specified, the problem can be solved, in principle. Actually, only if these three variables are *properly* assumed will it be possible to find a closed, analytic solution to the system of equations. For example, in the previous section it was noted that a solution could be found if A, E_y, and B_z were all assumed constant. A large number of other solutions have been found, each based on some different specification of the three necessary variables.[6-8]

In order to illustrate this procedure more clearly, the solution obtained when u, E_y, and B_z are all assumed constant will be presented first.[8] Then a method of allowing for both B_z and E_y variable along with a nonconstant σ' will be indicated. Finally, a solution will be developed for constant B_z but varying σ'.

The governing equations are (11.1), (11.27), and (11.28). Obviously, p or T as a function of x can be determined by a single integration, assuming σ' constant. First, however, dividing (11.27) by (11.28), using the perfect-gas law, and defining $K = E_y/uB_z$ as constant, we find

$$\frac{\gamma - 1}{\gamma}\frac{d \ln p}{d \ln T} = \frac{1}{K} \tag{11.39}$$

Integrating this and evaluating the constant at the entrance, this becomes

$$\frac{T(x)}{T_0} = \left[\frac{p(x)}{p_0}\right]^{K(\gamma-1)/\gamma} \tag{11.40}$$

This relation is clearly similar to the isentropic relation, the similarity being closest when $K \cong 1$.

Next, integrating Eq. (11.27) gives p as a function of x. Thus

$$p(x) = p_0 - \sigma' B_z^2(u - u_s)x \tag{11.41}$$

If, for convenience, we take the reference pressure to be $\rho_0 u_0^2$, then

$$\tilde{p} = 1 - (1 - K)I_x \tag{11.42}$$

Making use of this result, the remaining unknowns become

$$A/A_0 = [1 - (1 - K)I_x]^{-\left[\frac{\gamma(1-K)+K}{\gamma}\right]} \tag{11.43}$$

$$\mathfrak{M}/\mathfrak{M}_0 = [1 - (1 - K)I_x]^{[(\gamma-1)/2\gamma]K} \tag{11.44}$$

$$\frac{T}{T_0} = \left(\frac{\mathfrak{M}}{\mathfrak{M}_0}\right)^2 \tag{11.45}$$

The information that can be gained from this closed-form solution can be readily seen by plotting each variable versus I_x for $\gamma = \frac{5}{3}$ and two values of K. Such curves are shown in Fig. 11.6*a* and *b*.

The first observation to be made is that when $K < 1$, there is a value of I_x beyond which the solution cannot be carried; that is, p, T, and $\mathfrak{M}$ all become zero. Secondly, when energy is extracted from such a channel (corresponding to $K < 1$), then the pressure, temperature, and Mach number drop along the channel, but the area increases. For the example chosen, the Mach number decreases least rapidly. When energy is added to a channel flow (corresponding to $K > 1$), all variables increase or decrease with no limitation, as above. In this case the Mach number varies rather slowly while the channel area decreases. If the initial Mach number is supersonic in Fig. 11.6*a*, or subsonic in Fig. 11.6*b*, then the Mach number is seen to pass through unity smoothly in each case. As noted in the previous section, there is no choking problem for the constant-velocity case.

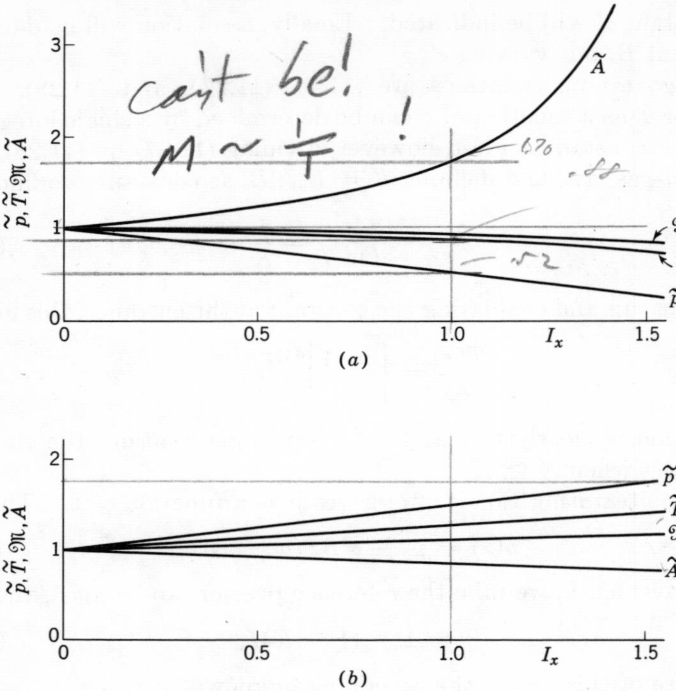

FIGURE 11.6 Solutions for constant-velocity channel flows: (*a*) Energy extraction channel with $\gamma = \frac{5}{3}$, $K = 0.5$; (*b*) energy addition channel with $\gamma = \frac{5}{3}$, $K = 1.5$.

Next, consider the possibility of having σ' and B_z varying with x. If we leave their axial distribution arbitrary, Eq. (11.27) is

$$\frac{dp}{dx} = -\sigma' B_z^2 u(1 - K) \tag{11.46}$$

where now we must recognize that for K to still be a constant, E_y must also change with x in such a way that $E_y/B_z = \text{const.}$ In any event, a new variable ξ can be defined as follows:

$$d\xi = \frac{\sigma' B_z^2}{(\sigma' B_z^2)_0}\, dx \tag{11.47}$$

In this case Eq. (11.46) becomes

$$\frac{dp}{d\xi} = -(1 - K)(\sigma' B_z^2)_0 u \tag{11.48}$$

which may be integrated immediately to give

$$p_0 - p(\xi) = (1 - K)(\sigma' B_z^2)_0 u \xi \tag{11.49}$$

A similar solution may be obtained for $T(\xi)$. Then since σ' is only a function of two state variables, knowing $p(\xi)$ and $T(\xi)$ enables us to determine $\sigma'(\xi)$. The dependence of ξ on x is then obtained by integration of Eq. (11.47). Thus,

$$\int_0^\xi \frac{d\xi}{\sigma'(\xi)} = \frac{1}{\sigma_0'} \int_0^x \left[\frac{B_z(x)}{(B_z)_0}\right]^2 dx \tag{11.50}$$

The variations of B_z and σ', as in the preceding section, may therefore be regarded as a "scaling" of the length parameter x; that is, the value of ξ which is required to obtain a given pressure drop is equal to the length x required to obtain the same pressure drop in a generator in which the magnetic field and effective conductivity remain constant. Decreases in either the magnetic field or the conductivity increase the length x required to obtain the same pressure drop.

If B_z is constant, however, a nonconstant conductivity σ' can be accounted for explicitly.[9] For example, consider a thermally ionized gas so that the conductivity is

$$\frac{\sigma'}{\sigma_0'} = \left(\frac{T}{T_0}\right)^{\frac{3}{4}} \left(\frac{p_0}{p}\right)^{\frac{1}{2}} e^{(E_i/2kT_0)(1-T_0/T)} \tag{11.51}$$

The use of an expression as complicated as this is not convenient, and so in order to simplify the analysis, let

$$\frac{\sigma'}{\sigma_0'} = \left(\frac{T}{T_0}\right)^{\omega} \left(\frac{p_0}{p}\right)^{\frac{1}{2}} \tag{11.52}$$

where ω is some constant chosen so that Eqs. (11.51) and (11.52) compare reasonably well in the temperature range of interest.

First, consider Eq. (11.28) with u = const.

$$\rho u C_p \frac{dT}{dx} = -K(1 - K)\sigma' u B_z^2 \tag{11.53}$$

Then use of the perfect-gas law, Eq. (11.40), and Eq. (11.52) in Eq. (11.53) gives

$$\left(\frac{T}{T_0}\right)^{\alpha-1} \frac{d}{dx}\left(\frac{T}{T_0}\right) = -\frac{1}{x^*} \tag{11.54}$$

where
$$x^* = \frac{\gamma p_0}{(\gamma - 1)uK(1 - K)\sigma_0' B_z^2}$$

$$\alpha = \omega - \frac{\gamma}{\gamma - 1}\frac{3}{2K}$$

This then integrates immediately to

$$\frac{T}{T_0} = \left[1 + \frac{\alpha x}{x^*}\right]^{-1/\alpha} \tag{11.55}$$

and with the use of Eq. (11.40) the corresponding pressure ratio can be found.

Other examples of direct integration are given in ref. 10, which includes the effects of electron-ion collisions and the Hall reduction in conductivity. The resulting expressions are generally more complex than Eq. (11.55).

The present discussion, although limited to constant-velocity flows, does serve to demonstrate the technique of finding analytic solutions for magnetohydrodynamic channel flows of perfect gases. In the next section, an alternate technique for obtaining simple closed-form solutions will be discussed.

11.6 THE ISENTROPIC APPROXIMATION

In the preceding section, solutions were discussed for those cases in which both the Lorentz force and Joule heating were important. It was pointed out that numerical solutions could be obtained for any gas, but that analytic solutions were possible only in special cases. In this section a perfect gas of infinite conductivity will be considered, so that Joule heating may be neglected. It will be shown that solutions are readily available.

Under such an assumption, the energy equation (11.3) is replaced by the isentropic relation

$$\frac{d}{dx}\left(\frac{p}{\rho^\gamma}\right) = 0 \tag{11.56}$$

The continuity and momentum equations (11.1) and (11.2) are unchanged,

$$\frac{d}{dx}(\rho u A) = 0 \tag{11.57}$$

$$\rho u \frac{du}{dx} + \frac{dp}{dx} = j_y B_z \tag{11.58}$$

and Ohm's law [Eq. (11.12)] becomes

$$E_y = u B_z \tag{11.59}$$

in order to ensure a finite current density j_y. The solution of the above system of equations has been considered by Podolsky and Sherman.[11] Their conclusions will be summarized here.

It is immediately seen that E_y need not be considered initially since, with B_z a known function of x, it can be determined once the solution for u is available. There remain, as a result, three equations (11.56) to (11.58), to be solved for the five unknowns: p, ρ, u, j_y, and A. The x dependence of two of these variables must be given along with the initial values of the other three before the problem can be solved. Omitting Eq. (11.35), the previous three equations can be written as

$$\rho u A = \rho_0 u_0 A_0 \tag{11.60}$$

$$\rho u \frac{du}{dx} + \frac{dp}{dx} = j_y B_z \tag{11.61}$$

$$\frac{p}{\rho^\gamma} = \frac{p_0}{\rho_0{}^\gamma} \tag{11.62}$$

where the subscript $(\quad)_0$ refers to some initial station.

In the event that any two of p, ρ, u, and A are specified, the problem can be solved directly. For example, assume that $u(x)$ and $A(x)$ are given. In this case, Eq. (11.60) gives $\rho(x)$, and Eq. (11.62) gives $p(x)$. From Eq. (11.61), knowing $\rho(x)$, $u(x)$, and $p(x)$, then $j_y(x)$ can be deduced and the problem is solved.

When, on the other hand, j_y is one of the variables specified, the problem is more complex. The principle difficulty lies in the fact that the momentum equation (11.61) will not be directly integrable unless some special assumption is made about the x dependence of the other variable: p, ρ, u, or A. For example, direct integration is possible in a constant-velocity flow since then the first term of the momentum equation is zero, and the pressure is obtained by a simple quadrature.

In general, problems of the first type (two of p, ρ, u, and A specified) will be of most interest, so that the ease with which solutions can be obtained should prove useful. Problems of the second type, although they cannot be solved under as general conditions as those of the first type, do offer one unique advantage, since the current density j_y can be specified as some function of x. For those solutions including Joule heating, this is not generally possible unless B_z, E_y, and u are all given quantities. The virtue of specifying j_y is that it can be taken to be some constant value equal to the maximum possible current density that can be emitted from an electrode (presumably by thermionic emission). Therefore, the local Lorentz force j_yB_z can be maximized for power-addition applications, or the local power generated per unit volume j_yE_y can be maximized for power-extraction applications.

Before leaving the subject of isentropic channel flows, some additional comments are necessary. In formulating the present problem [Eqs. (11.56 to 11.59)], it has been assumed that the induced magnetic field can be neglected. This was based on the presumption that the induced magnetic field will have the form shown in Fig. 11.2. In this case the induced field in the z direction is negligibly small, and the x component, although it may be large, results only in a crosswise pressure gradient. As noted earlier, if this pressure gradient becomes large enough, it can destroy the validity of the quasi-one-dimensional approximation.

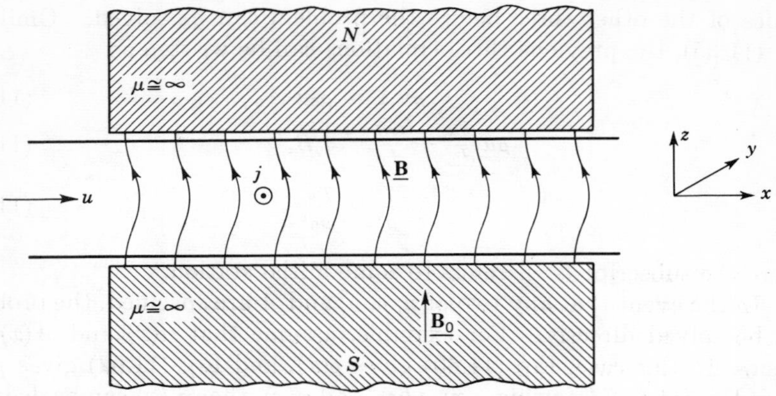

FIGURE 11.7 Induced magnetic field in presence of high-permeability pole pieces.

If on the other hand, one were to assume that there are magnet pole pieces adjacent to the channel wall of effectively infinite magnetic permeability, then the induced magnetic field would be of quite a different form. In this case B_z would be induced and B_x could be omitted, as shown in Fig. 11.7.

By choosing the above model for the induced field it must be realized that the problem must be reformulated. Now $B_z = B_z(x)$ is an essential part of the problem, and the Lorentz force term in Eq. (11.58) may be replaced by

$$j_y B_z = -B_z \frac{dB_z}{dx} \tag{11.63}$$

With the Lorentz force in this form, closed-form solutions are again possible for the isentropic flow.

11.7 NUMERICAL SOLUTIONS FOR REAL-GAS FLOWS

The preceding discussion has been limited to channel flows of perfect gases in order that the general behavior of such compressible channel flows might be illuminated. In addition, some analytic solutions were possible within this assumption. For practical channel flows, however, it frequently becomes necessary to consider a real rather than a perfect gas. No analytic solutions are possible in this case, and one must resort to numerical techniques. Fortunately, the numerical integration of a set of first-order ordinary differential equations with given initial conditions can be accomplished readily on a high-speed digital computor. The general equations that one would have to integrate are repeated here for convenience.

$$\rho u A = \text{const} \tag{11.64}$$

$$\rho u \frac{du}{dx} + \frac{dp}{dx} = \sigma'(E_y - uB_z)B_z \tag{11.65}$$

$$\rho u \frac{dh}{dx} + \rho u^2 \frac{du}{dx} = \sigma'(E_y - uB_z)E_y \tag{11.66}$$

These have then to be supplemented by either

$$h = h(p,\rho)$$

or

$$h = h(p,T) \quad \text{and} \quad p = p(\rho,T)$$

and three of the variables must be specified. Of course, the conductivity σ' must be calculable from the state of the plasma; that is, a relation such as $\sigma' = \sigma'(p,T)$ is also necessary. Methods of calculation of σ' have already been considered in Chap. 5; so it will not be necessary to discuss them further here. We will only note that σ' depends on the degree of ionization of the plasma, which must be obtained from thermodynamic considerations.

Unfortunately, there are numerous gases and gas mixtures that might be considered as the real gas. It is, therefore, not convenient to make any broad generalizations here. Instead, the technique for treating such problems will be illustrated for a plasma composed of a mixture of a diatomic (fully excited in rotation and vibration) inert gas (high ionization potential) and a monatomic seed gas (low ionization potential). The diatomic inert gas could correspond to the products of combustion. It will be assumed that electronic excitation of the seed atom above the ground state makes a negligible contribution to the plasma enthalpy.

Within the above restrictions, quite simple expressions for the enthalpy and the gas law can be obtained. The perfect-gas law for a mixture of perfect gases can be written as follows:

$$p\mathcal{V} = \sum_s n_s^* \mathcal{R} T \tag{11.67}$$

where the n_s^* are the number of moles for each species, and $\mathcal{R}$ is the universal gas constant. Based on mass density rather than volume $\mathcal{V}$, this becomes

$$\frac{p}{\rho} = \frac{\sum_s n_s^*}{m} \mathcal{R} T = \frac{\sum_s n_s^*}{n_0^* \bar{\mu}_0} \mathcal{R} T \tag{11.68}$$

where m is the total mass of the mixture, n_0^* is the original number of moles before ionization, and $\bar{\mu}_0$ is the mean molecular weight of the original mixture, which is

$$\bar{\mu}_0 = \frac{m_{\text{inert}} + m_{\text{seed}}}{n_{\text{inert}}^* + n_{\text{seed}}^*} = \frac{n_{\text{inert}}^* \mu_{\text{inert}} + n_{\text{seed}}^* \mu_{\text{seed}}}{n_{\text{inert}}^* + n_{\text{seed}}^*}$$

or

$$\bar{\mu}_0 = \mu_{\text{inert}}(1 - P) + \mu_{\text{seed}} P$$

where $P \equiv n^*_{\text{seed}}/(n^*_{\text{inert}} + n^*_{\text{seed}})$ in the original mixture. Returning to the perfect-gas law, we can write

$$\frac{p}{\rho} = \frac{(n_0^* + n_e^*)\mathcal{R}T}{n_0^*\bar{\mu}_0} = \frac{(1 + \alpha)\mathcal{R}T}{\bar{\mu}_0} \tag{11.69}$$

where we now define the degree of ionization α as n_e^*/n_0^*. In other words, the perfect-gas law can be applied to a reacting gas mixture as long as the change in mean molecular weight with gas conditions is accounted for.

Next an expression is needed for h for an ionizable gas mixture. Let us begin by noting that the internal energy of a mixture of gases is simply the sum of the internal energies of each constituent. Thus

$$E_m = \sum_s X_s E_s \tag{11.70}$$

where E is the energy per mole, X is the mole fraction, and $(\quad)_m$ denotes the reacting mixture. For the special case under consideration, the internal energy of each species is as follows:

$$\begin{aligned} E_{\text{inert}} &= \tfrac{7}{2}\mathcal{R}T \qquad \text{(diatomic)} \\ E_{\text{seed}} &= \tfrac{3}{2}\mathcal{R}T \\ E_{\text{ion}} &= E_0 + \tfrac{3}{2}\mathcal{R}T \\ E_{\text{electron}} &= \tfrac{3}{2}\mathcal{R}T \end{aligned}$$

where E_0 is the ionization energy of the seed atom. Substituting these in Eq. (11.70) gives

$$E_m = \frac{1}{n_m^*}\left[\tfrac{7}{2}n^*_{\text{inert}}\mathcal{R}T + \tfrac{3}{2}n^*_{\text{seed}}\mathcal{R}T + n_e^*(E_0 + 3\mathcal{R}T)\right] \tag{11.71}$$

Making use of the definitions of α and P, this can be rewritten in a more convenient form,

$$E_m = \frac{n_0^*}{n_m^*}\left[\tfrac{7}{2}(1 - P)\mathcal{R}T + \tfrac{3}{2}(P - \alpha)\mathcal{R}T + \alpha(E_0 + 3\mathcal{R}T)\right]$$

or in terms of energy per unit mass,

$$e = \frac{E_m}{\bar{\mu}_m} = \frac{n_0^*}{\bar{\mu}_m n_m^*}\left[\frac{7 - 4P}{2}\mathcal{R}T + (\tfrac{3}{2}\mathcal{R}T + E_0)\alpha\right]$$

or

$$e = \frac{1}{\bar{\mu}_0}\left[\frac{7 - 4P}{2}\mathcal{R}T + (\tfrac{3}{2}\mathcal{R}T + E_0)\alpha\right] \tag{11.72}$$

The enthalpy is then simply

$$h = e + \frac{p}{\rho} = e + \frac{1 + \alpha}{\bar{\mu}_0}\mathcal{R}T \tag{11.73}$$

and combining Eqs. (11.72) and (11.73) gives the desired relation:

$$h = \frac{1}{\bar{\mu}_0}\left[\frac{9-4P}{2}\,\mathcal{R}T + (\tfrac{5}{2}\mathcal{R}T + E_0)\alpha\right] \tag{11.74}$$

The second term on the right represents that portion of the enthalpy existing as energy of ionization. The first term is simply the enthalpy due to the translational, rotational, and vibrational energy of the particles.

In order to make use of these relations, an expression for α as a function of the gas state is necessary. Making note of the fact that α as defined here is slightly different than as defined in Eq. (6.88), the Saha relation [see Eq. (6.83)] becomes

$$\ln \frac{p\alpha^2}{(1+\alpha)(P-\alpha)} = -\frac{E_0}{\mathcal{R}T} + \tfrac{5}{2}\ln T + \ln\frac{2P_I{}^{\text{int}}}{P_n{}^{\text{int}}} + \ln\frac{(2\pi m_e)^{\frac{3}{2}}k^{\frac{5}{2}}}{h^3} \tag{11.75}$$

where $P_I{}^{\text{int}}$ = ionic state degeneracy
$P_n{}^{\text{int}}$ = atomic state degeneracy
m_e = electron mass
k = Boltzmann's constant
h = Planck's constant

It is interesting to note that for complete ionization $n_s \to 0$, the value attained by α is P. This is due to the particular definition for α chosen for the present case.

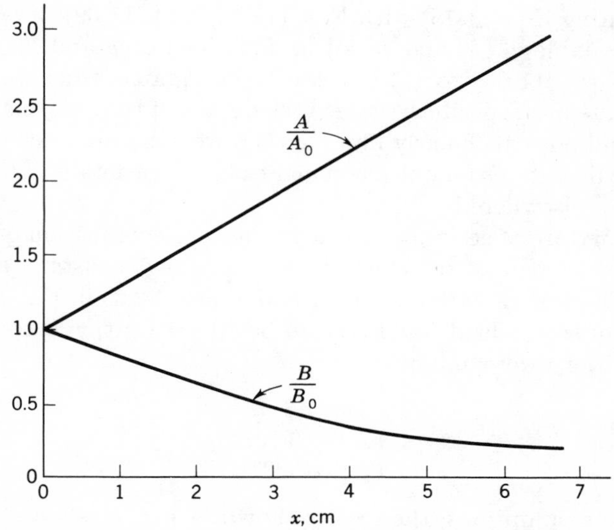

FIGURE 11.8 Channel shape and field variation for real-gas calculation where $A_0 = 1\ \text{cm}^2$, $B_0 = 15{,}000$ gauss.

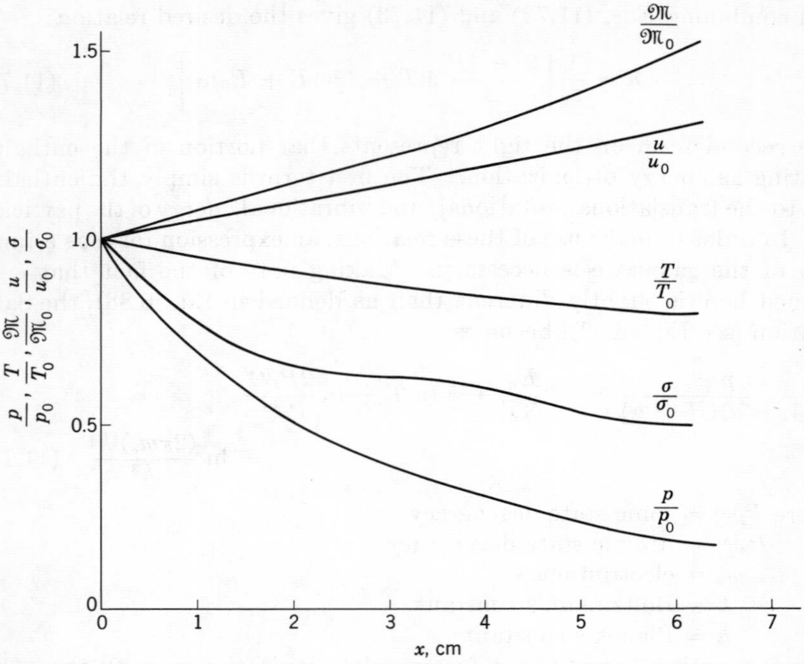

FIGURE 11.9 Real-gas channel flow solution—power-generating channel where $p = 3.9 \times 10^{-3}$ newton/m², $T_0 = 3730°\text{K}$, $\mathfrak{M}_0 = 1.3$, $u_0 = 1{,}320$ m/sec, $\sigma_0 = 655$ mhos/m.

Combining Eq. (11.75) with Eqs. (11.74) and (11.69), it is clear that one has available σ', h, and p, all as functions of ρ and T. Thus, in principle, Eqs. (11.63) to (11.65) can be integrated when three of the variables have been specified. Since the details of the analysis are rather involved, and not particularly illuminating, we will reproduce only a portion of the calculations for one particular case. The details of the analysis can be found elsewhere.[12]

For a mixture of cesium and the products of combustion of cyanogen and oxygen, a channel in which K was assumed constant at 0.5 was studied. The chosen variations of A and B are shown in Fig. 11.8. The percentage of seed added was taken to be 10 per cent, and the following initial conditions were assumed:

$$\mathfrak{M}_0 = 1.3$$
$$p_0^\circ = 1 \text{ atm}$$
$$T_0^\circ = 4520°\text{K}$$

Under these assumptions, the results shown in Fig. 11.9 were found.

For this case solid electrodes were assumed; so the conductivity σ' was reduced by the factor $1 + (\omega\tau)^2$. It can be seen first that the conductivity dropped off rapidly. The Mach number and velocity rose while the temperature and pressure dropped.

Calculations similar to those described here can be carried out for various carrier gases such as monatomic gases[13] or combustion products which are not fully excited. In the latter case one makes use of tabulated thermodynamic properties.[14]

REFERENCES CITED

1. Crocco, Luigi: In H. W. Emmons (ed.), *Fundamentals of Gas Dynamics*, Princeton University Press, Princeton, N.J., 1958.
2. Shapiro, A.: *The Dynamics and Thermodynamics of Compressible Fluid Flow*, vol. 1, The Ronald Press Company, New York, 1953.
3. Resler, E. L., Jr., and W. R. Sears: "The Prospects for Magneto-aerodynamics," *J. Aeron. Sci.*, **25**:235–246 (1958).
4. Neuringer, J. L.: "Optimum Power Generation Using a Plasma as the Working Fluid," *J. Fluid Mech.*, **7**:287 (1960).
5. Borman, G. L., and B. Podolsky: "One Dimensional Analysis of Plasma Accelerators," *Gen. Elec. TIS Rept.* R59AGT36, 1959.
6. Rosa, R. J.: Engineering Magnetohydrodynamics, part 2 of Ph.D. Thesis, Cornell University, Ithaca, N.Y., June, 1956.
7. Resler, E. L., Jr., and W. R. Sears: "Magneto-gasdynamic Channel Flow," *ZAMP*, **11b**:509–518 (1958).
8. Sutton, G. W.: "The Quasi-one Dimensional Flow of an Electrical Conducting Gas for the Generation of Electrical Power," *Gen. Elec. TIS Rept.* R59SD307, February, 1959.
9. Brocher, E. F.: "The Constant Velocity MHD Generator with Variable Electrical Conductivity," *J. Aerospace Sci.*, **29**:626 (1962).
10. Sutton, G. W.: "Magnetohydrodynamic Channel Flow of a Perfect Gas for the Generation of Electrical Power," *Gen. Elec. Rept.* R59SD473, December, 1959.
11. Podolsky, B., and A. Sherman: "Isentropic One Dimensional MHD Channel Flow," *Appl. Sci. Res. Sect. B*, **9**:567 (1961).
12. Sherman, A.: "A High Performance, Short Time Duration, MHD Generator System," in M. A. Zipkin (ed.), *Power Systems for Space Flight*, Academic Press Inc., New York, 1963.
13. Sherman, A.: "Theoretical Performance of a Crossed Field MHD Accelerator," *ARS J.*, **32**:414 (1962).
14. Blecher, S.: "Theoretical Performance Analysis of a Constant Velocity MHD Generator for Combustion Products of Hydrocarbon and Air," *ARS J.*, **32**:1394 (1962).

12

BOUNDARY LAYERS

12.1 INTRODUCTION

The subject matter to be covered in this chapter will consist of magnetohydrodynamic flows of a boundary-layer character. In conventional fluid dynamics, boundary-layer theory has been developed to a high degree of sophistication. No comparable extensive treatment will be attempted here. The problems which will be discussed will be chosen to illustrate those new features introduced by the interaction between currents flowing in the conducting fluid or plasma and the electromagnetic field. The principle interest in the present chapter will be in flows for which the magnetic Reynolds number is vanishingly small. For completeness, however, the boundary-layer character of flows with $R_m \to \infty$ will be treated in the last section.

The first problem considered will be the Rayleigh problem, in which a magnetic field is applied normal to the surface of an impulsively moved half plane. Its principle value will be that a solution can be obtained in closed form, so that the nature of magnetohydrodynamic boundary-layer flows can be inferred. Following this introductory treatment, the boundary-layer equations are obtained from the full equations by means of the well-known boundary-layer approximation. Based on these equations, incompressible boundary-layer flows are examined first. Two methods of solution of the nonlinear partial differential equations are developed. For flows which satisfy certain specified conditions, similarity exists, and the equations can be reduced to an ordinary differential equation, which must then be integrated numerically. For more realistic boundary conditions, similarity cannot exist, so that, in this instance, series solutions are necessary. For high-speed flows (hypersonic), compressibility effects must be considered, and so compressible boundary layers are considered next. In this case the boundary conditions are such that similarity conditions can be applied, and the solution to the problem reduces to the numerical integration of two coupled ordinary differential equations.

To conclude this chapter, the electric current and induced magnetic field boundary layers which can form on surfaces when the magnetic Reynolds number is very high are considered. Although the magnetic Reynolds is extremely small in almost all cases of interest in continuum magnetohydrodynamics, the above subject is important since it involves application of old boundary-layer concepts to a new physical problem.

12.2 THE RAYLEIGH PROBLEM

The problem which will be studied in this section is shown in Fig. 12.1. A field $\mathbf{B}_0$ is applied perpendicular to the plate and is assumed to be uniform in space and constant in time. The doubly infinite plate (a nonconductor) is assumed to move in the x direction impulsively at $t = 0$. The problem is to determine the induced flow and magnetic field due to the impulsive motion in general.

A number of authors have investigated the general problem[1,2] and have calculated the coupled flow and induced magnetic fields by means of various approximations. Of principle interest in this chapter will be flows in which $R_m \ll R_e$. In this case the problem reduces to one in which the flow disturbance is confined to a thin boundary-layer region while the induced field varies over a much larger region.

The equations appropriate to the present problem are essentially the same as those for the transient Couette flow, except that now the second, stationary wall is infinitely far away:

$$\rho \frac{\partial u}{\partial t} = \frac{B_0}{\mu_0} \frac{\partial b_x}{\partial y} + \eta \frac{\partial^2 u}{\partial y^2} \tag{12.1}$$

$$\frac{\partial b_x}{\partial t} = B_0 \frac{\partial u}{\partial y} + \frac{1}{\sigma \mu_0} \frac{\partial^2 b_x}{\partial y^2} \tag{12.2}$$

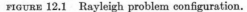

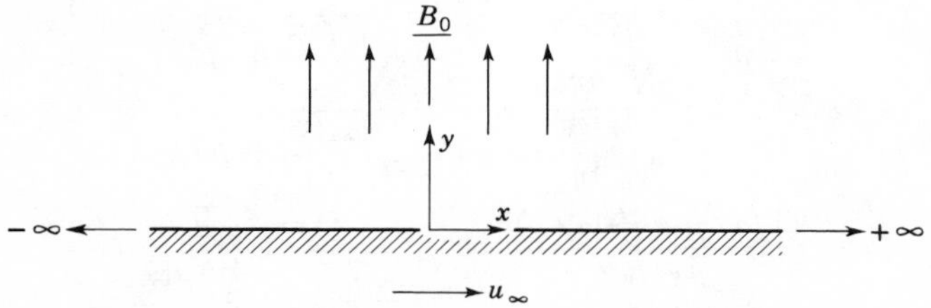

FIGURE 12.1 Rayleigh problem configuration.

The boundary and initial conditions are

$$\begin{aligned} t = 0: &\quad u(y,0) = 0 &\quad b_x(y,0) = 0 \\ t > 0: &\quad u(0,t) = u_0 &\quad b_x(0,t) = 0 \end{aligned}$$

where, of course, u and b_x must remain finite as $y \to \infty$. The requirement that $b_x = 0$ on the moving nonconductive wall is arrived at in much the same way as was done for Couette flow (see Sec. 10.3).

The above equations can be most readily treated with the aid of the Laplace transform defined by

$$L\{f(y,t)\} = \hat{f}(y,s) = \int_0^\infty e^{-st} f(y,t)\, dt$$

where s is some constant parameter. Taking the Laplace transform of (12.1) and (12.2) gives

$$s\hat{u} = \frac{B_0}{\rho\mu_0}\frac{d\hat{b}_x}{dy} + \nu\frac{d^2\hat{u}}{dy^2} \tag{12.3}$$

$$s\hat{b}_x = B_0\frac{d\hat{u}}{dy} + \frac{1}{\mu_0\sigma}\frac{d^2\hat{b}_x}{dy^2} \tag{12.4}$$

where $\nu = \eta/\rho$ = kinematic viscosity, and the boundary conditions are now

$$\hat{u}(0,s) = \frac{u_0}{s} \qquad \hat{b}_x(0,s) = 0$$

The solution of Eqs. (12.3) and (12.4) is readily found to be

$$\hat{u} = \frac{(m^2/\sigma\mu_0) - s}{mB_0} Ae^{-my} + \frac{(n^2/\sigma\mu_0) - s}{nB_0} Be^{-ny} \tag{12.5}$$

$$\hat{b}_x = Ae^{-my} + Be^{-ny} \tag{12.6}$$

where A and B are arbitrary constants. Terms which diverge at infinity have been omitted, and $\pm m$ and $\pm n$ are solutions of

$$\left(\frac{r^2}{\mu_0\sigma} - s\right)(\nu r^2 - s) - \frac{B_0{}^2}{\rho\mu_0} r^2 = 0 \tag{12.7}$$

which is satisfied if

$$m = \sqrt{\frac{\sigma B_0{}^2}{4\eta} + \alpha s} + \sqrt{\frac{\sigma B_0{}^2}{4\eta} + \beta s}$$

$$n = \sqrt{\frac{\sigma B_0{}^2}{4\eta} + \alpha s} - \sqrt{\frac{\sigma B_0{}^2}{4\eta} + \beta s}$$

where $$\alpha = \frac{(1/\sqrt{\mu_0\sigma} + \sqrt{\nu})^2}{4\nu/\mu_0\sigma} \qquad \beta = \frac{(1/\sqrt{\mu_0\sigma} - \sqrt{\nu})^2}{4\nu/\mu_0\sigma}$$

The constants A and B must be selected to satisfy the boundary conditions imposed. The solution then assumes the following form:

$$\frac{\hat{u}}{u_0} = \frac{1}{s(m-n)(1/\mu_0\sigma + s/mn)}\left[\frac{(m^2/\mu_0\sigma) - s}{m}e^{-my} - \frac{(n^2/\mu_0\sigma) - s}{n}e^{-ny}\right] \tag{12.8}$$

$$\frac{\hat{b}_x}{B_0} = \frac{u_0}{s(m-n)(1/\mu_0\sigma + s/mn)}(e^{-my} - e^{-ny}) \tag{12.9}$$

Inversion of these equations is quite difficult as they stand. Since our principle interest will be in flows in which $R_m \to 0$, and this implies $P_m = \sqrt{R_m/R_e} \to 0$ or $1/\sigma\mu_0 \gg \nu$, a solution of boundary-layer character can be anticipated and the problem accordingly simplified. Keeping $\sigma\mu_0$ finite, and letting $\nu \to 0$ while holding $y/\sqrt{\nu}$ fixed, leads to the following results:

$$m \to \left(\frac{\sigma B_0^2}{\eta} + \frac{s}{\nu}\right)^{\frac{1}{2}} \qquad n \to s\left(\frac{s}{\sigma\mu_0} + \frac{B_0^2}{\rho\mu_0}\right)^{-\frac{1}{2}}$$

and

$$\frac{\hat{u}}{u_0} = \frac{1}{s}e^{-\sqrt{\sigma B_0^2/\eta + (s/\nu)}\,y} \tag{12.10}$$

$$\hat{b}_x = 0$$

Accordingly, when $b_x = 0$ at the moving wall, it is zero throughout the velocity boundary-layer region. Such a result could have been anticipated. If, on the other hand, other boundary conditions had been selected for b_x, other results would have been obtained. If the problem geometry were such that for long times $b_x(0,t) \cong$ const rather than zero, then the boundary condition would be that b_x at the boundary be some function of time depending on the total current flow. Such a boundary condition could not be conveniently handled. Finally, if the moving wall is assumed to be a perfect conductor, the electric field in the fluid adjacent to the wall must be zero. Then from Eqs. (10.1) and (10.5*a*), we have

$$-\frac{\partial b_x}{\partial y} = \sigma(E_z + uB_0)$$

or

$$\frac{\partial b_x}{\partial y}(0,t) = -\sigma u_0 B_0 \tag{12.11}$$

which is the required boundary condition for this case. As has been shown by Ludford,[1] the solution when Eq. (12.11) is used as the boundary condition leads to a b_x which is constant throughout the boundary-layer region.

Returning now to the problem originally posed, the inverse of Eq. (12.10) is readily found to be

$$\frac{u}{u_0} = \frac{1}{2}\left[e^{-y\sqrt{\sigma B_0^2/\mu_0}}\operatorname{erfc}\left(\frac{y}{2\sqrt{\nu t}} - \sqrt{\frac{\sigma B_0^2}{\rho}t}\right) + e^{y\sqrt{\sigma B_0^2/\mu_0}}\operatorname{erfc}\left(\frac{y}{2\sqrt{\nu t}} + \sqrt{\frac{\sigma B_0^2 t}{\rho}}\right)\right] \tag{12.12}$$

This result is identical to that of Rossow,[2] although the induced magnetic field was not considered in that reference. The reason for the agreement is obvious, as $b_x = 0$ throughout the boundary-layer region. However, it should be noted that b_x will become finite above the boundary layer and approach some constant value at ∞. The value of formulating the complete problem before making the boundary-layer approximation will be seen shortly when the shear stress at the wall is calculated.

First, however, consider the solution for u found above. If B_0 is allowed to go to zero, Eq. (12.12) reduces to the classical Rayleigh problem:

$$\frac{u}{u_0} = 1 - \operatorname{erf} \frac{y}{2\sqrt{\nu t}} \tag{12.13}$$

In this case the velocity profile depends on only one variable $y/2\sqrt{\nu t}$, which is essentially the similarity variable to be discussed later. In the presence of magnetohydrodynamic effects, such similitude no longer exists, and there is no one variable on which u/u_0 depends. In order to illustrate the flow pattern, calculations based on Eq. (12.12) have been carried out and are presented in Fig. 12.2. It can be seen that application of the magnetic field increases the time required for the flow velocity above the plate to reach any specific value.

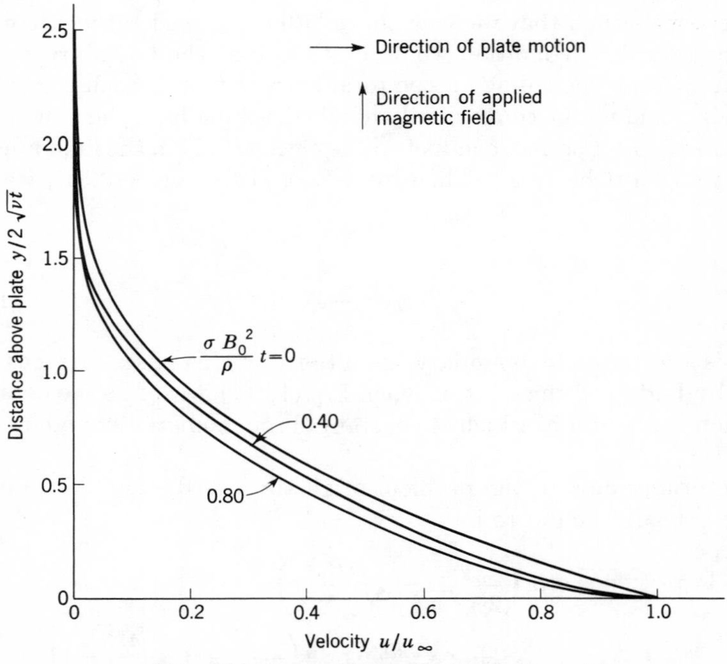

FIGURE 12.2 Velocity profiles in the Rayleigh problem.

If desired, the above solution can be interpreted as a boundary-layer flow with $t \rightarrow x/u_0$. In this case we observe that as the field strength is increased, the velocity profile becomes fuller. This result is analogous to that found for the Hartmann flow earlier. Also, the above results suggest that a natural variable to formulate the boundary-layer problem with should be $y/\sqrt{\nu x}$, just as in the case of conventional incompressible boundary layers.

Finally, the force on the moving plate will be considered. The shear stress is given simply as

$$(\tau)_w = \eta \left(\frac{\partial u}{\partial y}\right)_{y=0} \tag{12.14}$$

Now from Eq. (12.8) the transform of τ_w may be derived:

$$\hat{\tau}_w = \frac{\eta u_0}{1 + \sqrt{P_m}} \frac{\sqrt{\sigma B_0{}^2/\eta + (s/\nu)(1 + \sqrt{P_m})^2}}{s} \tag{12.15}$$

The inverse of this expression gives the following result,

$$\tau_w(t) = \frac{\eta u_0}{\sqrt{\nu}} \left(\frac{1}{\sqrt{\pi t}} e^{-\gamma t} + \sqrt{\gamma} \operatorname{erf} \sqrt{\gamma t}\right) \tag{12.16}$$

where
$$\gamma = \frac{\sigma B_0{}^2}{\rho(1 + \sqrt{P_m})^2}$$

which agrees with Rossow's[2] result when $P_m = 0$. The above equation is valid for arbitrary values of P_m and is thus a much more general result.

In order to illustrate the influence of P_m on the solution, Eq. (12.16) is plotted in Fig. 12.3.

A number of valuable observations can be made based on these results. First, it is clearly seen that as σ increases, the wall shear becomes larger for any given time. This increased shear arises as a result of the enhanced Lorentz force on the conducting fluid near the moving wall. At very long times, all the curves of Fig. 12.3 reach asymptotic values given by

$$\lim_{t \rightarrow \infty} \tau'_w = \frac{\sqrt{P_m}}{1 + \sqrt{P_m}}$$

Now in the nonmagnetohydrodynamic Rayleigh problem Eq. (12.13) shows that $u(y) \rightarrow u_0$ as $t \rightarrow \infty$, so that $\tau_w \rightarrow 0$, and it is of interest to inquire as to why in the present problem $\tau'_w \neq 0$ in the same limit. If we return to the original equations of the problem, (12.1) and (12.2), and assume $\partial/\partial t = 0$, the following solution is obtained for u and b_x:

$$\frac{u}{u_0} = e^{-\sqrt{\sigma B_0{}^2/\eta}\, y}$$

$$b_x = \sqrt{\sigma \eta}\, u_0 \mu_0 \left(\frac{u}{u_0} - 1\right)$$

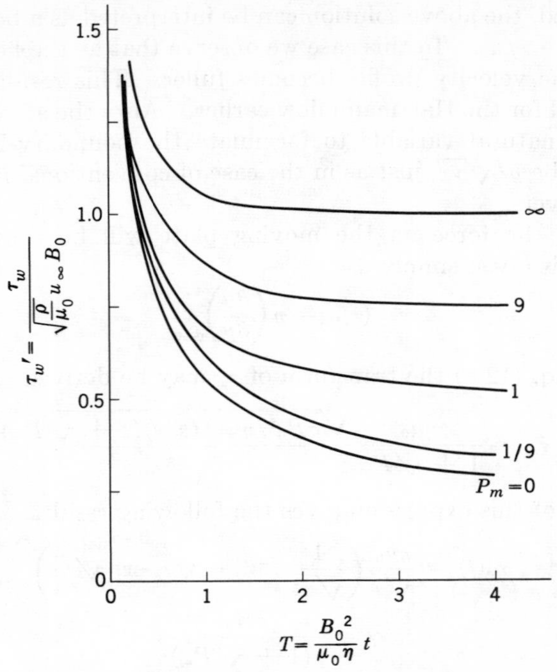

FIGURE 12.3 Wall shear in Rayleigh problem.

The steady-state long-time solution then has an exponential velocity profile rather than the constant one when, say, $\sigma = 0$. This shape of the profile arises because of the existence of the currents in the fluid and the attendant Lorentz force. The form of the current distribution is also exponential, decreasing from some finite value at the wall to zero at infinity.

From the point of view of the physical problem, the wall shear is balanced by the reaction force on the source of the magnetic field. When there is no magnetic field, there is nothing to balance this shear, and so it must be zero in the steady state.

12.3 FORMULATION OF BOUNDARY-LAYER EQUATIONS

The boundary-layer approximation in fluid mechanics has been discussed by many authors from the time of Prandtl; there is, therefore, no justification in repeating these arguments. What will be discussed in this section are those new terms which appear in the equations due to magnetohydrodynamic effects, and their simplification via the boundary-layer approximation. Attention for the present will be restricted to flows with $R_m \sim 0$, so that the magnetic field can be taken as the applied field (i.e., Sec. 10.8). The question of the boundary-layer approximation when $R_m \to \infty$ will be discussed later.

The general problem which will be considered is shown in Fig. 12.4. The magnetic field vector is assumed to lie in the xy plane, but may have x and y components. The Lorentz force for such a two-dimensional problem is given by

$$\mathbf{F} = \mathbf{j} \times \mathbf{B} = \sigma(\mathbf{E} + \mathbf{v} \times \mathbf{B}) \times \mathbf{B} \tag{12.17}$$

where the current is derived from Ohm's law since induced magnetic fields have been assumed negligible. Now since only steady-flow problems will be considered, it will be valid to take $\mathbf{E} = 0$ or, if desired, some constant. It may be recalled that in the unsteady problem (i.e., transient Couette flow), it is not, in general, valid to assume that $\mathbf{E} = 0$. For the present case, Eq. (12.17) can be written as

$$F_x = -\sigma(uB_y^2 - vB_xB_y) \tag{12.18}$$
$$F_y = \sigma(uB_xB_y - vB_x^2) \tag{12.19}$$

For purposes of order-of-magnitude arguments, one can assume that $B_y = \mathcal{O}(B_x)$. Then, since $v/u = \mathcal{O}(\delta)$ where δ is the boundary-layer thickness, the first of the above expressions can be written as

$$F_x \cong -\sigma B_y^2 u \tag{12.20}$$

where B_y can be a function of x and y in general.

In a boundary-layer calculation it will be exceedingly inconvenient to keep B_y a function of y. Accordingly, it is of interest to study $B_y(x,y)$ somewhat more carefully. For a two-dimensional field, one of Maxwell's

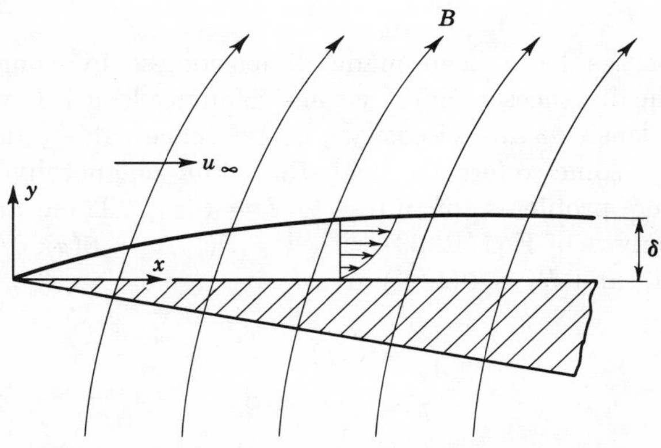

FIGURE 12.4 Magnetohydrodynamic boundary-layer problem.

equations ($\nabla \cdot \mathbf{B} = 0$) requires

$$\frac{\partial B_x}{\partial x} + \frac{\partial B_y}{\partial y} = 0$$

Now with $B_x = \mathcal{O}(B_y)$ and $\partial/\partial x = \mathcal{O}(1)$ while $\partial/\partial y = \mathcal{O}(\delta^{-1})$, we have

$$\frac{\partial B_y}{\partial y} = \mathcal{O}(1)$$

or

$$\Delta B_y = \mathcal{O}(\delta)$$

Thus, the change in B_y across the boundary layer will be the order of δ and can be neglected.

Making use of Eq. (12.20), assuming $p = p(x)$, and making the usual boundary-layer approximations, the x component of the momentum equation becomes

$$\rho\left(u\frac{\partial u}{\partial x} + v\frac{\partial u}{\partial y}\right) + \frac{dp}{dx} = -\sigma B_y{}^2 u + \frac{\partial}{\partial y}\left(\eta\frac{\partial u}{\partial y}\right) \tag{12.21}$$

Before proceeding further, the assumption that $p = p(x)$ must be examined. Again assuming $B_y = \mathcal{O}(B_x)$, Eq. (12.19) reduces to

$$F_y \cong \sigma u B_y B_x \tag{12.22}$$

Now the y component of the momentum equation can be written in the following form,

$$\rho u\frac{\partial v}{\partial x} + \rho v\frac{\partial v}{\partial y} + \frac{\partial p}{\partial y} = IuB_xB_y + \frac{1}{R_e}\frac{\partial}{\partial y}\left(\eta\frac{\partial v}{\partial y}\right) \tag{12.23}$$

where

$$I = \frac{\sigma B_R{}^2 L}{\rho_R u_\infty}$$

$$R_e = \frac{\rho_R u_\infty L}{\eta_R}$$

and the velocities have been made dimensionless by some reference velocity u_∞, the distances x and y by some reference length L, the pressure by $\rho_0 u_\infty{}^2$, the density ρ and viscosity η by reference values, and the magnetic field by some reference field B_R. For magnetohydrodynamic boundary-layer problems of interest, $I = \mathcal{O}(1)$. Then an order-of-magnitude analysis of Eq. (12.23) with $u = \mathcal{O}(1)$, $v = \mathcal{O}(\delta)$, $\partial/\partial x = \mathcal{O}(1)$, $\partial/\partial y = \mathcal{O}(1/\delta)$, and $R_e = \mathcal{O}(1/\delta^2)$ gives

$$\frac{\partial p}{\partial y} = \mathcal{O}(1)$$

or

$$\Delta p = \mathcal{O}(\delta) \sim 0$$

Thus, the pressure change across the boundary layer is of the order of δ (a small quantity) and can be neglected. It should be noted, however, that in the absence of magnetic forces $\Delta p = \mathcal{O}(\delta^2)$, so that it is less valid to assume $p = p(x)$ in the present case than it had been in the absence of a magnetic field.

Next, the Joule heating term which will enter into the energy equation must be considered.

$$\mathcal{H} = \frac{j^2}{\sigma} = \sigma(\mathbf{v} \times \mathbf{B}) \cdot (\mathbf{v} \times \mathbf{B}) \tag{12.24}$$

or $$\mathcal{H} = \sigma(u^2 B_y{}^2 + v^2 B_x - 2uvB_xB_y)$$

As before, the last two terms can be neglected since $v/u = \mathcal{O}(\delta)$. Thus,

$$\mathcal{H} \cong \sigma u^2 B_y{}^2$$

and the energy equation can be written as follows:

$$\rho u \frac{\partial h}{\partial x} + \rho v \frac{\partial h}{\partial y} - u \frac{dp}{dx} = \frac{\partial}{\partial y}\left(\frac{\eta}{P_R}\frac{\partial h}{\partial y}\right) + \frac{\partial}{\partial y}\left(\frac{5kjh}{2eC_p}\right) + \sigma u^2 B_y{}^2 + \eta\left(\frac{\partial u}{\partial y}\right)^2 \tag{12.25}$$

where the Prandtl number is

$$P_R = \frac{C_p \eta}{\mathcal{K}}$$

Finally, the mass-continuity equation must be added to complete the system of equations:

$$\frac{\partial}{\partial x}(\rho u) + \frac{\partial}{\partial y}(\rho v) = 0 \tag{12.26}$$

Before proceeding to the solution of specific problems, it will be of interest to study the general question of similar solutions for incompressible constant-property boundary-layer flows. Consider Eq. (12.21) evaluated in the inviscid free-stream flow:

$$\rho u_\infty \frac{du_\infty}{dx} + \frac{dp}{dx} = -\sigma B_y{}^2 u_\infty \tag{12.27}$$

Combining this with Eq. (12.21) leads to the following relation:

$$u\frac{\partial u}{\partial x} + v\frac{\partial u}{\partial y} - u_\infty \frac{du_\infty}{dx} + \frac{\sigma B_y{}^2}{\rho}(u - u_\infty) = \nu \frac{\partial^2 u}{\partial y^2} \tag{12.28}$$

Introducing $u = \partial\psi/\partial y$ and $v = -\partial\psi/\partial x$ satisfies continuity, and Eq. (12.28) becomes

$$\psi_y \psi_{yx} - \psi_x \psi_{yy} + \frac{\sigma B_y{}^2}{\rho}(\psi_y - u_\infty) = u_\infty \frac{du_\infty}{dx} + \nu \psi_{yyy} \tag{12.29}$$

The problem now is to determine whether or not the above can be reduced to an ordinary differential equation by a proper choice of variables. Let us assume

$$\psi(x,y) = \sqrt{u_\infty \nu x}\, f(\eta)$$

where $$\eta(x,y) = \frac{y}{2}\sqrt{\frac{u_\infty}{\nu x}}$$

and where it should be noted that u_∞ and B_y are known functions of x as yet unspecified. Substituting the above into Eq. (12.29) yields

$$2\frac{du_\infty}{dx}(f')^2 - \left(\frac{u_\infty}{x} + \frac{du_\infty}{dx}\right)ff'' - \frac{8\sigma B^2}{\rho}(1 - \tfrac{1}{2}f') = \frac{8du_\infty}{dx} + \frac{u_\infty}{x}f''' \quad (12.30)$$

Accordingly, similarity can be achieved if

$$\frac{du_\infty}{dx} \propto \frac{u_\infty}{x}$$

and

$$B_y \propto \sqrt{\frac{u_\infty}{x}}$$

so that u_∞ and B_y must be of the following form to permit a similar solution:

$$u_\infty = C_1 x^m$$
$$B_y = C_2 x^{(m-1)/2}$$

In fluid mechanics the x^m variation of u_∞ corresponds to the wedge flow solutions. In magnetohydrodynamic problems such a simple interpretation is not possible since the applied magnetic field interacts with the inviscid free-stream flow. We will return to this point in the next section.

A final point should be made in regard to the above treatment. In looking for similar solutions, only the incompressible boundary layer was studied. For a compressible flow the situation is much more complex. Now, for a similar solution to be found for the compressible boundary-layer problem, it is safe to say that a minimum condition would be that u_∞ and B_y satisfy the conditions already established for the incompressible case. In addition, many other assumptions and requirements will be necessary to obtain similarity in the compressible case. Some of the new phenomena associated with compressible magnetohydrodynamic boundary-layer flows will be treated in Sec. 12.5. The following section will be restricted to incompressible boundary layers.

12.4 INCOMPRESSIBLE BOUNDARY LAYERS

The distinguishing feature of an incompressible magnetohydrodynamic boundary layer is that the inviscid flow external to the boundary layer is also a conductor. Then, since it is not possible to restrict the magnetic field to the boundary-layer region alone, one has no choice but to incorporate the results of the inviscid magnetohydrodynamic analysis into the boundary-layer investigation. On the other hand, this may not be necessary in compressible flows in which the conductivity can vary, and for certain types of flows may be assumed zero external to the boundary layer. Application of the similarity solution to the incompressible boundary layer, although feasible in principle, will not be carried out, because of the difficulty of interpreting the resulting inviscid flow. Instead, two simple incompressible boundary-layer problems will be analyzed by the series-expansion technique.

12.4.1 Boundary Layer with Uniform Free Stream. The first problem will take as a model for the inviscid flow the flow through a parallel-walled two-dimensional channel and will consider the flat plate situated somewhere in the channel some distance from either wall. In this case, the free-stream velocity will be a constant, and the pressure gradient will be given by $dp/dx = -\sigma u_\infty B_y^2$. The applied magnetic field will be assumed constant so that the pressure will vary linearly along the channel. The equation to be solved is Eq. (12.29), which simplifies to the following,

$$\psi_y\psi_{yx} - \psi_x\psi_{yy} + \frac{\sigma B_y^2}{\rho}(\psi_y - u_\infty) = \nu\psi_{yyy} \tag{12.31}$$

where the boundary conditions are

$$\begin{aligned} \psi = \psi_y &= 0 \qquad \text{at } y = 0 \\ \psi_y &= u_\infty \qquad \text{at } y = \infty, x = 0 \end{aligned}$$

Since the pressure gradient in this problem is constant and favorable, it will be adequate to use a classical Blasius series expansion to effect a solution. Assume

$$\psi(x,y) = \sqrt{u_\infty \nu x}\left[f_0 + \frac{\sigma B_y^2}{\rho}xf_1 + \left(\frac{\sigma B_y^2}{\rho}x\right)^2 f_2 + \cdots\right] \tag{12.32}$$

where it is supposed that $\frac{\sigma B_y^2}{\rho}x$ is a small quantity, and the f_i are functions of $\eta = y\sqrt{u_\infty/\nu x}$. Introduction of the above assumption for ψ into Eq. (12.31) leads to the following infinite set of ordinary differential equations:

$$f_0''' + f_0 f_0'' = 0 \tag{12.33}$$

with the following boundary conditions:

$$f_0(0) = f_0'(0) = 0 \qquad f_0'(\infty) = 1$$

$$f_1''' + \tfrac{1}{2}f_0f_1'' - f_0'f_1' + \tfrac{3}{2}f_0''f_1 = f_0' - 1 \tag{12.34}$$

with $\qquad f_1(0) = f_1'(0) = 0 \qquad f_1'(\infty) = 0$

$$f_2''' + \tfrac{1}{2}f_0f_2'' - 2f_0'f_2' + \tfrac{5}{2}f_0''f_2 = (f_1')^2 - \tfrac{3}{2}f_1f_1'' + f_1' \tag{12.35}$$

with $\qquad f_2(0) = f_2'(0) = 0 \qquad f_2'(\infty) = 0$

etc.

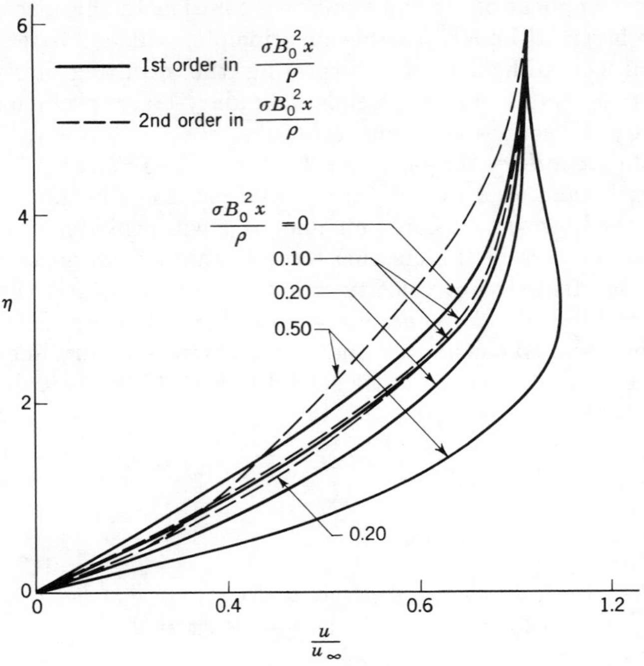

FIGURE 12.5 Incompressible boundary layer for uniform applied magnetic field and free-stream velocity. (After Rossow.[2])

The first of these is the well-known Blasius equation for which the solution has been tabulated for the boundary conditions shown. All subsequent equations are linear, but since they depend on the preceding solutions, numerical integration is necessary. The first two equations beyond the Blasius have been solved by Rossow.[2] The resulting velocity profiles are shown in Fig. 12.5.

Again these results are in agreement with the Hartmann flow treated in Chap. 10 and the Rayleigh problem solution discussed earlier in the present chapter. In other words, the presence of the applied magnetic field tends to make the velocity profile fuller.† If, on the other hand, the free-stream velocity had been decreasing with x, the pressure gradient would have become unfavorable, the boundary-layer profile would have become less full, and the possibility of flow separation would exist. Such a case will be considered next.

12.4.2 Boundary Layer Subject to Adverse Pressure Gradient. Consider, as an appropriate inviscid flow the flow through a parallel-

† The anomolous curve for $\sigma B_0^2 x/\rho = 0.50$ in the second-order solution is a consequence of the poor convergence for this large a value of the parameter.

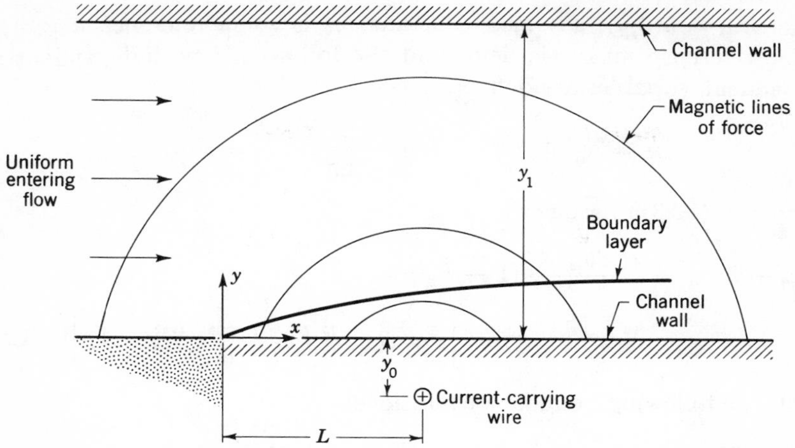

FIGURE 12.6 Boundary-layer development with magnetic field generated by current-carrying wire in lower wall.

walled channel when the applied magnetic field is created by a current-carrying wire aligned perpendicular to the flow direction and imbedded in the lower wall. As shown in Fig. 12.6, the boundary-layer development along the lower wall will be considered. One must, of course, assume that the boundary layer ahead of $x = 0$ can be removed, perhaps by a bleed port, shown schematically as the dotted region. The equation and boundary conditions for ψ have already been presented [Eq. (12.31)] and will also be used in the present problem. One should be aware, however, that requiring $\psi_y = u_\infty$ at $y = \infty$ means that the inviscid flow shear (see Fig. 10.33) at the lower wall is being neglected. In general, this shear can be neglected when the inviscid free-stream flow has been linearized.

As noted earlier, the existence of a nonuniform free-stream velocity, and the possibility of separation, requires the use of a series solution which is more sophisticated. A procedure frequently used for conventional boundary layers and ideally suited to the present problem is due to Görtler. Its extension to magnetohydrodynamics and its application to the present problem will be carried out now.

If the following dimensionless variables are defined,

$$\tilde{x} = \frac{xI}{y_0} \qquad \tilde{y} = \frac{y}{y_0}\sqrt{R_e I} \qquad \tilde{u}_\infty = \frac{u_\infty}{u_i}$$

$$\tilde{\psi} = \frac{\psi\sqrt{R_e I}}{y_0 u_i} \qquad \tilde{B}_y = \frac{B_y}{B_0}$$

and

$$R_e = u_i y_0 \nu \qquad I = \frac{\sigma B_0{}^2 y_0}{\rho u_i}$$

where $u_i = u(0,y)$, assumed constant; y_0 is some reference length; B_0 some reference magnetic field; and the following new independent and dependent variables are defined:

$$\xi = \int_0^{\tilde{x}} \tilde{u}_\infty \, d\tilde{x} \qquad \eta = \frac{\tilde{u}_\infty \tilde{y}}{\sqrt{2\xi}} \qquad F = \tilde{\psi}/\sqrt{2\xi}$$

then Eq. (12.31) becomes

$$F_{\eta\eta\eta} + FF_{\eta\eta} + \frac{2\xi \, d\tilde{u}_\infty/d\tilde{x}}{\tilde{u}_\infty{}^2}(1 - F_\eta{}^2) = 2\xi \left[F_\eta F_{\xi\eta} - F_\xi F_{\eta\eta} + \frac{\tilde{B}_y{}^2}{\tilde{u}_\infty{}^2}(F_\eta - 1) \right] \tag{12.36}$$

with the following boundary conditions:

$$\begin{aligned} F = F_\eta &= 0 \qquad \text{at } \eta = 0 \\ F_\eta &= 1 \qquad \text{at } \eta = \infty \end{aligned}$$

The problem can be solved in general by assuming the following expansions:

$$\begin{aligned} F(\xi,\eta) &= F_0(\eta) + \xi F_1(\eta) + \xi^2 F_2(\eta) + \cdots \\ \frac{2}{\tilde{u}_\infty{}^2}\frac{d\tilde{u}_\infty}{d\tilde{x}} &= \beta(\xi) = \beta_0 + \xi\beta_1 + \xi^2\beta_2 + \cdots \\ \frac{\tilde{B}_y{}^2}{\tilde{u}_\infty{}^2} &= g(\xi) = g_0 + \xi g_1 + \xi^2 g_2 + \cdots \end{aligned}$$

Substituting these into Eq. (12.36), one obtains, as before, an infinite set of equations. The first of these is the Blasius equation,

$$\begin{gathered} F_0''' + F_0 F_0'' = 0 \\ F_0(0) = F_0'(0) = 0 \qquad F_0'(\infty) = 1 \end{gathered} \tag{12.37}$$

The second and all later equations are linear, and are given by the following recursive system,

$$F_k''' + F_0 F_k'' - 2kF_0'F_k' + (2k+1)F_0''F_k + R_{k-1} = 0 \qquad k = 1, 2, 3, \ldots \tag{12.38}$$

where

$$\begin{aligned} R_{k-1} = \beta_{k-1}(1 - F_0'^2) &- \sum_{j=1}^{k-1}\sum_{i=1}^{k-j} \beta_{j-1}F_i'F_{k-i-j}' \\ &- F_0' \sum_{j=1}^{k-1} \beta_{j-1}F_{k-j}' - 2\sum_{j=1}^{k-1}(k-j)F_j'F_{k-j}' \\ &+ \sum_{j=1}^{k-1}(1+2j)F_jF_{k-j}'' + 2g_{k-1}(1 - F_0') - 2\sum_{j=1}^{k-1} g_{j-1}F_{k-j}' \end{aligned}$$

and

$$\begin{aligned} F_k = F_k' &= 0 \qquad \text{at } \eta = 0 \\ F_k' &= 0 \qquad \text{at } \eta = \infty \end{aligned}$$

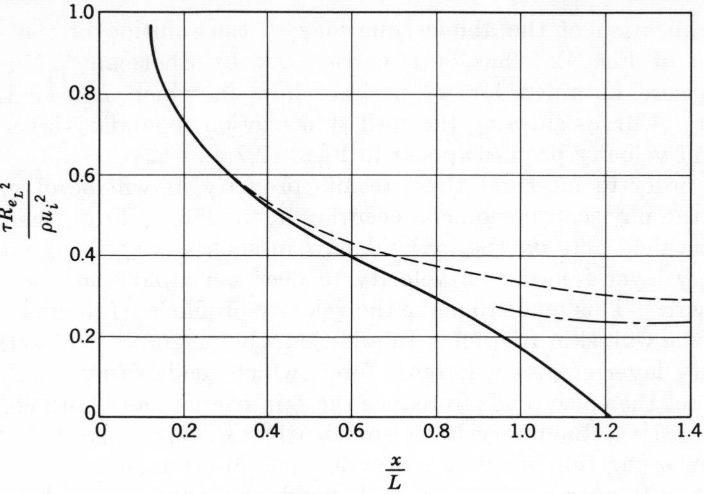

FIGURE 12.7 Wall skin friction versus distance from leading edge for $I = 0.1$ and $L/y_0 = 1.6$. Nonmagnetic case— — —; magnetic case, series solution———; magnetic case, integral approximation— · —.

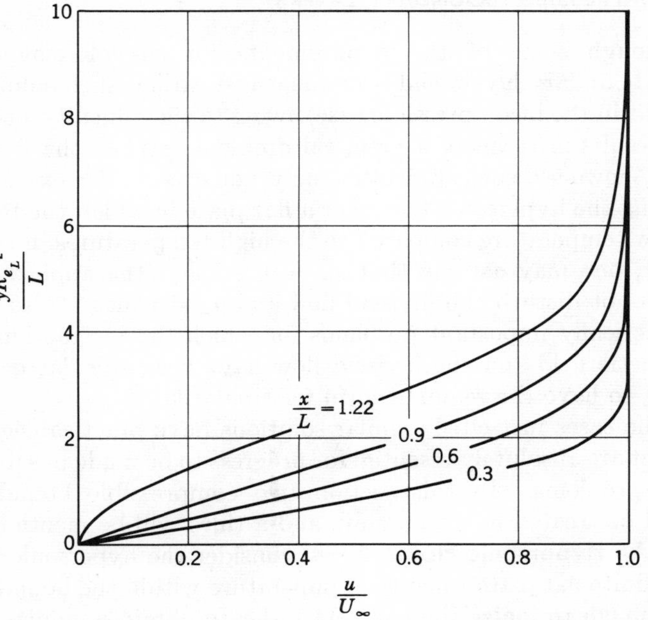

FIGURE 12.8 Boundary-layer velocity profiles at several positions downstream of leading edge for $I = 0.1$ and $L/y_0 = 1.6$.

Application of the above equations to the solution of the specific problem of Fig. 12.6 has been carried out by Sherman.[3] Numerical results were obtained for an inviscid flow in which $L/y_0 = 1.6$ and $I = 0.1$. Curves showing the wall skin friction, boundary-layer thickness, and velocity profiles appear in Figs. 12.7 and 12.8.

In order to interpret these results properly, it will be of value to review the physical phenomena occuring in the flow. First, the applied magnetic field acts on the inviscid flow in such a way as to cause the boundary-layer free-stream velocity to decrease rapidly in the vicinity of the wire. This tends to make the velocity profile less full, and thereby reduce the wall skin friction. In addition, the magnetic field within the boundary layer creates a Lorentz force, which tends to retard the flow. This effect then also tends to reduce the skin friction, and both combined may retard the boundary layer sufficiently to cause separation. That such flow separation is indeed a practical possibility is shown in Fig. 12.7, where $\tau = 0$ at $x = 1.22L$, just beyond the wire. For the present strongly retarded flow, the classical Karman-Pohlhausen integral approach is seen to be a poor approximation. The details of the velocity profiles are shown in Fig. 12.8, where it must be kept in mind that u_∞ is decreasing as x increases from zero.

12.5 COMPRESSIBLE BOUNDARY LAYERS

Although some of the requirements for similar magnetohydrodynamic boundary layers had been identified earlier, such solutions were not sought in the incompressible case, owing to the difficulty of interpreting the results in terms of a practical problem. When the flow is compressible, however, such difficulties may not exist. For example, when considering the hypersonic flow over a flat plate in which the free stream is at a low temperature compared to the high temperatures in the boundary layer, one may assume that $\sigma_\infty = 0$, so that the applied magnetic field does not disturb the inviscid flow and $u_\infty = \text{const}$. Also, there are some practically important problems for which the interaction between the magnetic field and the inviscid flow have been calculated and have shown u_∞ to have the required form for similarity.

In the cases just cited, similar solutions have practical significance, and in fact are absolutely essential for progress to be made in solving these complex problems. In this section two compressible boundary-layer flows will be treated in some detail, and a third will be mentioned.

12.5.1 Hypersonic Flow. First, consider the hypersonic flow over a semi-infinite flat plate when the temperature within the boundary layer is high enough to ionize the gas. In order to obtain a similar solution, the free-stream velocity is assumed constant (low free-steam temperature so that $\sigma = 0$), and the applied magnetic field B_y is assumed to vary inversely as the square root of x. In addition, the wall temperature is assumed constant, and the gas is considered to be in thermodynamic equilibrium. The geometry and coordinates of Fig. 12.4 will be used.

Neglecting heat flux due to diffusion of species (current does not flow across a temperature gradient), the Hall effect, and induced magnetic fields, and putting $dp/dx = 0$, then the boundary-layer equations are given by (12.21), (12.25), and (12.26). The magnetic field can be expressed as

$$B_y = \frac{B_0 \sqrt{L_0}}{\sqrt{x}}$$

The reduction of these equations to the ordinary differential equations corresponding to similarity is accomplished by the Crocco transformation.[4] The procedure will be sketched briefly.

If the independent variables of the problem are changed from x and y to x and u, and $\tau \equiv \eta\, \partial u/\partial y$, the transformation formulas can be written as follows:

$$\left(\frac{\partial}{\partial x}\right)_y = \left(\frac{\partial}{\partial x}\right)_u + \left(\frac{\partial u}{\partial x}\right)_y \left(\frac{\partial}{\partial u}\right)_x$$

$$\left(\frac{\partial}{\partial y}\right)_x = \left(\frac{\partial u}{\partial y}\right)_x \left(\frac{\partial}{\partial u}\right)_x = \frac{\tau}{\eta}\left(\frac{\partial}{\partial u}\right)_x$$

Recognizing that we can consider $y = y(x,u)$, the first of these leads to

$$0 = \left(\frac{\partial y}{\partial x}\right)_u + \left(\frac{\partial u}{\partial x}\right)_y \left(\frac{\partial y}{\partial u}\right)_x$$

or

$$\left(\frac{\partial u}{\partial x}\right)_y = -\frac{(\partial y/\partial x)_u}{(\partial y/\partial u)_x} = -\frac{y_x}{y_u}$$

and the second yields

$$1 = \frac{\tau}{\eta}\left(\frac{\partial y}{\partial u}\right)_x$$

or

$$y_u = \frac{\eta}{\tau}$$

Then the transformation equations can be rewritten to yield

$$\left(\frac{\partial}{\partial x}\right)_y = \left(\frac{\partial}{\partial x}\right)_u - \frac{y_x \tau}{\eta}\left(\frac{\partial}{\partial u}\right)_x$$

$$\left(\frac{\partial}{\partial y}\right)_x = \frac{\tau}{\eta}\left(\frac{\partial}{\partial u}\right)_x$$

Using these relations, the transformed boundary-layer equations become

$$\frac{\partial(\rho v)}{\partial u} = y_x \frac{\partial(\rho u)}{\partial u} - \frac{\eta}{\tau}\frac{\partial(\rho u)}{\partial x} \tag{12.39}$$

$$\rho v = \rho u y_x + \frac{\partial \tau}{\partial u} - \frac{\sigma B_0{}^2 L_0 \eta}{x}\frac{u}{\tau} \tag{12.40}$$

$$\rho u \frac{\partial h}{\partial x} + \left(\frac{\tau}{\eta}\frac{\partial \tau}{\partial u} - \sigma B_0{}^2 L_0 \frac{u}{x}\right)\frac{\partial h}{\partial u} = \frac{\tau}{\eta}\frac{\partial}{\partial u}\left(\frac{\tau}{P_R}\frac{\partial h}{\partial u}\right) + \frac{\sigma u^2 B_0{}^2 L_0}{x} + \frac{\tau^2}{\eta} \tag{12.41}$$

where the second term in the last of these has been simplified with the use of Eq. (12.40). Eliminating ρv from Eq. (12.40) by use of Eq. (12.39) gives

$$\rho u \left(\frac{\eta}{\tau}\right)_x + \frac{\eta}{\tau}(\rho u)_x + \frac{d^2\tau}{du^2} - B_0{}^2 L_0 \frac{d}{du}\left(\frac{\sigma \eta u}{\tau}\right) = 0$$

or

$$\left(\rho \frac{u\eta}{\tau}\right)_x + \frac{d^2\tau}{du^2} - B_0{}^2 L_0 \frac{d}{du}\left(\frac{\sigma\eta u}{\tau}\right) = 0 \tag{12.42}$$

Next assume that

$$\tau(x,u) = \frac{G(u)}{\sqrt{x}}$$

and

$$h(x,u) = h(u)$$

so that Eqs. (12.41) and (12.42) become

$$\frac{\rho u \eta}{2G}\frac{1}{\sqrt{x}} + \frac{1}{\sqrt{x}}\frac{d^2G}{du^2} - \frac{B_0{}^2 L_0}{\sqrt{x}}\frac{d}{du}\left(\frac{\sigma\eta u}{G}\right) = 0$$

or

$$G\frac{d^2G}{du^2} = -\frac{\rho u \eta}{2} + G B_0{}^2 L_0 \frac{d}{du}\left(\frac{\sigma \eta u}{G}\right) \tag{12.43}$$

and

$$\frac{G}{\eta x}\frac{dG}{du}\frac{dh}{du} - \frac{\sigma B_0{}^2 L_0 u}{x}\frac{dh}{du} = \frac{G}{\eta x}\frac{d}{du}\left(\frac{G}{P_R}\frac{dh}{du}\right) + \frac{\sigma u^2 B_0{}^2 L_0}{x} + \frac{G^2}{\eta x}$$

or

$$\frac{dG}{du}\frac{dh}{du} = \frac{d}{du}\left(\frac{G}{P_R}\frac{dh}{du}\right) + G + \frac{\sigma B_0{}^2 u L_0 \eta}{G}\left(\frac{dh}{du} + u\right) \tag{12.44}$$

These are then two ordinary differential equations for G and h as functions of u. The numerical procedure for their solution is given in detail by Bush,[5] where the method of expressing ρ, η, σ, and P_R as functions of h for high-temperature air are also described. Some of the results of calculations for the constant-wall-temperature case are shown in Fig. 12.9. The conditions chosen for the above case were $T_\infty = 222°\text{K}$, $p = 10^{-3}$ atm, $\mathfrak{M}_\infty = 25$, and a wall temperature of $\sim 2000°\text{K}$. The subscript NM stands for nonmagnetic, and $\bar{I}$ is the interaction parameter proportional to $B_0{}^2$.

The above results bear a striking resemblance to the real-gas Couette flow results described in Chap. 10. Again, a hysterisis effect exists,

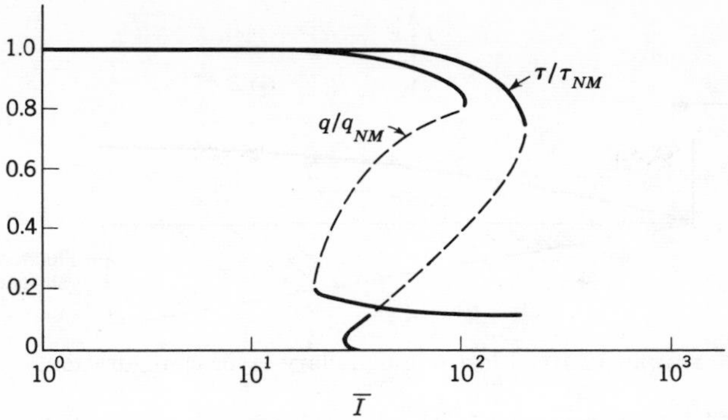

FIGURE 12.9 Shear stress and heat flux for hypersonic boundary layer. (After Bush.[5])

owing to the form of the σ versus T curve, and the dashed portions of the curves are unstable. The principle new information here is that in allowing the boundary layer to grow in height (in the Couette flow δ is fixed), a reduction in heat flux of 80 per cent is possible where little if any heat-flux reduction had been predicted earlier. The shear stress does, however, behave as previously predicted.

12.5.2 Crossed-field MHD Channel Flow. Another compressible boundary-layer flow of practical interest is one which grows along the electrode surface of a crossed-field MHD channel. The principal new feature here is that a current flows normal to the boundary-layer surface (see Fig. 12.10), so that the contribution to the heat flux due to the diffusion of electrons associated with the current cannot be neglected. Since the boundary layer under consideration will be developing within a finite-width channel, the usual assumption must be made that the boundary-layer thickness is not large enough to disturb the inviscid flow. In addition, it is necessary to assume that the electrical resistance of the boundary layer is small compared to the resistance of the inviscid flow, so that the overall current flow is determined external to the boundary layer.

The momentum equation is given by Eq. (12.21), except that now the Lorentz force is written as jB_y since j is now some known function of x.

$$\rho u \frac{\partial u}{\partial x} + \rho v \frac{\partial u}{\partial y} + \frac{dp}{dx} = \frac{\partial}{\partial y}\left(\eta \frac{\partial u}{\partial y}\right) + jB_y \qquad (12.45)$$

The energy equation written in terms of temperature ($h = C_pT$) is given by Eq. (12.25), except that here the Joule heating is written as j^2/σ, again due to the fact that $j = j(x)$ is a given quantity. The continuity equation is, of course, Eq. (12.26).

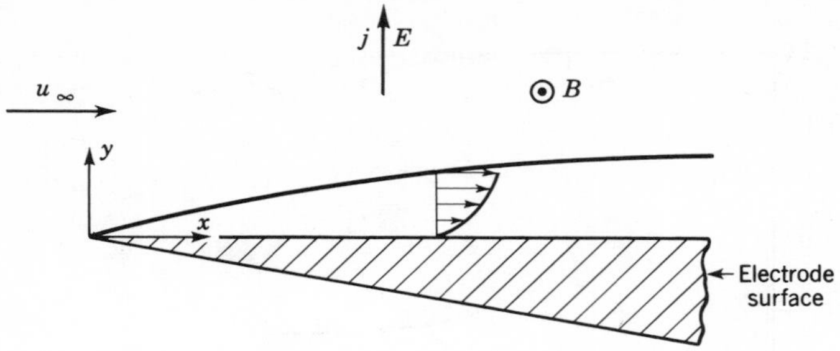

FIGURE 12.10 Electrode boundary-layer configuration.

Since j is the same within the boundary layer as in the free stream, the momentum equation in the free stream is

$$\rho_\infty u_\infty \frac{du_\infty}{dx} + \frac{dp}{dx} = jB_y \tag{12.46}$$

and combining this with Eq. (12.45) gives

$$\rho u \frac{\partial u}{\partial x} + \rho v \frac{\partial u}{\partial y} = \frac{\partial}{\partial y}\left(\eta \frac{\partial u}{\partial y}\right) + \rho_\infty u_\infty \frac{du_\infty}{dx} \tag{12.47}$$

The energy equation evaluated in the free stream yields

$$\rho_\infty u_\infty C_p \frac{dT_\infty}{dx} = u_\infty \frac{dp}{dx} + \frac{j^2}{\sigma_\infty} \tag{12.48}$$

which when combined with Eq. (12.25) yields the following relation:

$$\rho C_p\left(u \frac{\partial T}{\partial x} + v \frac{\partial T}{\partial y}\right) = \frac{\partial}{\partial y}\left(\mathcal{K} \frac{\partial T}{\partial y} + \frac{5kj}{2e} T\right) + \eta\left(\frac{\partial u}{\partial y}\right)^2 + \rho_\infty u_\infty C_p \frac{dT_\infty}{dx}\frac{u}{u_\infty} + \frac{j^2}{\sigma_\infty}\left(\frac{\sigma_\infty}{\sigma} - \frac{u}{u_\infty}\right) \tag{12.49}$$

It is interesting to note at this point that the momentum equation for the present case is independent of B_y. The principal magnetohydrodynamic effects appear in the energy equation.

For convenience, in the boundary-layer analysis η and $\mathcal{K}$ will be assumed proportional to T, despite the fact that for constant mean free path, kinetic theory leads to a $T^{\frac{1}{2}}$ dependence. In general (see Chap. 5), the electrical conductivity σ can be determined as a function of pressure and temperature. This time, for convenience, in both the free-stream and boundary-layer analyses the pressure dependence will be ignored. Finally, the gas will be assumed perfect so that

$$p = \rho RT \tag{12.50}$$

Now, the boundary conditions which are needed are

$$T_\infty = T_\infty(x) \qquad u_\infty = u_\infty(x) \tag{12.51}$$

In addition, expressions are needed for $p(x)$ as well as $j(x)$. All four of these relations can be obtained from the solution of the inviscid problem. For the inviscid flow, it will be assumed that T_∞ and E_∞ are constant, the former also leading to a constant σ_∞ if the pressure dependence of σ is neglected. Within these assumptions, the solution, based on the methods of Chap. 11, is

$$\begin{aligned} u_\infty &= \alpha x^n \\ p &= \frac{\sigma_\infty (RT_\infty E_\infty)^2}{\alpha^2} \frac{5n-1}{n^2} x^{1-5n} \\ j &= \frac{\sigma_\infty R T_\infty E_\infty}{\alpha^2 n} (5n-1) x^{-2n} \end{aligned} \tag{12.52}$$

were one must have $n > \frac{1}{5}$.

As noted earlier, u_∞ in the above form may make a similarity solution possible. The feasibility of reducing the equations to similar form will be taken up next. Define the following independent variables,

$$\xi = \int_0^x \frac{p}{p_0} \frac{u_\infty}{u_0} \, dx \tag{12.53}$$

and

$$\zeta = \frac{u_\infty}{u_0} \sqrt{\frac{u_0}{2\nu_0}} \, \xi^{-\frac{1}{2}} \int_0^y \frac{\rho}{\rho_0} \, dy \tag{12.54}$$

where $(\ )_0$ denotes some convenient reference x position. Next, define a stream function in order that mass continuity be satisfied,

$$\psi_y = \frac{\rho u}{\rho_0} \qquad \psi_x = -\frac{\rho v}{\rho_0}$$

and then redefine the stream function to be

$$\psi = \sqrt{2\nu_0 u_0} \sqrt{\xi} f(\zeta)$$

The momentum equation then becomes

$$f''' + ff'' + \frac{2\xi}{u_\infty} \frac{du_\infty}{dx} \left[\frac{\rho_\infty}{\rho} - (f')^2 \right] = 0 \tag{12.55}$$

If a dimensionless temperature is defined as $\theta = T/T_0$, the energy equation becomes

$$\begin{aligned} \frac{1}{P_R} \frac{\partial^2 \theta}{\partial \zeta^2} + f \frac{\partial \theta}{\partial \zeta} = 2f'\xi \frac{\partial \theta}{\partial \xi} &- (\gamma - 1) \mathfrak{M}_\infty^2 (f'')^2 \\ &- \frac{5kj}{e} \left(\frac{u_0}{2\nu_0} \right)^{\frac{1}{2}} \frac{\sqrt{\xi}}{C_p \rho_0 u_\infty} \frac{p_0}{p} \frac{\partial \theta}{\partial \zeta} \\ &- \frac{j^2}{\sigma} \frac{2u_0 \xi}{C_p T_\infty \rho_\infty u_\infty^2} \frac{p_0}{p} \theta \left(\frac{\sigma_\infty}{\sigma} - f' \right) \end{aligned} \tag{12.56}$$

Using the results of the inviscid analysis [Eqs. (12.52)] to determine ξ and restricting the value of n so that $n < \frac{1}{2}$, we find

$$\frac{x}{x_0} = \left[(2 - 4n) \frac{\xi}{x_0} \right]^{1/(2-4n)} \tag{12.57}$$

and the energy and momentum equations can be written as follows:

$$\begin{aligned} \frac{1}{P_R} \frac{\partial^2 \theta}{\partial \zeta^2} + f \frac{\partial \theta}{\partial \zeta} = 2f'\xi \frac{\partial \theta}{\partial \xi} &- (\gamma - 1)\mathfrak{M}_\infty^2 (f'')^2 \\ &- \frac{\gamma - 1}{\gamma} \left(\frac{5n - 1}{1 - 2n} \right)^{\frac{1}{2}} \frac{5kT_0}{2e} \left(\frac{\sigma_0}{\eta_0 R T_0} \right)^{\frac{1}{2}} \frac{\partial \theta}{\partial \zeta} \\ &- \frac{\gamma - 1}{\gamma} \frac{5n - 1}{1 - 2n} \theta \left(\frac{\sigma_\infty}{\sigma} - f' \right) \end{aligned} \tag{12.58}$$

and

$$f''' + ff'' + \frac{n}{1 - 2n} [\theta - (f')^2] = 0 \tag{12.59}$$

Accordingly, it can be seen that since $\mathfrak{M}_\infty = \mathfrak{M}_\infty(\xi)$, the first two terms on the right-hand side of Eq. (12.58) are functions of ξ and prevent a similar solution. If, however, the wall temperature is constant, then $\theta \neq \theta(\xi)$, and the first of these terms vanishes. Finally, when $\mathfrak{M}_\infty^2 \cong 0$, the second term can be neglected, and a similar solution is feasible. If $\mathfrak{M}_\infty^2 \neq 0$, it can be taken to be a constant, and the similarity is then inexact. In the present example one can clearly see that when the flow is compressible, the specification that $u_\infty \propto x^n$ is not sufficient to ensure a similar solution, but that additional conditions and assumptions are necessary.

Calculations based on the above equations have been carried out by Kerrebrock[6] for helium seeded with cesium. The free-stream temperature and Mach number were taken to be 3000°K and unity, respectively. A wall temperature of 1500°K was also chosen.

Within the boundary layer being considered, heat is generated by two mechanisms: viscous dissipation and Joule heating. Energy is transported from these two sources and from the high-temperature free stream to the wall by both conduction and diffusion of electrons. For the selection of parameters made by Kerrebrock, both viscous dissipation and Joule heating are of comparable importance, and energy transport by electrons is only a few per cent of the overall heat transfer.

To see more clearly the influence of the above heat sources on the boundary layer, velocity and temperature profiles are shown in Fig. 12.11. Increasing values of n correspond to free streams with increasing acceleration. This is seen to correspond to the fact that the velocity profiles tend to become fuller as n increases. The temperature profile marked "flat plate" corresponds to the case for which there is no current

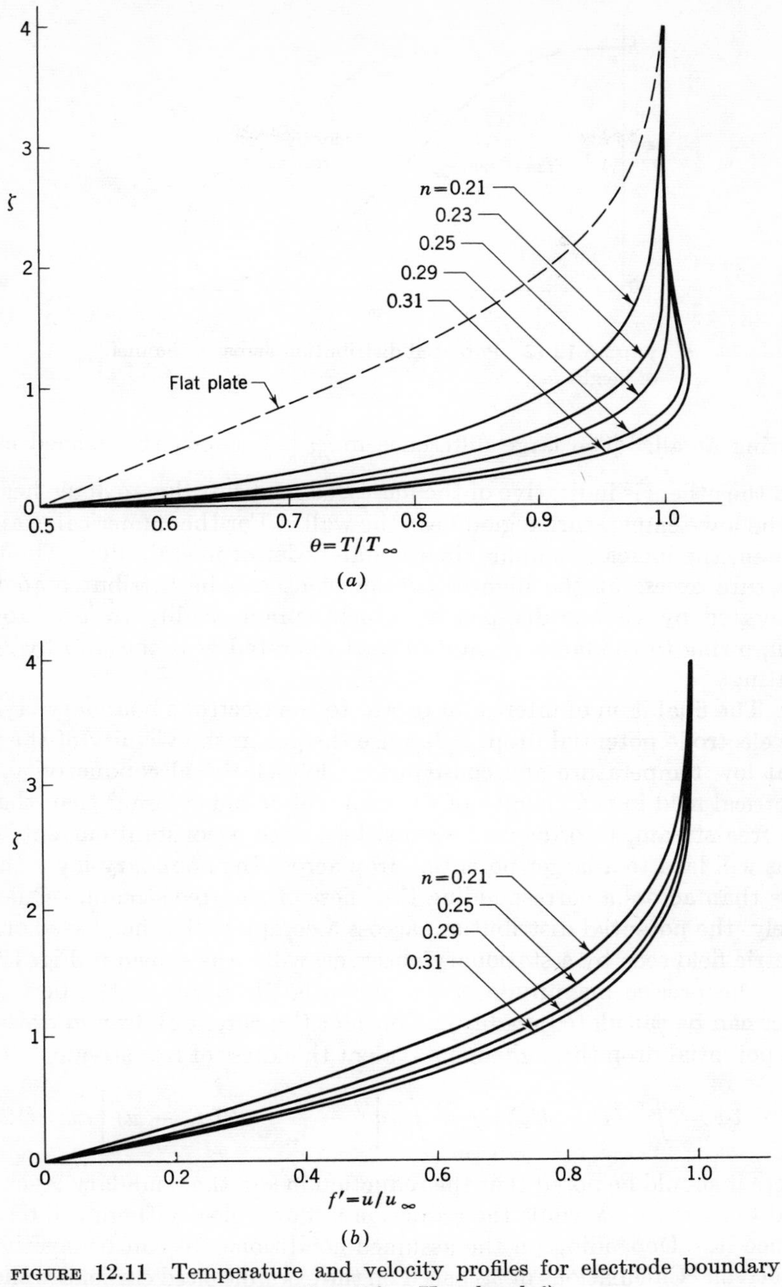

FIGURE 12.11 Temperature and velocity profiles for electrode boundary layer where $\mathfrak{M}_\infty = 1$, $\theta_\omega = 0.5$. (After Kerrebrock.[6])

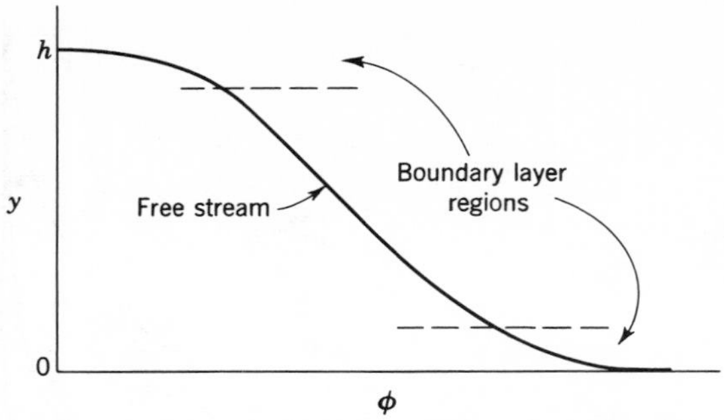

FIGURE 12.12 Potential distribution across a channel of height h.

flowing at all. The large difference in $\left.\frac{\partial \theta}{\partial \zeta}\right|_0$ between the dashed curve and the others is indicative of the increased heat flux due to Joule heating in the low-temperature region near the wall. For the numerical example chosen, the increase is approximately an order of magnitude. The temperature excess at the highest accelerations can be attributed to heat generated by viscous dissipation, which cannot readily transfer to the wall, owing to the large amount of heat liberated near the wall by Joule heating.

The final item of interest in regard to the electrode boundary layer is the electrode potential drop. Because the gas in the vicinity of the wall is at low temperature and consequently low electrical conductivity, the electrical field in the vicinity of the wall will be much larger than that in the free stream, in order to be consistent with a constant-current flow. This will lead to a larger potential drop across the boundary-layer thickness than across a corresponding thickness of the free stream. Qualitatively, the potential distribution, across a complete channel, based on the electric field seen by a stationary observer, will be as shown in Fig. 12.12.

The precise magnitude of the potential drop across the boundary layer can be calculated readily. Consider the potential drop in excess of the potential drop through an equivalent thickness of free stream. Then

$$\delta\phi = \int_0^\infty (E - E_\infty)\,dy = \int_0^\infty \left[\frac{j}{\sigma} - \frac{j}{\sigma_\infty} - B(u_\infty - u)\right] dy \quad (12.60)$$

where it should be noted that the reduction in σ in the boundary layer will tend to increase $\delta\phi$, while the reduction in flow velocity there will tend to reduce it. Depending on the assumed conditions, $\delta\phi$ can be positive or negative. Calculations of $\delta\phi$ based on the example cited earlier are shown in Fig .12.13. It is interesting to observe that $\delta\phi$ is positive for this case, so that the potential drop through the boundary layer is indeed greater than in the free stream over the same distance.

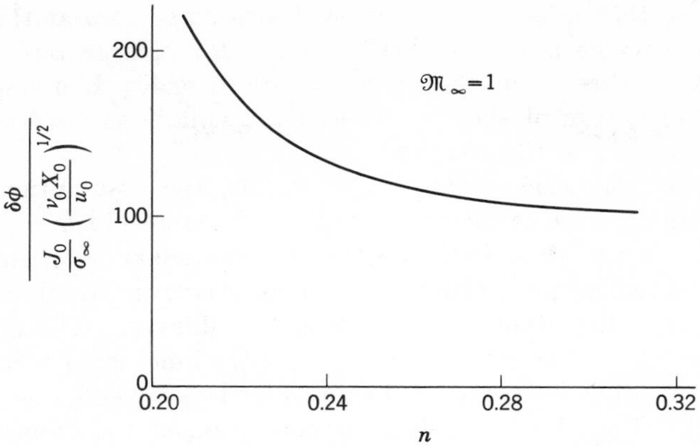

FIGURE 12.13 Boundary-layer potential excess. (After Kerrebrock.[6])

Finally, mention should be made of the magnetohydrodynamic compressible boundary layer in the region of the stagnation point on a blunt body. The practical example is, of course, the reentering nose cone. For this problem the inviscid flow has been calculated, and it has been shown that $u_\infty = \alpha x$ when B_y is a constant, the magnitude of α being reduced as the strength of the magnetic field is increased. These are precisely the minimum requirements for a similar solution, as noted earlier, and with several additional simplifying assumptions, similarity solutions can indeed be obtained.[7]

12.6 MAGNETIC BOUNDARY LAYERS

Up to this point in the present chapter, and in fact so far in the book, problems of external flow (over closed bodies such as airfoils) have not been discussed. It will be of interest, however, to consider qualitatively some new boundary-layer phenomena that mainly arise in such flows when R_m is large and P_m is small.[8]

The particular overall problem that will be investigated will be the so-called "aligned flows." These are flows in which the flow velocity and magnetic field vectors far from the body are parallel. Now when $R_m = \infty$ and the electric field $\mathbf{E}$ is zero, Ohm's law requires that $\mathbf{v} \times \mathbf{B} = 0$, so that $\mathbf{v}$ and $\mathbf{B}$ are not only parallel at infinity but also parallel everywhere. For a body of finite conductivity $\mathbf{E} = 0$ implies $\mathbf{j} = 0$, so that the magnetic field is harmonic within the body. Since it must be a constant on the surface, the mean-value theorem of potential theory tells us that it must be zero everywhere within the body. Accordingly, the tangential component of $\mathbf{B}$ at the surface must jump from a finite value to zero. As was shown in Chap. 2, this corresponds to a current sheet at the surface. Since **v** must also go to zero at the surface, there must also be a vortex sheet. When R_m is large but no longer infinite, these current and vortex sheets are in reality boundary layers. The physical nature of such layers and the equations governing them will be the subject of this section.

Since, as was seen earlier, $P_m = R_m/R_e$, the assumption of large R_m and small P_m is tantamount to assuming R_m large and R_e much larger. Accordingly, it can be anticipated that the boundary layer in question will really be two layers. One will be an outer layer in which viscosity is negligible, and the other will be a viscous sublayer. The outer-layer thickness will be of the order of $R_m^{-\frac{1}{2}}$, while the inner layer will be of the order of $R_e^{-\frac{1}{2}}$. The flow external to the outer layer, where $\mathbf{v} \propto \mathbf{B}$, will be irrotational. The above physical interpretation of the boundary-layer region is illustrated in Fig. 12.14.

Before considering the equations and specific boundary conditions in detail, it will be of value first to discuss the procedure for solution. First, the potential flow must be determined, neglecting both boundary layers. The boundary conditions for such a solution are that the surface be both a fluid and magnetic streamline. From such a solution one obtains values of u and B_x at the wall. These, then, will serve as outer boundary conditions for the inviscid layer. The inner conditions for this layer are evaluated by assuming the viscous layer to be of negligible thickness. Thus, one of the inner conditions on the inviscid layer will be $v = 0$ while $u \neq 0$. Another inner boundary condition on the magnetic field will be needed to complete the formulation of the inviscid boundary layer. The viscous layer will then use $u(x,0)$ as obtained from the inviscid-layer solution as its outer boundary condition along with $v = 0$. The inner

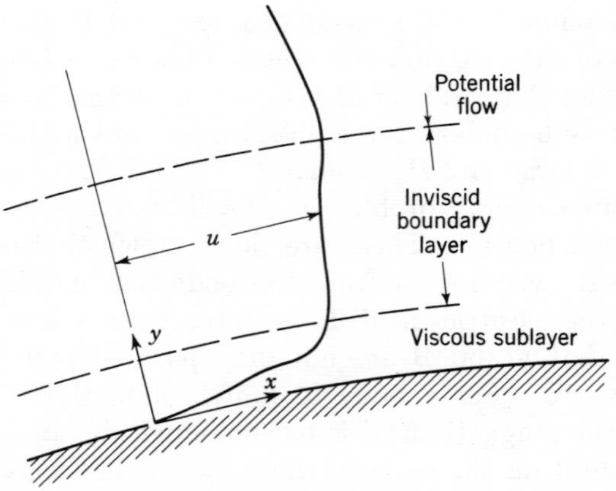

FIGURE 12.14 Sketch showing inviscid magnetohydrodynamic boundary layer and viscous sublayer. (Adapted from Sears.[8])

boundary conditions on the viscous layer are the conventional ones of $u = v = 0$.

So far little has been said about the boundary conditions on **B**. The difficulty lies in the fact that when R_m is no longer infinite, then **B** is no longer zero within the body and B_x and B_y at the surface are not known before the solution of the problem. The one thing we do know, however, is that when $R_m \to \infty$, then B_x and B_y should both $\to 0$ within the body.

Before resolving the above question of the boundary values of B_x and B_y, it will be necessary to introduce some order-of-magnitude arguments. It will be assumed that the thickness of the inviscid magnetic boundary layer δ_i is $\mathcal{O}(R_m^{-\frac{1}{2}})$, and that the thickness of the viscous sublayer δ_v is $\mathcal{O}(R_e^{-\frac{1}{2}})$. Also, differentiation with respect to x will not alter the order of magnitude of a quantity, but differentiation with respect to y will change the order of magnitude by δ^{-1}. Whether it is δ_i or δ_v will depend on which layer is being discussed.

It was noted earlier that B_x and B_y tend to zero as $R_m \to \infty$, so that it will be valid to assume them both $\mathcal{O}(R_m^{-\frac{1}{2}})$ at the wall. Since the viscous sublayer is extremely thin, neither should vary appreciably from its value at the wall within this region. Next, consider the following relation,

$$\nabla \times \mathbf{B} = R_m \mathbf{v} \times \mathbf{B} \tag{12.61}$$

where **v** and **B** have been made dimensionless by reference values of v and B, where Ohm's law has been used, and $\mathbf{E} = 0$. Or, for the present two-dimensional problem,

$$\frac{\partial B_y}{\partial x} - \frac{\partial B_x}{\partial y} = R_m(uB_y - vB_x) \tag{12.62}$$

Within the viscous layer the first two terms have the following orders of magnitude:

$$\frac{\partial B_y}{\partial x} \to \mathcal{O}(R_m^{-\frac{1}{2}}) \qquad \frac{\partial B_x}{\partial y} = \mathcal{O}(P_m^{-\frac{1}{2}})$$

so that $\partial B_y/\partial x \ll \partial B_x/\partial y$. Also, within the viscous layer, $v \ll u$ and B_y and B_x are of comparable orders of magnitude, so that $vB_x \ll uB_y$. Accordingly Eq. (12.61) can be simplified, within the viscous layer, to

$$-\frac{\partial B_x}{\partial y} = R_m u B_y \tag{12.63}$$

or, integrating over the viscous layer,

$$B_x = B_x(x,0) + \mathcal{O}(R_m^{\frac{1}{2}} R_e^{-\frac{1}{2}})$$

or

$$B_x = \mathcal{O}(R_m^{-\frac{1}{2}}) + \mathcal{O}(P_m^{-\frac{1}{2}})$$

Accordingly, one can assume $B_x \cong 0$ throughout the viscous sublayer and take this as the other inner boundary condition for the inviscid layer.

The equations governing both boundary layers will be deduced next, by similar order-of-magnitude arguments. Within the *inviscid* layer, $\partial B_x/\partial x + \partial B_y/\partial y = 0$, so that assuming $B_x = \mathcal{O}(1)$ leads to $B_y = \mathcal{O}(R_m^{-\frac{1}{2}})$. Next, the two momentum equations, (8.17) and (12.62), are considered:

$$\underset{\mathcal{O}(1)}{\rho u \frac{\partial u}{\partial x}} + \underset{\mathcal{O}(1)}{\rho v \frac{\partial u}{\partial y}} + \underset{\mathcal{O}(1)}{\frac{\partial P}{\partial x}} = N\left(\underset{\mathcal{O}(1)}{B_x \frac{\partial B_x}{\partial x}} + \underset{\mathcal{O}(1)}{B_y \frac{\partial B_x}{\partial y}}\right) \tag{12.64}$$

$$\underset{\mathcal{O}(R_m^{-\frac{1}{2}})}{\rho u \frac{\partial v}{\partial x}} + \underset{\mathcal{O}(R_m^{-\frac{1}{2}})}{\rho v \frac{\partial v}{\partial y}} + \frac{\partial P}{\partial y} = N\left(\underset{\mathcal{O}(R_m^{-\frac{1}{2}})}{B_x \frac{\partial B_y}{\partial x}} + \underset{\mathcal{O}(R_m^{-\frac{1}{2}})}{B_y \frac{\partial B_y}{\partial y}}\right) \tag{12.65}$$

$$\underset{\mathcal{O}(R_m^{-\frac{1}{2}})}{\frac{\partial B_y}{\partial x}} - \underset{\mathcal{O}(R_m^{\frac{1}{2}})}{\frac{\partial B_x}{\partial y}} = R_m(\underset{\mathcal{O}(R_m^{-\frac{1}{2}})}{uB_y} - \underset{\mathcal{O}(R_m^{-\frac{1}{2}})}{vB_x}) \tag{12.66}$$

where $P = p + B^2/2$ and $N = B_\infty^2/\mu_0\rho u_\infty^2$ and it will be assumed that P and N are $\mathcal{O}(1)$. The resulting boundary-layer equations in dimensional form for the *inviscid* layer are

$$\rho u \frac{\partial u}{\partial x} + \rho v \frac{\partial u}{\partial y} + \frac{\partial P}{\partial x} = B_x \frac{\partial B_x}{\partial x} + B_y \frac{\partial B_x}{\partial y} \tag{12.67}$$

$$-\frac{\partial B_x}{\partial y} = \sigma\mu_0(uB_y - vB_x) \tag{12.68}$$

$$\frac{\partial u}{\partial x} + \frac{\partial v}{\partial y} = 0 \tag{12.69}$$

$$\frac{\partial B_x}{\partial x} + \frac{\partial B_y}{\partial y} = 0 \tag{12.70}$$

with the boundary conditions

$$y = \infty: \quad u = u_\infty(x), \quad B_x = B_{x\infty}(x) \propto u_\infty(x)$$

$$y = 0: \quad v = 0, \quad B_x = 0$$

It is interesting to see that a boundary condition on B_y at $y = 0$ is not needed, since when B_y is eliminated from the equations by Eq. (12.70), they become second order in B_x and two boundary conditions on B_x are available. The value of B_y at $y = 0$ is part of the solution being sought, and, accordingly, it is not a suitable boundary condition. From Eq. (12.65) it can also be seen that $\partial P/\partial y = \mathcal{O}(R_m^{-\frac{1}{2}})$ and $P = P(x)$ alone. Accordingly, $\partial P/\partial x$ can be evaluated from the free-stream solution.

The boundary-layer equations within the viscous layer are precisely those obtained earlier in this chapter. The applied magnetic field B_y is taken to be the value found at $y = 0$ from the inviscid boundary-layer solution. The pressure p to be used is $P(x)$, obtained from the potential flow solution.

In conclusion, then, when $R_m \to \infty$, boundary-layer phenomena very similar to conventional boundary layers can exist. They do, however, offer a number of new features for future studies.[8]

REFERENCES CITED

1. Ludford, G. S. S.: "Rayleigh's Problem in Hydromagnetics: The Impulsive Motion of a Pole Piece," *Arch. Rational Mech. and Anal.*, **3**:14 (1959).
2. Rossow, V. J.: "On Flow of Electrically Conducting Fluids over a Flat Plate in the Presence of a Transverse Magnetic Field," *NASA Rept.* 1358, 1958.
3. Sherman, A.: "Viscous Magnetohydrodynamic Boundary Layer," *Phys. Fluids*, **4**:552 (1961).
4. Howarth, L. (ed.): *Modern Developments in Fluid Dynamics*, vol. 1, *High Speed Flow*, Oxford University Press, Fair Lawn, N.J., 1953.
5. Bush, W. B.: "Compressible Flat Plate Boundary Layer Flow with an Applied Magnetic Field," *J. Aerospace Sci.*, **27**:49 (1960).
6. Kerrebrock, J. L.: "Electrode Boundary Layers in Direct Current Plasma Accelerators," *J. Aerospace Sci.*, **28**:631 (1961).
7. Bush, W. B.: "The Stagnation-point Boundary Layer in the Presence of an Applied Magnetic Field," *J. Aerospace Sci.*, **28**:610 (1961).
8. Sears, W. R.: "On a Boundary Layer Phenomenon in Magneto-Fluid Dynamics," *Astronaut. Acta*, **7**:223 (1961).

part III

APPLICATIONS

13

MAGNETOHYDRODYNAMIC PROPULSION

13.1 INTRODUCTION

To complete this presentation of engineering magnetohydrodynamics, two areas of application, namely, magnetohydrodynamic propulsion and power generation, will be treated. This chapter will deal with the former. Because of the considerable amount of current work in this area it will not be possible to cover the subject completely. An attempt will be made, rather, to describe the physical operation of a number of different types of propulsion units, to identify their unusual characteristics, and to define desirable operating modes.

Magnetohydrodynamic accelerators are only one of several types of electrical propulsion devices being proposed for use in space flight. Although the application of electrical propulsion devices to space propulsion has been studied extensively,[1] it may be in order to discuss this question briefly. Up to the present time all space propulsion has been accomplished with chemical rockets. They give thrust-to-weight ratios greater than unity and are in a high state of development. Their limitation is that they can give, at most, specific impulses (rocket exhaust velocity/acceleration due to gravity at earth's surface) in the order of 400 sec. This limitation is due to the fact that there is a practical limit to the energy available from a chemical reaction, so that the total enthalpy available for conversion into exhaust kinetic energy is limited. If, however, the molecular weight of the exhaust gases is lowered, the specific impulse can be raised. This is the principle employed in the nuclear rocket concept where gaseous hydrogen is used as the propellant. In other words, for a given initial total temperature, the limiting exhaust velocity (exhaust temperature zero) is given by

$$u_{\text{limit}} = \sqrt{2C_p T_0/M} \tag{13.1}$$

where C_p now is the molar specific heat, which does not vary appreciably from one gas to another, and where M is the molecular weight. Thus, the specific impulse varies inversely as the square root of the molecular weight, and hydrogen is an obvious choice. Since 3000°K is the upper limit of T_0 in a nuclear rocket utilizing a heat exchanger, the specific impulse will be limited to less than 1,000 sec. When the limitation on total temperature is removed, as in an electrical rocket, then there is no limit to the specific impulse that may be achieved. There is a limit, however, to the specific impulse that may be achieved efficiently. The question of efficiency is an essential one since the electrical rocket uses energy provided by some power supply, and if it does not use it efficiently, the power supply becomes excessively heavy. Another essential feature of the electrical propulsion system is that it has a thrust-to-weight ratio much less than unity, so that it must be launched, or placed into orbit, by a chemical or nuclear rocket.

The desirability of a high value of specific impulse for space flight can be established by a simple argument. Consider a spacecraft moving at a constant velocity ($\sim$ exhaust velocity) between two points in space. Now a mission can generally be defined in terms of the thrust on the vehicle times the length of time it is applied. In other words, the total impulse is

$$I \equiv \int_0^{t_f} T\,dt = \int_0^{t_f} \dot{m}v\,dt = mv \tag{13.2}$$

where T is thrust, $\dot{m}$ is propellant flow rate, and m is total propellant mass expended during the mission.† It is clear that the higher the exhaust velocity, the less propellant mass used. Where the total mass of propellant is limited, as, for example, in extremely long missions ($\sim$ 1 year), the above considerations become critical.

Actually, from the above simple argument, one would suppose that the maximum possible specific impulse would be the most desirable. This is not the case. In fact, there is an optimum specific impulse for each vehicle and mission. This can be illustrated by considering the weight of the electric power supply needed to operate the electrical rocket. First, define the mass advantage γ of the electrical system over the chemical system as

$$m_{\text{elec}} + m_{ps} \equiv \gamma m_{\text{chem}} \tag{13.3}$$

† Equation (13.2) illustrates the alternate definition of specific impulse as $I_{\text{sp}} = T/\dot{m}$, where its units are those of velocity. If, however, the $\dot{m}$ is given in terms of weight flow rather than mass flow, then I_{sp} is again in units of time. For the purposes of this chapter I_{sp} will be defined as v/g as noted earlier.

where m_{ps} is the mass of the electric power supply, m_{chem} is the total mass of the chemical propellant, m_{elec} is the total mass of the electrical rocket propellant, and $\gamma < 1$. If the same mission is to be performed by both devices, then

$$I = m_{\text{chem}}v_{\text{chem}} = m_{\text{elec}}v_{\text{elec}} \tag{13.4}$$

or, using (13.3),

$$\frac{m_{ps}}{m_{\text{elec}}} = \gamma \frac{v_{\text{elec}}}{v_{\text{chem}}} - 1 \tag{13.5}$$

If the quantity α, the specific weight of the power supply, is defined as the ratio of m_{ps} to power-supply power level P, then

$$\alpha = \frac{m_{ps}}{P} \tag{13.6}$$

Assuming an electrical rocket with an efficiency η, we can write

$$\eta P = \tfrac{1}{2}\dot{m}_{\text{elec}}v_{\text{elec}}^2$$

so that

$$\frac{m_{ps}}{m_{\text{elec}}} = \frac{\frac{1}{2}\alpha\dot{m}_{\text{elec}}v_{\text{elec}}^2}{\eta m_{\text{elec}}} = \frac{\alpha v_{\text{elec}}^2}{2t_f\eta} \tag{13.7}$$

Substituting this into Eq. (13.5) yields an expression for γ:

$$\gamma = \frac{v_{\text{chem}}}{v_{\text{elec}}} + \frac{1}{2}\frac{\alpha}{t_f\eta}v_{\text{elec}}v_{\text{chem}} \tag{13.8}$$

Clearly there is some value of v_{elec} (or specific impulse) which makes γ a minimum. Taking $d\gamma/dv_{\text{elec}} = 0$, the above yields this optimum:

$$(v_{\text{elec}})_{\text{opt}} = \sqrt{\frac{2t_f\eta}{\alpha}} \tag{13.9}$$

According to this simple relation, the longer the mission, the higher the optimum specific impulse. Also, the heavier the power supply, the smaller the optimum value, so that one can anticipate that if the power supply is too heavy, the optimum I_{sp} will become so low that a chemical rocket can do the job with less total weight. Also note that the electrical rocket inefficiency can be absorbed directly in a larger power-supply specific weight. Assuming an α of 30 lb_m/kw, Eq. (13.9) shows that $(I_{\text{sp}})_{\text{opt}} \sim 4{,}000$ sec for lunar missions (100 days), and $\sim$12,000 sec for interplanetary missions (1,000 days). These values are surprisingly close to the results of more precise calculations.[2,3] Also, Eq. (13.8) shows that $\gamma \sim 0.20$ for the former and $\sim$0.07 for the latter, illustrating the anticipated superiority of the electrical propulsion system compared to the chemical system as far as payload mass is concerned. Finally, it can be seen that using Eq. (13.9), then Eq. (13.7) yields the interesting conclusion that the optimum condition for a mission is that the power supply and propellant masses be equal.

As a result of the above discussion, it should now be clear that in order for an electrical propulsion system to be useful for space missions, it must have a lightweight power supply (small α), and it must have an electrical rocket capable of efficient operation at impulse values in the range of 2,000 to 20,000 sec. It is because the magnetohydrodynamic propulsion unit offers the potential for efficient operation in this specific-impulse range that there is much current interest in it.[4,5]

In the remainder of this chapter a number of specific devices will be discussed in detail. No attempt will be made to classify them in any precise way. The first section will deal with crossed-field devices operating at sufficiently high pressures that the Hall effect is of secondary importance. These will generally be high-thrust-per-unit-area machines. Following this, related devices operating at lower pressures will be discussed, in which the Hall currents dominate. The subject of the basically unsteady pulsed accelerator with electrodes will be taken up next. Concluding the chapter will be a discussion of pulsed accelerators operating on induced currents (electrodeless). Compared to the crossed-field device, these others are all essentially low-thrust-per-unit-area machines. Compared to the ion rocket, however, they can all be considered as having a high thrust per unit area.

13.2 CROSSED-FIELD ACCELERATORS

As pointed out earlier, the specific impulse of an electrical rocket can be made to exceed that of a chemical rocket by the simple expedient of raising the propellant's total temperature before expansion through the nozzle. If the question of efficiency is considered, however, it is quickly seen that such a process cannot go on indefinitely. As a gas is heated to higher and higher temperatures, it dissociates and ionizes, and the energy invested in these modes will generally be lost in the subsequent frozen expansion, causing the entire process to be inefficient. In order to avoid this difficulty as higher specific impulses are sought, it would seem advisable to maintain a more modest static temperature and add additional energy directly into kinetic energy via the Lorentz force. This approach is common to all the devices considered in this chapter. In this section an accelerator in which mutually perpendicular applied electric and magnetic fields create the Lorentz force will be treated. As could have been anticipated, the principal questions will concern specific impulse and efficiency.

Since crossed-field devices have been described several times (i.e., Chaps. 10 and 11), there is no need to repeat these descriptions here. It should suffice to point out that for such a device to operate as an accelerator, the vector product of the current and magnetic field should lie in the flow direction. Basically, the device will operate with a relatively high-pressure compressible reacting plasma in supersonic flow. The induced magnetic field will be negligible, but the Hall effect may not, in which case segmented electrodes may be used.

Before discussing some of the theoretical and experimental studies that have been carried out, it would be of value to consider the questions of specific impulse and efficiency in the broad sense. In general, the accelerating capability of any crossed-field device will depend on the magnetic-interaction parameter based on its length, $I = \sigma_0 B_0^2 L/\rho_0 u_0$. It is obvious, then, that one way to obtain a very high I_{sp} in a short distance is to reduce the gas density. Doing this, however, will require the use of segmented electrodes to avoid the Hall current flow. Generally speaking, modest increases in I_{sp} can be achieved without the need to consider the Hall effect or use segmented electrodes, but it will have to be taken into account for higher I_{sp} values.

In regard to efficiency, the important problem is the losses. They may be enumerated as follows:

1. Thermal energy remaining in plasma stream at accelerator exit
2. Ionization and dissociation energy remaining in stream at accelerator exit
3. Heat and momentum transferred from main stream into accelerator walls

If regenerative cooling is used, some of item 3 may be recovered, and will not properly count as an energy loss. It will, in any event, degrade the performance of the crossed-field accelerator (i.e., require additional length to achieve some desired I_{sp}). End effects which can also degrade the performance will be neglected here. They are considered in some detail in Chap. 14.

As was seen in Chap. 11, a large number of solutions are possible to the quasi-one-dimensional equations, many of which can be utilized for crossed-field accelerators. Recalling the requirement to minimize frozen-flow losses, a logical choice would at least have $T =$ const. Following this reasoning, Wood[6] and Kerrebrock[7] have analyzed constant-temperature quasi-one-dimensional flows. The former also assumed constant area and constant magnetic field and included the Hall effect. The latter neglected the Hall effect, assumed constant electric field, and took the flow velocity proportional to a power of x. The per cent ionization was also assumed small; so the gas was assumed perfect. In order to illustrate the information available from these analyses, consider the illustrative example calculated by Kerrebrock. Assuming helium seeded with cesium at 3000°K, an initial B_z of 10,000 gauss, and an initial $\mathfrak{M}$ of unity, he calculated an $I_{sp} \cong 670$ sec for an accelerator length of

10 cm. As will be seen shortly, much higher specific impulses can be obtained at higher temperatures and percentages of seed material.

For the accelerator proposed by Wood,[6] $E_x \neq 0$ and E_y varies with x, since B_z is assumed constant and no Hall currents are permitted to flow. Here, segmented electrodes are essential. In the other calculation,[7] it was assumed that $u \propto x^n$, so that the channel cross-sectional area depends on the choice of n, being constant when $n = 0.25$. Regardless of the area variation for this second case, the distance between electrodes must be constant since E_y is assumed constant and continuous electrodes are used.

An alternative approach to the problem of accelerating a plasma in a crossed-field device without excessive increase of static temperature is to rapidly increase the flow area in the flow direction. This has the effect of converting the Joule heat into kinetic energy by the usual thermodynamic expansion process. Since the more rapid the channel expansion, the less valid the quasi-one-dimensional theory, Podolsky[8] and Sherman[9] have postulated a source-flow model of the accelerator. Such a model is shown in Fig. 13.1. Here it is assumed that a radial flow occurs in the presence of an azimuthal B field which varies in magnitude as r^{-1}. The electrodes are plane surfaces perpendicular to the source axis. The accelerator then can have any divergence angle θ, if it is assumed to be that portion of the source flow located between two radii. The geometry is shown in Fig. 13.2.

The equations governing this flow are Eqs. (8.23) to (8.26) written in cylindrical coordinates. For $\partial/\partial\theta = \partial/\partial z = 0$, the following system of equations are found.

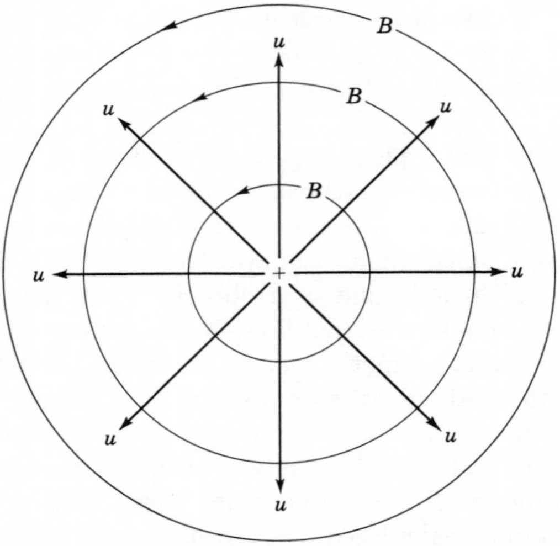

FIGURE 13.1 Source-flow model of crossed-field accelerator.

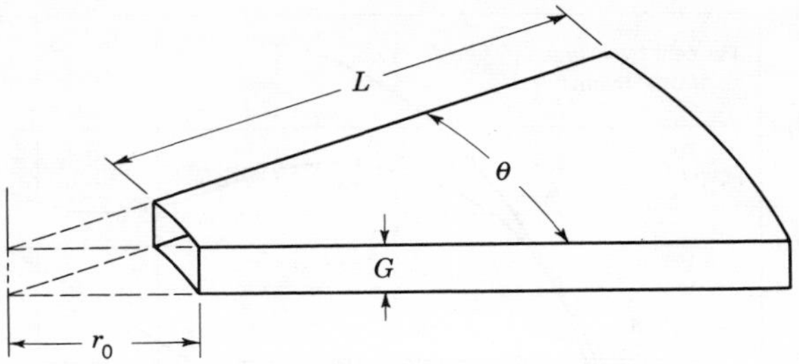

FIGURE 13.2 Accelerator duct geometry.

Equation of motion:

$$\rho u \frac{du}{dr} = -\frac{dp}{dr} + \frac{\sigma' B_0 r_0}{r}\left(E_0 - \frac{u r_0 B_0}{r}\right) \tag{13.10}$$

Conservation of energy:

$$\rho u \frac{de}{dr} = -\frac{p}{r}\frac{d}{dr}(ru) + \left(\sigma' E_0 - \frac{u r_0 B_0}{r}\right)^2 \tag{13.11}$$

Mass conservation: $$\rho u r = \rho_0 u_0 r_0 \tag{13.12}$$

where $$\sigma' = \frac{\sigma}{1 + (\sigma\beta B)^2} \qquad \sigma\beta B = \omega\tau$$

and the subscript zero denotes conditions at the accelerator entrance.

The plasma can be assumed to be a perfect gas, or, if desired, property variations can be included.[8,9] Also, one can assume the electrodes segmented and thereby neglect $\omega\tau$,[8] or they can be assumed solid so that $\omega\tau$ is calculated during the course of the solution and σ' used.[9] In the former case, calculations have been made for pure lithium vapor at low pressures ($p_i^0 \sim 1$ mm Hg), and it has been shown that I_{sp} values in the range of 5,000 to 6,000 sec should be possible over reasonable accelerator lengths. For the latter analysis, in which solid electrodes were assumed, calculations have been carried out under the following conditions:

$$\begin{aligned} r_0 &= 1 \text{ cm} & \mathfrak{M}_0 &= 1.5 \\ B_0 &= 11{,}000 \text{ gauss} & K &= 1.5 \\ p^0 &= 0.233 \text{ atm} & & \\ T^0 &= 5000^\circ\text{K} & & \end{aligned}$$

for various mixtures of lithium and helium. Some typical results for pure lithium are shown in Fig. 13.3. It should be noted that provision was made in the calculation to assume that either the flow was in a shifting ionization equilibrium or the ionization was frozen. The essential feature shown in these calculations is that even for frozen flow an $I_{sp} \sim 2{,}200$ sec is possible, along with an efficiency greater than 70 per cent, and the accelerator is only 8 cm long. Even better perform-

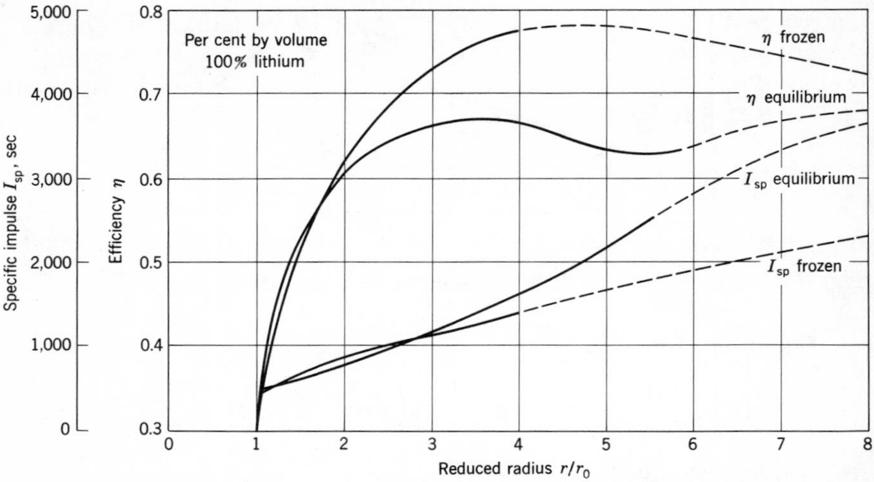

FIGURE 13.3 Crossed-field accelerator specific impulse and efficiency.

ance would have been calculated had the electrodes been assumed segmented.

So far it has been shown both by the quasi-one-dimensional analysis and the source-flow model that higher specific impulses than are possible with plasma jets should be possible without excessive thermal, dissociation, or ionization losses. The question of thermal losses into the channel walls has not yet been considered, and will be taken up next.

In Chap. 12 an analysis of a compressible magnetohydrodynamic boundary layer was described for which the free-stream velocity varied as x^n. If the results of this analysis are applied to the crossed-field accelerator, some estimates of the heat loss to the wall can be made. In particular, when $n = 0.25$, the following relation was derived for $\mathfrak{M} < 2.5$:

$$\frac{N_u}{\sqrt{R_e}} \cong 5 \tag{13.13}$$

where $P_R = 1$ was assumed, and the Nusselt number was defined as

$$N_u \equiv -\frac{q_w x}{\mathcal{K}_\infty(T_\infty - T_w)} \tag{13.14}$$

where $(\ )_\infty$ denotes some reference point in the free stream, so that the lower the flow Reynolds number, the lower the magnitude of the heat flux. Since such fluxes can be of the order of magnitude of several kilowatts per square centimeter, the practical problem of finding a way to remove so much heat may make it necessary to reduce the flux by lowering the Reynolds number or the temperature difference $T_\infty - T_w$ or both. As far as the accelerator efficiency is concerned, however, it will be shown that high Reynolds numbers would be desirable. Define an efficiency as the ratio of the exhaust kinetic energy to the exhaust total enthalpy plus heat losses along the way. Then

$$\eta' = \frac{\frac{1}{2}\rho_e v_e^3 A_e}{\rho_e v_e A_e(\frac{1}{2}v_e^2 + C_p T_e) + q_w LC} \tag{13.15}$$

If q_w is taken from Eq. (13.14) with N_u given by Eq. (13.13), the above expression for efficiency can be rewritten as

$$\eta' = \left\{1 + \frac{2}{(\gamma - 1)\mathfrak{M}_e^2}\left[1 + \frac{60(1 - T_w/T_\infty)\sqrt{v_0/v_e}}{R_e^{\frac{1}{5}}}\right]\right\}^{-1} \tag{13.16}$$

where the Reynolds number is based on the exit velocity and channel width, and v_0 is a reference velocity near the accelerator entrance. It was also assumed that the channel was square, so that $A_e = w^2$, and C (the circumference) $= 4w$. Since $q_w \propto 1/x$ in Eq. (13.14), an average length of $L/3$ was used. The variation of ρ along the channel was neglected, and the reference length x_0 was assumed equal to w.

Qualitatively then, the accelerator efficiency will be maximized when $\mathfrak{M}_e$ and R_e are as large as possible. It is also desirable to have $T_w \sim T_\infty$ and $v_e \gg v_0$, as one might have expected. Strictly speaking, the above relation applies only to the special case considered by Kerrebrock (Chap. 12). Nonetheless, the Mach number and Reynolds number dependencies should be valid for any crossed-field accelerator of this type.

Before concluding the discussion of the theoretical aspects of the crossed-field accelerator, the result of some quantitative calculations of heat loss[10] will be mentioned. Making use of the example just described, with argon seeded with potassium, with $T_w = 1500°K$ and $T_\infty = 3000°K$, integration of the heat flux over the channel length leads to a heat loss of 3.26 kw/electrode. Then, in hopes of reducing the heat flux as well as the leaving thermal losses noted earlier, the possibility of operation in a nonequilibrium mode can be considered. In this case Joule heating in the low-temperature layer near the wall is substantially reduced since the electron temperature can be quite high in this region. The principal heat flux then occurs by virtue of the electron flux in the presence of a temperature gradient. For the same case cited above, the heat flux is calculated to be[10]

$$q_{\text{anode}} = 0.972 \text{ kw} \qquad q_{\text{cathode}} = 0.065 \text{ kw}$$

where $(T_e)_\infty = 3500°K$ and $T_\infty = 1746°K$ while $T_w = 1500°K$. As can be seen, the total heat flux is considerably reduced, and the asymmetry due to the direction of electron flux is apparent. Although the above

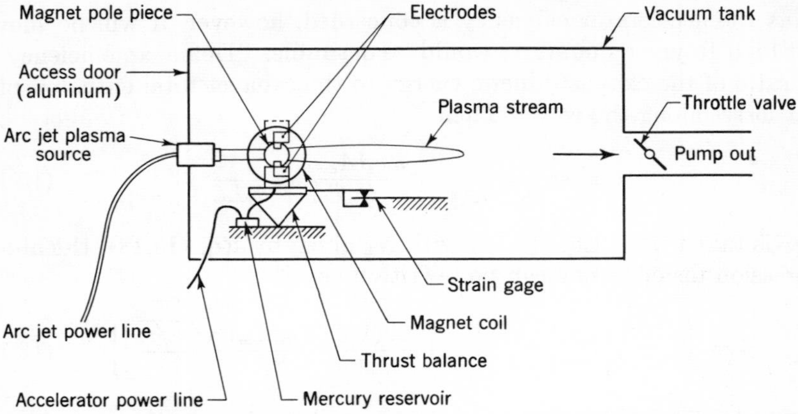

FIGURE 13.4 Experimental apparatus for crossed-field accelerator experiments. (After Demetriades and Ziemer.[13])

analysis is certainly quite preliminary and involves many assumptions, the trend of the results seems to be in the correct direction. Finally, it should be noted that operating under nonequilibrium conditions should not reduce frozen-flow losses but only thermal leaving losses, and perhaps heat flux.

Turning now to the experimental verification of the above developments, only very preliminary results are presently available. It will be of interest, however, to review work currently in progress. Perhaps the first experimental crossed-field accelerator was built by Carter and Wood.[11] The device they conceived is designed according to the constant T, E, and A analysis mentioned earlier, and so has segmented electrodes. A flow of 2.6 g/sec of nitrogen seeded with cesium is heated to a total temperature of 6900°K before entering the 1-cm^2 channel at $\mathfrak{M} = 2$. With the use of a 12,000-gauss magnet, preliminary experiments have demonstrated the feasibility of the concept, but have not yielded any detailed measurements. More recently, Hogan[12] in a shock-tube experiment demonstrated a twofold increase in specific impulse in a crossed-field device. In this experiment, a $1\frac{1}{2}$-in.-diameter combustion-driven shock tube heats pure argon to 12,000°K at 1 atm while accelerating it to $\mathfrak{M} = 2$. Under these conditions, $\sigma \sim 4{,}500$ mhos/m, and the interaction parameter I is sufficiently large to create a sizable influence on the flow. Starting with an $I_{sp} \sim 500$ sec, Hogan measures an $I_{sp} \sim 1{,}000$ sec after acceleration by the use of a magnetic field of 1,500 gauss. He also estimates $\eta \cong 50$ per cent. Although these results are encouraging, the specific impulse is still too low. Since these experiments were run at relatively high pressures, $\omega\tau$ was small enough to be neglected, and electron heating did not occur.

Most recently, some continuous experiments have been carried out by Demetriades,[13] in which a crossed-field accelerator was operated on unseeded argon but at lower pressures and temperatures than used by Hogan. In this case, the Hall effect must be considered, and non-equilibrium ionization of the plasma is a real possibility. A diagram of the experimental apparatus is shown in Fig. 13.4. In this arrangement the arc jet exhausts into the vacuum tank, and the crossed-field accelerator acts on the jet itself. The entire accelerator assembly is balanced on a thrust stand, and thrust is measured directly by means of strain gauges. Some typical experimental data are reproduced in Fig. 13.5. The drop-off in thrust with B can be generally attributed to the Hall reduction in crosswise current occurring when solid electrodes are used and $\omega\tau > 1$. For the above data a maximum specific impulse of 660 sec (counting the 400 sec available initially from the arc jet) is obtained at an efficiency of 42 per cent. Specific impulses as high as 1,400 sec have also been reported, presumably at similarly high efficiencies. Complete data on this device which demonstrates $I_{sp} \sim 2{,}000$ sec at high efficiencies are not available as yet.

In summary, then, theoretical calculations indicate that the crossed-field accelerator should operate in the I_{sp} range over 1,500 sec with reasonable efficiencies. It is unlikely that efficient operation will be

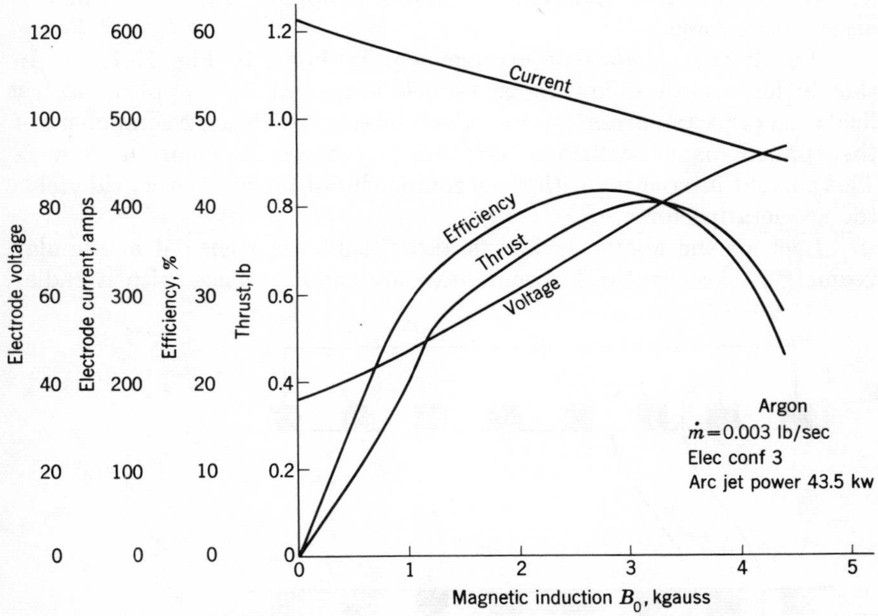

FIGURE 13.5 Typical performance of a crossed-field accelerator. (After Demetriades and Ziemer.[13])

possible for $I_{sp} \geqq 4{,}000$ sec. To date, experimental verification has been achieved of the basic feasibility of such devices, but detailed demonstration of both high I_{sp} and η for long periods of time has not yet been accomplished.

13.3 HALL CURRENT ACCELERATOR

As was shown in the preceding section, there is a general desire to increase the magnetic field and lower the density, in order to create larger values of I, the interaction parameter. This, of course, raises $\omega\tau$ to quite high values, and the question must be raised as to whether or not there may be other accelerator geometries more suitable for high $\omega\tau$ operation. Two configurations which have been suggested, and which we will call *Hall current accelerators,* will be discussed here.

Both devices, in their two-dimensional configuration, use segmented electrodes in this case to encourage the flow of Hall currents rather than suppress them. In these devices it is the Lorentz force due to the Hall currents that does the accelerating. The first device is shown in Fig. 13.6.[5] Here a voltage is applied between electrodes at the channel inlet and outlet. The resulting current flow interacting with the transverse B field induces a Hall current to flow across the channel. Short-circuiting each pair of opposing electrodes allows this current to flow unimpeded. Interaction between this Hall current and the applied B field yields the accelerating force.

An alternate geometric arrangement is shown in Fig. 13.7.[5,14] In this device now an oblique magnetic field is applied. An applied electric field then causes a current to flow, which interacts with the x component of the applied magnetic field to create a transverse Hall current flow j_z. This current interacting with the y component of the magnetic field yields the accelerating force.

Each of the above devices is also feasible in a coaxial or annular geometry. Accelerator I would have an annular space with a radial

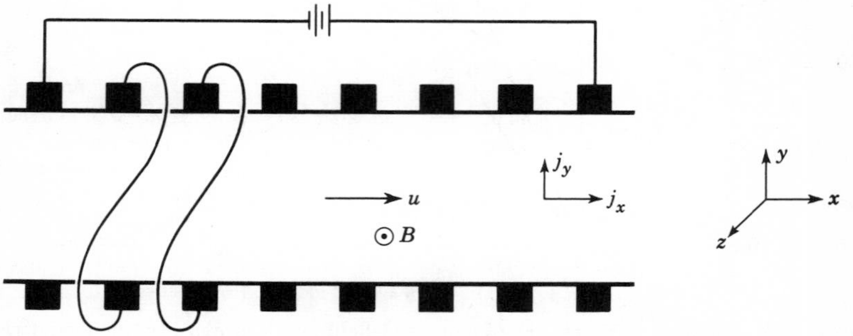

FIGURE 13.6 Hall current accelerator I.

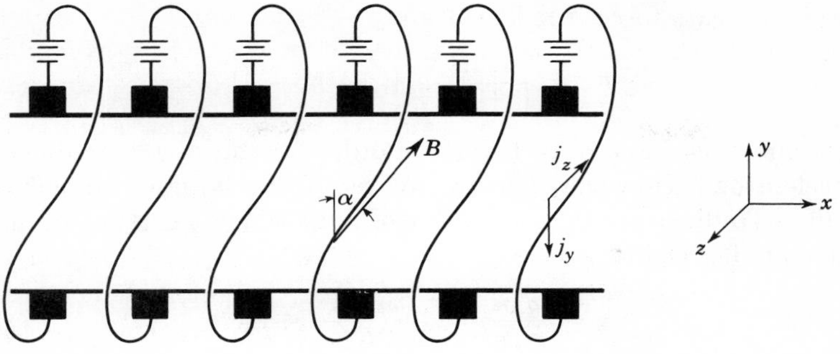

FIGURE 13.7 Hall current accelerator II.

magnetic field. Applying a longitudinal electric field would now cause an azimuthal Hall current which would, as before, interact with the radial magnetic field to yield the accelerating force. In accelerator II the inner and outer walls of the annulus would be composed of concentric rings, between which an applied electric field would be applied. In fact, this geometry is generated if the channel of Fig. 13.7 is rotated about an axis parallel to the flow and below the channel. The mode of operation is precisely as before. The advantage of the annular geometry lies principally with accelerator I where, by this device, the multitude of short-circuited electrodes is avoided.

For simplicity, a brief analysis of each of the above accelerators will be given, when the flow velocity is assumed to be uniform, for the two-dimensional configurations (small crossflows will be neglected). Expanding the generalized Ohm law [Eq. (8.26)] into its three components yields

$$j_x = \sigma_0[E_x + vB_z - wB_y - \beta(j_yB_z - j_zB_y)] \tag{13.17}$$
$$j_y = \sigma_0[E_y + wB_x - uB_z - \beta(j_zB_x - j_xB_z)] \tag{13.18}$$
$$j_z = \sigma_0[E_z + uB_y - vB_x - \beta(j_xB_y - j_yB_x)] \tag{13.19}$$

For accelerator I, however, $j_z = B_x = B_y = E_z = v = w = 0$. Thus,

$$j_x = \frac{\sigma_0}{1 + (\omega\tau)^2}[E_x - \omega\tau(E_y - uB_z)] \tag{13.20}$$

$$j_y = \frac{\sigma_0}{1 + (\omega\tau)^2}(E_y - uB_z + \omega\tau E_x) \tag{13.21}$$

Or defining $E_x = K\omega\tau uB_z$, these become

$$j_x = \frac{\sigma_0 uB_z(\omega\tau)}{1 + (\omega\tau)^2}(1 + K) \tag{13.22}$$

$$j_y = \frac{\sigma_0 uB_z}{1 + (\omega\tau)^2}[(\omega\tau)^2K - 1] \tag{13.23}$$

Then the Lorentz force, $\mathbf{j} \times \mathbf{B}$, is simply

$$F_x = \frac{\sigma_0 u B_z^2}{1 + (\omega\tau)^2} [(\omega\tau)^2 K - 1] \tag{13.24}$$

Clearly one must have $K > 1/(\omega\tau)^2$ in order for this device to operate as an accelerator. However, one cannot set K too large or the efficiency will fall. To illustrate this, the value of K at which η is a maximum will be calculated. Define η as

$$\eta = \frac{F_x u}{E_x j_x} = \frac{(\omega\tau)^2 K - 1}{(\omega\tau)^2 K(1 + K)} \tag{13.25}$$

Differentiating and setting equal to zero yield

$$K_{\text{opt}} = \frac{1 + \sqrt{1 + (\omega\tau)^2}}{(\omega\tau)^2} \tag{13.26}$$

When $\omega\tau$ becomes very large, $K_{\text{opt}} \rightarrow (\omega\tau)^{-1}$ and $\eta \rightarrow (1 + 2/\omega\tau)^{-1}$. Also the axial force $F_x \rightarrow \sigma_0 u B_z^2/\omega\tau$. If desired, this can be compared to the axial force in a crossed-field device with high $\omega\tau$ and segmented electrodes. For this case, $F_{x_1} = \sigma u B^2(K_1 - 1)$, where now $K_1 \equiv E_y/uB$, and the efficiency is $\eta = K_1^{-1}$. For the same efficiency in each accelerator, we find $F_{x_1} = 2\sigma u B^2/\omega\tau$, which is double the value for the Hall accelerator. At first glance it would seem that the crossed-field device is twice as effective as the Hall accelerator I. That this is not necessarily true can be seen by considering Eqs. (13.24) and (13.25) again. As shown in Fig. 13.8, the efficiency does not drop off very rapidly at all for $K > K_{\text{opt}}$. Thus, let us consider an example for which $\omega\tau = 10$ and $K = 0.2$. In this case $\eta \cong 79$ per cent as contrasted to 83 per cent when $K = 0.1$. However, now $F_x = 0.19\sigma_0 u B_z^2$. For the crossed-field accelerator with $\eta = 79$ per cent, the axial force is now $F_{x_1} = 0.26\sigma_0 u B_z^2$, so that apparent disadvantage is greatly reduced.

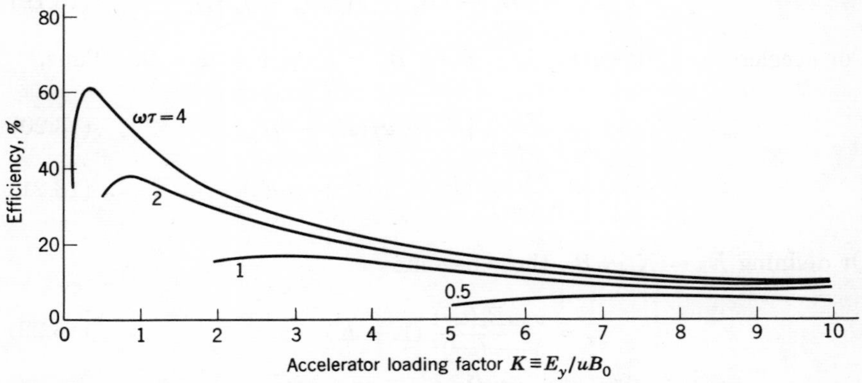

FIGURE 13.8 Hall accelerator I efficiency versus loading factor.

In general then, the Hall accelerator I will be comparable in performance to the crossed-field device at large $\omega\tau$ values. Despite this and the fact that a single power supply may be used, this device has been relatively little explored to date.

Consideration will now be given to the second type of Hall accelerator illustrated in Fig. 13.7. For this case it will be assumed that $j_x = B_z = E_z = v = w = 0$, so that the current relations yield

$$j_y = -\frac{\sigma u B \cos\alpha[K_2 + (\omega\tau)^2 \sin^2\alpha]}{[1 + (\omega\tau)^2 \sin^2\alpha](\omega\tau \sin\alpha)} \tag{13.27}$$

$$j_z = -\frac{\sigma u B \cos\alpha(K_2 - 1)}{1 + (\omega\tau)^2 \sin^2\alpha} \tag{13.28}$$

where
$$K_2 = \frac{-\omega\tau E_y \sin\alpha}{uB\cos\alpha}$$

and B denotes the magnitude of $\mathbf{B}$. The axial propulsive force is $F_x = -j_z B_y = -j_z B \cos\alpha$, so that we must require $K_2 > 1$ in order for the device to function as an accelerator.

Without going into any more detailed analysis, some of the operating characteristics of this device can be deduced. First, if $\alpha = 0$, nothing occurs other than Joule heating of the plasma, since $\mathbf{j} \times \mathbf{B} = 0$. Alternatively, when $\alpha = 90°$, both an azimuthal and a radial current will flow again, resulting in Joule heating. If the coaxial geometry is employed, a rotational flow will be induced, and if $\omega\tau \gg 1$, most of the energy will appear as rotational kinetic energy. This rotational kinetic energy can, perhaps, be converted into directed kinetic energy.

When $j_x = 0$ as has been assumed, the efficiency of the above device can be shown to be comparable to the crossed-field device.[14,26] If, however, segmented electrodes are not used, $E_x = 0$, and the device's performance will be quite poor.[5]

13.4 PULSED ACCELERATORS USING ELECTRODES

For the remainder of this chapter the discussion will be devoted to accelerators which operate in an unsteady fashion. Generally speaking, the basic advantage of an unsteady device is that a plasma of very high energy or temperature can be created and handled without any severe wall-erosion problem so that efficiencies can be kept high. In other words, the thermal lag of the accelerator and the short time of plasma contact with it combine to keep the material surface temperatures low.

Attention will be devoted in this section to those pulsed accelerators which use electrodes to bring current into and out of the plasma. The related device which operates inductively without electrodes will be treated next.

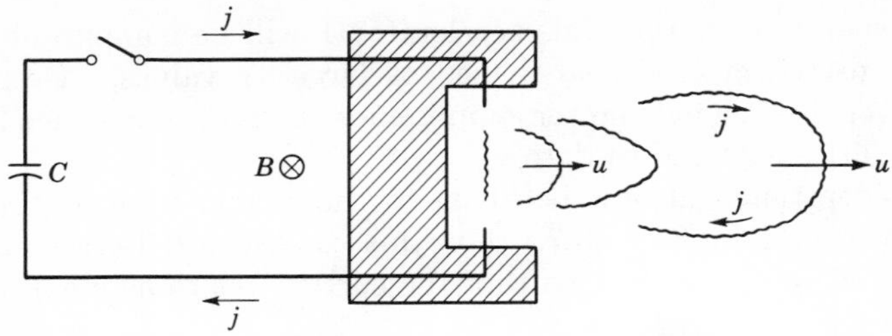

FIGURE 13.9 Schematic diagram of a pulsed accelerator with electrodes.

The basic mode of operation of the pulsed accelerator with electrodes is best illustrated by the sketch shown in Fig. 13.9. When the switch is closed, a very high voltage is applied to the gas between the electrodes. An arc then forms, creating a plasma and discharging the capacitor. As the current flows, a strong magnetic field B is generated, and the plasma is blown away from the electrodes by the Lorentz force, owing to the current in the arc. With sufficiently large current flows, the plasma ejected can reach very high velocities.

Since the plasma in a device such as this is essentially unconfined, much of the energy imparted to it appears as radial motion. In addition, the Lorentz force is applied for only a very short time since the arc column quickly grows in length and detaches from the electrodes. For these two reasons the efficiency of the simple device is quite poor.

One approach taken to improve the efficiency of such a device was to confine the arc within a T-tube geometry[15] such as shown in Fig. 13.10*a*. Also, in order to get the largest Lorentz force, the current return lead from the capacitor was passed close to the region of the initial discharge. Although originally conceived as a device to generate high velocities alone, it has achieved efficiencies in the 5 to 10 per cent range when operated as a propulsion device.[16]

An alternative approach to a higher-efficiency device is the rail accelerator shown in Fig. 13.10*b*. Here rails help carry the current to the arc as it accelerates, so that the propulsive force acts on the plasma for a longer time. Despite this, experiments with such devices have yielded very low efficiencies since the plasma is still relatively unconfined.

A logical combination of the above two approaches should, however, yield an efficient device. Such in fact has been found to be the case. The first device combining both these features, rails and confinement, was built by Marshall.[17] Basically, this device consists of a pair of concentric rails whereby the confinement is accomplished between the two cylindrical electrodes. Schematically it is shown in Fig. 13.11. Experiments carried out on this and related devices have shown that specific impulses in the range of 5,000 to 25,000 sec are possible with efficiencies

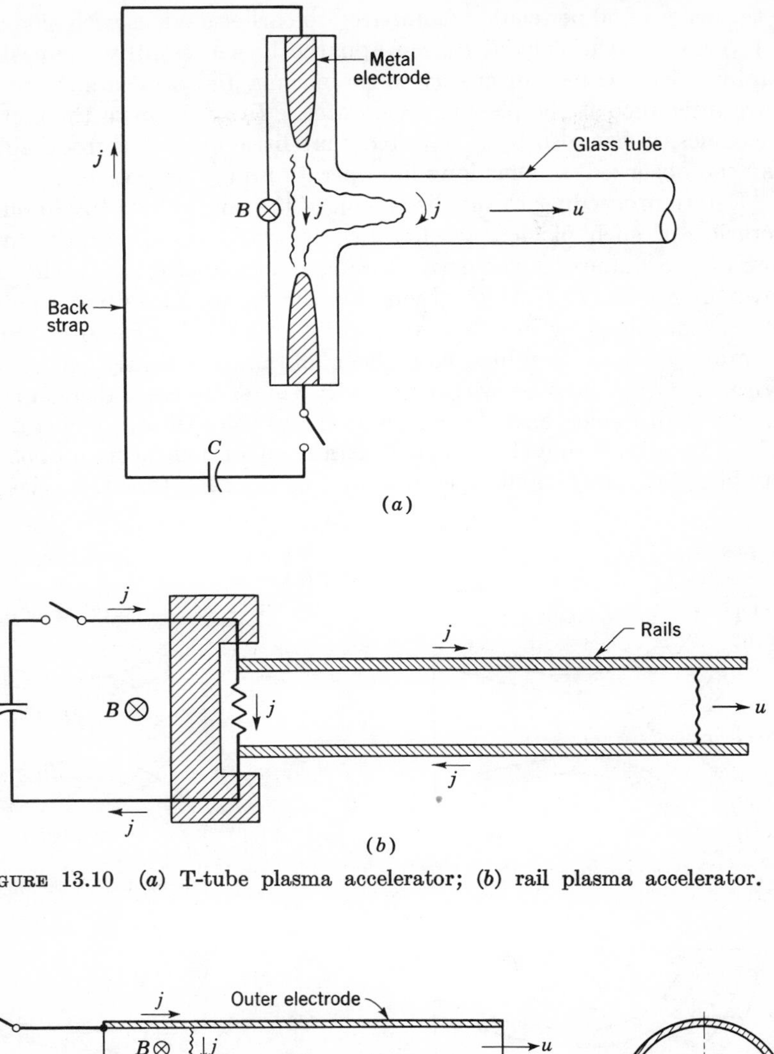

FIGURE 13.10 (a) T-tube plasma accelerator; (b) rail plasma accelerator.

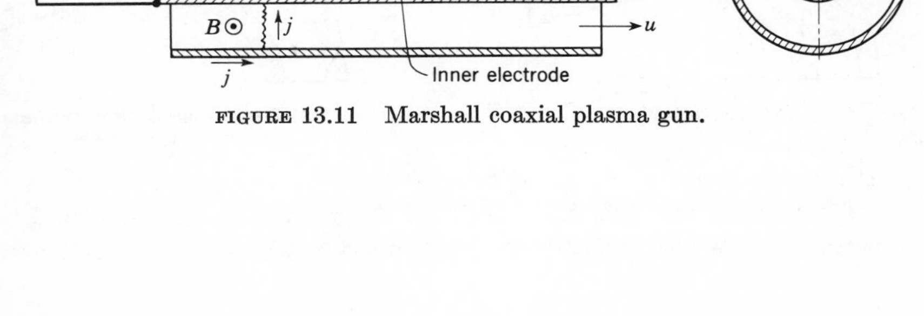

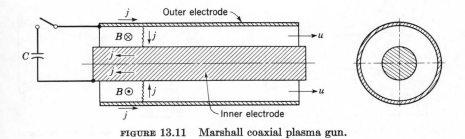

FIGURE 13.11 Marshall coaxial plasma gun.

on the order of 50 per cent. Compared to earlier devices with efficiencies of 1 per cent, the coaxial device apparently successfully increases the coupling of the capacitor energy to the plasma and prevents the increase in arc resistance as the plasma accelerates. In addition to the increased efficiencies, it has also been reported that little or no electrode ablation has been observed, so that long life operation may be possible.

Before proceeding to the discussion of the continuous (rapid pulsing) operation of such plasma accelerators, it would be of interest to note some of the numerous geometric arrangements analogous to the device shown in Fig. 13.11. Most obvious is the simple two-dimensional rail system contained within an appropriate channel structure. Similar favorable I_{sp} and η values have been obtained recently with such a device.[18] Other devices with essentially the same coaxial geometry as the Marshall device have been operated by AVCO[19] and General Electric.[20] Finally, a novel geometric arrangement has been proposed by Republic Aviation,[21] and is shown in Fig. 13.12. If this device were

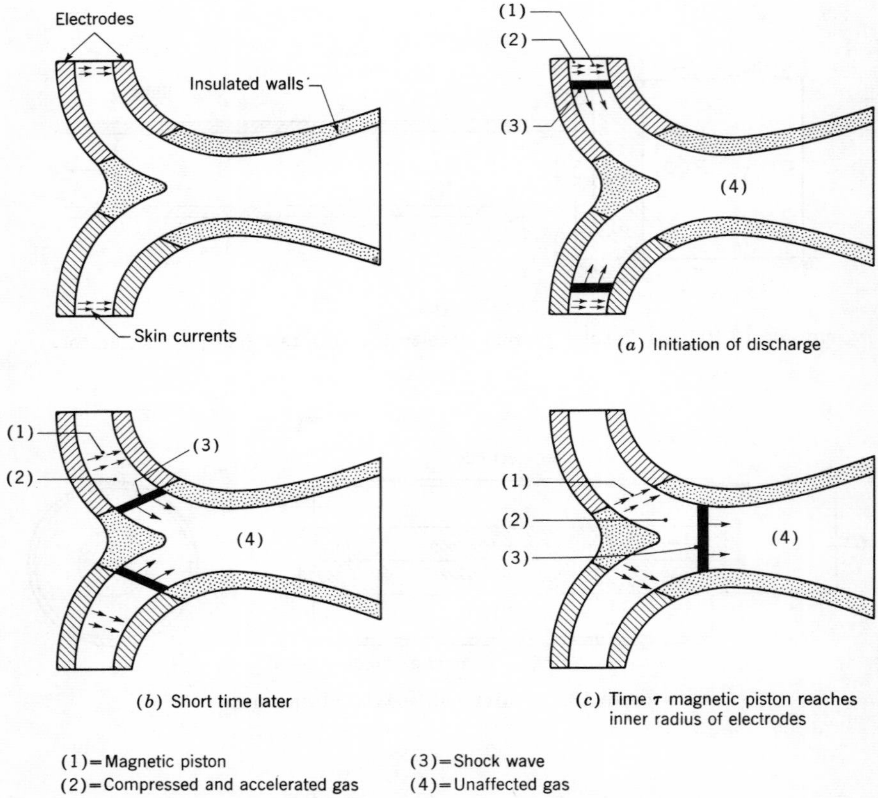

FIGURE 13.12 Pulsed pinch plasma accelerator.

two-dimensional, it would be, essentially, a shaped rail system followed by an aerodynamic nozzle. In this way reasonably good confinement is obtained and, in addition, some of the plasma thermal energy can be converted to axial kinetic energy by the nozzle.

So far no distinction has been drawn between the mode of operation in which the gas is admitted in a pulse and the high voltage breaks it down, and the mode in which the gas flows in continuously and is broken down by a pulsed electric field. The distinction is essential, however, if the pulsed electrodeless accelerator is to be used for continuous operation as a space propulsion device. In general, the weight of the capacitors needed for a given size of engine will be minimized if a high pulsing rate is possible. This is due to the fact that the stored energy per pulse required is less, the more pulses per second; and the greater the stored energy, the heavier the capacitor. Now, when the gas flow is continuous, a high-power fast-acting switch is needed, and there is some question as to whether such a switch would be reliable over extended periods of time. An alternative approach would be to pulse the gas in and maintain a constant applied voltage. The problem that arises here is that the low-pressure gas at the front of the gas pulse tends to break down first, and the magnetohydrodynamic interaction is poor. One of perhaps several solutions is to use a two-stage device.[22] Here a low-power switch triggers a small T tube which then discharges into a larger coaxial accelerator, across which is placed the main power supply. The partially ionized plasma entering the second stage has a sharp pressure front, so that the breakdown is favorable to good accelerating action. Using this device, a life test of 60 hr with a pulsing rate of 1,000 per min was achieved. For this particular test, a thrust of 0.02 lb, an I_{sp} of 9,000 sec, and an η of 52 per cent were reported.[22]

Clearly, then, the pulsed magnetohydrodynamic accelerator employing electrodes seems capable of long-time operation at high specific impulses and efficiency. It is yet to be demonstrated that they can operate well in the 2,000- to 4,000-sec range also. If this can be shown, however, they may provide the interesting possibility of a *single* engine capable of operation over a wide range of I_{sp}.

13.5 ELECTRODELESS ACCELERATORS

In this final section of the chapter, the type of pulsed accelerator which operates inductively will be discussed. The principle of operation can be readily illustrated in terms of the single-pulse mode of operation. Consider a tube filled with ionized gas, open at one end, and with a single-turn coil around the closed end, as shown in Fig. 13.13. When the switch is closed, discharging the capacitor, a rapidly time-varying magnetic field is generated. This, in turn, creates an azimuthal electric field, and

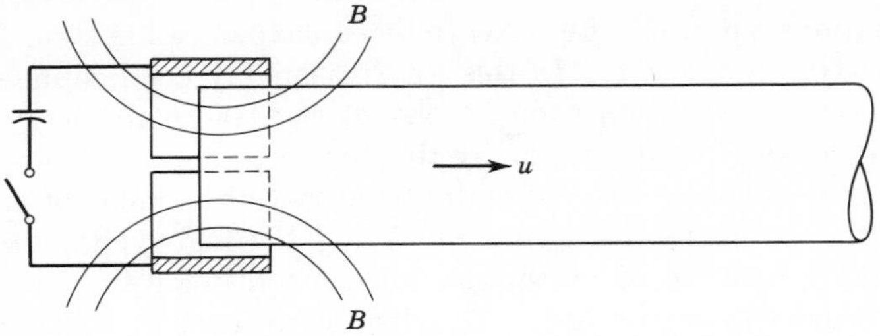

FIGURE 13.13 Single-pulse electrodeless accelerator.

since the plasma is a conductor, an azimuthal current flows. The interaction of this *induced* current and the radial component of the magnetic field present results in a Lorentz force in the axial direction. In the event that the plasma is a poor conductor, the fraction of energy input which goes into work by the Lorentz force will be small compared to energy input into Joule heating of the coil. One measure of the efficiency capability of such a device will then be the magnetic Reynolds number, since in general this parameter describes the coupling between the applied magnetic field and the induced current.

So far nothing has been said concerning the method for initially ionizing the plasma. Most investigators have actually started with initially cool gas and used the single-turn coil to break down the gas as well as provide the accelerating action just described. This technique of ionizing a gas is an old one known as the *ring discharge*. In simplest terms, the azimuthal electric field is made strong enough to create a discharge in the gas. Since this field is at a maximum near the wall, the discharge initiates there and the resulting current sheet is driven inward toward the tube axis.[23] As can be seen, when the ring discharge is used to establish the conductivity, the acceleration process is extremely complicated, and because of this, principally experimental analyses have been carried out.

One of the more extensive studies has been carried out by Miller,[23] whose measurements can be interpreted in terms of specific impulse and efficiency. Measurements of I_{sp} up to $\sim$1,700 sec were made. The measured overall efficiencies were on the order of 1 to 2 per cent, and can be explained as follows. It was found that of the initial stored energy in the capacitors, only one-third reached the field. Of this amount only 5 to 10 per cent was successfully transferred to the plasma. Finally, the total energy of the plasma stream was apparently evenly split between thermal and kinetic energies. Clearly, poor coupling between the magnetic field and the plasma accounts for a major energy loss. Actually there is no reason to assume that using a ring discharge in this device would be more efficient than preionizing and then activating the coil. In fact, it would seem that preionizing the plasma so that σ is high initially should lead to a more efficient coupling. Carrying this concept further, experiments have been conducted in which the preionization is provided by an RF coil and the single drive coil is operated with 10 kc alternating current.[24] With the drive coil operating this way, the accelerator operated in a quasi-steady fashion, and some plasma acceleration was measured.

In addition to the possibility of operating the single coil on alternating current, one can also build an accelerator tube with a number of coils. If the coils are then fired in succession with the proper timing, the plasma pulse should receive several accelerations before being ejected. In this way it may be possible to achieve higher specific impulses at a corresponding higher efficiency.

A logical extension of this idea would be to operate each coil on alternating current, again with the proper timing. This then brings us to the consideration of the traveling-wave concept of the electrodeless accelerator. A number of investigators have studied the traveling-wave accelerator from several points of view. Basically, they are all manifestations of the simple arrangement shown in Fig. 13.14. The mode of operation is as follows: At $t = 0$, a step function of voltage is applied, and a current pulse begins to travel down the helical transmission coil. When it reaches position 1, it accelerates plasma in the downstream direction. As the plasma reaches position 2, the first current pulse arrives there and gives it a second push. At about this time another current pulse arrives at position 1 again, and the process is repeated. Preliminary experiments with a device similar to that described have demonstrated that an interaction can be achieved, but efficiency and specific impulse are still low:[25] $I_{sp} \cong 1{,}000$ sec, $\cong 1$ per cent. If the coils are spaced more closely than shown in Fig. 13.14 and the plasma pressure is low enough so that it is collisionless, then one has, effectively, a series of magnetic bottles such as shown in Fig. 13.15. Such a device is still only in the conceptual stage.[19]

It should also be noted that if the current is reversed in every other coil, then one can create what is essentially a traveling-wave machine which behaves as though a series of cusps rather than magnetic mirrors

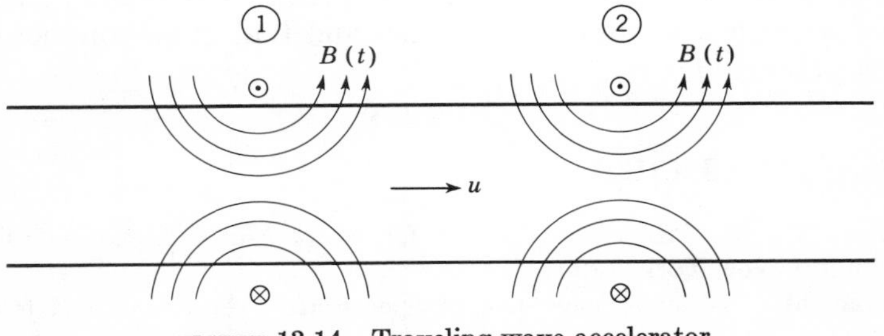

FIGURE 13.14 Traveling-wave accelerator.

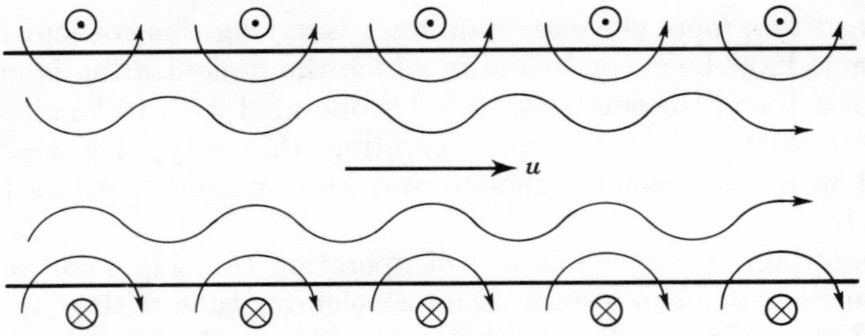

FIGURE 13.15 Traveling-wave accelerator with magnetic confinement.

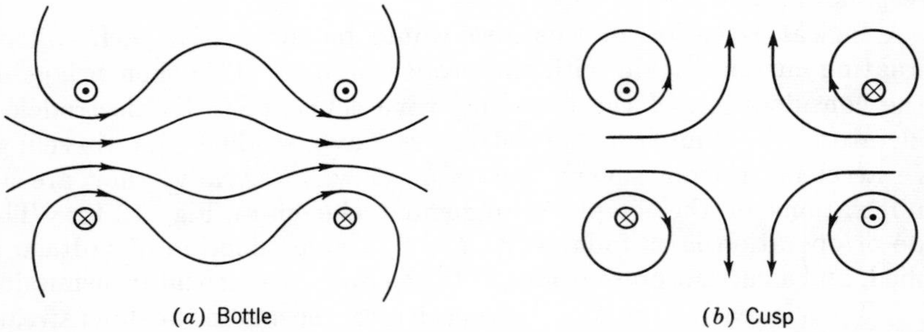

FIGURE 13.16 Comparison of (a) magnetic bottle and (b) cusp field configurations.

were traveling in the flow direction. The cusp geometry has been proposed for thermonuclear fusion work in which the stability of confinement is the essential problem. Whether or not a similar approach is necessary or desirable for a plasma propulsion device is not as yet clear.

As noted earlier, the successful operation of all such devices will depend on effective coupling between the applied magnetic field and the plasma. The ideal situation would involve zero slip between the magnetic field lines and the plasma. In other words, one would want $R_m \to \infty$. Practically speaking, such a condition will be difficult to obtain in a basically low-temperature and low-conductivity plasma. For solid copper wires with their very high electrical conductivity, it is well known that such a condition can be met and that induction motors are indeed a practical reality.

REFERENCES CITED

1. Corliss, W. R.: *Propulsion Systems for Space Flight,* McGraw-Hill Book Company, New York, 1960.
2. Camac, M.: "Plasma Propulsion of Spacecraft," *Astronautics,* **4** (October, 1959).

3. Demetriades, S. T.: "Plasma Propulsion: part I," *Astronautics,* **7** (March, 1962).
4. Gourdine, M. C.: "Recent Advances in Magnetohydrodynamic Propulsion," *ARS J.*, **31**:1670 (1961).
5. Sutton, G. W., and P. Gloersen: "Magnetohydrodynamic Power and Propulsion," published in *Magnetohydrodynamics;* A. B. Cambel, T. P. Anderson, and M. M. Slawsky (eds.), *Proc. 4th Biennial Gas Dynamics Symp.*, Northwestern University, Evanston, Ill., 1962.
6. Wood, G. P., A. F. Carter, H. K. Lintz, and J. B. Pennington: "A Theoretical Treatment of the Steady Flow, Linear, Crossed Field, Direct Current Plasma Accelerator for Inviscid, Adiabatic, Isothermal, Constant Area Flow," *NASA Tech. Rept.* R-114, 1961.
7. Kerrebrock, J., and F. E. Marble: "Constant Temperature Magnetogasdynamic Channel Flow," *J. Aerospace Sci.*, January, 1960.
8. Podolsky, B., and G. Borman: In S. W. Kash (ed.), *Plasma Acceleration,* Stanford University Press, Stanford, Calif., 1960.
9. Sherman, A.: "Theoretical Performance of a Crossed Field MHD Accelerator," *ARS J.*, **32**:414 (1962).
10. Oates, G. C., J. K. Richmond, Y. Aoki, and G. Grohs: "Loss Mechanisms of a Low Temperature Plasma Accelerator," published in *Magnetohydrodynamics;* A. B. Cambel, T. P. Anderson, and M. M. Slawsky (eds.), *Proc. 4th Biennial Gas Dynamics Symp.*, Northwestern University, Evanston, Ill., 1962.
11. Wood, G. P., A. F. Carter, A. P. Sabol, and R. H. Weinstein: "Experiments in Steady State Crossed Field Acceleration of Plasmas," *Phys. Fluids,* **4**:652 (1961).
12. Hogan, W. T.: "Experiments with a Transient D. C. Crossed Field Accelerator at High Power Levels," in N. W. Mather and G. W. Sutton (eds.), *Proc. 3d Annual Symposium on Engineering Aspects of Magnetohydrodynamics*, pp. 479–506, Gordon and Breach, Science Publishers, Inc., New York, 1964.
13. Demetriades, S. T., and R. W. Ziemer: "Energy Transfer to Plasmas by Continuous Lorentz Forces," published in *Magnetohydrodynamics;* A. B. Cambel, T. P. Anderson, and M. M. Slawsky (eds.), *Proc. 4th Biennial Gas Dynamics Symp.*, Northwestern University, Evanston, Ill., 1962.
14. Sevier, J. R., R. V. Hess, and P. Brockman: "Coaxial Hall Current Accelerator Operation at Forces and Efficiencies Comparable to Conventional Crossed Field Accelerators," *ARS J.*, **32**:78 (1962).
15. Kolb, A. C.: "Production of High Energy Plasmas by Magnetically Driven Shock Waves," *Phys. Rev.*, **107**:345 (1957).
16. Harned, B. W.: "Magnetic Effect in a T-tube," *ARS J.*, **30**:656 (1960).
17. Marshall, J., Jr.: "Performance of a Hydromagnetic Plasma Gun," *Phys. Fluids,* **3**:134 (1960).
18. Maes, M. E.: "Experimental Investigation of the Confined Parallel Rail Pulsed Plasma Accelerator," in N. W. Mather and G. W. Sutton (eds.), *Proc. 3d Annual Symposium on Engineering Aspects of Magnetohydrodynamics*, pp. 439–465, Gordon and Breach, Science Publishers, Inc., New York, 1964.
19. Janes, G. S.: "Magnetohydrodynamic Propulsion," *AVCO-Everett Res. Lab. Res. Rept.* 90, August, 1960.
20. Gloersen, P., B. Gorowitz, and W. Palm: "Experimental Performance of a Pulsed Gas Entry Coaxial Plasma Accelerator," *ARS J.*, **31**:1158 (1961).

21. Granet, I., and W. J. Guman: "Experimental Program for Plasma Pinch Space Engine," *J. Am. Soc. Naval Engrs.*, **73**:745 (1961).
22. Gloersen, P., B. Gorowitz, W. A. Hovis, Jr., and R. B. Thomas, Jr.: "An Investigation of the Properties of a Repetitively-fired Two-stage Coaxial Plasma Engine," in N. W. Mather and G. W. Sutton (eds.), *Proc. 3d Annual Symposium on Engineering Aspects of Magnetohydrodynamics*, pp. 465–478, Gordon and Breach, Science Publishers, Inc., New York, 1964.
23. Miller, D. B.: "Measurements on an Experimental Induction Plasma Accelerator," *ARS J.*, **32**:549 (1962).
24. Barger, R. L., J. D. Brooks, and W. D. Beasley: "The Design and Operation of a Continuous Flow Electrodeless Plasma Accelerator," *NASA Tech. Note* D-1004, February, 1962.
25. Jones, R. E., and R. W. Palmer: "Traveling Wave Plasma Engine Program at NASA," in N. W. Mather and G. W. Sutton (eds.), *Proc. 3d Annual Symposium on Engineering Aspects of Magnetohydrodynamics*, pp. 383–400, Gordon and Breach, Science Publishers, Inc., New York, 1964.
26. Hess, R. V.: "Experiments and Theory for Continuous Steady Acceleration of Low Density Plasmas," *Proc. 11th Intern. Astronaut. Federation Congr.*, Stockholm, 1960, vol. 1, Springer-Verlag OHG, Vienna, 1961.

GENERAL REFERENCES

Alperin, M., and G. P. Sutton (eds.): *Advanced Propulsion Systems*, Pergamon Press, New York, 1959.

Corliss, W. R.: *Propulsion Systems for Space Flight*, McGraw-Hill Book Company, New York, 1960.

14

MAGNETOHYDRODYNAMIC POWER GENERATION

14.1 INTRODUCTION

The magnetohydrodynamic (MHD) electric power generator is based upon the Faraday effect; that is, a conductor which moves through a magnetic field generates within it an induced electric field; if suitable electric connections are made to an electric load, then electric current will flow through the load. At present, all Faraday generators utilize conductors made of solid metal, driven by a prime mover which is operated by a chemical or nuclear fuel. The Faraday principle is also widely used with liquids in flowmeters; however, the power generation per se is negligible. However, the MHD generator is based on the concept of using ionized gases as the moving conductor. This gas is heated by chemical or nuclear fuel, and then flows through the MHD generator when the energy is extracted directly in the form of electric energy. Thus, the MHD generator removes the intermediate step of the prime mover.

In addition, the MHD generator has the potential capability of utilizing working fluids at higher temperatures than are compatible with prime movers, since the MHD generator has no moving parts, and therefore the level of mechanical stresses can be greatly reduced. This higher temperature can lead to increased conversion efficiencies, or in the case of closed cycles for space power, to a reduction in the size of the radiator. Unfortunately, in order to achieve reasonable amounts of thermal ionization, very high temperatures may be required (see Sec. 14.4).

At present, the primary interest is in d-c generators, because of the problems associated with a-c generators (see Sec. 14.3.4). Also, primary interest is in the use of ionized gases as the working fluid, although there is some interest in the use of two-phase fluids in which the liquid phase is a liquid metal (see Sec. 14.8.3).

Two types of gases are generally used. The first is combustion gas, where chemical energy is used directly to heat the gas. This is generally referred to as the *open cycle*. Because the products of combustion are generally polyatomic, the only feasible method of ionization is thermal ionization of elements or compounds with a low ionization potential, which may be an additive (seed) to the gas.

For economical operation, it is desirable to use air as the oxidizer. Unfortunately, the combustion of most fuels with air does not achieve a sufficiently high temperature to obtain enough ionization, even with seeding.

Thus, the air must either be preheated or enriched with oxygen to increase the flame temperature. Even then, the combustion gas becomes essentially nonconducting at temperatures below 2500°K, but this gas still contains a large amount of thermal energy. This energy can be utilized either to preheat the incoming air or to generate steam to operate auxiliary equipment such as the air compressor or separator.

For closed cycles, the gas must be heated by direct contact with a heat exchanger. The high temperatures generally require the use of noncorrosive gases, such as noble gases. Conversely, if noble gases are used, it is necessary to use a closed cycle because of the cost of noble gases. Fortunately, several methods are available for achieving nonthermal ionization of noble gases or their mixtures with or without seeding, and the required temperatures therefore are not so high as is necessary for thermal ionization.

In this chapter, we will introduce this subject by examination of the three generator geometries of most present interest; however, the linear channel and its variations will be emphasized. The theoretical performance of the linear geometry will be derived including the Hall effect and ion slip. This is considered first for a short section of the generator, and includes a discussion of the continuous electrode, segmented electrode, and Hall geometries. In addition, the performance of the a-c induction generator is derived. Following this, the application of thermal- and magnetically induced ionization is considered theoretically.

The factors which affect the overall generator efficiency are then considered, including the effects of viscous friction, heat transfer, end losses, and electrode geometry, and general expressions are derived for the polytropic efficiencies of the linear geometry. In addition, the results of Chap. 11 are applied to the linear geometry in order to obtain expressions for the overall performance. Finally, there is a discussion of the application of the MHD generator to various cycles, and a description of the experimental results which have been achieved.

14.2 MHD GENERATOR GEOMETRIES

There are several different MHD generator geometries presently under consideration. The chief requirement for any geometry is that there be a component of the gas velocity which is not parallel to the magnetic field, so that a Faraday electric field $\mathbf{v} \times \mathbf{B}$ is created. This field will then cause electric currents and fields in the plane normal to the magnetic field. For d-c machines, the second requirement is that there be electrodes which collect the current for the electric load. The simplest geometries for accomplishing this are the linear (together with its many variations), vortex, and radial outflow (see Fig. 14.1). These are described qualitatively below, and the linear geometry is examined more thoroughly in the remaining sections of this chapter.

14.2.1 Linear MHD Generator—"Duct or Channel" Geometry. The simplest MHD generator geometry is the *linear* geometry, in which the gas flows through a linear duct or channel (see Fig. 14.1). The magnetic field is at right angles to the gas-flow velocity, which induces a Faraday electric field at right angles to both the flow velocity and the magnetic field. If suitable electrodes are placed on either side of the channel and connected through an electric load or resistance, then current will flow through the gas, electrodes, and load.

In addition to the Faraday electric field, the magnetic field causes a Hall current to flow in the direction of fluid flow; that is, the current does not flow straight across the duct. This phenomenon can be prevented by employing *segmented electrodes,* which are a variation of the linear generator. This allows a Hall electric field to develop in the flow direction. In the "Hall" variation of the linear generator, the Faraday current is short-circuited, and the Hall current is allowed to flow through the electric load.

14.2.2 Vortex MHD Generator. In addition to the linear geometry with its many variations, there is also interest in the vortex or spiral geometry, in which the gas is introduced tangentially into a cylindrical geometry, and withdrawn along the surface of an inner coaxial cylinder (see Fig. 14.1). The magnetic field is in the axial direction, and the inner and outer cylinders are the two electrodes. Under open-circuit conditions, free-vortex flow should result; that is, the tangential velocity should be inversely proportional to the radial position. Under load, the tangential velocity is practically constant in the radial direction. When the inner cylindrical diameter is much smaller than the outer cylinder, the gas makes several revolutions in the generator; thus, this geometry permits a longer magnetic-interaction length; or, alternately, for a given interaction length, the vortex generator has a more compact magnetic field. On the other hand, the Hall currents tend to flow in the tangential direction; thus, to prevent the Hall reduction in electrical conductivity,

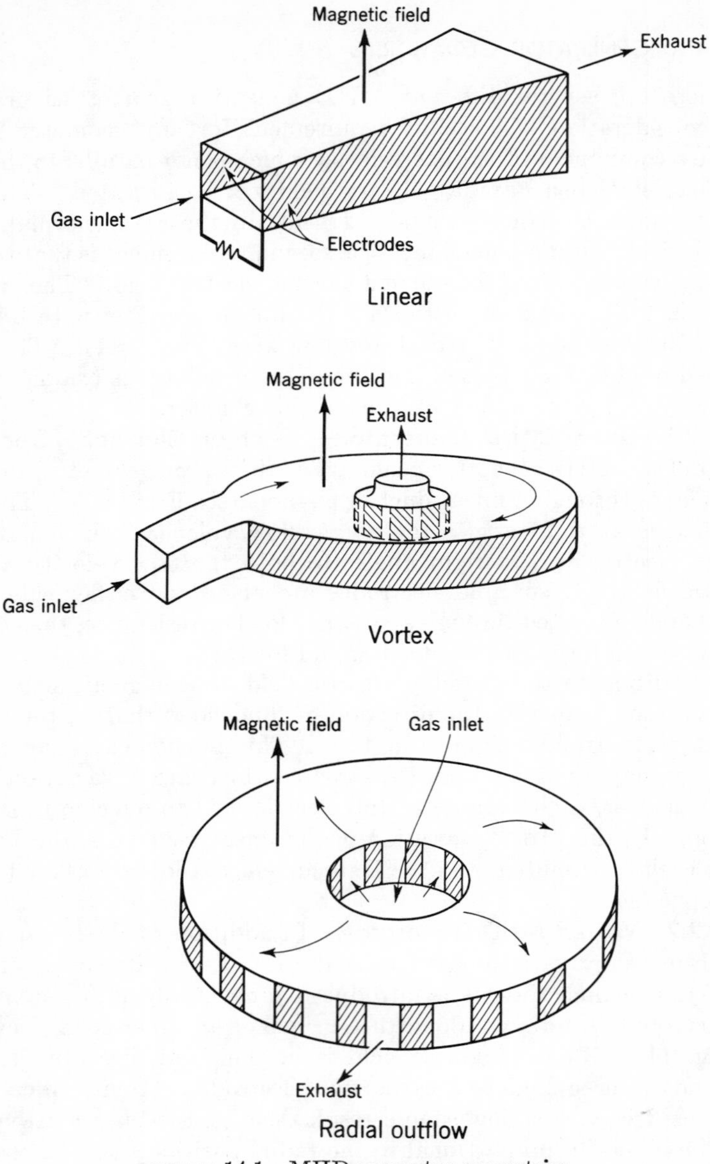

FIGURE 14.1 MHD generator geometries.

the gas pressure must be sufficiently high that $\omega_e \tau_e < 1$ at the exit. (Note that when the inner radius is almost equal to the outer radius, the vortex geometry is very similar to the linear geometry.)

14.2.3 Radial Outflow MHD Generator. A variation of the vortex generator is one in which the gas is injected radially outward from the inner cylinder. In this case, the Faraday current flows tangentially, and the Hall current flows radially; the latter interacts with the magnetic field to rotate the flow, so that flow becomes a spiral outward. This variation is essentially the same as the Hall geometry, with the duct bent so that the Lorentz force caused by the Hall current is equal to the centrifugal force in the fluid.

14.3 LOCAL INVISCID ANALYSES OF LINEAR MHD GENERATORS

In the local analysis of an MHD generator, one usually assumes that the properties, such as conductivity, density, gas velocity, and Hall parameter, are all constant. The advantage of such an analysis is that the gross operating characteristics can be determined. In the following analysis, viscosity and thermal conductivity will also be neglected. The velocity U is taken constant in the x direction, and the magnetic field is taken constant in the z direction (see Fig. 14.2). The induced electric field $\mathbf{v} \times \mathbf{B}$ is then UB in the negative y direction. Then, from Eq. (5.178), the components of the current for a slightly ionized gas become

$$
\begin{aligned}
j_x &= \frac{\sigma}{(1 + \beta_I\beta_e)^2 + \beta_e^2}\,[(1 + \beta_I\beta_e)E_x - \beta_e(E_y - UB)] \\
j_y &= \frac{\sigma}{(1 + \beta_I\beta_e)^2 + \beta_e^2}\,[(1 + \beta_I\beta_e)(E_y - UB) + \beta_e E_x]
\end{aligned}
\tag{14.1}
$$

where, omitting the asterisks, $\beta_I = \omega_I\tau_{In}$, and $\beta_e = \omega_e\tau_e$

In the absence of velocity or thermal boundary layers, both E_x and E_y may be considered constant (although more generally they may be a function of x). Then all variables are constant across a cross section, so

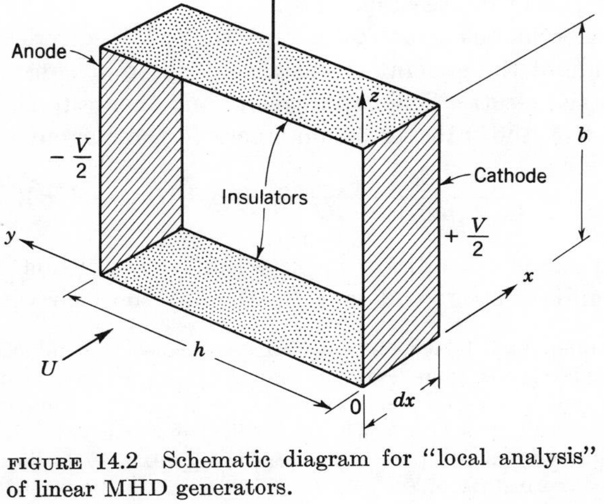

FIGURE 14.2 Schematic diagram for "local analysis" of linear MHD generators.

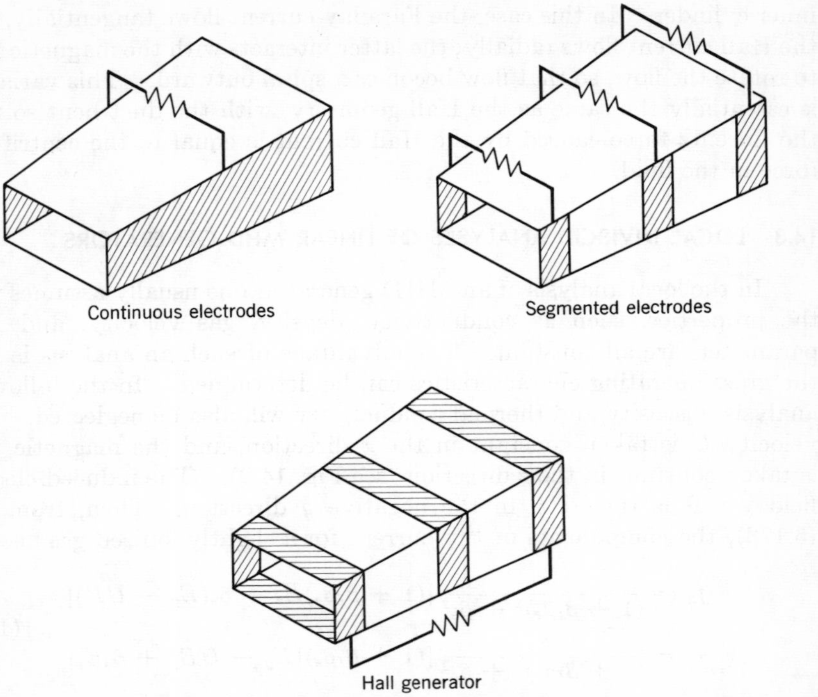

FIGURE 14.3 Linear-generator geometries having rectangular cross sections.

that the electric field and current in the direction of the magnetic field are zero.†

We will next use this simple model to analyze the three most common types of linear generators: continuous electrodes, segmented electrodes, and the Hall generator (see Fig. 14.3).

14.3.1 Continuous Electrodes. With the electrodes continuous along each side of the generator and with a different constant potential on each, no axial electric field can develop, and therefore $E_x = 0$. Then from Eqs. (14.1), the transverse component of the current is

$$j_y = \frac{\sigma}{(1 + \beta_e\beta_I)^2 + \beta_e^2} [(1 + \beta_e\beta_I)(E_y - UB)] \tag{14.2}$$

The open-circuit condition implies that $j_y = 0$; thus, from (14.2), the open-circuit electric field is UB. Under short-circuit conditions,

† Velocity boundary layers on the insulators cause the induced field $\mathbf{v} \times \mathbf{B}$ within the boundary layer to be less than that at the center line. Under these conditions, the current in the boundary layer may be in the opposite direction to that in the main flow and thus may constitute a "leakage" current. However, if the electrical conductivity is constant, then the average axial velocity across a cross section may be used instead of U.

$E_y = 0$ (except for the finite electrical resistance of the electrodes and external connection). Thus, in general, $0 < E_y < UB$. It is common to express the electric field under load as a fraction K of the open-circuit electric field; thus, for the continuous electrode geometry,

$$K = \frac{E_y}{UB} \tag{14.3}$$

where for generation of electric power, $0 < K < 1$. Note that j_y is then negative, and the Lorentz force $\mathbf{j} \times \mathbf{B}$ is in the negative x direction, that is, *opposite* to the flow direction. Thus, in the generator, the Lorentz force tends to *retard* the flow. (If, on the other hand, the electrodes were attached to a voltage source so that $E_y > UB$, that is, $K > 1$, then j_y is positive, and the Lorentz force tends to accelerate the flow. If the polarity of the imposed voltage is reversed so that $E_y < 0$, the Lorentz force will retard the flow; the energy added to the flow from the voltage source then increases the thermal energy of the gas.)

In addition to the transverse component of the electric current, there is also a component in the downstream direction given by

$$j_x = \frac{\sigma\beta_e(1 - K)UB}{(1 + \beta_I\beta_e)^2 + \beta_e^2} \tag{14.4}$$

where use has been made of (14.3). Thus, the current, as it flows across the generator, also tends to flow downstream. Actually, it is the current in the downstream direction which is responsible for the Lorentz force on the gas through collision between the electrons and heavy particles.

The power generated per unit volume is $P = -\mathbf{E} \cdot \mathbf{j}$, which becomes $-j_yE_y$ since $E_x = 0$. From Eqs. (14.2) and (14.3), this becomes

$$P = \frac{\sigma K(1 - K)U^2B^2(1 + \beta_e\beta_I)}{(1 + \beta_e\beta_I)^2 + \beta_e^2} \tag{14.5}$$

Equation (14.5) can also be written as

$$P = \frac{n_em_eU^2K(1 - K)}{\tau_e} \cdot \frac{\beta_e^2[1 + \beta_e^2(\mu_I/\mu_e)]}{\left(1 + \beta_e^2\dfrac{\mu_I}{\mu_e}\right)^2 + \beta_e^2} \tag{14.6}$$

where μ_I and μ_e are the electron and ion mobilities $e\tau_{In}/m_I$, $e\tau_e/m_e$, respectively. The coefficient of (14.6), $n_em_eU^2\nu_e$, has a simple interpretation: Consider that after each collision with a heavy particle, the electron acquires the gas velocity U in the downstream direction. But then the magnetic field turns the electron velocity in the $+y$ direction parallel to the electric field, so that its kinetic energy is transformed into potential energy. If the electron is then hit again by a heavy particle, it again acquires a velocity U in the downstream direction. The rate at which an electron acquires kinetic energy from the gas is thus approximately $\frac{1}{2}m_e U^2 \nu_e$; the total rate at which all electrons acquire energy from the gas is therefore $\approx \frac{1}{2}n_e m_e U^2/\tau_e$.

The factor on the right side of Eq. (14.6) represents the effects of the Hall reduction in electrical conductivity and ion slip for this geometry, and has two asymptotes. The first asymptote is obtained by taking μ_I equal to zero, which is equivalent to stating that the ion velocity is equal to the gas velocity. This factor then becomes $\beta_e^2/(1 + \beta_e^2)$. Thus, for a given value of τ_e, the power P initially increases quadratically with the magnetic field, since $\beta_e = \mu_e B$. This is shown in Fig. 14.4. As the magnetic field is increased further, the first asymptote is reached as $\beta_e^2/(1 + \beta_e^2) \to 1$. Thus, the *maximum* energy transfer or power generation due to the electrons is $n_e m_e U^2 \nu_e$, modified, of course, by the loading-factor term $K(1 - K)$. In Fig. 14.4, the inflection point near unity represents this first asymptote. Since magnets generally consume power and are expensive or heavy, it is desirable to operate at a point somewhat below this point; suppose the power level is set at $P\tau_e/n_e m_e U^2 K(1 - K)$ equal to 80 per cent of the first asymptote, then $\beta_e^2/(1 + \beta_e^2) = 0.8$, so that $\beta_e = \sqrt{5} = 2.24$. Thus, a magnetic field which corresponds to a value of the Hall parameter greater than 2 will not lead to substantially greater power generation by electrons.

With β_I nonzero, Eq. (14.6) predicts a second asymptote for the right-hand factor, equal to the mobility ratio μ_e/μ_I, which is generally much greater than unity. This is shown on the right side of Fig. 14.4 for

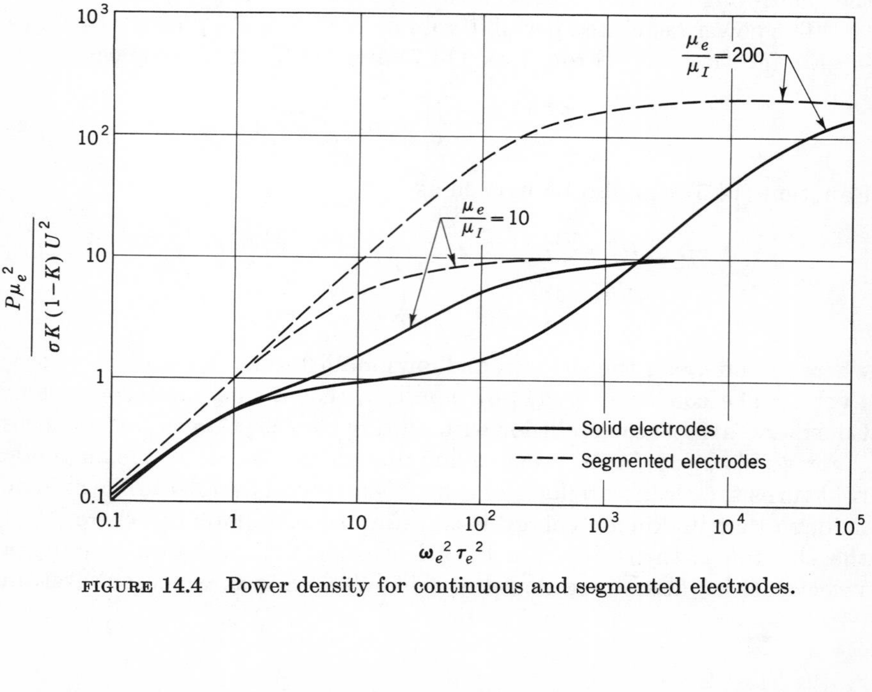

FIGURE 14.4 Power density for continuous and segmented electrodes.

very large values of $\omega_e\tau_e$. The power extraction is then of the order of $P \approx n_I m_I U^2/\tau_{In}$, which shows that for very large values of $\omega_e\tau_e$, the positive ions are responsible for the power generation. However, it appears unlikely that an MHD generator can be designed to utilize the ion current with continuous electrodes.

From Eq. (14.5), it is obvious that the power generation density is a maximum when $K = \frac{1}{2}$, which corresponds to matched impedance, that is, when the load resistance is equal to the generator internal resistance. However, for some applications, it may not be desirable to operate at maximum power density, but instead, closer to maximum efficiency. For the purpose of a local analysis, a local conversion efficiency may be defined as the ratio of the generated power to the flow work which is required to overcome the Lorentz force, or

$$\eta_L = \frac{P}{\mathbf{v} \cdot \mathbf{j} \times \mathbf{B}} \tag{14.7}$$

In the present geometry, the denominator of (14.7) is Uj_yB, while the numerator is E_yj_y; thus, the local efficiency for this geometry is $E_y/UB = K$, from (14.3).

The local efficiency, as defined by (14.7), is also equal to the local adiabatic or polytropic efficiency (also called the *stage* efficiency) when $\frac{1}{2}(\gamma - 1)\mathfrak{M}^2(1 - K)$ is small compared to unity (see Sec. 14.5). Thus, if a high polytropic efficiency is required, it is necessary to operate at values of K near unity.

Since the load voltage is $KUBh$, and the load current per unit length of generator is $\sigma_e(1 - K)UBb$, where σ_e is the "effective" electrical conductivity; the external load resistance per unit length of generator is therefore

$$R_L = \frac{V}{J} = \frac{Kh}{(1 - K)\sigma_e b} = \frac{K}{1 - K} R_i \tag{14.8}$$

where R_i is the effective internal resistance of the generator, $h/\sigma_e b$ (see Fig. 14.2). Solving (14.8) for the value of K, one obtains

$$K = \frac{1}{1 + R_i/R_L} \tag{14.9}$$

which, for this geometry, is also equal to the conversion efficiency. One therefore obtains the familiar result that the conversion efficiency increases as the ratio of external to internal load increases.

14.3.2 Segmented Electrodes. In the previous section, it was shown that with increasing magnetic field, the generated power density has a low first asymptote, $n_e m_e U^2 K(1 - K)\nu_e$, because of the Hall reduction in electrical conductivity in the direction of the electric field. To increase the power density, the segmented-electrode generator has been devised,[1,2] in which each opposite pair of electrodes is connected to a single load (see Fig. 14.3). In this arrangement, the current flow is essentially transverse to the gas flow, and no net Hall current exists in the downstream direction. Since the gas is electrically neutral, this means, of course, that the electron and ion velocities in the downstream direction are equal to each other, but are slightly lower than the gas velocity owing to ion slip.

With the Hall current j_x equal to zero, Eq. (14.1) predicts that an electric field will develop in the axial direction given by

$$E_x = \frac{\beta_e}{1 + \beta_e \beta_I}(E_y - UB) \tag{14.10}$$

so that the current in the y direction becomes

$$j_y = \frac{\sigma}{1 + \beta_e \beta_I}(E_y - UB) \tag{14.11}$$

As in the previous section, the open-circuit voltage corresponding to $j_y = 0$ is UB; we therefore take the electric field under load as KUB. The Lorentz force $\mathbf{j} \times \mathbf{B}$ now acts only in the negative x direction so that it acts only to retard the flow. This force is caused mainly by collisions between the neutral particles and the ions, between which there exists a velocity difference.

The power density is $-\mathbf{E} \cdot \mathbf{j} = -E_y j_y$, or

$$\begin{aligned} P &= \frac{K(1 - K)\sigma U^2 B^2}{1 + \beta_e \beta_I} \\ &= \frac{n_e m_e U^2 K(1 - K)}{\tau_e} \cdot \frac{\beta_e^2}{1 + \beta_e^2 \mu_I / \mu_e} \end{aligned} \tag{14.12}$$

As with continuous electrodes, the power density initially increases quadratically with increasing magnetic field (since $\beta_e = e\tau_e B/m_e$); and the last factor of (14.12) becomes asymptotic to μ_e/μ_I (see Fig. 14.4). However, for intermediate values of β_e, no first asymptote appears in the power density, as was the case for continuous electrodes. Thus, for $1 < \beta_e < (\mu_e/\mu_I)$, the generated power of the segmented-electrode geometry greatly exceeds that of the continuous-electrode geometry.

The local efficiency is still equal to K, since $\eta_L = E_y j_y / UB j_y$. Thus, the increase in power density has been obtained with no sacrifice in efficiency. The power density is still a maximum when $K = \frac{1}{2}$.

The segmented-electrode generator has the disadvantage, as compared to the continuous-electrode or Hall generator, of requiring a multiplicity of loads, each at a different potential. This can be corrected by providing external connections between electrode segments on opposite sides of the generator which are at the same potential. In this way, the number of loads can be reduced to a few or even one.

14.3.3 Hall Generator.[3] When the electrodes are segmented, it was shown in the previous section that an electric field develops in the flow direction. This electric field is maximum when the opposite electrodes are short-circuited, that is, when $E_y = 0$. If the electrode pair at the inlet is connected through a load to the pair at the exit, a current should then flow through the load. With $E_y = 0$, the current density in the $+x$ direction is obtained from Eq. (14.1):

$$j_x = \frac{\sigma}{(1 + \beta_e\beta_I)^2 + \beta_e^2}[(1 + \beta_e\beta_I)E_x + \beta_e UB] \tag{14.13}$$

When open-circuited, the axial electric field is $-\beta_e UB/(1 + \beta_e\beta_I)$; under load, the axial electric field will be some fraction K_H of this value, $E_x = -\beta_e K_H UB/(1 + \beta_e\beta_I)$, so that

$$j_x = \frac{\sigma\beta_e(1 - K_H)UB}{(1 + \beta_e\beta_I)^2 + \beta_e^2} \tag{14.14}$$

Note that the definition of K_H is different from K for the continuous- and segmented-electrode geometries. The generated power density is

$$\begin{aligned} P &= -E_x j_x \\ &= \frac{K_H(1 - K_H)\sigma\beta_e^2U^2B^2}{(1 + \beta_e\beta_I)[(1 + \beta_e\beta_I)^2 + \beta_e^2]} \\ &= \frac{n_e m_e U^2 K_H(1 - K_H)}{\tau_e} \cdot \frac{\beta_e^4}{(1 + \beta_e^2\mu_I/\mu_e)[(1 + \beta_e^2\mu_I/\mu_e)^2 + \beta_e^2]} \end{aligned} \tag{14.15}$$

In this geometry, as the magnetic field is increased from zero, the power increases as the fourth power of the magnetic field, in contrast to the quadratic dependence of the continuous- and segmented-electrode geometries. An asymptote is reached when $\beta_e > \mu_e/\mu_I$, equal to $(\mu_e/\mu_I)^3\beta_e^{-2}$, which is considerably smaller than the asymptote of μ_e/μ_I obtained in the continuous- and segmented-geometry generators. However, for $2 < \beta_e < (\mu_e/\mu_I)^{\frac{1}{2}}$, the power density approaches that of the segmented-electrode geometry.

The retarding Lorentz force j_yB becomes

$$F_x = \frac{-\sigma UB^2}{1 + \beta_e\beta_I} \cdot \frac{1 + \beta_e'^2 K_H}{1 + \beta_e'^2} \tag{14.16}$$

where β_e' is the effective Hall parameter for electrons defined in (5.183). Note that the retarding Lorentz force is a minimum when the load is short-circuited, that is, when $K_H = 0$. This is in sharp contrast to the previous geometry, where the retarding force is a maximum when short-circuited.

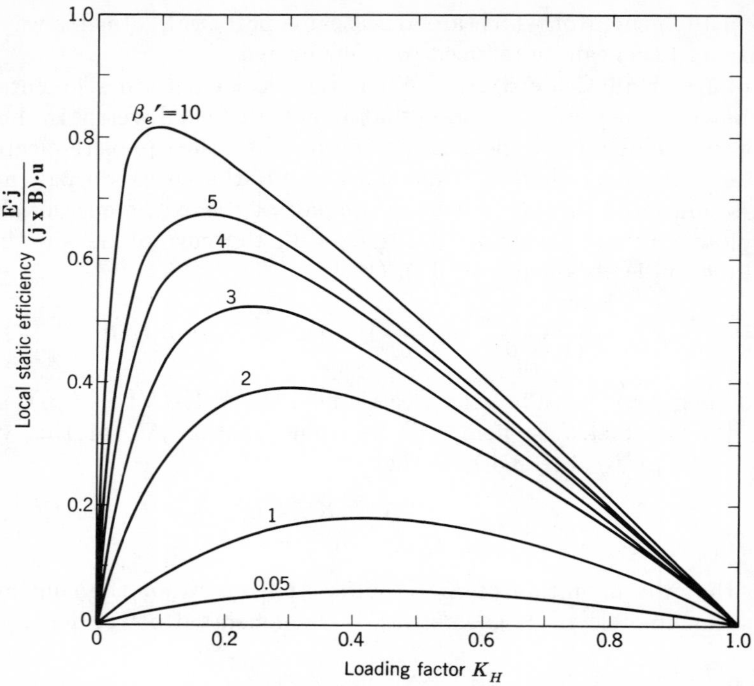

FIGURE 14.5 Local static efficiencies, Hall MHD generator for various values of $\beta_e' = \omega_e\tau_e/(1 + \omega_e\tau_e\omega_I\tau_{In})$.

The local efficiency of the Hall generator is the ratio of the power (14.15) to the flow work UF_x when F_x is given by Eq. (14.16). Thus,

$$\eta_L = \frac{\beta_e'^2 K_H(1 - K_H)}{1 + \beta_e'^2 K_H} \tag{14.17}$$

For small values of $\beta_e'^2$, the efficiency is proportional to $\beta_e'^2$ and is maximum when $K_H = \frac{1}{2}$. For large values of $\beta_e'^2$, the efficiency becomes

$$\lim_{\beta_e' \to \infty} \eta_L \to 1 - K_H \tag{14.18}$$

that is, the efficiency is a *maximum* when K_H is small (that is, when close to short-circuited). For arbitrary values of β_e', as K_H is increased, the efficiency at first increases, then decreases, as shown in Fig. 14.5. Thus, for any given value, there is a value of K_H which yields the maximum efficiency. This value is obtained by differentiation of (14.17) with respect to K_H; the result is

$$\beta_e'^2 = \frac{1 - 2K_m}{K_m^2} \tag{14.19}$$

Substitution of (14.19) into (14.17) yields η_{L_m} in terms of K_m:

$$\eta_{L_m} = 1 - 2K_m \tag{14.20}$$

Substitution of K_m from (14.20) into (14.19) yields an alternate form for the maximum local efficiency:

$$\frac{4\eta_{L_m}}{(1 - \eta_{L_m})^2} = \beta_e'^2 \tag{14.21}$$

Thus, β_e' must be large in order for the local efficiency to be close to unity. Note, however, that as the magnetic field is increased from zero, that is, as β_e is increased, β_e' first increases, reaches a maximum, and then decreases. The maximum value of β_e' is obtained by setting equal to zero the derivative of $\beta_e/(1 + \beta_e{}^2\mu_e/\mu_I)$ with respect to β_e. The result is

$$\beta'_{e_{\max}} = \sqrt{\frac{\mu_e}{\mu_I}} \tag{14.22}$$

Thus, if the mobility ratio is 100, the maximum value of β_e' is 10, and the maximum local efficiency is slightly over 80 per cent.

It is desirable to compare the power densities of the Hall generator to those of the segmented-electrode generator for the same values of η_L. From (14.12) and (14.15),

$$\frac{P_{\text{Hall}}}{P_{\text{seg}}}(\eta_L) = \frac{K_H(1 - K_H)\beta_e'^2}{\eta_L(1 - \eta_L)(1 + \beta_e'^2)} \tag{14.23}$$

where $K_H = K_H(\eta_L)$, given by (14.17). This ratio is shown in Fig. 14.6 as a function of the parameter β_e'. It is seen that for the same efficiency, the power density of the Hall generator approaches that of the segmented-electrode generator. Of course, the latter generator can be operated at any local efficiency, while the maximum efficiency of the Hall generator depends on the value of β_e'; this maximum efficiency is shown as the dashed line in Fig. 14.6.

Since the Hall current is allowed to flow, a Lorentz force will exist in the $-y$ direction, as in the case of continuous electrodes. The ratio of this transverse force to the retarding Lorentz force is j_x/j_y, or

$$\frac{F_y}{F_x} = \frac{\beta_e'(1 - K_H)}{1 - \beta_e'^2 K_H} \tag{14.24}$$

which is of order-of-magnitude unity, for $\beta_e > 1$; this must be balanced by a pressure gradient of the gas normal to the plane of the electrodes similar to continuous electrodes.

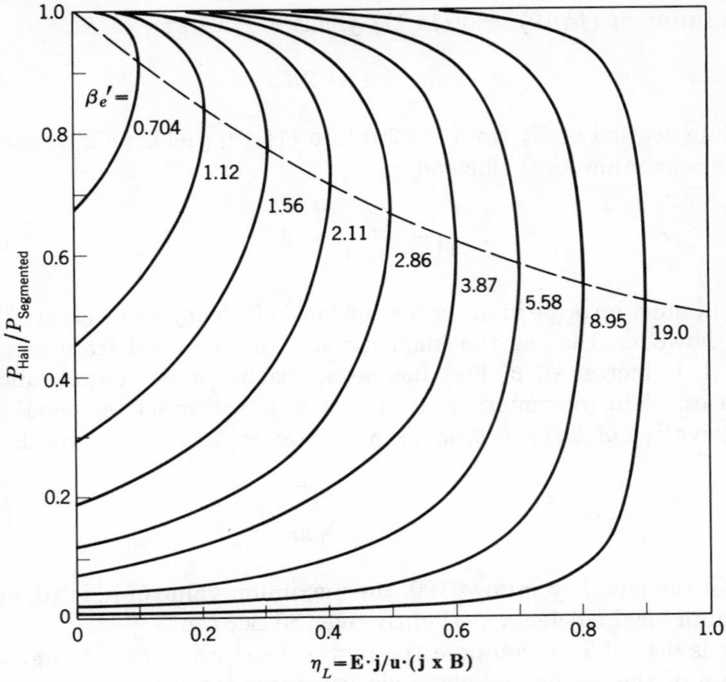

FIGURE 14.6 Comparison of power density of Hall generator to power density of segmented-electrode generator, for various values of $\beta_e' = \omega_e\tau_e/(1 + \omega_e\tau_e\omega_I\tau_{In})$.

14.3.4 Induction MHD Generator.

The electrodeless induction-type MHD generator operates by means of a traveling, alternating magnetic field, which induces currents in the gas. In turn, this induced current creates an induced magnetic field which cuts the field windings of the magnet. If the gas velocity is greater than the velocity of the traveling magnetic field, the induced currents will be in such a direction that the Lorentz force retards the flow; and in addition, there will be power output from the field windings.

A simplified analysis of the induction generator will illustrate its performance. It is assumed that the generator channel is infinite in the y direction. The field coils are also taken in the y direction, and are so excited that the z component of the magnetic field is approximately sinusoidal and moving in the downstream direction x with velocity u_B (see Fig. 14.7). The gas is assumed to have a constant scalar conductivity, to be incompressible, and to be moving in the downstream direction with constant velocity U. Also, it is assumed that the induced current loops close at $y = +\infty$. In practice, this may be accomplished by the use of an annular geometry.

In the absence of a conducting fluid in the generator, the imposed magnetic field B_0 is given by

$$B_{z_0} = \Re\, B_0^* e^{(i2\pi/\lambda)(x-u_Bt)} \tag{14.25}$$

where λ is the wavelength of the magnetic field. In the presence of a conducting fluid, there will also be an induced magnetic field B_{z_i} caused by the currents in the fluid, which may be represented by

$$B_{z_i} = \Re\, B_i^* e^{(i2\pi/\lambda)(x-u_Bt)} \tag{14.26}$$

such that

$$\nabla \times \mathbf{B}_i = \mu_0 \mathbf{j}_i \tag{14.27}$$

where $\mathbf{j}_i$ is the induced current in the fluid. It is assumed that the variation of the magnetic field is only in the x direction. Then (14.27) becomes

$$\frac{\partial B_{z_i}}{\partial x} = -\mu_0 j_{y_i} \tag{14.28}$$

Use of (14.26) for B_{z_i} yields

$$\frac{i2\pi}{\lambda} B_{z_i} = -\mu_0 j_{y_i} \tag{14.29}$$

The induced current may also be obtained from Ohm's law. First, the

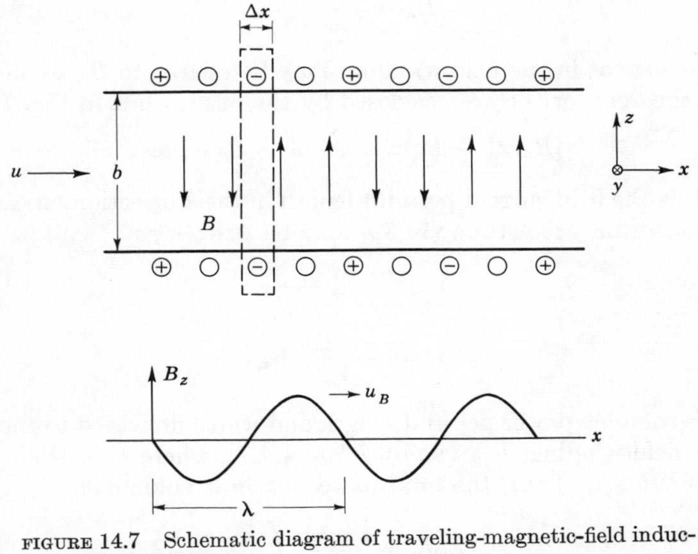

FIGURE 14.7 Schematic diagram of traveling-magnetic-field induction generator.

electric field in the y direction is obtained from Maxwell's equation:

$$\frac{\partial E_y}{\partial x} = -\frac{\partial B_z}{\partial t}$$

Let

$$E_y = E_0^* e^{(i2\pi/\lambda)(x-u_Bt)}$$

$$B_z = B_{z_0} + B_{z_i} = B_z^* e^{(i2\pi/\lambda)(x-u_Bt)}$$

Thus,

$$E_y = u_B B_z$$

Ohm's law then yields

$$\begin{aligned} j_{y_i} &= \sigma(E_y - UB_z) \\ &= \sigma(u_B - U)B_z \\ &= -(1 - S)\sigma U(B_{z_i} + B_{z_0}) \end{aligned} \tag{14.30}$$

where S is the slip, $S = u_B/U$. Equating the two expressions for the induced current (14.29) and (14.30), one may solve for the induced magnetic field,

$$B_{z_i} = \frac{B_{z_0}}{i/R_m - 1}$$

where R_m is a magnetic Reynolds number defined by

$$R_m = \frac{\mu_0 \sigma U \lambda (1 - S)}{2\pi}$$

The total magnetic field is given by

$$B_z = B_{z_i} + B_{z_0} = \frac{B_{z_0}}{1 + iR_m}$$

Thus,

$$E_y = \frac{u_B B_{z_0}}{1 + iR_m} \tag{14.31}$$

Now the current in the field windings may be related to B_{z_0} by means of Stokes' theorem for the area enclosed by the dashed line in Fig. 14.7,

$$[B_{z_0}(x) - B_{z_0}(x + \Delta x)]b = 2\mu_0 J_y \, \Delta x \tag{14.32}$$

where J_y is the field current per unit length in the x direction on each side of the generator. Equation (14.32) may be written as

$$-\frac{\partial B_{z_0}}{\partial x} = \frac{2\mu_0 J_y}{b} \tag{14.33}$$

Thus,

$$J_y = -\frac{i2\pi b}{2\mu_0 \lambda} B_{z_0} \tag{14.34}$$

Now the complex power per unit length and width delivered to the upper or lower field windings is given by $P^* = \frac{1}{2}\tilde{E}_y J_y$, where $\tilde{E}_y$ is the complex conjugate of E_y. Thus, the total power per unit volume is

$$P^* = \tfrac{1}{2}\tilde{E}_y J_y = \frac{\pi B_0{}^2 u_B}{\mu_0 \lambda}\left(\frac{R_m - i}{1 + R_m{}^2}\right) \tag{14.35}$$

where Eqs. (14.31) and (14.34) have been used. The real power is given by the real part of (14.35), while the reactive power is given by the imaginary part of (14.35). Equation (14.35) thus clearly illustrates that the reactive power is larger than the actual power when $R_m < 1$. To increase the power factor, R_m must be increased, but then the power density will decrease for $R_m > 1$. Equation (14.35) may also be compared to the d-c generator by substitution of R_m in the numerator:

$$\mathcal{R}\, P^* = \frac{1}{2} \frac{S(1 - S)\sigma U^2 B_0^2}{1 + R_m^2} \tag{14.36}$$

Thus, the slip velocity S replaces the load factor K. The factor of $\frac{1}{2}$ is caused by the sinusoidal variation of power output, as is usually associated with a-c power. Equation (14.36) clearly shows that increasing the magnetic Reynolds number will decrease the power density. However, it is unlikely that magnetic Reynolds numbers in excess of unity can be achieved, so that the main problem is the power factor. From (14.35), it is seen that the phase angle between the voltage and current is given by $\theta = \tan^{-1} R_m^{-1}$; more detailed analyses have verified this poor power factor.[4]

Another problem is the high frequency of the current; the frequency is given by $u_B/\lambda = U/S\lambda$. The gas velocity must be high in order to have a high power density. Thus, the frequency will be quite high, unless the wavelength is made exceptionally long, which will cause the generator length also to be long.

14.4 SEEDING AND IONIZATION IN MAGNETOHYDRODYNAMIC GENERATORS

Two types of ionization are most promising for MHD generators: thermal ionization and magnetically induced ionization. Other types of ionization processes have been little investigated for MHD generators. For example, an electric arc can be used to ionize the gas, but this consumes power, and its effectiveness depends on the rate of electron recombination; the same is true of low-frequency-induction ionization of gases. Although radio-frequency waves can be used to produce a low degree of ionization in a gas, the high degree of ionization required for MHD generators leads to a very small skin depth, so that the RF field cannot produce the required degree of ionization before the plasma becomes self-shielding. Radioactivity can also produce ionization, but a practical method has not yet been suggested for utilizing this in a generator. Photo-ionization, although relatively efficient, requires a very long light path in the gas for the ionizing light to be absorbed, because of the small photo-ionization cross section of most atoms and molecules. Electron-beam ionization may prove effective if the recombination rate is sufficiently low. For flames, a certain amount of chemi-ionization has been observed, but the amount is usually insufficient. For these reasons, the first two methods of ionization have received the most attention. These are covered in more detail below.

14.4.1 Thermal Ionization. When a gas is raised to a sufficiently high temperature, some of the atoms or molecules in the gas will lose one or more of their outer electrons. The energy required to separate an electron from an atom (or a molecule) is called the *ionization energy* and is commonly measured in electron volts, or in terms of the ionization "potential," measured in just volts. Values of the ionization potential are shown in Table 6.3 for most gases. The ionization energy is supplied to the particle by the relative kinetic energy of two particles during a collision, or from the energy of an electronically excited state.

If the gas is in equilibrium (including radiation equilibrium), then statistical mechanics can be used to determine the degree of ionization from Saha's equation, given by (see Chap. 6)

$$\frac{n_e n_I}{n_n} = \frac{2P_I}{P_n}\left(\frac{2\pi m_e kT}{h^2}\right)^{\frac{3}{2}} e^{-E_I/kT} \tag{14.37}$$

for the reaction $n \rightleftharpoons e + n^+$, where E_I is the ionization energy for this reaction, and P_I and P_n are the internal partition functions for the ion and neutral, respectively (see Table 6.2). From Table 6.3, it is obvious that sufficient thermal ionization cannot be achieved in air, combustion gases, or noble gases at the temperatures corresponding to ordinary combustion temperatures, or heat exchangers. However, by the addition to the carrier gas of small amounts of an easily ionized compound such as the alkali metals, sufficient thermal ionization can be achieved.

Even then, only a small fraction of the ionizable material is ionized. Generally, the electron cross section of the seed material is much larger than the gas cross section; hence, as seed material is added to a gas, the corresponding conductivity at first increases, then decreases. This is shown in Fig. 14.8, for a mixture of cesium and argon. The optimum seeding can be determined by differentiating the total scalar resistivity with respect to the number density n_n, of neutral seed atoms for the temperature and pressure fixed. The total number density is $n = n_g + n_n + n_e + n_I$; hence the number density of the carrier gas is $n_g = n - n_n - 2n_e$, since the gas is essentially neutral. The average cross section of the carrier gas is taken as Q_{eg}. Then the scalar resistivity, from (5.130), can be written as

$$\eta = \frac{m_e\langle c\rangle_e}{n_e e^2}\left[(n - n_n - 2n_e)Q_{eg} + n_n Q_{es}\right] + \alpha T^{\frac{3}{2}} \ln \frac{\gamma T^{\frac{3}{2}}}{n_e^{\frac{1}{2}}} \tag{14.38}$$

Substitution of (14.37) into (14.38) and equating to zero the derivative

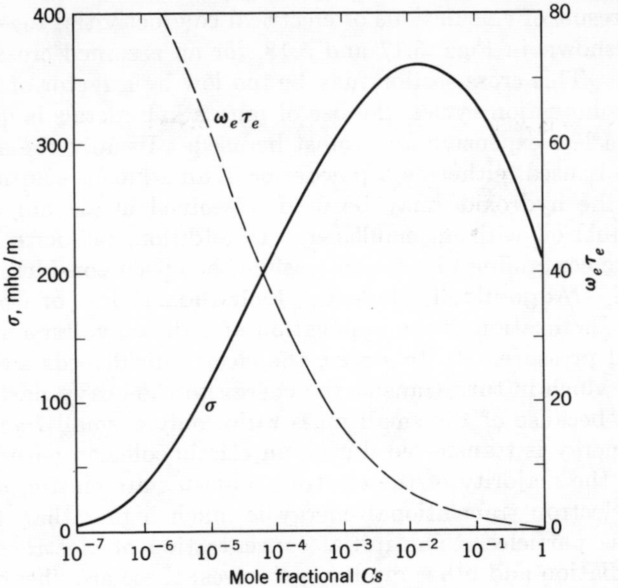

FIGURE 14.8 Electrical conductivity and Hall parameter in a mixture of cesium and argon at 1 atm pressure and 2500°K, where $Q_{eCs} = 3.5 \times 10^{-15}$ cm², $Q_{eA} = 2 \times 10^{-17}$ cm², B = 10,000 gauss.

with respect to n_n yield

$$\frac{n_n/n - Q_{eg}/(Q_{es} - Q_{eg})}{n_n/n + (1 - n_e/n)Q_{eg}/(Q_{es} - Q_{eg})} = \frac{\sigma_{en}}{2(\ln \Lambda)\sigma_{eI}} \tag{14.39}$$

Since $n_e \ll n$, (14.39) can be solved for n_n/n:

$$\frac{n_n}{n} = \frac{1 + \sigma_{en}/2(\ln \Lambda)\sigma_{eI}}{Q_{es}/Q_{eg} - 1} \tag{14.40}$$

Equation (14.40) must be solved iteratively; as a first approximation, the ratio σ_{en}/σ_{eI} can be taken as zero; then n_n is calculated, and the numerator of (14.40) is determined, giving a new value of n_n/n. The amount of seed atoms which must be added to the gas is given by $n_s = n_n + n_I = n_n + n_e$; the fractional seeding is then $(n_n + n_e)kT/p$.

Note that the cross sections of the alkali metals are usually much larger than those of combustion gases or noble gases, so that the optimum seeding ratio is only a few per cent.

In addition to the ionization of the alkali metals, one must also take into account the production of negative ions by electron attachment to atoms, molecules, or radicals. This effect is important at the lower ranges of temperature.

The result of calculations of electrical conductivities for combustion gases[5] is shown in Figs. 5.17 and 5.18, for an assumed cross section of 10^{-15} cm^2. This cross section may be too low by a factor of 2 or 3.

For combustion cycles, the use of pure alkali metals is quite expensive, and a less expensive form must be used. Usually the alkali metal carbonate is used, either as a powder or in an aqueous solution. Alternatively, the hydroxide may be used, dissolved in alcohol, and mixed with the fuel oil with an emulsifier. In addition, pollucite, which is a natural ore containing 27 per cent cesium, has been considered.

14.4.2 Magnetically Induced Ionization. One of the simplest methods of ionization is the application of a direct voltage across a gas at reduced pressure. In this case, the electric field feeds energy to the electrons, which in turn transfer the energy to the heavy particles in the gas. But because of the small mass ratio, only a small fraction of the electron energy is transferred during an elastic collision with heavy particles. If the majority of the electron collisions are elastic, the effect is that the electron translational energy is much higher than that of the heavier gas particles. The initial concentration of electrons is due to cosmic radiation and other random processes; these are "heated" by the above process, and as they acquire energies greater than the ionization energy, cause additional ionization. This process is known as a *glow discharge*, and was one of the first demonstrations of sustained electrical discharges in gases.

Only recently was it demonstrated that the same effect could be achieved in seeded noble gases, if the gas temperature was elevated.[6] Equation (5.196) describes the electron heating; if one assumes that gradients in the gas may be neglected, this becomes

$$\mathbf{E}^* \cdot \mathbf{j}_e = 3kn_e m_e(T_e - T) \sum_{s \neq e} \frac{\delta_s \nu_{es}}{m_s} \tag{14.41}$$

The electron current is given by (5.124) and (5.125), and the degree of ionization may be obtained from Saha's equation (14.37), based on the electron temperature. Saha's equation may be used because the ionization cross section is much larger for electron impacts than for heavy-particle impacts. Thus, at high electron densities, electron impacts are mainly responsible for ionization. Because of microscopic balancing, deionization is the reverse process. Thus, the ionization and deionization processes depend only on the electron temperature, and are insensitive to the temperature of the heavy particles. Therefore, the degree of ionization should be predicted by Saha's equation, based on electron temperature. The agreement between theory and experiment[7] is shown in Fig. 14.9. Note that the discrepancy between theory and experiment decreases with increasing electron density. This difference can be explained on the basis of radiation losses.[8] In general, the resonant

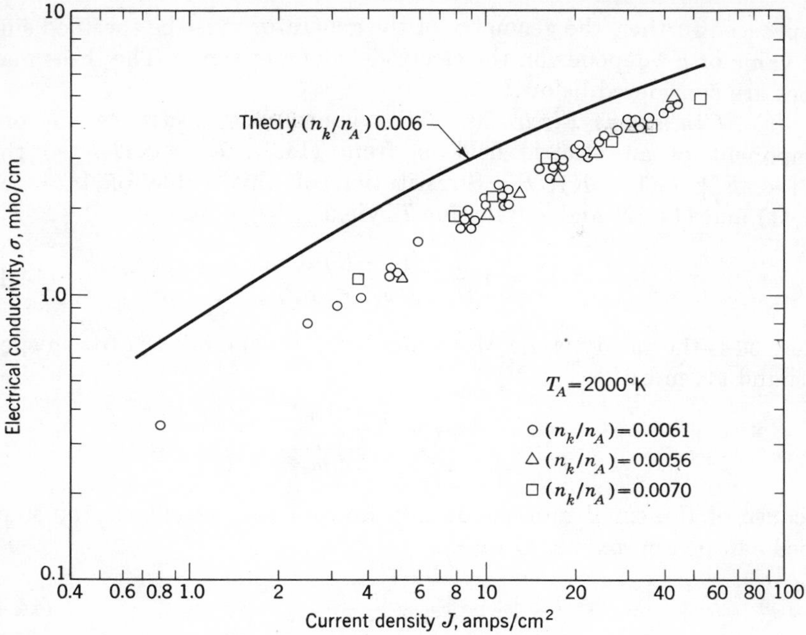

FIGURE 14.9 Dependence of steady-state conductivity on current density.[7]

radiation from the first excited level of the seed atoms is trapped within the gas because of the high population of seed atoms in the ground state; but the population of upper states is insufficient to trap radiation from the transitions of upper states. The net effect is a loss of electron energy, so that the electron temperature is not as high as that predicted by the assumption of only elastic collisions. The theory can be corrected for this effect by taking values of δ_s greater than unity. This effect can be minimized by the use of a carrier gas whose first excitation energy is greater than the ionization energy of the seed material, although it may be possible to achieve magnetically induced ionization without seeding.

In applying this technique to MHD generators, it is obvious that the carrier gas must be an inert gas because the values of δ_s for diatomic and polyatomic gases are too great to allow for appreciable electron heating (see Fig. 5.6); thus a closed cycle must be used. On the other hand, it should not be necessary to impress an external electric field on the gas as in a glow discharge; the combined Faraday and Hall electric fields which are induced in the gas by virtue of its motion may provide the required electric field. The electron current is given by (5.124) and (5.125) with the electric field perpendicular to the magnetic field; thus the left side of (14.41) becomes

$$\mathbf{E}^* \cdot \mathbf{j}_e = \frac{\sigma}{1 + \beta_e^2} |\mathbf{E}^*|^2 \tag{14.42}$$

To proceed further, the geometry of the generator must be specified since the value of E^* depends on the electrode configuration. The three main types are considered below.[7]

(*a*) *Continuous Electrodes.* With continuous electrodes, the only component of an electric field is, from (14.3), $E_y = KUB$, so that $|E^*| = |E_y^*| = (1 - K)UB$. Substitution of this value of $|E^*|$ into (14.41) and (14.42) and solving for T_e yield

$$\frac{T_e}{T} = 1 + \frac{\gamma(1 - K)^2\beta_e{}^2\mathfrak{M}^2}{3\delta(1 + \beta_e{}^2)} \tag{14.43}$$

where $\mathfrak{M}$ is the gas dynamic Mach number U/a, and a is the frozen speed of sound given by

$$a^2 = \frac{\gamma p}{\rho} = \frac{\gamma \sum_s n_s kT_s}{\Sigma n_s m_s}$$

Because of the small number density and mass of electrons, the sound speed can be approximated by

$$a^2 = \frac{\gamma kT}{\sum_{s \neq e} X_s m_s} \tag{14.44}$$

where X_s is the number fraction of the s species, n_s/n. In (14.43), δ is the average correction factor for inelastic collisions, given by

$$\delta = \frac{\left(\sum_{s \neq e} X_s m_s\right)\left(\sum_{s \neq e} X_s Q_{es}\delta_s/m_s\right)}{\sum_{s \neq e} X_s Q_{es}} \tag{14.45}$$

From (14.45), it can be seen that if the species with the largest cross section also has a large mass, then it is possible to obtain values of δ less than unity.[8]

Now it is more convenient to compare the electron temperature to the stagnation temperature of the flow, given by

$$\frac{T_0}{T} = 1 + \frac{\gamma - 1}{2}\mathfrak{M}^2 \tag{14.46}$$

The ratio of the electron temperature to the local stagnation temperature is therefore

$$\frac{T_e}{T_0} = \frac{1 + [\gamma(1 - K)^2\beta_e{}^2/3\delta(1 + \beta_e{}^2)]\mathfrak{M}^2}{1 + \frac{1}{2}(\gamma - 1)\mathfrak{M}^2} \tag{14.47}$$

In order for the electron temperature of the gas to exceed the local stagnation temperature, it is necessary for the coefficient of $\mathfrak{M}^2$ in the numerator of Eq. (14.47) to exceed the coefficient of $\mathfrak{M}^2$ in the denominator; that is,

$$\frac{2}{3\delta}\frac{\gamma}{\gamma - 1}(1 - K)^2\frac{\beta_e^2}{1 + \beta_e^2} \equiv \psi \tag{14.48}$$

must exceed unity. To make ψ large, it is necessary for β_e to be large and δ small. In addition, the generator should be close to short-circuited, so that $K \approx 0$. Under these conditions, the maximum value of ψ is $\frac{5}{3}\delta$. Thus, if the Mach number of the flow is large, $T_e/T_0 \rightarrow 5/3\delta$.

(*b*) *Segmented Electrodes.* In the segmented-electrode generator, the total Hall current is zero so that the electric field from (14.10) is given by

$$\begin{aligned} E_y^* &= -(1 - K)UB \\ E_x^* &= -\frac{(1 - K)\beta_e UB}{1 + \beta_e\beta_I} \end{aligned} \tag{14.49}$$

Substitution of (14.49) into (14.42) yields

$$\mathbf{E}^*\cdot\mathbf{j}_e = \frac{\sigma(1 - K)^2U^2B^2}{1 + \beta_e^2}\left[\frac{1 + \beta_e^2 + 2\beta_e\beta_I + \beta_e^2\beta_I^2}{(1 + \beta_e\beta_I)^2}\right] \tag{14.50}$$

In the numerator in the brackets, β_I may be neglected in comparison to β_e; substitution of (14.50) into (14.41) yields

$$\frac{T_e}{T} = 1 + \frac{\gamma(1 - K)^2\beta_e^2\mathfrak{M}^2}{3\delta(1 + \beta_e\beta_I)^2} \tag{14.51}$$

for the asymptotic electron temperature; the ratio of the electron temperature to the local stagnation temperature is then

$$\frac{T_e}{T_0} = \frac{1 + \gamma(1 - K)^2\beta_e^2\mathfrak{M}^2/3\delta(1 + \beta_e\beta_I)^2}{1 + \frac{1}{2}(\gamma - 1)\mathfrak{M}^2} \tag{14.52}$$

Comparison of (14.52) with the corresponding expression for continuous electrodes (14.47) shows that the factor $\beta_e^2/(1 + \beta_e^2)$ which is always less than unity is replaced by $\beta_e^2/(1 + \beta_e\beta_I)$, which can be much greater than unity. In fact, as the magnetic field, i.e., β_e, is increased, $\beta_e^2/(1 + \beta_e\beta_I)$ has a maximum when $\beta_e = (\mu_e/\mu_I)^{\frac{1}{2}}$, which can be of the order of 10 to 20. The maximum value of the factor is therefore

$$\left.\frac{\beta_e^2}{(1 + \beta_e\beta_I)^2}\right|_{\max} = \frac{\beta^2_{e_{\max}}}{4} = \frac{1}{4}\frac{\mu_e}{\mu_I} \tag{14.53}$$

which is of the order of 25 to 250. Thus, considerable electron heating is possible in a segmented-electrode generator.

(*c*) *Hall Generator.* For the Hall generator, the components of the electric field are given by

$$\begin{aligned} E_y^* &= -UB \\ E_x^* &= \frac{\beta_e K_H UB}{1 + \beta_e\beta_I} \end{aligned} \tag{14.54}$$

Use of (14.54), (14.42), and (14.41) yields the following expression for the electron temperature:

$$\frac{T_e}{T} = 1 + \frac{\gamma \mathfrak{M}^2 \beta_e^2}{3(1 + \beta_e^2)} \left[\frac{K_H^2 \beta_e^2}{(1 + \beta_e \beta_I)^2} + 1 \right] \tag{14.55}$$

As the magnetic field is increased, the first factor $\beta_e^2/(1 + \beta_e^2)$ rapidly reaches a maximum of unity. The factor in the brackets reaches a maximum when $\beta_e^2 = \mu_e/\mu_I$; thus, this value of β_e yields the maximum electron temperature. Note that this maximum is the same as that for the segmented-electrode geometry. The maximum value of the coefficient of $\gamma \mathfrak{M}^2/3$ is then $1 + \frac{1}{4}K_H^2\beta_e^2$, which compares to $\frac{1}{4}(1 - K)^2\beta_e^2$ for the segmented-electrode generator. Since in the Hall generator K_H is comparable to $1 - K$ in the segmented-electrode generator, the maximum electron temperature is approximately the same in both generators.

(*d*) *Relaxation Length.* In addition to considering the asymptotic electron temperature and ionization which correspond to the homogeneous solution of Eq. (5.196), one should also consider the distance necessary to achieve this after the gas enters the generator. There are actually two processes which occur: the electron heating and the ionization by the heated electrons. Since the former is much faster than the latter, one may consider that the process occurs by two independent steps: first, the electrons are heated, and, second, the heated electrons ionize the neutral seed atoms. Although the ionization process occurs at the expense of the electron energy, it is sufficiently slow so that the electron ohmic heating maintains the electron temperature at the asymptotic value. Of course, the electron heating and ionization occur at the expense of the total enthalpy of the carrier gas, but if the degree of ionization is not very high, the gas temperature will not decrease appreciably, and one may take T and other gas properties as constant during the two processes. Thus, ignoring heat conduction, (5.196) predicts that the electron temperature is given by

$$\frac{T_e(x) - T_{e_a}}{T - T_{e_a}} = e^{-x/L_T} \tag{14.56}$$

where the relaxation length L_T is the length required for the electron temperature to reach 65 per cent of its asymptotic value, T_{e_a}, and is given by

$$L_T = \frac{5}{6} \frac{u}{\delta} \frac{\langle m \rangle}{m_e \nu_e} \approx \frac{\mathfrak{M}}{\delta} \left(\frac{\langle m \rangle}{m_e} \right)^{\frac{1}{2}} \lambda_e \tag{14.57}$$

Thus, the relaxation length for electron heating is several hundred mean free paths.

During the ionization process, the ohmic heating of the electrons supplies the ionization energy; thus,

$$\mathbf{j}_e \cdot \mathbf{E}^* = E_I \dot{n}_e \tag{14.58}$$

For the right side of (14.58) the continuity equation for electrons may be used, while for the left side one may use Ohm's law. For example, for segmented electrodes, neglecting ion slip, the electron-continuity equation becomes

$$\frac{d \ln n_e}{dx} = (1 - K)^2 \omega_e{}^2 \tau_e{}^2 n_e \nu_e u E_I{}^{-1} \tag{14.59}$$

from which a relaxation length for ionization L_c may be obtained,

$$L_c = \frac{E_I \lambda_e}{(1 - K)^2 \omega_e{}^2 \tau_e{}^2 m_e u \langle c \rangle_e}$$

or, in terms of dimensionless groups,

$$L_c \approx \frac{E_I}{3kT_e} \left(\frac{\langle m \rangle}{m_e} \right)^{\frac{1}{2}} \frac{1}{(1 - K)^2 \omega_e{}^2 \tau_e{}^2} \frac{\lambda_e}{\mathfrak{M}} \tag{14.60}$$

Experimentally, it has been found that the relaxation length is about 10 times longer[9] than that corresponding to Eq. (14.60), which verifies that the ionization length is indeed longer than the electron-temperature relaxation length. The ionization length should next be compared to the length of the MHD generator. Based on an interaction length of unity, the generator length is

$$L = \frac{p}{\sigma u B^2 (1 - K)} \approx \frac{n}{n_e} \left(\frac{\langle m \rangle}{m_e} \right)^{\frac{1}{2}} \frac{\lambda_e}{(1 - K) \omega_e{}^2 \tau_e{}^2 \mathfrak{M}} \tag{14.61}$$

Since the degree of ionization n_e/n is usually much smaller than the ratio of the electron thermal energy to ionization by two to three orders of magnitude, the generator length should be one to two orders of magnitude longer than the ionization length.

14.5 CONVERSION EFFICIENCY OF MHD GENERATORS

The local efficiency which was defined in the previous section is not useful for thermodynamic cycles, the reason being that the previous definition was based on local conditions instead of stagnation conditions. The local efficiency was defined by (14.7) as follows:

$$\eta_L = \frac{\mathbf{E} \cdot \mathbf{j}}{\mathbf{v} \cdot \mathbf{j} \times \mathbf{B}} = \frac{-\mathbf{E} \cdot \mathbf{j}}{\mathbf{j} \cdot (\mathbf{v} \times \mathbf{B})} = \frac{-\mathbf{E} \cdot \mathbf{j}}{-\mathbf{E} \cdot \mathbf{j} + \mathbf{E}^* \cdot \mathbf{j}}$$

Since the power density is $-\mathbf{E} \cdot \mathbf{j}$, and the ohmic heating per unit volume is $\mathbf{E}^* \cdot \mathbf{j}$, this definition is the same as

$$\eta_L = \frac{\text{power}}{\text{power} + \text{dissipation}}$$

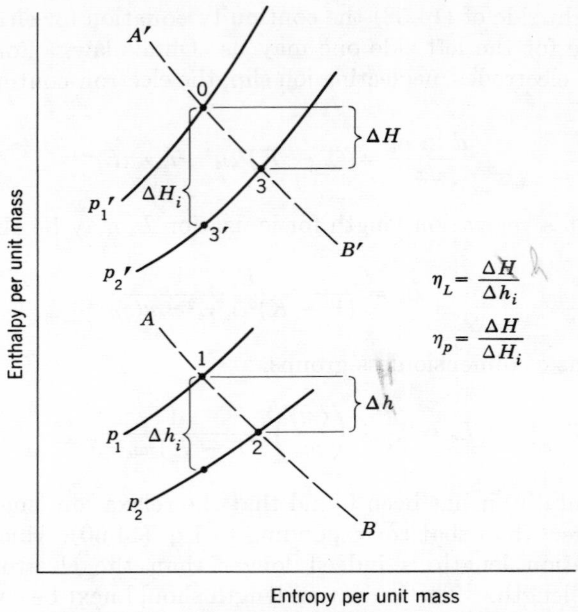

FIGURE 14.10 Relation between local and polytropic efficiencies.

The local efficiency can also be represented on a Mollier diagram along the static line AB (see Fig. 14.10). Consider two axial stations 1 and 2 along an MHD generator which are a distance Δx apart. As the gas passes between these two stations, the total enthalpy per unit mass is changed by ΔH, which is also equal to the change in static enthalpy if the change in gas velocity is negligible, while the static-pressure change is $p_1 - p_2$. The ideal change in static enthalpy between these two pressures is Δh_i. The *local* efficiency may therefore also be defined as

$$\eta_L = \frac{\Delta H}{\Delta h_i} \tag{14.62}$$

However, the thermodynamicist is usually interested in the *stagnation* behavior of the gas, as along the line $A'B'$. The reason for this is that the gas usually starts at a small Mach number in a combustor or heat exchanger, and after being accelerated in a nozzle and passing through the generator, is again brought almost to rest to recover the pressure or to pass the gas through a heat exchanger or some other low-speed device. The local efficiency calculated on the basis of stagnation conditions is called the *polytropic* efficiency η_p, sometimes called the *stage* or *local adiabatic* efficiency. From Fig. 14.10, $\eta_p = \Delta H/\Delta H_i$. Now because of the spreading of the constant-pressure lines with increasing enthalpy, $\Delta H_i > \Delta h_i$; hence, $\eta_p < \eta_L$.

A slightly different definition of the polytropic efficiency is

$$\eta_p = \frac{dH_e}{dH_i} \tag{14.63}$$

where dH_e is the increment in total enthalpy due to electric power generation, $-\mathbf{E} \cdot \mathbf{j}$, and dH_i is the isentropic or ideal change in total enthalpy within the same increment in pressure. The difference in dH_e and the actual change in total enthalpy dH is due to heat transfer from the gas. In this definition, the heat transfer is charged as a loss against the generator, although this energy may be utilized elsewhere in the cycle. For the ideal or isentropic generator with zero heat transfer, the first law of thermodynamics yields

$$dQ_i = 0 = dH_i - \frac{dp_s}{\rho_s} \tag{14.64}$$

where p_s and ρ_s are the stagnation pressure and density, respectively. Substitution of (14.64) into (14.63) and use of the ideal-gas law for the stagnation density yields

$$\eta_p = \frac{p_s}{RT_s} \cdot \frac{dH_e}{dp_s} = \frac{p_s}{RT_s} \cdot \frac{dH_e}{dH} \cdot \frac{dH}{dp_s} \tag{14.65}$$

The ratio dH_e/dH is the fraction of the total enthalpy which is converted into electric energy; the remainder is heat transfer from the generator; let this fraction be $a_e = dH_e/dH$. Also $dH = C_pT_s$, and $C_p/R = \gamma/(\gamma - 1)$ where γ is the ratio of specific heats. Then (14.65) may be written as

$$\eta_p = \frac{a_e\gamma}{\gamma - 1} \cdot \frac{d \ln H}{d \ln p_s} \tag{14.66}$$

which may be integrated to obtain

$$\frac{H}{H_0} = \left(\frac{p_s}{p_{s_0}}\right)^{\langle \eta_p(\gamma-1)/a_e\gamma \rangle} \tag{14.67}$$

where the exponent of the stagnation-pressure ratio is an average defined by the integration of (14.66) as follows:

$$\left\langle \frac{\eta_p(\gamma - 1)}{a_e\gamma} \right\rangle = \frac{\int_{p_{s_0}}^{p_s} \frac{\eta_p(\gamma - 1)}{a_e\gamma} \, d \ln p_s}{\int_{p_{s_0}}^{p_s} d \ln p_s} \tag{14.68}$$

Now, in the complete MHD generator, the stagnation enthalpy progresses from 0 to 3 (see Fig. 14.11), that is, from H_0 to H_3. The ideal change in enthalpy between the same stagnation pressures is given by $H_0 - H_{3'}$.

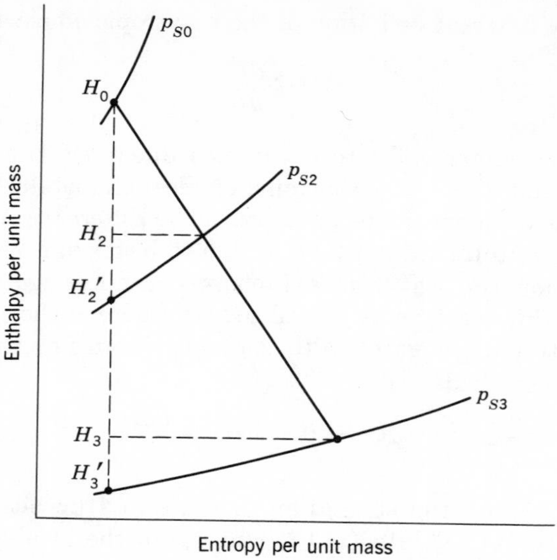

FIGURE 14.11 Effect of large stagnation pressure ratios on generator efficiencies.

The overall generator efficiency is defined as

$$\eta_g = \frac{a_e(H_0 - H_3)}{H_0 - H_{3'}} \tag{14.69}$$

since only the fraction a_e of $H_0 - H_3$ is converted into electric energy. The relation between $H_{3'}$ and H_0 is obtained from (14.67) with $\eta_p = a_e = 1$:

$$\frac{H_{3'}}{H_0} = \left(\frac{p_{s_3}}{p_{s_0}}\right)^{\langle(\gamma-1)/\gamma\rangle} \tag{14.70}$$

while H_3 is obtained from (14.67) directly. The generator efficiency therefore becomes

$$\eta_g = a_e \frac{[1 - (p_{s_3}/p_{s_0})^{\langle\eta_p(\gamma-1)/a_e\gamma\rangle}]}{[1 - (p_{s_3}/p_{s_0})^{\langle(\gamma-1)/\gamma\rangle}]} \tag{14.71}$$

For small pressure ratios across the generator, that is, for $p_{s_3}/p_{s_0} \approx 1$, the generator efficiency given by (14.71) becomes just η_p. But for large pressure ratios, the pressure-ratio terms in (14.71) become small, and the generator efficiency approaches a_e; if the pressure ratio is sufficiently large, the generator efficiency becomes independent of the polytropic efficiency. This effect is well known in the design of steam turbines and is the reason for designing them for very large pressure ratios. The reason for the high efficiency is as follows: The dissipation in each stage, or at each section of the generator, appears as heat energy which is passed onto the next stage or section. The main effect of the dissipation is that the loss of total pressure is small owing to the flattening of the constant-pressure lines at low pressure on the Mollier diagram, as shown in Fig. 14.11. For moderate pressure ratios, η_g is equal to an $(H_0 - H_2)/(H_0 - H_{2'})$. For large pressure ratios, η_g is shown as an $(H_0 - H_3)/(H_0 - H_{3'})$. From Fig. 14.11, it is seen that the generator efficiency is larger for the larger pressure ratio. Note that large pressure ratios imply large temperature ratios, since (14.71) can also be written as

$$\eta_g \approx \frac{a_e[1 - (T_{s_{3'}}/T_{s_0})^{\eta_p/a_e}]}{1 - T_{s_{3'}}/T_{s_0}} \tag{14.72}$$

with the use of (14.70).

However, in an MHD generator in which combustion gases are used at pressures greater than one atmosphere, the lowest total temperature at which the gas still has sufficient electrical conductivity is about 4000°R; the highest possible flame temperature is about 8000°R. For these conditions, it is important that the polytropic efficiency be as high as possible because the generator efficiency, as calculated from (14.71) or (14.72), will be only slightly larger than η_p. The generator efficiency will be improved appreciably over the polytropic efficiency if the pressure ratio is very large, which requires some method for improving the electrical conductivity at low temperatures.

14.5.1 Polytropic Efficiency in Linear MHD Generators. In this section, the general expression is derived for the polytropic efficiency in linear MHD generators under steady flow conditions at a particular generator station x, where the flow velocity in the x direction is $u(x)$, and the transverse velocity components are negligible. As before, the local magnetic field is transverse to the generator in the z direction. It is assumed that the magnetic Reynolds number is small, so that perturbations of the imposed magnetic field may be neglected. If current is allowed to flow, then there will be a Lorentz force in the direction of the flow, and power generation per unit volume equal to $-\mathbf{E} \cdot \mathbf{j}$. In addition, there is a friction pressure drop $(dp/dx)_f$ which is also negative, given as follows:

$$\left(\frac{dp}{dx}\right)_f = -\frac{\tau_w C}{A} \tag{14.73}$$

where τ_w is the average shear stress at the wall, C is the perimeter length of the cross section, and A is the cross-sectional area; each of these will generally be a function of the generator station x. In general, a friction factor c_f is defined as follows:

$$\tau_w = \tfrac{1}{2}\rho u^2 c_f \tag{14.74}$$

In addition to the skin friction, there may also be heat transfer from the gases in the MHD generator to the walls; this is given by

$$\rho u \left(\frac{dH}{dx}\right)_q = -\, q_w \frac{C}{A} \tag{14.75}$$

where q_w is the average heat-transfer rate per unit area over the perimeter of the cross section. The heat-transfer rate is generally related to the film coefficient h as follows:

$$q_w = h(T_s - T_w) \tag{14.76}$$

where T_s is the local bulk gas-stagnation temperature, and T_w is the wall temperature; the film coefficient is usually made nondimensional as follows:

$$S_t = \frac{h}{\rho u C_p} \tag{14.77}$$

where S_t is the local Stanton number. Now, if the Prandtl number of the gas, $C_p\eta/\mathcal{K}$, is close to unity, as is the case for most gases when the degree of ionization is less than a few per cent, then, as a general rule, the Stanton number is equal to half the friction factor,† or

$$S_t \approx \tfrac{1}{2}c_f \tag{14.78}$$

To apply these relations to a linear MHD generator, Eqs. (11.2) and (11.3) are utilized, with the assumption that all quantities vary only in the flow direction x. These equations then become

$$\rho u \frac{du}{dx} + \frac{dp}{dx} = (\mathbf{j} \times \mathbf{B})_x + \left(\frac{dp}{dx}\right)_f = \frac{(\mathbf{j} \times \mathbf{B})_x}{b_e} \tag{14.79}$$

$$\rho u \frac{dH}{dx} = \mathbf{E} \cdot \mathbf{j} - \frac{q_w C}{A} = \frac{\mathbf{E} \cdot \mathbf{j}}{a_e} \tag{14.80}$$

where b_e is the fraction of the total pressure drop due to the Lorentz force,

$$b_e = \frac{(\mathbf{j} \times \mathbf{B})_x}{(\mathbf{j} \times \mathbf{B})_x + (dp/dx)_f} \tag{14.81}$$

and a_e is the fraction of the enthalpy drop which is due to electric power generation, as previously defined. From (14.80),

$$\frac{dH_e}{dx} = \frac{\mathbf{E} \cdot \mathbf{j}}{\rho u} \tag{14.82}$$

and, from (14.65), the polytropic efficiency is

$$\eta_p = \frac{p_s}{RT_s} \frac{dH_e/dx}{dp_s/dx} = \frac{\mathbf{E} \cdot \mathbf{j}}{\rho u R T_s \, d(\ln p_s)/dx} \tag{14.83}$$

† The presence of a magnetic field may alter this relation, if the magnetic interaction parameter is much larger than unity.

To evaluate $d(\ln p_s)/dx$, use is made of the following isentropic relation,

$$\frac{p_s}{p} = \left(\frac{T_s}{T}\right)^{\gamma/(\gamma-1)}$$

or

$$\ln p_s = \ln p + \frac{\gamma}{\gamma - 1} \ln T_s - \frac{\gamma}{\gamma - 1} \ln T \tag{14.84}$$

Differentiation with respect to x yields

$$\frac{d(\ln p_s)}{dx} = \frac{p'}{p} - \frac{\gamma}{\gamma - 1}\frac{T'}{T} + \frac{\gamma}{\gamma - 1}\frac{T'_s}{T_s} \tag{14.85}$$

where $(\quad)' \equiv d/dx$. Next, substitute

$$H' = C_p T' + uu' \tag{14.86}$$

into the energy equation, and eliminate $\rho uu'$ between the energy equation and the momentum equation. The result is

$$\frac{p'}{p} - \frac{\gamma}{\gamma - 1}\frac{T'}{T} = \frac{1}{p}\left[\frac{(\mathbf{j} \times \mathbf{B})_x}{b_e} - \frac{\mathbf{E} \cdot \mathbf{j}}{u}\right] \tag{14.87}$$

Also, from the energy equation,

$$T'_s = \frac{\mathbf{E} \cdot \mathbf{j}}{a_e \rho u C_p} \tag{14.88}$$

Substitution of (14.87) and (14.88) into (14.85), and then into (14.83), yields

$$\eta_p = \frac{a_e}{\dfrac{\mathbf{v} \cdot (\mathbf{j} \times \mathbf{B})}{\mathbf{E} \cdot \mathbf{j}} \cdot \dfrac{a_e}{b_e} \cdot \dfrac{T_s}{T} + 1 - \dfrac{T_s}{T}} \tag{14.89}$$

since $u(\mathbf{j} \times \mathbf{B})_x \equiv \mathbf{v} \cdot (\mathbf{j} \times \mathbf{B})$; hence, the first factor in the denominator is just the reciprocal of the previously defined "local" electrical efficiency η_L. Thus, the polytropic efficiency becomes

$$\eta_p = \frac{a_e}{a_e T_s/\eta_L b_e T + 1 - T_s/T} \tag{14.90}$$

where T_s/T is the ratio of the local stagnation temperature to static temperature, and for a perfect gas is given by

$$\frac{T_s}{T} = 1 + \frac{\gamma - 1}{2}\mathfrak{M}^2 \tag{14.91}$$

where $\mathfrak{M}$ is the local Mach number. To proceed, expressions are required for a_e and b_e. Several possible cases will be examined in the next two sections.

14.5.2 Polytropic Efficiency for Zero Friction and Zero Heat Transfer. For this case $a_e = b_e = 1$, and use of (14.91) in (14.90) yields

$$\eta_p = \frac{\eta_L}{1 + \frac{\gamma - 1}{2} \mathfrak{M}^2(1 - \eta_L)} \tag{14.92}$$

Thus, for the polytropic efficiency to be close to the local efficiency η_L, either η_L must be close to unity or else $\frac{1}{2}(\gamma - 1)\mathfrak{M}^2$ must be small. Thus, the local efficiency η_L is identically equal to the polytropic efficiency of a subsonic, zero-heat-transfer, zero-friction flow. For combustion gases where $\gamma \approx 1.2$, $\mathfrak{M} \approx 1$, and $\eta_L = 0.8$, the polytropic efficiency is only 2 per cent less than η_L. But for gases in which $\gamma = \frac{5}{3}$, $\mathfrak{M} = 2$, and $\eta_L = 0.8$, the polytropic efficiency is almost 25 per cent less than the local efficiency η_L.

14.5.3 Polytropic Efficiency with Friction but Zero Heat Transfer. With friction but zero pressure drop, $a_e = 1$, and from the definition of b_e,

$$\frac{1}{b_e} = 1 - \frac{\tau_w C/A}{(\mathbf{j} \times \mathbf{B})_x} \tag{14.93}$$

To proceed further, an expression is needed for $(\mathbf{j} \times \mathbf{B})_x$, which requires that the geometry be specified. Actually, since the local efficiency is equal to K for both the continuous- and segmented-electrode geometries, they may be considered as one case with an effective transverse electrical conductivity, which is evaluated as follows:

Continuous electrodes: $\sigma_{\text{eff}} = \dfrac{\sigma}{(1 + \beta_e\beta_I)^2 + \beta_e^2}$

Segmented electrodes: $\sigma_{\text{eff}} = \dfrac{\sigma}{1 + \beta_e\beta_I}$

Since the local efficiency is different for the Hall generator, this will be considered separately.

(*a*) *Continuous- and Segmented-electrode Generators.* For these two geometries, $(\mathbf{j} \times \mathbf{B})_x = (K - 1)\sigma_{\text{eff}} u B^2$, so that the expression for b_e becomes

$$\frac{1}{b_e} = 1 + \frac{c_f}{2I(1 - K)} \tag{14.94}$$

where I is the magnetic interaction parameter based on a length equal to A/C as follows:

$$I = \frac{\sigma_{\text{eff}} B^2 A}{\rho u C} \tag{14.95}$$

Finally, a parameter Z may be defined as

$$Z = \frac{c_f}{2I} \tag{14.96}$$

so that b_e is given by

$$\frac{1}{b_e} = 1 + \frac{Z}{1 - K} \tag{14.97}$$

Substitution of (14.97) into the expression for the polytropic efficiency yields

$$\eta_p = \frac{1}{\{[(1 - K + Z)/K(1 - K)] - 1\}T_s/T + 1} \tag{14.98}$$

Now, for any given value of Z and T_s/T, there is a value of K which minimizes the expression in braces in (14.98), and which therefore yields the highest polytropic efficiency. This value of $K = K_m$ is given by

$$K_m = 1 + Z - \sqrt{Z + Z^2} \tag{14.99}$$

or, alternatively,

$$Z = \frac{(1 - K_m)^2}{2K_m - 1} \tag{14.100}$$

The maximum polytropic efficiency is therefore

$$\eta_{pm} = \frac{2K_m - 1}{1 + (1 - K_m)(\gamma - 1)\mathfrak{M}^2} \tag{14.101}$$

For subsonic flows where the Mach number is negligible, $\eta_{pm} = 2K_m - 1$; substitution of K_m in terms of η_{pm} into Eq. (14.100) then yields

$$Z\bigg|_{\mathfrak{M} \ll 1} = \frac{(1 - \eta_{pm})^2}{4\eta_{pm}} \tag{14.102}$$

which is identical to the expression for the maximum *local* efficiency of a Hall generator, given by (14.21) with Z replacing $1/\beta_e'^2$. This indicates that small values of Z are required to achieve high values of the polytropic efficiency. Now, I based on A/C will seldom be more than 0.1, while the friction factor f is generally inversely proportional to the Reynolds number raised to the power of $\frac{1}{2}$ for laminar flows and 0.2 for turbulent flows.† The result is that very large flow Reynolds numbers are required to obtain high values of the polytropic efficiency; that is, Z must be small.

For Z much less than unity, and finite Mach number, the above expressions may be simplified as follows:

$$Z \ll 1: \qquad K_m \approx 1 - \sqrt{Z} \tag{14.103}$$

$$\eta_{pm} \approx 1 - 2\sqrt{Z}\left(1 + \frac{\gamma - 1}{2}\mathfrak{M}^2\right) \tag{14.104}$$

which clearly shows that the polytropic efficiency decreases with both increasing Z and Mach number.

† It has been assumed here that the magnetic field does not affect the friction factor.

(*b*) *Hall Generator.* From (14.16) and (14.81) the expression for b_e becomes

$$\frac{1}{b_e} = 1 + \frac{1 + \beta_{e1}'^2}{1 + \beta_e'^2 K} Z \tag{14.105}$$

so that the expression for the polytropic efficiency (14.90) becomes

$$\frac{1}{\eta_p} = 1 - \frac{T_s}{T} + \frac{1}{K(1-K)}\left[\frac{1+Z}{\beta_e'^2}(1+Z) + K + Z\right] \tag{14.106}$$

This expression is essentially the same as that given by (14.92) in the absence of friction, except that in computing the local efficiency of the Hall generator, $\beta_e'^2$ should be divided by the factor $1 + Z + \beta_e'^2 Z$.

14.6 ELECTRICAL LOSSES IN MHD GENERATORS

In addition to the friction losses described in Sec. 14.5, there may be electrical losses in the MHD generator, caused by inhomogeneous current flow in the generator. Generally, there are three types of such losses:

1. End losses, associated with eddy currents at the inlet and exit of the generator
2. Effects in the vicinity of segmented electrodes, especially when the conductivity is tensor
3. Inhomogeneities in the electrical properties of the gas, which tend to short-circuit the Hall current[10]

At present, the first two effects are the best known, and so this section will concentrate on these. To solve such problems, it is usually assumed that the gas properties, velocity, and magnetic field are constant; that the boundary layer is negligible; and that the sides of the generator are straight and parallel. With these assumptions, there is no variation in the direction of the magnetic field, so that the problem becomes two-dimensional in the plane normal to **B**. Also, because of the assumption of constant properties, both the electric field potential and electric current stream function obey Laplace's equation. Thus, the problem can generally be solved by conformal mapping. The solutions to the first two problems are given below.

14.6.1 End Losses.[11,12] End losses are caused by the flow of current from the positive electrode to the negative electrode in the ionized gas upstream and downstream of the magnetic field. For $L/h > 0.7$, this effect can be computed by calculating the effect separately for each end and summing the two effects; in the following these two losses are taken as equal, corresponding to the model of constant properties and cross

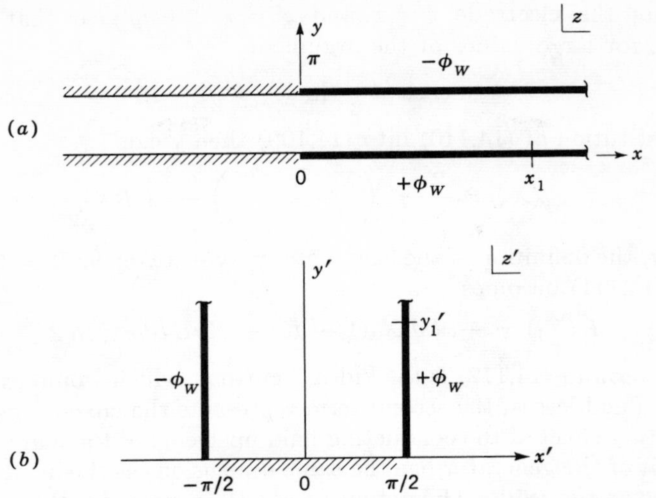

FIGURE 14.12 Conformal mapping of end losses. (a) Physical plane; (b) transformed plane $z = \ln \sin z'$.

section. It is also assumed that the Hall effect is negligible. Since $\nabla \cdot \mathbf{j} = 0$, from Ohm's law, it follows that $\nabla^2\phi = 0$, where ϕ is the electric field potential and $\mathbf{E} = -\nabla\phi$. The electrode voltages are taken as $\pm\phi_w$, so that the generator voltage is $2\phi_w$. Upstream of the electrodes, outside the magnetic field, the current j_y is zero, so that $\partial\phi/\partial y$ is also zero (see Fig. 14.12) because it is assumed that for $x < 0$, $B = 0$. In the remainder of this section, X and Y refer to dimensional coordinates, and x and y are made nondimensional by the scale factor h/π. The generator is conformally mapped into the z plane by

$$z = \ln \sin z' \tag{14.107}$$

From the boundary conditions, the complex potential $\Phi = \phi + i\psi$ is given by

$$\Phi = \frac{2\phi_w z'}{\pi} \tag{14.108}$$

where ψ is the current stream function, so that the total current from the end of the electrode to some point on the electrode is

$$J_y(x_1) = -\sigma\left[\psi\left(\frac{\pi}{2}, 0\right) - \psi\left(\frac{\pi}{2}, y_1'\right)\right] - \frac{\sigma UBh}{\pi}x_1$$

or, from (14.108),

$$J_y(X_1) = \frac{2\sigma\phi_w y_1'}{\pi} - \sigma UBX_1 \tag{14.109}$$

Along the electrode $z = x$ and $z' = \pi/2 + iy'$, so that (14.107) becomes, for large values of the argument,

$$x = \ln \cosh y' \approx \ln \tfrac{1}{2}e^{y} \approx y' - \ln 2 \tag{14.110}$$

Substitution of (14.110) into (14.109) then yields

$$J_y(X_1) = \frac{2}{\pi}\sigma\phi_w\left(\frac{X_1\pi}{h} + \ln 2\right) - \sigma UBX_1 \tag{14.111}$$

Now, the definition of the load factor may be taken as $K = 2\phi_w/UBh$ so that (14.111) becomes

$$J_y(X_1) = -\sigma UBX_1(1 - K) + K\sigma UBh\pi^{-1}\ln 2 \tag{14.112}$$

The first term in (14.112) is the "ideal" current, which would exist in the absence of end losses; the second term represents the current loss, due to the shunting effect of the conducting fluid upstream of the magnetic field. If the exit of the generator has the same dimensions as the inlet, a similar loss exists at the exit. The actual power P_a is given by the product of the voltage $KUBh$ and the total current as follows:

$$P_a = \sigma U^2B^2Kh[(1 - K)L - 2\pi^{-1}h\ln 2] \tag{14.113}$$

To calculate the efficiency, the flow work W through the generator must be found:

$$W = \int_0^h \int_0^L \mathbf{v}\cdot\mathbf{j}\times\mathbf{B}\,dY\,dX$$

$$= -\sigma\int_0^L \int_0^h \left(\frac{\partial\phi}{\partial Y} + UB\right)UB\,dX\,dY \tag{14.114}$$

The integration is taken over X to obtain the average flow work across the generator, while the integration over Y is taken only where the magnetic field is nonzero. Integration with respect to Y and then X and use of the definition of K yield

$$W = -\sigma(1 - K)U^2B^2Lh \tag{14.115}$$

which is identical to the expression which one obtains if the end regions are ignored. The efficiency is then given by

$$\eta = -\frac{P_a}{W} = K\left(1 - \frac{Ka^*}{1 - K}\right) \tag{14.116}$$

from (14.115) and (14.114), where a^* is proportional to the generator aspect ratio,

$$a^* = \frac{2}{\pi}\frac{h}{L}\ln 2 \tag{14.117}$$

Note that as the generator becomes very long, that is, as $a^* \to 0$, then the expression for the efficiency becomes identical to the local efficiency K. Also, $K = 0$ still corresponds to short circuit, but open-circuit

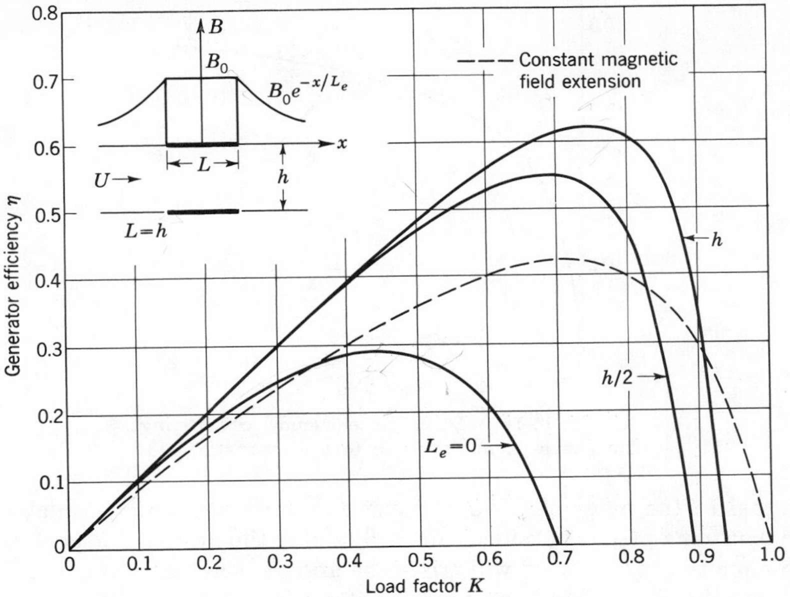

FIGURE 14.13 Generator efficiency, for channel length equal to channel width.

conditions correspond to the expression in parentheses in (14.116) equal to zero, e.g., when

$$K_{OC} = \frac{1}{1 + a^*} \tag{14.118}$$

Thus, the larger the value of a^*, the smaller the open-circuit voltage. However, when the voltage is equal to the open-circuit voltage, the efficiency is equal to zero, instead of equal to K as for the ideal generator. A typical efficiency curve is shown in Fig. 14.13 for an aspect ratio $L/h = 1$. Note that the maximum efficiency is only 0.29, corresponding to a loading factor of 0.45. As the aspect ratio L/h increases, a^* decreases, and both the maximum efficiency and loading factor at maximum efficiency increase. For any given aspect ratio, the maximum efficiency is obtained by equating to zero the derivative of (14.116). The maximum efficiency is then given by

$$\eta_m = \frac{\sqrt{1/a^* + 1} - 1}{\sqrt{1/a^* + 1} + 1} \tag{14.119}$$

This maximum efficiency is shown in Fig. 14.14. It is seen that large aspect ratios are required to obtain efficiencies greater than 0.6.

For a given aspect ratio, the efficiency can be improved by the insertion of insulating vanes at the inlet and exit, parallel to the flow but

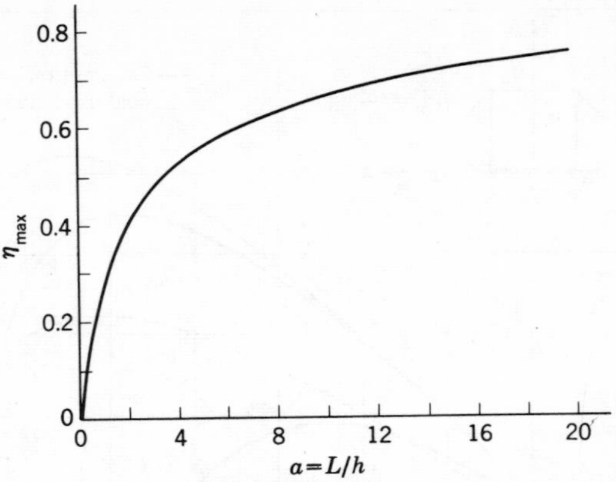

FIGURE 14.14 Maximum efficiency considering end losses—zero extension to the magnetic field.

external to the magnetic field region. For example, a single inlet vane and exit vane placed in midstream will double the apparent aspect ratio; two equally spaced vanes will triple the apparent aspect ratio, etc.

Another method of improving the efficiency is to extend the magnetic field. Actually, most magnetic fields decrease exponentially away from the pole faces. Hence, this type of "shading" is considered next.

Now, for this case,

$$B = B_0 e^{x/L_e} \qquad \text{for } x < 0$$

so that along the insulator, for j_y to be zero,

$$\frac{\partial \phi}{\partial y} = -\frac{h}{\pi} U B_0 e^{x/L_e} \qquad \text{for } x < 0 \tag{14.120}$$

The resulting efficiencies are shown in Fig. 14.13 for two different e-folding lengths of the magnetic field, $\frac{1}{2}h$ and h. It is seen that considerable improvement in the efficiency is obtained by slight shading of the magnetic field.

14.6.2 Effect of Hall Currents. In Sec. 14.3 it was shown that segmentation of electrodes should stop the axial Hall currents. In this section, we will examine in detail the current flow in the vicinity of such electrodes. The components of current are given by

$$\begin{gathered} j_{B_x} = \frac{\sigma' \beta_e' U B}{1 + \beta_e'^2} \qquad j_{B_y} = -\frac{\sigma' U B}{1 + \beta_e'^2} \\ j_{\phi_x} = \frac{\sigma'}{1 + \beta_e'^2}\left(-\frac{\partial \phi}{\partial x} + \beta_e' \frac{\partial \phi}{\partial y}\right) \\ j_{\phi_y} = \frac{\sigma'}{1 + \beta_e'^2}\left(-\frac{\partial \phi}{\partial y} - \beta_e' \frac{\partial \phi}{\partial x}\right) \end{gathered} \tag{14.121}$$

where $\mathbf{j}_B$ is the induced current $\boldsymbol{\sigma} \cdot (\mathbf{v} \times \mathbf{B})$ and $\mathbf{j}_\phi = -\boldsymbol{\sigma} \cdot \nabla\phi$. Thus, if j_{ϕ_y} is specified as zero on a boundary, then $\partial\phi/\partial y = -\beta_e(\partial\phi/\partial x)$. Therefore the equipotential lines have a slope of β_e^{-1} with respect to the x axis.

To solve this type of problem, one may conformal-map the original region such that the equipotential lines are straight and equally spaced in the transformed plane.[2] The boundaries along which the potential lines are sloped are then mapped at the appropriate angle to the equipotential lines. This problem may also be solved by numerical solution of Laplace's equation, with these boundary conditions. For example, the performance of continuous electrodes has been calculated[2] when the electrical conductivity upstream of the electrode region is zero.

Using this same technique, the potential field and current have been obtained when the magnetic field and electrical conductivity are extended infinitely upstream of the electrodes[13] and when the electrodes are skewed with respect to one another.[14] The mapping technique has also been used to determine the current flow in the vicinity of segmented electrodes[2] (see Chap. 10); numerical techniques have also been used.[15]

If the electrode-pitch distance were infinitely small, the effective transverse conductivity would be equal to the scalar electron conductivity σ'. However, the current concentration (for constant electrical conductivity) causes an additional impedence, which causes the effective transverse conductivity to be reduced. Since the Hall electric field is directly proportional to the transverse current density, any decrease in transverse current immediately reduces the axial electric field. This relationship is given below, for $(\omega_e\tau_e)' > 1$,

$$\frac{\sigma_{\text{eff}}}{\sigma'} = \frac{E_x}{\beta_e' UB(1-K)} = \left[1 + \frac{d}{h}\left[(\omega_e\tau_e)' - 0.441\right]\right]^{-1} \tag{14.122}$$

where d is the electrode pitch. Equation (14.122) shows that for large values of $(\omega_e\tau_e)'$, very small electrode pitches are required in order that the transverse conductivity σ_{eff} be close to the theoretical value, σ'.

The effect of end losses with segmented electrodes has also been investigated theoretically.[16,17] It is found that as $(\omega_e\tau_e)'$ increases, the end losses decrease because the eddy currents become skewed, and thereby decreased.

14.7 COMPRESSIBLE FLOW IN FARADAY–CURRENT MHD GENERATORS

In this section, expressions are derived for the change in properties in an MHD generator, taking into account the compressibility of the gas. We shall concentrate on linear flows with variable cross section. Friction and heat transfer will be neglected; this is permissible if the Z factor given by Eq. (14.96) is sufficiently small. As in Sec. 14.5, the quasi–one-

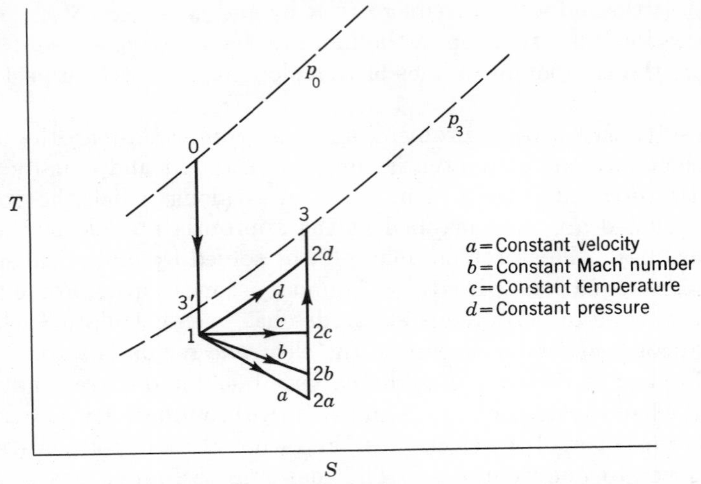

FIGURE 14.15 Paths on a Mollier diagram for various linear MHD generators. Point 0 = stagnation conditions upstream of generator; 1 = generator inlet; 2 = generator exhaust; 3 = stagnation conditions corresponding to generator exhaust.

dimensional flow equations will be used [Eqs. (14.79) and (14.80)], together with the perfect-gas law, since the degree of ionization is generally so low that the compressibility factor is unity. In addition, the conservation of mass is used,

$$\rho u A = \dot{m} = \text{const} \tag{14.123}$$

and the magnetic field is specified, usually constant. With these equations, there are always two more unknowns than equations; hence, no general solution is possible. Two additional relations are required. In the following, the ratio K, of E_y to uB, will be specified, since this ratio is related to polytropic efficiency and one would normally wish to design the generator with η_p nearly constant. In addition, one of the flow variables, such as u, $\mathfrak{M}$, T, p, ρ, or A, can be specified. The path of gas on a temperature-entropy diagram is shown in Fig. 14.15. The initial stagnation conditions are shown as subscript zero. The gas is then isentropically accelerated to some velocity (1) in a nozzle; this velocity may be either subsonic or supersonic. The gas then enters the generator and as a result of ohmic heating of the gas, the entropy increases (2). The effect of the entropy change is that the exit stagnation pressure p_3 is always less than the inlet stagnation pressure p_0.

For Faraday generators, the transverse electric current density from (14.2) and (14.11) may be written as

$$j_y = -\sigma(1 - K)uB \tag{14.124}$$

so that the momentum equation (14.79) becomes

$$\text{Momentum:} \qquad \rho u \frac{du}{dx} + \frac{dp}{dx} = -\sigma(1 - K)uB^2 \tag{14.125}$$

For either the segmented- or continuous-electrode generator, $E_x j_x = 0$, so that the only contribution to the energy equation (14.80) is $E_y j_y$. Thus,

$$\text{Energy:} \qquad \rho u \frac{d}{dx}(C_p T + \tfrac{1}{2}u^2) = -\sigma K(1 - K)u^2B^2 \tag{14.126}$$

The effect of any transverse pressure gradients due to Hall currents is generally neglected. In the remainder of this section, several solutions will be given.

14.7.1 Constant-velocity Generator.† In the constant-velocity generator, u is taken as constant. The first integral was then obtained in Sec. 11.5 as follows:

$$\frac{T(x)}{T_1} = \left[\frac{p(x)}{p_1}\right]^{K(\gamma-1)/\gamma} \tag{14.127}$$

The usual isentropic expression corresponds to $K = 1$, so that (14.127) shows that for the same pressure ratio, the temperature decrease in an MHD generator is *always* less than isentropic.

The entropy change may be calculated from

$$\Delta S = C_p \ln \frac{T}{T_1} - R \ln \frac{p}{p_1} = C_p \frac{1 - K}{K} \ln \frac{T_1}{T} \tag{14.128}$$

which shows the rapid increase in entropy with decreasing K. The variation with x is given directly by integration of (14.125), for σ constant,

$$p_1 - p = \sigma(1 - K)uB^2x \tag{14.129}$$

so that the generator length is given by

$$L = \frac{p_1 - p_2}{(1 - K)\sigma u B^2} \tag{14.130}$$

The pressure drop may also be expressed in terms of the magnetic interaction parameter I, equal to $\sigma B^2 L/\rho u$, as follows:

$$\frac{p_2}{p_1} = 1 - \mathfrak{M}^2\gamma(1 - K)I \tag{14.131}$$

† For the case of constant-velocity flow, (14.123) to (14.126) were integrated in Sec. 11.5. The results for constant E_y are given by (11.41) to (11.45), while for constant K, (11.49) corresponds to (14.129).

Now, in order for an appreciable fraction of the energy to be extracted, the temperature ratio T_2/T_1 should be small, which means from (14.127) that $p_2/p_1 \ll 1$. Thus, (14.131) shows that I must be of the order of unity.

From (14.130) one may also observe that the length is minimized when the product $\sigma u/p_1$ is a maximum. For thermal ionization, however, as u is increased, the static temperature decreases [see (14.126)], and the degree of ionization also decreases. One therefore finds that there is an optimum inlet temperature ratio, given by

$$\frac{T_1}{T_0} = \frac{\xi + \zeta \pm \sqrt{\xi^2 - 2\xi\zeta + \zeta^2 + \frac{4}{3}\zeta}}{2\xi - \frac{2}{3}} \tag{14.132}$$

where

$$\xi = \frac{\gamma}{\gamma - 1} - \frac{1}{2}$$

$$\zeta = \frac{E_I}{3kT_0}$$

From (14.132) one may show that for combustion gases the optimum inlet Mach number is slightly supersonic.

The above results were obtained by assuming the conductivity was constant; however, the equations may also be integrated directly† for thermal ionization, neglecting the Hall effect.[18] The result is given by Eq. (11.55). Assuming that α is approximately constant, the generator length is minimized by minimizing x^*; that is, $p_1/\sigma_1 u$; yielding the same results as given by (14.132).

For constant specific heat C_p, the generator efficiency, as defined by (14.69), becomes

$$\eta_G = \frac{T_0 - T_3}{T_0 - T_{3'}} = \frac{1 - T_3/T_0}{1 - T_{3'}/T_0} \tag{14.133}$$

where $T_{3'}$ is the temperature corresponding to an isentropic expansion from (T_0, p_0) to pressure p_3:

$$\frac{T_{3'}}{T_0} = \left(\frac{p_3}{p_0}\right)^{(\gamma-1)/\gamma} \tag{14.134}$$

For low subsonic Mach numbers, the generator efficiency is always greater than the polytropic efficiency, that is, greater than the loading factor, owing to the reheat factor; but for supersonic Mach numbers, the generator efficiency can be considerably less than K, owing to the Mach number effect given in (14.92).

14.7.2 Constant-Mach-number Generator. In the constant-velocity generator described above, the gas temperature decreases so that the Mach number at the exit is greater than at the inlet, increasing sub-

† An alternate method of integration, useful for either variable σ or B was given in Chap. 11.

sequent diffuser losses. This can be alleviated by designing the generator for constant Mach number. Since $u^2 = \mathfrak{M}^2\gamma RT$, differentiation yields

$$uu' = \tfrac{1}{2}\mathfrak{M}^2\gamma RT' \tag{14.135}$$

Use of (14.135) in the momentum and energy equations leads to the following first integral,

$$\frac{p}{p_1} = \left(\frac{T}{T_1}\right)^{\gamma/(\gamma-1)\eta_p} \tag{14.136}$$

where η_p is the polytropic efficiency given by (14.92). If K is constant, then η_p is constant since $\mathfrak{M}$ is constant. With the use of (11.49), (14.135), and (14.136), the energy equation can be integrated to obtain the variation of temperature with distance; the result is identical to (11.52), except that the value of x^* is increased by the factor $[1 + \frac{1}{2}(\gamma - 1)\mathfrak{M}^2]$, and α must be increased by 0.5.

Because the Mach number is constant, the stagnation-temperature ratio is equal to the static-temperature ratio. Thus, the generator efficiency is given by

$$\eta_G = \frac{1 - (p_3/p_0)^{\eta_p(\gamma-1)/\gamma}}{1 - (p_3/p_0)^{(\gamma-1)/\gamma}} \tag{14.137}$$

14.7.3 Constant-temperature Generator. The first integral, obtained from the energy and momentum equations, is

$$\frac{p(x)}{p_1} = \exp\left[(u_1^2 - u^2)\frac{K-1}{2KRT_1}\right] \tag{14.138}$$

For the electrical conductivity given by (11.49) and constant K and B, the variation of velocity with distance along the generator is given by[19]

$$\int_1^{F\mathfrak{M}_2/\mathfrak{M}_1} e^{\xi^2}\,d\xi = \frac{F\sigma K(1-K)u_1B^2}{p_1\mathfrak{M}_1^2} \tag{14.139}$$

where
$$F = \left[\frac{3(1-K)\gamma\mathfrak{M}_1^2}{4K}\right]^{\frac{1}{2}}$$

The generator efficiency may be derived in the same manner as in the previous sections.

14.7.4 Constant Cross-sectional Area.[20] For the purposes of performing experiments on magnetohydrodynamic electric power generation, the most convenient channel configuration is a straight, rectangular duct of constant width and height, and hence constant area. For continuous electrodes, the voltage difference between the two electrodes will be constant, and hence the electric field will be a constant. This causes the loading factor K to vary along the length of the generator, so that the local conversion efficiency varies. In fact, it is possible to have one part of the duct acting as a generator while some other part is acting as an accelerator. The flow Mach number tends toward $\mathfrak{M} \approx 1$. If the flow was initially subsonic, the temperature decreases while the velocity increases. Thus, additional thermal energy is converted into kinetic energy, which is not recoverable in the generator. If the flow was initially supersonic, the velocity will decrease and temperature will increase, so that some thermal energy cannot be converted. For these reasons, the constant cross-sectional-area generator does not appear to be practical. The solution for constant transverse electric field is given by (11.35). Based on that solution the length required to reach $\mathfrak{M}_2 = 1$ has been calculated in ref. 21, and is shown in Fig. 14.16. It is seen that

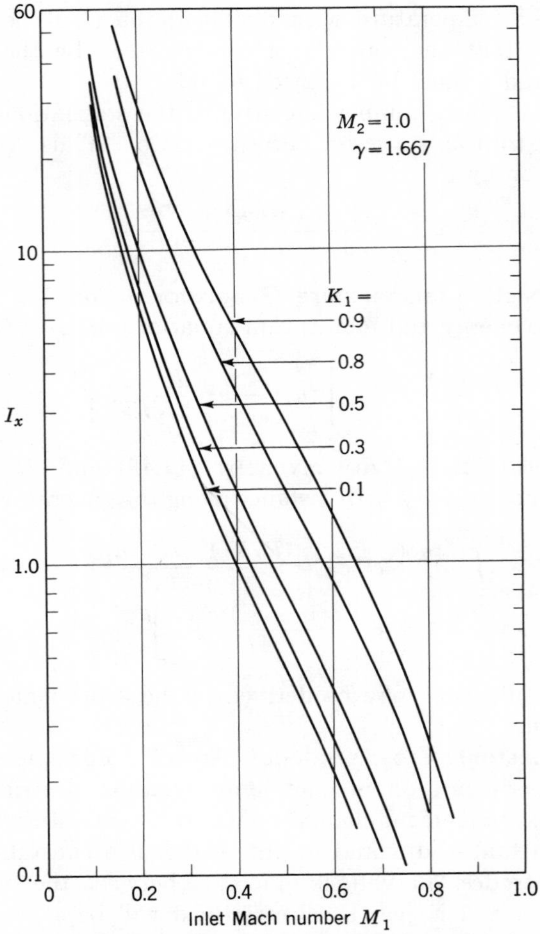

FIGURE 14.16 Length to reach Mach 1.0 at outlet. (From ref. 21.)

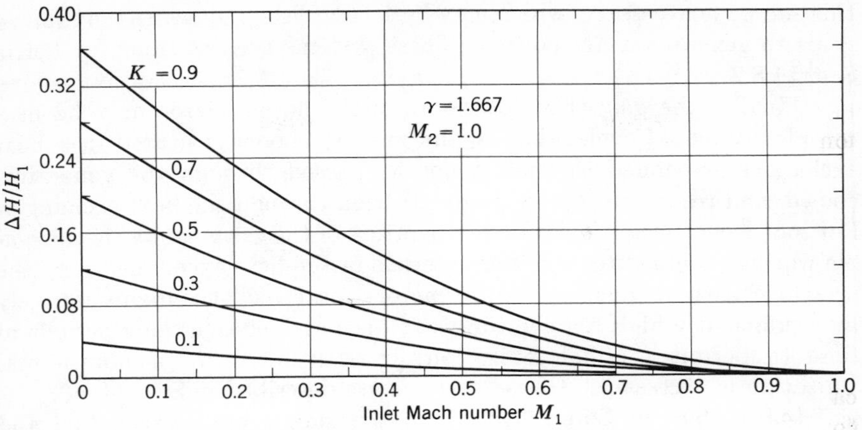

FIGURE 14.17 Energy extraction as a function of inlet Mach number. (From ref. 21.)

the higher the initial load factor K_1 or the lower the inlet Mach number, the longer the generator length.

Also, high loading factors or low inlet Mach number lead to the largest electric energy extraction from the flow, as is shown in Fig. 14.17. On the other hand, the largest average power density is obtained when $K_1 \approx 0.5$, for any subsonic inlet Mach number.

14.8 MHD POWER GENERATION SYSTEMS

There are three general types of MHD generator systems. In the simplest system, liquid or solid fuel and liquid oxidizer are burned, seed is added, and the resulting gas mixture is passed through the generator with no further recovery of the remaining thermal energy or seed material in the exhaust gases. Such a system is feasible only for small or short-duration generators. Since the amount of energy required to pump the liquid (or solid) fuel and oxidizer is small, all the generated electric power is available for the load except that required to energize the magnet, if it is an electromagnet. This system will be discussed further in Sec. 14.8.1.

For the generation of bulk power, fossil fuel must be used for economic reasons, and the oxidizer must be air, although some enrichment with additional oxygen may be possible. In order for the combustion temperature to be high enough for thermal ionization, preheating of the incoming air is necessary. The exhaust temperature of the gas from the generator is determined by the decrease in the ionization of the gas; but because combustion gases must be thermally ionized, the exhaust temperature is still very high. For economic operation further extraction of this energy is necessary, which may be accomplished by using the exhaust gases to generate steam power. These systems are described further in Sec. 14.8.2.

Finally, the gas which passes through the generator may be in a completely closed cycle; that is, the gas (or vapor) is heated in a heat exchanger, expanded through a nozzle, passed through the generator, cooled, and recompressed (or pumped) back through the heat exchanger. For such a cycle, the maximum temperature of the gas is set by the allowable working temperature of the materials in the heat exchanger. At the present state of development of refractory materials, it is highly unlikely that sufficiently high temperatures can be sustained over long periods of time to permit thermal ionization; thus, some form of nonthermal ionization is necessary. These systems are described in Sec. 14.8.3.

14.8.1 Simple Open Cycle. In the simple open cycle, fuel and oxidizer are burned and "seed" material is added without preheating. The combustion products are accelerated by a nozzle and passed into the generator and exhausted into the atmosphere. Since seeded combustion gases are not sufficiently conducting below about 4000°F at a pressure of 1 atm, the flame temperature must exceed 4000°F in order to extract any electric power. Since the temperature of most flames with air is below 4000°F, it is necessary to use either pure oxygen or a chemical oxidizer. Even if pure oxygen is used, the flame temperature with ordinary hydrocarbons is not especially high because of dissociation of the products of combustion (see Table 14.1). The overall efficiency for this type of open-cycle generator can be expressed in terms of the enthalpy difference between the flame temperature and ambient,

$$\eta_t = \frac{\text{net electric energy/unit mass of gas}}{H_0 - h_a}$$

where H_0 is the total enthalpy of the products of combustion at the combustor pressure, and h_a is the sensible enthalpy of the same gas if cooled to ambient pressure and temperature. The net energy is the difference between the generator inlet total enthalpy and the exit total enthalpy, less any heat transfer, and power for auxiliary equipment. Thus,

$$\eta_t = \frac{H_0 - h_2 - \frac{1}{2}u_2^2 - Q - P_{\text{aux}}}{H_0 - h_a}$$

The thermal efficiency is therefore limited by the minimum temperature $T_{\min}$ at which there is sufficient ionization, and by the exhaust velocity. If the exhaust velocity is reduced by adjusting the cross-sectional area, then additional energy can be extracted from the gas before $T_{\min}$ is reached; however, decreasing the gas velocity generally increases the generator length. For this reason, it is desirable to use the higher flame temperatures.

Table 14.1 Flame Temperatures of Fuels Burned with Liquid Oxygen at 20 Atm Pressure

Fuel	*Flame temperature, °F*
Ethyl alcohol†	5250
Kerosene†	5570
Hydrogen†	~5400
Methane†	5040
Cyanogen	~8200

† From G. P. Sutton, *Rocket Propulsion Elements*, 2d ed., John Wiley & Sons, Inc., New York, 1956.

Also listed in Table 14.1 is the flame temperature with cyanogen, C_2N_2. The high flame temperature results not so much from a larger heat of combustion, but from the fact that the products CO and N_2 of combustion do not dissociate. Detailed calculations of the performance of an oxycyanogen generator indicate that over 36 per cent of the input chemical energy can be converted into terminal power.[22] This is to be compared to about 15 per cent for hydrocarbon fuels.

14.8.2 Open Cycle with Recovery. The previous open cycle is clearly unsuited for economic operation for three reasons: The seed material is not recovered; liquid or gaseous oxygen is expensive; and finally, the thermal energy of the exhaust gases is not recovered. For the economic generation of bulk power these three problems must be considered.

The cheapest available oxidizer is obviously air, although power is required to compress it to the required combustion pressure. In addition, common fossil fuels must be used if the fuel cost is to be minimized. Since it is impossible to burn fossil fuels with air and achieve sufficiently high combustion temperatures to ionize the seed material, preheating of the inlet air with possible oxygen enrichment is required to increase the combustion temperature; that is, a regenerative cycle is required[23] (see Figs. 14.18 and 14.19).

Now, because the specific heat of combustion gas is larger than that for air, the regenerator hot-side exit temperature T_4 will normally be considerably higher than the regenerator cold-side inlet temperature, and additional energy can be recovered from the exhaust gases by producing steam and using a steam turbine. It is possible to couple the turbine directly to the air compressor, and to use any remaining shaft power to generate electric power. The net power output is then the direct current generated in the MHD generator, plus any remaining steam power, less the magnet power and auxiliary power. For this type of hypothetical cycle, overall thermal efficiencies up to 56 per cent have been calculated.[23]

Several problems in the cycle are evident. First, for combustion products and about 1 per cent molar potassium seeding, T_2 is about

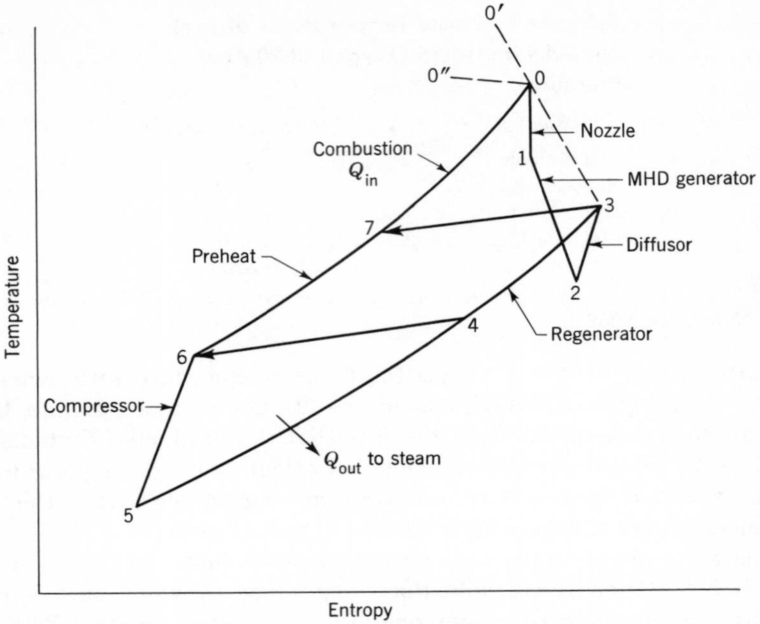

FIGURE 14.18 Regenerative open cycle, temperature-entropy diagram.

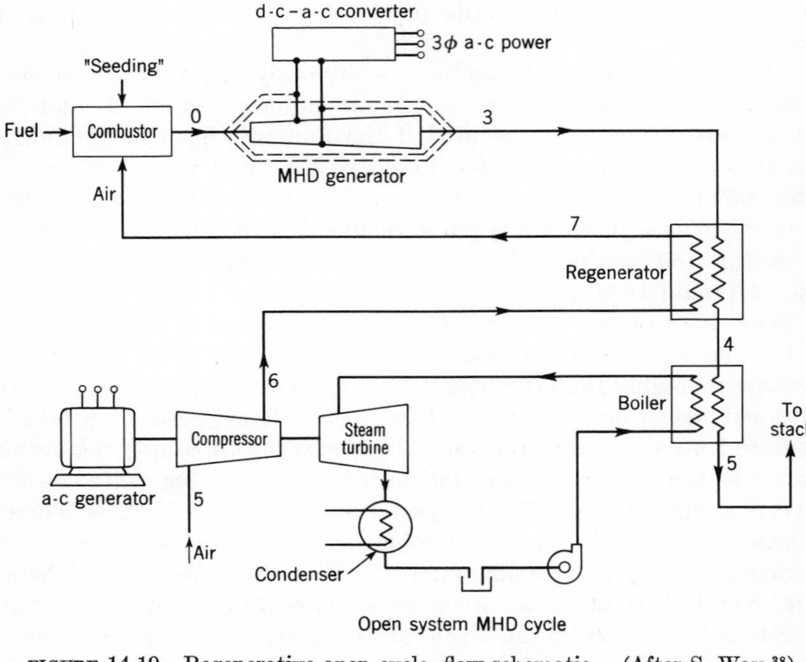

FIGURE 14.19 Regenerative open cycle, flow schematic. (After S. Way.[38])

4000°F, and the regenerator walls will then be close to this temperature. At the present time, economic materials which will withstand this temperature for long periods of time are not known. To reduce the regenerator surface temperature, several possibilities have been explored. First T_7 can be reduced, which will help lower the regenerator surface temperature. However, this reduces the combustion temperature and the power generated in the MHD generator. An alternative to this is to cool the gases from temperature T_3 by use of a steam superheater, before passing the gases into the regenerator.[24] This also reduces the combustion temperature T_0.

A different solution is to reduce T_7, as explained above, but to obtain the same combustion temperature by enriching the inlet air with oxygen.[25] Although this alleviates the regenerator materials problems, for a given mass flow of combustion products, additional fuel is required to burn the additional oxygen, which reduces the thermal efficiency somewhat; furthermore, additional investment in oxygen separation equipment and additional auxiliary power are required.

A more novel remedy which has been suggested is to use molten ash as the regenerator,[26] which is similar in concept to the "rotating regenerator" under development for gas turbines. The exhaust gases from the MHD generator are used to heat ash until molten; the molten ash is then sprayed through the compressed air in a counterflow arrangement. The ash solidifies as granules, and is mechanically recirculated to the exhaust gas heater.

A more practical method of reducing the regenerator temperature is to use pollucite as the seed, in order to utilize the lower ionization potential of cesium; and to use the higher field strengths that may become available through the development of high-field superconductors. The latter also has the advantage that the magnetic field itself consumes no power; the only power consumed by the magnet system is that required to recondense liquid helium to keep the windings superconducting. With these two modifications, it has been estimated that a reduction in temperature of as much as 700°C can be expected.[38]

On the basis of fuel cost and preheat, coal seems to be the best fuel for economic operation of an MHD generator. On the other hand, the high ash content of coal causes additional difficulties. Although it is possible to remove as much as 90 per cent of the ash in a "cyclone" burner, the remaining ash becomes mixed with the seed material, which may be a potassium compound or pollucite. Since economic operation requires recovery of the seed material, this means that the 10 per cent ash must be recovered as well, and recirculated. To keep the "seed" makeup at a minimum, scrubbers and electrostatic precipitators are required; but a more important problem is the large weight of ash that must be recirculated through the system in order to make use of the seed trapped in it.

In addition, the molten ash will coat out on the inside of the generator and will quite likely short-circuit the electrodes, and will coat out on the regenerator. Thus, the problems of burning coal are quite difficult.

In addition to the problems caused by ash, there are two other important problems associated with continuously operated generators. First, the potassium attacks insulating materials and makes them conducting. Second, the electrode materials—tungsten, carbon, or silicon carbide—are chemically eroded by combustion gases. This last problem might be solved by using consumable electrodes; that is, feed the electrodes continuously into the generator in a manner similar to that used in electric arc furnaces.

The greatest problem that is faced by large-scale, continuous generation of power by fossil-fuel MHD generators is economics. Although this system shows promise of increasing the overall thermal efficiency to as much as 56 per cent as compared to 40 per cent for conventional steam plants, the additional investment in the magnet, generator duct, compressors, regenerator, scrubbers, precipitators, d-c to a-c inverters if alternating current is required, causes the plant cost of the generated electric power to be essentially the same as that for present-day steam plants.[24]

14.8.3 Closed Nuclear-MHD Cycle. A third possible application for MHD power generation is a closed cycle with a nuclear heat source. This appears to be especially attractive for the generation of electric power in space, where the heat rejection must be by radiation, because the heat rejection per unit area varies as the fourth power of the surface temperature, and therefore high-temperature nuclear reactors are under development; but the corresponding development of turbogenerators is difficult because of the combination of high operating temperatures, blade stresses in the turbine, and the corrosive properties of some high-temperature working fluids, such as liquid metals. The advantage of the MHD generator is that the stress level is reduced drastically. On the other hand, it is not likely that the reactor temperature will be sufficiently high that thermal ionization of the working fluid in the MHD generator will be possible; thus, some form of nonthermal ionization will be required.

The Rankine (vapor) cycle is extremely attractive for space applications because the heat rejection is at constant temperature, and the pumping power is small. For such cycles, the optimum condenser temperature is 75 to 80 per cent of the boiling temperature.[27] At the present state of development of refractory materials, it appears that the upper temperature for Rankine cycles may be about 2500°R, with a corresponding reject temperature of 1900°R. These temperatures require the use of a liquid metal, such as potassium or sodium, for the working fluid, but are too low for thermal ionization even with the addition of cesium, so that some form of nonthermal ionization must be used. Calculations for magnetically induced ionization, however, indicate that this may be possible with potassium for relatively high field strengths.

The Rankine cycle has one main disadvantage: at the high temperatures necessary to minimize the radiator size, liquid metals are quite corrosive. On the other hand, an inert gas such as helium, which could be used in a gas cycle, is not corrosive. The gas cycle has two disadvantages for space applications: namely, a large compressor is required; and the heat rejection is at a continuously varying temperature which causes the radiator area to be 6 to 10 times that of a Rankine cycle with the same T_0. However, since a corrosionless noble gas can be used, the reactor can be operated at a higher temperature. Also, regeneration may be used; thus the radiator areas can be equalized. This temperature is probably too high for the use of gas turbines, but not for MHD generators.

Of course, a magnetic field must be incorporated into a nuclear-MHD space power system, which raises two additional problems, namely, the weight of the magnet, and the rejection of heat from the magnet. These problems may be solved by the use of high-field superconducting materials. The high electric current densities of superconductors reduce the weight of the windings, while the only required heat rejection is that which is conducted into the magnet Dewar, which tends to boil off the liquid helium in which superconductors are kept. Either the liquid helium can be recooled by a cryostat which requires additional weight, power, and radiators; or sufficient liquid helium can be stored to allow boil-off of the helium during the required mission time.

MHD–nuclear gas cycles for terrestial applications differ from those for space applications in one very important aspect: The heat rejection can be at low temperatures, corresponding to ambient cooling water. This allows use of a waste-heat cycle for a turbocompressor cycle. Two such cycles are shown in Fig. 14.20. In both these cycles the steam is used *only* to drive the compressor. Figure 14.21 shows the results of some calculations for which the steam-cycle efficiency was taken as 40 per cent, and the compressor and generator efficiencies were taken as 80 per cent. It is seen that substantial improvements in efficiency can be obtained as the inlet temperature to the MHD generator increases from 2000 to 3000°F.

The use of regeneration usually increases the overall efficiency. The compressor pressure ratio was taken as 2.34, and the generator pressure ratio as 2.06; the difference allows for pressure drop through the reactor and regenerator. The results are also shown in Fig. 14.21. Comparing the cycles with and without regeneration, it is seen that regeneration gives a greater efficiency up to 3000°F, but that the pressure ratio, and hence number of compressor stages, is less. For the point at which the two efficiencies cross, factors other than efficiency will determine whether the regenerator is more or less desirable than the added number of compressor stages.

Instead of regeneration, one could use the thermal energy in the MHD generator exhaust to generate steam-electric power. However, since the efficiency of the steam portion of the cycle is 40 per cent, such a use of the steam will decrease the overall plant efficiency. Thus, a proposed cycle[28] in which no attempt was made at either balancing the compressor–steam-turbine work or regeneration yielded an overall thermal efficiency of only 47 per cent at 3000°F in comparison to the present calculation of 55 per cent.

Of course, it is not necessary for the working fluid of an MHD generator to be an ionized gas; it could, for example, be a liquid metal, or a mixture of gas or vapor and liquid metal. Such a generator has the advantage of the very high electrical conductivity of liquid metals at

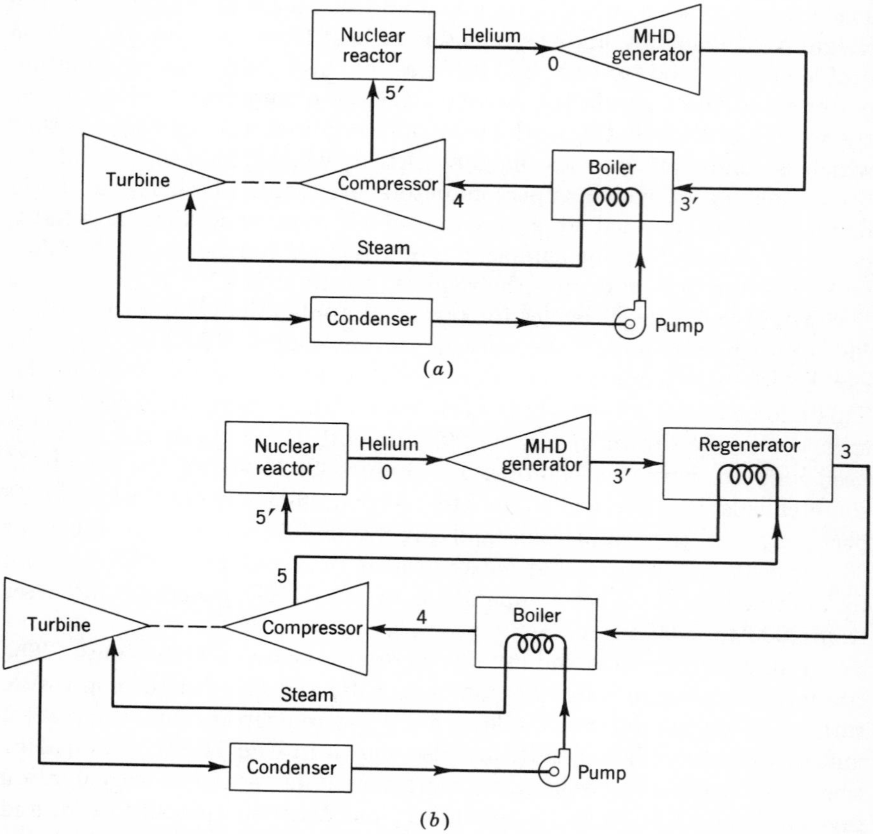

FIGURE 14.20 Waste-heat turbocompressor closed cycles: (*a*) Without regeneration; (*b*) with regeneration.

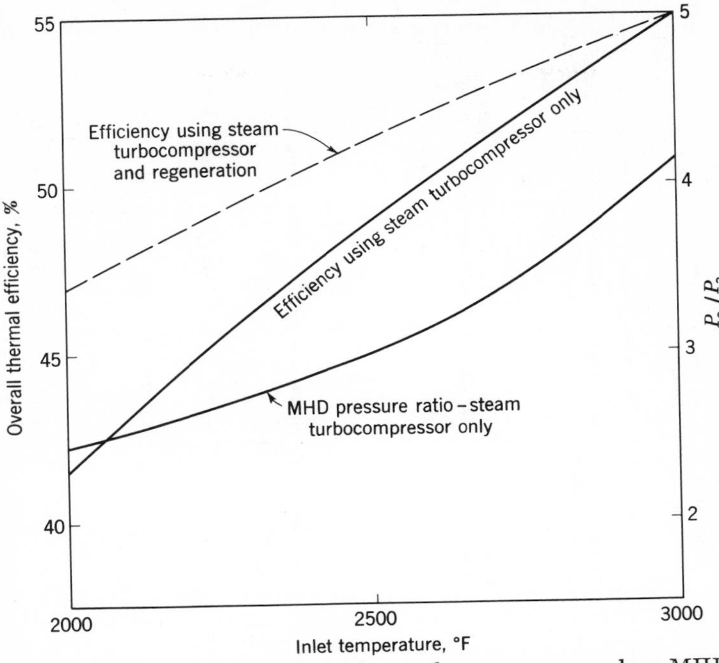

FIGURE 14.21 Efficiencies for steam turbocompressor nuclear MHD closed cycles.

all temperatures. The main problem is the conversion of the thermal energy from the nuclear reactor into kinetic energy of motion of the liquid metal of low vapor pressure. The hot liquid metal from the reactor can be mixed with a liquid metal of high vapor pressure, causing the latter to vaporize. The mixture is passed into a nozzle which allows the vapor to expand and accelerate the droplets of liquid metal. The mixture is then separated, without appreciable loss of kinetic energy or head of the liquid metal, and this head then forces the liquid metal through the generator against the Lorentz force.[29]

14.9 MHD GENERATOR EXPERIMENTS

The first MHD generator experiments were those of Halász and Karlovitz,[30] which were carried out at Westinghouse up to about 1946, using electron-beam ionization. Owing to rapid recombination and formation of negative ions, the generated power density was far below theoretical. No further experiments were performed until about 1958, when operations were initiated using thermal ionization of seeded gases (see Table 14.2). The earliest of these experiments utilized plasma jets as the method for thermal heating of the gas, since gas temperatures could easily be obtained which are much higher than those available from com-

Table 14.2 Summary of MHD Experiments

Characteristic	MHD research	AVCO		General Electric Space Sciences Laboratory	General Electric Research Laboratory	General Electric Research Laboratory	Westinghouse	
		Mark I	Mark II				Model I	Model 2
Working gas	Kerosene and ethanol (plus oxygen)	Argon with arc heater	Ethanol or kerosene (plus oxygen)	Nitrogen with plasma jet heating	Propane (plus oxygen)	H_2 (plus air)	Diesel oil + octoate soap (plus O_2 + N_2)	*n*-Heptane (plus $O_2 + 0.47$ molar N_2)
Temperature, °K	3000	2800	3000	3200	2300	2550	2800–3000	2570
Gas velocity	500–1000 m/sec	Mach 0.7	1000 m/sec	700 m/sec	56.8 m/sec	Mach 0.8	500–865 m/sec	757 m/sec
Seeding	1 %	K_2CO_3	1 % molar KOH powder	K_2CO_3	K_2CO_3	KOH	1.5 % (molar K in gas) as soap in fuel	0.3 % (molar K in gas) as K_2CO_3 slurry in fuel
Generator size, in.	$\frac{1}{2} \times 2 \times 16$	$1 \times 3 \times 20$	$60 \times \begin{cases} 3 \times 9 \text{ inlet} \\ 3 \times 13 \text{ exit} \end{cases}$	$\frac{1}{2} \times 4 \times 29$	$1 \times 2 \times 2$	$2 \times 4 \times 12$	$1\frac{5}{8} \times 4\frac{5}{7} \times 16$	$\frac{3}{4} \times \frac{3}{4} \times 16$
Electrode material	Tungsten (segmented, 5 electrodes 3 in. long)	....	Graphite (segmented)	Graphite (4)	Graphite	Silicon carbide	C, ZrO_2, ZrB_2, W, etc.	ZrB_2
Insulator material	MgO	....	Nonablating	Zirconia	MgO	MgO	MgO or cooled ZrO_2	MgO
Magnetic field, gauss	20,000	....	32,000	11,000	4,250	12,000	5,000–14,000	10,000
Emf generated, d-c volts	50–100	55	Up to 1,400	75–90	0.7	90	30–100 open circuit	7.7 open circuit
Power generated, kw	1.03	11.6	600	6	0.00002	1.9	1.5–10.4	3 watts per in. of length
Test duration	30 min	10 sec	10 sec	5 sec	5 min	6 min	3–50 min	40 min
Efficiency (heat to electricity), %	0.1	....	3	0.1	....	....	~0.3	
Reference	32	37	25	36	33	35	31	

bustion flames. In these experiments, the measured electrical conductivity and generated power agreed within a factor of 2 of the theoretically predicted performance, although the total power was small (less than 12 kw) and the run times were less than 10 sec. These experiments mainly verified the validity of the physical principle of MHD power generation.

The first combustion experiment was performed at Westinghouse Electric,[31] in which over 10 kw was generated; this was followed rapidly by similar experiments.[32,33] The largest combustion experiment at the present time is the AVCO Mark 6,[34] which has generated 11 Mw. A Hall generator has also been successfully operated on an air-hydrogen flame.[35]

For the plasma jet and combustion experiments, some initial trials were made using stabilized zirconia for the insulator; however, at high temperatures the zirconia generally becomes electrically conducting, and most experimenters have changed to magnesia for the insulator. One unexpected effect is that the resistivity of the ceramic decreases during an experiment;[35] it is not yet known whether this is due to the presence of potassium which could change the chemical composition of the surface of the insulator. The presence of molten ash will probably intensify this problem.

For very large MHD generators, wall cooling may be possible without adversely affecting the performance, and experiments have been performed in which water-cooled tubes were used as the insulator. These same tubes can also serve as the electrodes if the tubes follow equipotential lines as in the series-segmented geometry, and if an insulation is placed in between the tubes. Since the temperature of the tubes is low, presumably the temperature of the insulation between them will also be low, and hence alumina may be satisfactory.

The most commonly used electrode material has been graphite, although silicon carbide has also been utilized.[35] However, zircon compounds have also been utilized because of their relatively high electrical conductivity, both with and without embedded tungsten.[32] In general, if the electrodes are sufficiently hot to emit electrons thermionically, there has been almost zero cathode voltage drop;[36] otherwise voltage drops to 100 volts have been observed. The graphite and carbide electrodes have been observed to erode very rapidly when used with products of combustion.

The seed has generally been injected as a salt, a carbonate, or a hydroxide. The salt dissolves readily in water which provides a convenient method for injection, but powdered potassium carbonate has also been used. The hydroxide dissolves easily in alcohol, which then can be mixed directly with the fuel,[31] eliminating the necessity for a separate injection system, and also allowing for more precise control of the seed injection rate. For closed-cycle operation, pure alkali metal is required for the seed. This can be provided by injection of the liquid metal; or use of a side stream which is bubbled through the liquid metal, a spray evaporator, or a direct boiler for the liquid metal.

REFERENCES CITED

1. Steg, L., and G. W. Sutton: "The Prospects of MHD Power Generation," *Astronautics*, August, 1960, pp. 22–25, 82, 84–86.
2. Hurwitz, H., Jr., R. Kilb, and G. W. Sutton: "Influence of Tensor Conductivity on Current Distribution in a MHD Generator," *J. Appl. Phys.*, **32**:205–216 (1961).
3. Harris, L. P., and J. D. Cobine: "The Significance of the Hall Effect for Three MHD Generator Configurations," *Trans. ASME, Ser. A*, **83A**:392–396 (1961).
4. Bernstein, I. B., J. B. Fanucci, K. H. Fischbeck, J. Jarem, N. I. Korman, R. M. Kulsrud, M. Lessen, and N. Ness: "An Electrodeless MHD Generator," in C. Mannal and N. W. Mather (eds.), *Proc. 2d Symp. Eng. Aspects Magnetohydrodynamics*, pp. 255–276, Columbia University Press, New York, 1962.
5. Moffatt, W. C.: "Thermodynamics and Electrical Properties of Dissociated Combustion Gases," *MIT Magnetogasdynamic Lab. Rept* 5, 1961.
6. Kerrebrock, J. L.: "Conduction in Gases with Elevated Electron Temperatures," in C. Mannal and N. W. Mather (eds.), *Proc. 2d Symp. Eng. Aspects Magnetohydrodynamics*, pp. 327–346, Columbia University Press, New York, 1962.
7. Hurwitz, H., Jr., G. W. Sutton, and S. Tamor: "Electron Heating in Magnetohydrodynamic Power Generators," *ARS J.*, **32**:1237–1243 (1962).
8. Byron, S., P. Bortz, and G. Russell: "Electron-Ion Reaction Rate Theory," *Proc. 4th Symp. Eng. Aspects Magnetohydrodynamics*, pp. 93–101, IEEE, New York, 1964.
9. Zukoski, E. E., T. A. Cool, and E. G. Gibson: "Experiments Concerning Non-equilibrium Conductivity in a Seeded Plasma," *AIAA J.*, **2**:1410 (1964).
10. Rosa, R.: "Hall and Ion-slip Effects in a Non-uniform Gas," *Phys. Fluids*, **9**:1081–1090 (1962).
11. Sutton, G. W., H. Hurwitz, Jr., and H. Poritsky, Jr.: "Electrical and End Losses in a Magnetohydrodynamic Channel Due to End Current Loops," *Trans. AIEE Commun. and Electron.*, **801**:687–696 (1962).
12. Fishman, F.: "End Effects in Magnetohydrodynamic Channel Flow," *AVCO-Everett Res. Lab. Res. Rept.* 78, June, 1959.
13. Podolsky, B., and A. Sherman: "Some Aspects of the Hall Effect in Crossed Field MHD Accelerators," *ARS Preprint* 1531-60, 1960.
14. Podolsky, B., and A. Sherman: "The Influence of Tensor Conductivity on End Currents in Crossed Field MHD Channels with Skewed Electrodes," *J. Appl. Phys.*, **33**:1414–1418 (1962).
15. Crown, J. C.: "Analysis of Magnetohydrodynamic Generators Having Segmented Electrodes and Anistropic Conductivity," *United Aircraft Res. Lab. Rept.* R-1852-2, February, 1961.

16. Sutton, G. W.: "End Losses in Magnetohydrodynamic Channels with Tensor Electrical Conductivity and Segmented Electrodes," *J. Appl. Phys.*, **34**:396–403 (1963).
17. Dzung, L. S.: "Hall Effect and End Loop Losses of MHD Generators," *Symposium on Magnetoplasmadynamic Electrical Power Generation*, Newcastle on Tyne, England, Sept. 6–8, 1962.
18. Brocher, E. F.: "The Constant Velocity MHD Generator with Variable Electrical Conductivity," *J. Aerospace Sci.*, **29**:626–627 (1962).
19. LeBouc, F.: "Conversion de la chaleur en électricite par magnetohydrodynamique," *Inst. Franc. du Petrole Rept.* 6647, Rueil-Malmaison (S. et-0.), August, 1961.
20. Neuringer, Joseph L.: "Optimum Power Generation from a Moving Plasma," *J. Fluid Mech.*, **7**(2):287–301 (February, 1960).
21. Talaat, Mostafa E.: "Magnetohydrodynamic Electric Power Generators," *Advan. Energy Conversion*, **1**:19–35 (1961).
22. Sherman, A.: "A High Performance Short Time Duration, MHD Generator System," *ARS Space Power Conf. Preprint* 2558-62, Santa Monica, Calif., September, 1962.
23. Sporn, P., and A. Kantrowitz: "Magnetohydrodynamics: Future Power Process?" *Power*, **103**(11):62–65 (November, 1959).
24. Brown, J. W. W.: "Some Aspects of MHD Power Plant Economics," in N. W. Mather and G. W. Sutton (eds.), *Proc. 3d Symp. Eng. Aspects Magnetohydrodynamics*, pp. 223–242, Gordon and Breach, Science Publishers, Inc., New York, 1964.
25. Brogan, T. R., J. F. Louis, R. J. Rosa, and Z. J. J. Stekly: "A review of Recent MHD Generator Work at the AVCO-Everett Research Laboratory," in N. W. Mather and G. W. Sutton (eds.), *Proc. 3d Symp. Eng. Aspects Magnetohydrodynamics*, pp. 243–259, Gordon and Breach, Science Publishers, Inc., New York, 1964.
26. Allen, R. C.: "Feasibility of 300 Mwe MHD Power Plant," *American Power Conference*, Chicago, March, 1962.
27. Pitkin, E. T.: "Optimum Radiator Temperature for Space Power Systems, *ARS J.*, **29**:596–597 (1959).
28. Gunson, W. E., E. E. Smith, J. H. Wright, and T. C. Tsu: "Gas-cooled Reactors for Magnetohydrodynamic Power Generation," *Trans. Am. Nucl. Soc.*, **5**:438 (November, 1962).
29. Elliot, D. G.: "Two-fluid Magnetohydrodynamic Cycle for Nuclear-Electric Power Conversion," *ARS J.*, **32**:924–928 (1962).
30. Karlovitz, B., and D. Halász: "History of the K&H Generator and Conclusions Drawn from the Experimental Results," in N. W. Mather and G. W. Sutton (eds.), *Proc. 3d Symp. Eng. Aspects Magnetohydrodynamics*, pp. 187–204, Gordon and Breach, Science Publishers, Inc., New York, 1964.
31. Way, S., S. M. De Corso, R. L. Hundstad, G. A. Kemeny, W. Stewart, and W. E. Young: "Experiments with MHD Power Generation," *Trans. ASME* (*J. Eng. for Power*), **83A**:397 (1961).
32. Blackman, V. H., M. S. Jones, Jr., and A. Demetriades: "MHD Power Generation Studies in Rectangular Channels," in C. Mannal and N. W. Mather (eds.), *Proc. 2d Symp. Eng. Aspects Magnetohydrodynamics*, pp. 180–210, Columbia University Press, New York, 1962.

33. Mullaney, G. J., and N. R. Dibelius: "Small MHD Power Generator Using Combustion Gases as an Energy Source," *ARS J.*, **31**:555–557 (1961).
34. Louis, J. F., G. Gal, and P. R. Blackburn: "Detailed Theoretical and Experimental Study on a Large MHD Generator," *Proc. 5th Symp. Eng. Aspects Magnetohydrodynamics*, IEEE, New York, 1964.
35. Harris, L. P., and G. E. Moore: "Some Electrical Measurements on MHD Channels," in N. W. Mather and G. W. Sutton (eds.), *Proc. 3d Symp. Eng. Aspects Magnetohydrodynamics*, pp. 259–278, Gordon and Breach, Science Publishers, Inc., New York, 1964.
36. Sutton, G. W., and F. Robben: "Preliminary Experiments on MHD Channel Flow with Slightly Ionized Gases," *Proc. Symp. Electromagnetics and Fluid Dynamics of Gaseous Plasma*, pp. 307–321, Polytechnic Press, Brooklyn, N.Y., 1962.
37. Rosa, R.: "Physical Principles of Magnetohydrodynamic Power Generation," *Phys. Fluids*, **4**:182–198 (1961).
38. Way, S.: "Reduction of Operating Temperature or Generator Length in MHD Power Plants," *Westinghouse Res. Lab. S. P.* 66-111-600-P2, AIEE Pacific Energy Conversion Conf., San Francisco, August, 1962.

GENERAL REFERENCES

Engineering Aspects of Magnetohydrodynamics: C. Mannal and N. W. Mather (eds.), *Proc. 2d Symp.*, Columbia University Press, New York, 1962; N. W. Mather and G. W. Sutton (eds.), *Proc. 3d Symp.*, Gordon and Breach, Science Publishers, Inc., New York, 1964.

Kaye, Joseph, and J. A. Welsh (eds.): *Direct Conversion of Heat to Electricity*, John Wiley & Sons, Inc., New York, 1960.

Magnetohydrodynamic Electrical Power Generation, Proc. of Int. Symp., Paris, July, 1964: European Nuclear Energy Agency OECD, Paris, 1964.

Magnetohydrodynamics Generation of Electrical Power: R. A. Coombe (ed.), Chapman and Hall, Ltd., London, 1964.

Spence, Barbara A.: "Magnetohydrodynamic Power Generation, a Bibliography," *AVCO-Everett Res. Lab. AMP* 110, June, 1963.

PROBLEMS

CHAPTER 2

2.1 Consider an infinitely long, thin-walled solenoid with circumferential current I per unit length. Determine the expression for the internal magnetic pressure in the solenoid.

2.2 Consider a straight, infinitely long wire of radius a and electrical conductivity σ carrying a uniform current density j. Determine (*a*) the electric field distribution; (*b*) the magnetic field $\mathbf{B}(r)$; (*c*) the value of Poynting's vector integrated around the surface of the wire per unit length of wire, that is, $\int_0^L \int_0^{2\pi} \mathbf{S} \cdot d\mathbf{S}$, where dS is an element of surface area $a\, d\phi\, dz$; (*d*) the electric field pressure; and (*e*) the magnetic field pressure. Compare the ohmic heating per unit length in the wire to the flux of Poynting's vector into the wire. Explain.

2.3 (*a*) Derive an expression for the axial magnetic $B_z(0,0,z)$ for a circular coil, radius a, in the xy plane, carrying a current I.

(*b*) Consider two such coils, parallel to each other, one at $z = 0$ and the other at $z = h$. Show that between the two coils, at $r = 0$, $z = h/2$, $\partial^2 B_z/\partial z^2 = 0$ when $h = a$. (Because of the resulting field uniformity, such spacing is frequently used, and is called a *Helmholtz pair*.)

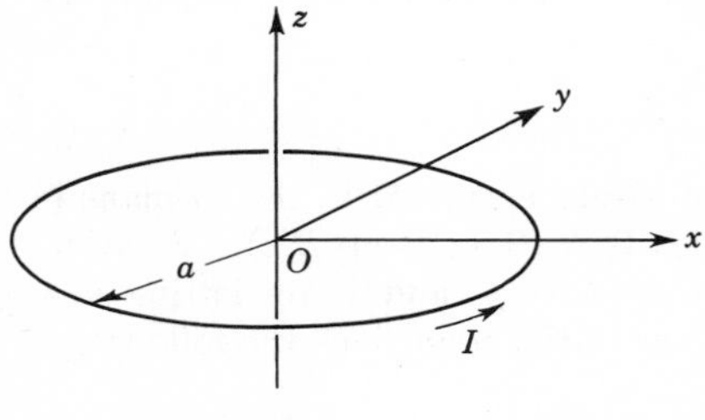

2.4 Consider an axially symmetric solenoidal magnetic field in cyclindrical coordinates r, ϕ, z, such that $\mathbf{B} = (B_r,0,B_z)$. Assume also that the field is symmetrical about $z = 0$. Now in the plane defined by $z = 0$ a charged particle with velocity $(v_0,0,0)$ approaches the magnetic field. Show that the distance of minimum approach is given by

$$\frac{r_{\min}}{2\pi \int_0^{r_{\min}} rB_z(r)\,dr} = \frac{ez}{2\pi m v_0}$$

2.5 Consider a volume in which the current density is unidirectional and constant. Show that the net magnetic force on the volume is given by the following surface integral:

$$F = -\mathbf{j} \times \int_s \mathbf{A} \times d\mathbf{S}$$

2.6 (*a*) For a non-time-varying situation, show that the electrostatic field energy within a fixed volume may be expressed as

$$E_e = -\tfrac{1}{2}K_0 \int_s \phi \mathbf{E} \cdot d\mathbf{S} + \frac{1}{2} \int_{\mathcal{V}} \phi \rho_e \, d\mathcal{V}$$

Assume the permittivity is that of vacuum.

(*b*) For a non-time-varying situation, show that the magnetostatic field energy within a fixed volume may be expressed as

$$E_m = \tfrac{1}{2}\mu_0 \int \mathbf{A} \times \mathbf{B} \cdot d\mathbf{S} + \frac{1}{2} \int \mathbf{J} \cdot \mathbf{A} \, d\mathcal{V}$$

Assume the permeability is that of vacuum.

2.7 A uniform oscillating electric field $E_0 e^{j\omega t}$ is applied tangentially to the surface of a semi-infinite conductor with scalar electrical conductivity σ. Derive an expression for the electric field as a function of distance x below the surface. Determine the *skin depth*, that is, the distance δ below the surface at which $E(\delta)/E_0 = e^{-1}$.

2.8 Show that the wave equations (2.91) and (2.92) satisfy conservation of electric current equation (2.62).

2.9 If coordinate system (x',y',z') is moving at velocity $(v',0,0)$ with respect to (x,y,z), and coordinate system (x'',y'',z'') is moving at velocity $(v'',0,0)$ with respect to (x',y',z'), find the velocity of coordinate system (x'',y'',z'') with respect to (x,y,z).

2.10 Derive Maxwell's equations, from Eq. (2.110).

CHAPTER 3

3.1 Consider an electron moving in the xy plane in the following inhomogeneous magnetic field: $\mathbf{B} = (0, 0, B_0 + B'x)$. Solve for the first- and second-order components of velocity v_0 and v_1 by letting $v = v_0 + B' r_{L_0} v_1 / B_0$ where $r_{L_0} = v_\perp m_e / eB_0$. Use as initial conditions the following:

$$v_{0_x}(0) = -v_\perp \qquad x_0(0) = 0$$
$$v_{0_y}(0) = 0 \qquad y_0(0) = -r_{L_0}$$

3.2 Consider an electron in a central electrostatic force field $\phi(r)$ moving in a circular orbit of radius a such that the centrifugal force is balanced by the electrostatic force. Show that the sum of kinetic and potential energy is given by

$$\epsilon(a) = -\left(\frac{e}{2r}\frac{\partial}{\partial r}r^2\phi\right)_{r=a}$$

CHAPTER 4

4.1 Consider a stationary, equilibrium, isothermal single species gas in a uniform gravitational field. Derive the expression for the spatially dependent distribution function.

4.2 For Knudsen diffusion of a perfect gas with no internal energy, obtain the expression for the energy flux per unit area through the hole. Compare your expression with the usual expression for enthalpy flux,

$$\rho \mathbf{v}\left(\frac{1}{2}v^2 + \frac{5}{2}\frac{k}{m}T\right) + \mathbf{q}$$

Explain any differences.

4.3 Derive the expression for the potential distribution near an insulated wall for a singly ionized gas in equilibrium. (Do not linearize.)

4.4 Derive the expression for the Debye shielding length when the ions and electrons have maxwellian velocity distribution functions about different temperatures, for the one-dimensional linearized case.

CHAPTER 5

5.1 For an inverse-fifth-power interaction for electrons, show that the ratio of the electric current to the projection of the electric field in the direction of the current vector is equal to the scalar electrical conductivity.

5.2 The Hall effect causes the angle between the electric field and the current to be approximately $\tan^{-1}\omega_e\tau_e$. Derive an approximate expression for σ_1, taking into account that the electric field in the direction of the current is reduced, and the apparent resistance is increased due to the longer path length of the electric current vector between equipotential lines.

5.3 Consider the steady conduction equation in two dimensions

$$j = \frac{\sigma}{1+\beta^2}\left(\mathbf{E} - \beta\frac{\mathbf{E}\times\mathbf{B}}{B}\right)$$

with

$$\mathbf{E} = (E_x,E_y,0) \qquad \mathbf{B} = (0,0,B_z)$$

Determine the expression for the complex electrical conductivity which relates the complex current $\tilde{j} \equiv j_x + ij_y$ to the complex electric field $\tilde{E} = E_x + iE_y$.

5.4 Consider a two-dimensional uniformly ionized gas; that is, $c^2 = c_x^2 + c_y^2$, $c_z = 0$.

(*a*) Letting $\langle c^2\rangle_e = 2kT/m_e$, show that the maxwellian distribution function is given by

$$f_0 = \frac{n_e m_e}{2\pi k T_e} e^{-m_e c_e^2/2kT_e}$$

(b) Prove that the average thermal speed is $\langle c \rangle_e = (\pi k T_e / 2 m_e)^{\frac{1}{2}}$

(c) For zero magnetic field and an electric field in the xy plane, prove that the electrical conductivity is given by

$$\sigma = \frac{e^2}{2kT} \int \frac{c^2 f_0 \, d\mathbf{c}}{\nu(c)}$$

(d) For constant free path, $\lambda_e = nQ$, show that the Lorentz conductivity is given by

$$\sigma = \frac{\pi}{4} \frac{n_e e^2}{m_e \langle c \rangle_e nQ}$$

5.5 (a) For the Druyvesteyn distribution function given by (5.71), determine the normalization constant a, the mean electron temperature in terms of the electric field, and average electron speed.

(b) Determine the scalar electrical conductivity in terms of the electric field.

5.6 For ω_e / ν_e small, Eq. (5.78) can be integrated by expansion of the denominator. The first integral in the series is the scalar electrical conductivity, while the second term is

$$\sigma_{1_c} = -\frac{e^2 \omega_e^2}{3k} \int \frac{c_e^2 f_0 \, d\mathbf{c}_e}{\nu_e^3 T^*}$$

where

$$\nu_e = \eta_s c_e Q_{es}$$

$$Q_{es} = 2\pi c_e^{-4/(s-1)} \left(\frac{\alpha_{es}}{m_e} \right)^{2/(s-1)} A_1(s)$$

where $A_1(s)$ is independent of c_e. Assume T^* is constant, equal to T_e. Calculate the ratio of σ_{1_c} for $s = 2$ to σ_{1_c} for $s = 5$.

5.7 Carry out the steps which lead to Eqs. (5.88) and (5.89) starting from the Boltzmann equation.

5.8 Invert the electrical conductivity tensor (5.106a) to obtain the resistivity tensor.

5.9 Evaluate the electron thermal conductivity $\mathcal{K}_{33}$, for maxwellian molecules ($s = 5$) in terms of n_e, $\langle c \rangle_e$, $\langle \nu \rangle_e$. Compare to the electrical conductivity for the same case.

5.10 Derive the expression for the coefficient of thermal diffusion parallel to a magnetic field (α_{33}) for electrons, using the Lorentz approximation, for an inverse-power law of interaction ($F_{es} = \alpha_{es} r^{-s}$). Express the results in terms of s, m_e, n_e, $\langle c_e \rangle$, $\langle \nu_e \rangle$.

5.11 Using the relaxation model of the Boltzmann equation for electrons,

$$\frac{\partial f_e}{\partial t} + \mathbf{c}_e \cdot \nabla f_e - \frac{e}{m_e} (\mathbf{E} + \mathbf{c}_e \times \mathbf{B}) \cdot \nabla_{c_e} f_e = \nu_e (f_0 - f_e)$$

where ν_e is a function of c_e, and letting

$$f_e = f_0 + \frac{e}{m_e} \mathbf{E} \cdot \mathbf{c}_e f_1 - \frac{e}{m_e} \mathbf{E} \times \mathbf{B} \cdot \mathbf{c}_e h_1$$

derive the expressions for f_1 and h_1, and compare the results to Eqs. (5.23) and (5.24). Let $\mathbf{E}$ and $\mathbf{B}$ be mutually perpendicular.

5.12 Carry out the indicated steps which lead to Eq. (5.155).

5.13 Prove the results of (5.148).

CHAPTER 6

6.1 Saha's equation can be derived on the basis that the reaction

$$N_e + N_I \rightleftharpoons N_n$$

is in equilibrium and therefore constitutes a system. Thus, the ratio of the reactants on the left side of the reaction to the products on the right side is

$$\frac{N_e N_I}{N_n} = \frac{P_e P_I}{P_n}$$

From this relation, derive Eq. (6.83).

6.2 In the same manner as Prob. 6.1, thermionic emission may be regarded as the process $N_e(g) \rightleftharpoons N_e(s)$ where (g) and (s) refer to gas and solid, respectively. Thus,

$$\frac{N_e(g)}{N_e(s)} = \frac{P_e(g)}{P_e(s)}$$

Using $N_e(s)/P_e(s) = \lambda$, derive Eq. (6.151).

CHAPTER 7

7.1 Derive an expression for the dispersion relation $k(\omega)$ for ion longitudinal waves in a neutral plasma, using the ion-momentum, Poisson's, and the conservation equations of ions. Neglect thermal motion and collisions, and assume that the frequency is sufficiently low that the electrons equilibrate instantaneously; that is, $n_e = n_{e0} \exp(e\phi/RT)$. Show that in the limit $\omega/\omega_{PI} \rightarrow 0$, the phase velocity is $v \equiv \omega/\kappa = \sqrt{kT/m_I}$.

7.2 For a uniform-plasma Lorentz approximation, consider the relaxation mode of the electron Boltzmann equation,

$$\frac{\partial f_e}{\partial t} + \mathbf{c}_e \cdot \nabla f - \frac{eE}{m_e} \cdot \nabla_c f_e = \nu_e(f_0 - f)$$

where f_0 is the local maxwellian. For an oscillating electric field $\mathbf{E} = (E_x \sin \omega t, 0, 0)$, derive the expression for the electron current $\mathbf{j}_e(t)$. Assume that ν_e is constant.

7.3 Determine the expression for the frequency of longitudinal electron oscillations in the presence of a transverse magnetic field B_z, using the conservation, electron-momentum, and Poisson's equations.

Ans: $\omega = \sqrt{\omega_e^2 + \omega_{pe}^2}$

Draw plots of v_{e_x} as a function of v_{e_y} for $\omega_e/\omega_{pe} = (0,1,10)$.

CHAPTER 8

8.1 It is often stated that when the electrical conductivity of a fluid is considered infinite one may conceive of the magnetic field lines as *frozen* into the fluid. Prove that the above statement is valid for an incompressible fluid when the Hall effect can be neglected. *Hint:* Consider a closed contour in the fluid which at every point has the fluid velocity. Show that the material derivative of the flux ($\varphi = \iint \mathbf{B} \cdot d\mathbf{S}$) through this surface is zero.

8.2 Considering a magnetic tube of force, show that for magnetic lines frozen to the fluid the magnetic field intensity within the tube is directly proportional to the fluid density and tube length as the tube moves about with the fluid.

8.3 For the case of no fluid motion, Eq. (8.31) reduces to the diffusion equation, where α is the magnetic diffusivity. Calculate the decay time of a magnetic field due to diffusion for a 1-cm-diameter copper sphere and the earth.

8.4 When, in a plasma, the electron temperature is higher than the heavy particle temperature, the plasma is said to be in a state of nonequilibrium. Since the stronger the electric field, the greater this nonequilibrium, it has been suggested that this phenomenon can be described macroscopically by considering the electrical conductivity σ to be a function of the electric field. More conveniently it can be taken to be a function of the absolute magnitude of the current density, since the current and electric field must be related through Ohm's law. For a static system neglecting the Hall effect and ion slip, show that when conductivity depends linearly on current density, a nonlinear Ohm's law results. Also, verify that there is a critical value of applied electric field beyond which Ohm's law is no longer valid.

CHAPTER 9

9.1 Show that when the mass flow through the discontinuity surface is zero, we have a "contact" discontinuity across which the entropy and density jumps but the pressure, *flow velocity*, and magnetic field are continuous. This is in contrast to the conventional fluid dynamic "contact" discontinuity across which the flow velocity may jump.

9.2 Verify the form of Eq. (9.65) as derived from Eqs. (9.59), (9.60), and (9.64).

9.3 Show that for fast or slow shocks, the magnetic field ahead of the shock is not rotated (the shock is two-dimensional) in general when $B_x \neq 0$. *Hint*: Choose a coordinate system such that $B_{z_1} = 0$ and verify that $B_{z_2} = 0$.

9.4 For an incompressible fluid consider a magnetic field applied in the x direction and a wave motion in which $\partial/\partial y = \partial/\partial z = 0$. Under these conditions show that the induced magnetic field and transverse flow velocity undergo wave motion of *finite* amplitude for which the wave speed is the Alfvén speed.

CHAPTER 10

10.1 Consider a two-dimensional magnetohydrodynamic flow as follows:

$$\mathbf{E} = [0,0,E_z(x,y,t)]$$
$$\mathbf{B} = [B_x(x,y,t),B_y(x,y,t),0]$$
$$\mathbf{v} = [v_x(x,y,t),v_y(x,y,t),0]$$

Assume that the electrical conductivity is constant and scalar.

(*a*) Derive the differential equation for the transport of the magnetic potential A in terms of (A,v,ϕ), neglecting electromagnetic wave phenomena.

(*b*) To what other familiar differential equation in fluid mechanics is the equation for A similar?

10.2 Show that if the following complex variables are defined,

$$\tilde{u} = u + iv \qquad \tilde{\jmath} = j_y - ij_x \qquad \tilde{E} = E_y - iE_x$$
$$\tilde{\sigma} = \frac{\sigma}{1 + i\omega\tau} \qquad \tilde{p} = \frac{\partial p}{\partial x} + i\frac{\partial p}{\partial y}$$

then Eqs. (10.74) and (10.75) can be reduced to a single equation of the form of Eq. (10.8), and Eqs. (10.69) and (10.70) can be reduced to an equation analogous to Eq. (10.7). Accordingly, the solution to the Hartmann flow with Hall effect can be expressed in terms of the classical Hartmann problem.

10.3 In order to account for nonequilibrium ionization in flow problems it has been suggested that σ be assumed to be some function of the current density. For the case where $\sigma = d|j|^n$:

(*a*) Derive the appropriate Ohm's law and determine if the value of n which one may assume need be restricted.

(*b*) With this Ohm's law derive the differential equation for the velocity in the Hartmann problem.

(*c*) Noting that $d^2u/dz^2 = \frac{1}{2}d/du(du/dz)^2$, show that for the special case of $n = \frac{1}{2}$, the velocity equation can be integrated once in closed form and the remaining integration leads to elliptic functions. *Hint*: Separate integration into regions where $u < K$ and $u > K$.

10.4 For the case in which the Hall effect must be considered, derive the appropriate equations governing the flow field for the Couette flow problem. Verify that additional velocity and current components exist due to the Hall effect and that the equations are linear. Assume all electric fields to be short-circuited.

10.5 Consider a two-dimensional vortex flow of conducting fluid, and assume it to be steady and incompressible. Neglect θ and axial variations and postulate a radial electric field and axial magnetic field. Within the assumption of a vanishingly small magnetic Reynolds number derive the linear second-order ordinary differential equation governing the θ component of flow velocity. How can the radial pressure gradient be determined?

CHAPTER 11

11.1 For an isentropic MHD channel flow with magnet pole faces of infinite permeability material, the Lorentz force is expressible as in Eq. (11.63). Making use of this expression, show that the velocity and area changes along the channel are related as follows:

$$\frac{1}{u}\frac{du}{dx} = \frac{a^2}{u^2 - a^2 - B^2/\mu_0 p}\frac{1}{A}\frac{dA}{dx}$$

where a is the conventional speed of sound. Since $a^2 + B^2/\mu p$ is the speed of propagation of infinitesimal disturbances, we observe that the flow velocity must now attain this velocity rather than Mach 1 at the nozzle throat.

11.2 Show that if one assumes $B_z =$ const, $E_y = \frac{3}{2}uB_z$, and $\rho =$ const for the quasi-one-dimensional flow of a perfect gas, a plasma accelerator is found which has a linearly increasing velocity. Also, verify that the then increasing velocity causes an increase in temperature.

11.3 Calculate the induced magnetic field strength at the surface of a channel, such as shown in Fig. 11.3, for a channel height of 5 cm and a current density of 2 amp/cm². Assume the channel to be doubly infinite.

11.4 Verify that choking cannot occur in a constant-temperature channel flow of a perfect gas. Derive equations analogous to (11.17) to (11.20) for this case.

CHAPTER 12

12.1 Consider the motion of a doubly infinite flat plate in an unbounded fluid, where the motion is assumed to be periodic (the Stokes problem). If the fluid is electrically conducting, and a magnetic field is applied normal to the plate, show that the equations governing the induced magnetic field and flow velocity are identical to Eqs. (12.1) and (12.2). Solutions for this case are correspondingly simpler compared to the Rayleigh problem since no inversion of the transformed variables is necessary.

12.2 For the special case of vanishingly small Prandtl number show that the energy equation corresponding to the problem of 12.4.1 can be reduced to the following linear equation from (12.25),

$$u_\infty \frac{\partial h}{\partial x} = \alpha \frac{\partial^2 h}{\partial y^2}$$

where $\alpha = \mathcal{K}/\rho C_p$ is the thermal diffusivity.

12.3 Determine the conditions under which similar solutions may be obtained for the inviscid boundary layer described in Sec. 12.6.

CHAPTER 13

13.1 For the source problem of Eqs. (13.10) to (13.12) where the electrodes are assumed continuous, there will be a radial current flow. Express this radial current from Ohm's law in terms of u. Explain why this expression for $j_r = j_r(r)$ differs from the expression required by imposing $\nabla \cdot \mathbf{j} = 0$. Also, formulate the expression for the z pressure gradient due to j_r also in terms of u.

13.2 For a constant-area duct determine the value of E/B which gives rise to maximum acceleration of the plasma. Assume a quasi-one-dimensional flow of a perfect gas.

CHAPTER 14

14.1 For the local inviscid approximation, draw the vector diagrams for the Faraday, segmented-electrode, and Hall-type generators. Include the following vectors:

$$\mathbf{U}, \mathbf{B}, \mathbf{U} \times \mathbf{B}, \mathbf{E}, \mathbf{E}^*, \mathbf{j}.$$

14.2 Consider an "ideal" Hall generator, with

$$\mathbf{B} = (0,0,B_z)$$
$$\mathbf{E} = (E_x,0,0)$$
$$\mathbf{u} = (U,0,0)$$

where U = const; that is, a "local" inviscid non-heat-conducting model, with magnetic Reynolds number $\ll 1$. The magnetic field varies in the downstream direction as follows:

$$x < 0 \qquad B_z = 0$$
$$0 \leq x \leq L \qquad B_z = B_0 \sin \frac{\pi x}{L}$$
$$x > L \qquad B_z = 0$$

In terms of both the ratio of output voltage to open-circuit voltage, and the rms magnetic field, determine: (*a*) axial current density, (*b*) power per unit cross-sectional area, (*c*) total pressure drop = Δp, (*d*) conversion efficiency η.

$$\eta = \frac{\text{power per unit cross-sectional area}}{U\,\Delta p}$$

NOTE: Neglect ion slip; that is, let $w_I \tau_I = 0$. Also, be sure that the current obeys the conservation equation $\nabla \cdot \mathbf{j} = 0$.

14.3 Derive the expression for the local conversion efficiency for a series-segmented electrode generator for off-design performance when the magnetic field is adjusted so that the open-circuit voltage remains constant. Express results in terms of K, K_0, β_e', where K_0 is the design load factor.

14.4 Calculate n_e, σ, $\omega_e \tau_e / B$ in a gas seeded with 1 per cent molar potassium, for thermal ionization for pressures of 1, 2, 5, 10 atm, for the temperature range of 4000 to 5000°F. Neglect chemical reactions and electron attachment. Assume $Q_{eK} = 20 \times 10^{-15}$ cm^2, $Q_{eg} = 2 \times 10^{-15}$ cm^2.

14.5 (*a*) Carry out the derivation which leads to Eq. (14.40).

(*b*) Using the results of Eq. (14.40), calculate the optimum concentration of potassium seed in argon gas at 1500°K and 1 atm pressure, for thermal ionization. Assume $Q_{eK} = 20 \times 10^{-15}$ cm^2, $Q_{eA} = 2 \times 10^{-17}$ cm^2.

14.6 (*a*) Prove that the average value of δ as used in Eq. (14.45) is given by

$$\delta = \frac{\sum_{s \neq e} m_s^{-1} X_s \delta_s Q_{es} \sum_s X_s m_s}{\sum_{s \neq e} X_s Q_{es}}$$

(*b*) For δ_s equal, and Q_{es} equal, for all species, show that $\delta \geq 1$.

(*c*) For a gas mixture containing only two species, show that δ is a minimum when the mass fraction of one species is given by

$$X_1 = \frac{1}{\sqrt{Q_1/Q_2} + 1}$$

and that

$$\delta_{\max} = \frac{m_2}{m_1} \frac{(\sqrt{Q_1/Q_2} + m_1/m_2)^2}{(\sqrt{Q_1/Q_2} + 1)^2}$$

(*d*) For Prob. *c*, show that $\delta < 1$ only for

$$\frac{Q_1}{Q_2} > \frac{m_1}{m_2} > 1$$

(*e*) For the results of *c*, show that the optimum value of m_1/m_2 is given by

$$\frac{m_1}{m_2} = \sqrt{\frac{Q_1}{Q_2}}$$

for which

$$\delta_{\max} = \frac{4\sqrt{Q_1/Q_2}}{(\sqrt{Q_1/Q_2} + 1)^2}$$

(*f*) Plot $\delta_{\max}$ versus $\sqrt{Q_1/Q_2}$.

14.7 From Eq. (14.71), show that the generator efficiency approaches the polytropic efficiency for stagnation pressure ratios close to unity.

14.8 Assuming that the skin friction owing to the magnetic field remains unchanged, calculate the maximum polytropic efficiency for $R_e = 2{,}000$, $I = 0.1$.

14.9 For a given total mass flow rate, and for $c_f/\sigma B^2$ equal to a constant, show that parameter Z defined by Eq. (14.96) is a maximum when the flow Mach number is unity.

14.10 Integrate the momentum and energy equations for a constant-density generator. Assume that the magnetic field and effective electrical conductivity are constant.

14.11 The ohmic heating I^2R in a magnet is to be rejected to space by radiation, by the use of a heat pump. Assume a Carnot cycle for the heat pump, with heat absorbed from the magnet at temperature T_1 and rejected to space at temperature T_2.

The radiator weight per unit area is β, and the power-supply weight per unit power is α. Show that for T_1 fixed, the sum of the weight of the power supply and radiator is a minimum when $T_2 = (3\beta/\sigma E)^{\frac{1}{4}}$, where σ is the Stefan-Boltzmann constant and E is the emissivity.

INDEX